BEER PACKAGING

A Manual for the Brewing and Beverage Industries

EDITOR
Harold M. Broderick
Technical Director
Master Brewers Association
of the Americas

i

Published 1982
Master Brewers Association of the Americas
Madison, Wisconsin 53705

Copyright 1982
Master Brewers Association of the Americas
All rights reserved
Library of Congress Catalog Card Number
80-82264

Printed in the United States of America
By Impressions, Inc.
Madison, Wisconsin

FOREWORD

As part of a continuing effort toward providing sources of basic information on the Art and Practice of Brewing, the Master Brewers Association of the Americas has prepared this volume on Beer Packaging. It is one more block in the foundation upon which to build and advance our own knowledge as well as our industry's technology.

Once again, it is the voluntary efforts of some of our members that make possible works such as this, and we thank them for sharing with us their expertise.

Fred J. Gerhardt *President*
Master Brewers Association of the Americas

CONTENTS

v

PREFACE

The Committee of Past Presidents of the Master Brewers Association of the Americas, meeting during the 1979 Annual convention in response to a proposal by William Hipp, recommended that the Association publish a textbook on Beer Packaging that would serve as a companion volume to *The Practical Brewer*.

The Executive Committee, after a survey found that there was a widespread and definite need for such a book, voted in January 1980 in favor of the proposal, and President Codd appointed a Committee consisting of H. Broderick, J. Cleasby, W.A. Hipp and D.G. Ruff to look into the matter and to present its findings and recommendations to the Board of Governors. The Study Committee found that Bottling and Canning of Beer written by Donald G. Ruff (a member of the present Editorial Board) and Kurt Becker, published by Siebel Publishing Company in 1955 was out of print and unavailable. There was "general agreement that this text, while a landmark in its own right, needs updating and revision as well as coverage of additional topics to meet the changes in technology that have occurred in the 25 years since it was written."

In April, 1980, the Board of Governors approved the recommendation of the Study Committee and authorized the Editorial Board, subject to the control of the Executive Committee, "to undertake the steps necessary to complete the preparation and publication of the book".

Coverage of beverage packaging in one volume of reasonable size must involve compromise. Consequently, the Editorial Board felt that a detailed discussion of equipment available would require many volumes which would quickly be made obsolete by the continual modification of existing machines as well as the introduction of new ones: such an exposition, it was felt, was best left to the individual manufacturer's manuals and training material. It was decided that the industry would be best served by a volume that concentrated on other important (and more permanent) elements of operation found in a packaging department. Such elements include not only the principles, maintenance and problems involved in the various unit operations; they also include the management functions and controls necessary to produce a quality product with high overall efficiency, to maintain a clean and safe working environment and to meet regulatory requirements.

Lack of space, therefore, dictates that the number of machines mentioned in a chapter be severely limited. Such mention is usually only to illustrate a point and should not be construed by the reader to mean that there are no others available to do the job equally well. Nor should such mention be construed as representing an endorsement by the authors, the Editorial Board or by the Master Brewers Association of the Americas.

The Editorial Board was fortunate in being able to select from the large pool of capable packaging personnel the authors it felt had the necessary expertise. The treatment of topics by these authors reflects North American practice in the main, but it should be emphasized that there is *no one* accepted approach. Methods used, and equipment selected, for a given plant reflect the experience of managerial personnel, the restraints of space and capital, managerial resources available, as well as overall corporate philosophy. Consequently, this diversity of background, experience and style is reflected, as it should be, in each author's approach to his subject, providing the reader with a representative cross section of actual practice.

It is impossible to acknowledge in this space all those whose comments and suggestions to the Editorial Board helped shape this book, but it is to be hoped that they will recognize that their contribution made it more useful. However, particular mention must be made of: Daniel Sommers, our Executive Secretary, and Mrs. Irene Venn, our Office Manager, for their unfailing and cheerful help; the members of the various Executive Committees who supported our efforts; the numerous equipment manufacturers who supplied data and illustrations, Mrs. Dorothy Haines and staff of Impressions, Inc., for their patience and skill in transmuting difficult manuscripts into printed pages; William Marten, who prepared the index; and, last but not least, my wife Elinor Broderick who patiently served as "go-fer", proof reader and counsel.

Our heartfelt thanks go to the members of the Editorial Board and to the contributing authors who made this volume possible. The authors somehow found time in their busy schedules to complete their assignments, in many cases at the expense of more pleasurable pursuits. The members of the Editorial Board gave cheerfully and without stint the time necessary to complete our task. Together, their joint labors and enthusiasm shaped this volume.

Harold M. Broderick

Stuart, Florida, July, 1982

INTRODUCTION

For the convenience of the reader and also as an aid in the teaching of packaging courses, the chapters in this book are grouped together in seven sections that follow logically from the major activities in a Packaging Department. Section I sets the stage. Sections II through V follow the process flow in operations such as bottling, canning, etc. Soft Drink Operations warrants, and has, a separate section of its own. The various support activities, such as 'Maintenance, Quality Assurance, etc., together with other necessary functions such as Safety, Cleaning and Sanitation, etc., comprise the seventh section.

SECTION I, MANAGEMENT OF PACKAGING should serve as a frame of reference for the reader not working in brewery packaging. For those who are in training for positions in packaging, it will show how they will fit into the overall scheme. These five chapters explain why packaging is important, how a typical packaging department is organized to carry out its many interrelated functions. Chapter IV discusses how standards of performance are set up and used to measure the efficiency of the plant and the effectiveness of supervision. Chapter V goes to the core of the packaging operation, the line layout.

Chapter III, The Human Element, is offered to offset the unintended, but quite often, mechanistic approach to packaging. It discusses one company's program to enlist the whole-hearted cooperation of its most important resource, its employees. The identical approach may not be readily transferable to other settings, but the goals it sets forth are worthy of attention.

SECTION II, BOTTLE OPERATIONS covers bottling from the manufacture of the bottle through filling, crowning and labeling. The glass container is one of the oldest in use for beverages, its use going back to Roman times. The development of the automatic glass forming machine early in this century made possible today's large shipping breweries. The many virtues of glass offset its disadvantages so that it remains the beverage container most commonly used throughout the world. In the United States, 43% of packaged beer shipments in 1981 were in glass; in Mexico 77%; and in Canada over 95%. The continued research and development work by the glass industry ensures a prominent role for the glass bottle in the beverage industry.

SECTION III, CANNING OPERATIONS covers canning from the manufacture of cans through filling and seaming. The metal can is a relative newcomer to the beverage packaging. Its strength, imperviousness to light, ease of handling and low unit weight have made it increasingly popular in the United States. In 1981, 57% of the beer shipped in the United States was in cans; in Mexico 22% and growing; and in Canada less than 8%. Noteworthy is the fact that 92% of the beverage cans sold in the United States are aluminum.

Cans have become such an important part of beer sales that several major U.S. brewers have set up wholly or jointly owned can manufacturing facilities to insure a source of supply.

SECTION IV, DRAFT OPERATIONS covers an important part of the brewery packaging operation. Until World War I, most of the beer sold was draft, but the percentage declined gradually as shown in Table I on page 4. However, the use of stainless steel kegs, the remarkable improvement made in tapping systems and the development of associated equipment, which automatically cleans, sanitizes and fills these units, all helped to provide better product integrity. Consequently, in the United States draft sales seemed to have stabilized in 1981 at 12%. However, in the rest of the Western Hemisphere they continue to be only a minor part of sales: in Canada, less than 5%; in Mexico, 1.3%.

SECTION V, OPERATIONS COMMON TO BOTTLING, CANNING & DRAFT covers the proper handling of beer from the packaging cellar through warehousing and distribution. The important methods of microbiological stabilization, in-package pasteurization, bulk pasteurization and "sterile" filtration are introduced and their advantages and disadvantages compared. Some common methods of putting the container into packs and cases are discussed, and under Product Identification the need for, and methods of, coding products for quality control and legal purposes are discussed.

Warehousing & Shipping in many companies constitutes an interface between brewery and customer. It receives product from the packaging lines for palletizing for storage and/or shipment on railcars or trucks. In many cases it also does all the production planning for the entire packaging department as well as the scheduling of shipments of finished product. As such it is responsible for satisfying the sometimes conflicting demands of customer requirements and the scheduling of lines and vehicles for the most efficient operation.

SECTION VI, SOFT DRINK OPERATIONS points out that these operations are similar to those in brewery packaging. Indeed, in many countries soft drink lines are an integral part of the brewery packaging operation. The cans and bottles used, and the equipment used to fill and process them are much alike. However, there are differences: and the major ones, such as the treatment of water, preparation of syrups, blending and carbonation of product as well as the use of plastic bottles and cases, are covered in Chapter XX.

SECTION VII, RELATED PACKING FUNCTIONS includes the many support activities and functions necessary to operate a well-run packaging department. Safety is covered in Chapter XXI primarily from the viewpoint of a supervisor, and what he can do to contribute to a safe work place.

The all important subject of quality is covered under four separate topics that have a direct bearing on ultimate product quality; Cleaning & Sanitation; Pest Control; The Influence of Packaging Materials on Beer Quality; and Quality Assurance itself.

In addition, there are two chapters that have a bearing on the efficient operation of equipment: Maintenance & Lubrication; and Packaging Line Instruments & Control. The microcomputer has found a place in all new packaging lines. Programmable logic controllers permit high speed operation of units as well as providing flexibility in line control.

Finally, the subject of Waste & Effluent is worthy of coverage, since its control falls under increasingly restrictive environmental regulations.

Section I: Management of Packaging

CHAPTER I

THE IMPORTANCE OF BEER PACKAGING

BY PETER CODD

INTRODUCTION

Historically man has invariably consumed his drinks from a *package*. The goatskin of the bible, the horn of the Vikings, the goblet of the medieval table, the barrel throughout all ages, the bottle, the jug, and more recently the can—all have been packages for his drinks. Barrels have been used for many hundreds of years; bottled beer was first introduced in the 17th Century, whilst canned beer is the product of the 20th Century. Packaging is not new, nor is its importance to the brewer, who has always needed to have a "package" to take the liquid beer to the consumer.

However, it is in this century that beer packaging has grown so tremendously.

This chapter examines briefly the recent historical growth of beer packaging importance. This is followed by an examination of the areas in which packaging is important and why. The conclusion is drawn, somewhat provocatively perhaps, that nothing is more important to the brewer than packaging, not even the beer itself. Yet, it must be stated immediately, this is tempered by the knowledge that for the whole they can only coexist. We can't have one without the other, and perhaps they are better described as "equally important".

The point of emphasis to the reader is the magnitude of the importance. Only if this is understood and agreed will all disciplines of science, engineering, brewing, marketing and economics be able to evaluate the knowledge in the chapters that follow.

To know the importance of beer packaging is the key to understanding the importance of this book and all of its chapters.

HISTORICAL GROWTH OF PACKAGING IMPORTANCE

In this century until the late 1930's the bulk of the beer produced was for draught beer. Consumption was mainly on-premise and oriented to the retailer rather than the consumer. Packaging was in barrels or kegs, with bottled beer and some beer in cans occupying a minor area of importance to the brewer.

3

After the second World War there was a dramatic rise in consumer-oriented packaging, with all of its attendant technology. This occurred in many consumer goods markets, particularly, and almost explosively, in the beer market. Additionally, social trends led to more drinking away from bars and taverns, and more off-premise sales, accelerating the growth of packaged beer.

Table I shows the volume of beer produced between 1935 and 1980 in the U.S.A., and the percentage of packaged and draught beer that made up this volume. It illustrates the present dominance of packaged beer and its importance. In 1980, package beer is almost 90% of the total U.S. beer market.

TABLE I
U.S.A. BEER PRODUCTION 1935-1980
Showing Percentage of Packaged and Draught Beer

Year	Total Beer Volume produced (in million of US Bbls.)	Percentage of Packaged Beer	Percentage of draught beer
1935	48.0	29.5	70.5
1940	53.8	51.7	48.3
1945	88.2	64.3	35.7
1950	88.1	71.8	28.2
1955	90.2	77.9	22.1
1960	93.4	80.7	19.3
1965	108.2	82.3	17.7
1970	133.1	85.9	14.1
1975	160.6	87.6	12.4
1980	194.1	87.9	12.1

One must be careful not to subtract percentages between years in Table I and call this true growth percentage, because the total volume of beer sales has changed each year. Examination of *true* package beer growth is shown in Table II, where the total beer sales are shown by volume in package and draught for the years 1935 to 1980, and the true percentage growth each year then calculated.

In the past fifteen years in the U.S.A., beer packaging has been growing at about 5% per year average, and the total packaged beer volume produced has more than doubled in that same time. Draught beer, while a decreasing percentage of the *total* volume, has remained relatively stable at the same actual volume figure for the past twenty-five years.

Packaged beer growth has been such that it is now the dominant component of the American beer market.

ECONOMIC IMPORTANCE OF BEER PACKAGING

The economic importance of beer packaging, when measured in dollars, is staggering. For the beer produced in 1980 in the United States, approximately 3½ billion dollars was expended in packaging materials alone. The

TABLE II
U.S. BEER PRODUCTION 1935-1980
Showing True Percentage Growth of Packaged and Draught Beer

Year	Total Beer Volume		Packaged Beer		Draught Beer	
	Total Production Millions Bbls. U.S.	Percentage Change	Total Production Millions Bbls. U.S.	Percentage Change	Total Production Millions Bbls. U.S.	Percentage Change
1935	48.0		14.2		33.8	
1940	53.8	+ 12	27.8	+ 96	26	− 23
1945	88.2	+ 64	56.7	+104	31.5	+ 21
1950	88.1	+ 0	63.0	+ 11	24.8	− 21
1955	90.2	+ 2.4	70.0	+ 11	19.9	− 20
1960	93.4	+ 3.5	75.4	+ 8	18.0	− 9
1965	108.2	+ 15.8	89.0	+ 19	19.2	+ 6
1970	133.1	+ 23	114.3	+ 39	18.8	− 2
1975	160.6	+ 21	140.7	+ 22	19.9	+ 6
1980	194.1	+ 21	170.6	+ 18.1	23.5	+ 18

suppliers to the brewing industry, the brewing industry itself, and the distribution industry, with all their employees involved, make up a dollar total of investments, manpower, and employed capital, many times the three billion dollar figure for materials alone. This importance of beer packaging is by itself sufficient reason for all concerned with packaging to pay close attention to every aspect of beer packaging to ensure the careful and optimum use of the financial and human resources involved. The beer industry is not merely involved in producing six-packs for leisure, but embraces a whole important economic segment of United States industry.

What now follows is an examination in more depth of the aspects of importance of packaging.

EXAMINATION OF THE IMPORTANCE OF PACKAGING TO THE BREWER

The word "Packaging" is used rather loosely in two different ways, one as a noun to describe the package itself, which is a commodity or unit of product, uniformly wrapped and sealed. The other use is as a verb, describing the act or process of making into a package. For easier examination of the importance, considerations are made here under these two definitions separately, namely, the package importance, and then the importance of the act of making the package.

THE PACKAGE

One can consider the importance of the package under six headings, each identifying a separate area of major importance. All areas combined give the total importance of the package. The areas are:

> Fundamental
> Technical
> Financial
> Marketing
> Resource Conservation
> Legislative

Fundamental

Beer is a liquid, and one must contain a liquid in a hollow, rigid, or semi-rigid solid container for transportation and distribution to the ultimate consumer. Beer is an acidic, carbonated beverage, subject to alteration in its flavour and appearance by contact with and exposure to outside materials and conditions. The choice or nature of a package is governed by these technical factors and other factors, such as economics and marketing.

Overriding all these is the fundamental fact that no liquid can be moved or sold without being in a package and without being packaged. Out of this fact arises the basic importance of packaging to the brewer. A co-existence of package and product must prevail. Without it, beer cannot be distributed nor consumed. The package and the packaging must be such that the product arrives at the consumer's lips in virtually the same condition as the brewer intended it to be when it left the brewery. It must be unchanged in taste, appearance, carbonation and clarity.

The basic unit or pack for beer is usually a keg, can or bottle. For practical transportation it is grouped within some form of secondary package, such as a case, carton, or a tray. This serves to protect the individual container and to allow further grouping into a larger unit of packages for commercial movement, usually involving palletization or containers.

Both primary and secondary packaging are of fundamental importance. This fundamental importance of the package is, then, its essential purpose for moving the liquid beer around.

Technical Importance

The properties of beer include being an acidic, carbonated liquid, susceptible to flavour change and deterioration. These properties govern the technical importance of the package, and the package's specification. Beer must be protected from deterioration, from changing composition, organoleptic variation, agitative and thermal damage and physical damage. The package, both the basic container and all of its supplemental packaging, must not affect the product adversely.

Glass, cans and kegs are the common beer containers. It is well known that they are selected for their inertness and protective properties. Glass is usually amber to protect the beer from light deterioration but may for traditional or marketing reasons be green. Cans are lined to protect taste. Both are cushioned by secondary packaging to prevent physical damage, breakage and crushing.

Because beer deteriorates with age and temperature, refrigeration properties of the package are important.

Further consideration of some of these important technical properties is given to this subject in the chapter in the book on "Beer Handling", and many of these topics are considered in detail in other subsequent chapters. It is sufficient to say here that the technical importance of the package is a prime concern of the brewer.

Financial

For competitive sale a beer package must be "economical" in its component costs. Relative importance of cost can be demonstrated pictorially by examining the percentage cost of components of a pallet of cans and bottles as shown in Figure 1-1.

COST COMPONENTS OF A PALLET OF BEER
SHOWING PERCENTAGES OF COMPONENT COSTS

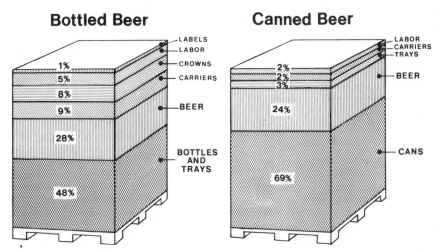

Figure 1-1. Cost Components of a Pallet of Beer, Showing Percentages of Component Costs

The total cost of packaging materials is two to three times the cost of the beer involved and ten to thirty times the cost of direct labor. Obviously then, the financial importance of a package is another prime area of concern for all involved in beer packaging. Selection of materials, usage control, minimum wastage, and an understanding of the economics of package costs must temper many areas of how packaging is conducted and controlled.

Marketing

Very often the package is its own selling message and this makes the package an important factor to the sale of the product. Distinct shapes and colors, graphics and decorations are all used to build consumer awareness, product image and appeal. A package must often say "Buy me, please" to the consumer. Packages therefore become a marketing tool, rather than merely a transporting container.

A display of contents or of appeal and a visual impact coaxing the consumer to purchase are features built into many beer packages, both in the container itself, and the container's "overwraps". Individual bottle shapes, dressing with foil labels and capsuling, can and carton printing, six-pack carriers and baskets—all are the concern of marketing and production and also of cost departments.

The package therefore assumes a real importance in the market area.

Resource Conservation

Here the importance of the package lies in the fact that brewers have a social responsibility to practice resource conservation in their choice of packaging in a logical, objective and unemotional fashion. This should be done so that packages produced are harmonious with the needs of the economy and ecology, without being prejudicial to the brewer.

Recyclable materials, reusable containers, bio-degradable components, all have come into the forefront of resource, solid waste and litter considerations. Some have reached the point where legislative action and regulation are now in force.

There are important considerations here, not always the concern of the production areas of brewing and packaging, but frequently impacting upon them.

Legislative

Packages must conform to restrictions and regulations imposed on packages in general, and alcoholic beverages in particular. Beer packages have to conform to many State and Federal regulations in the U.S.A., and similar legislative rulings in other countries. Contents labeling, ingredients, strengths, product code dating and identification are some of the areas. Legislation on taxation, on recycling, and even on the advertising printed on packaging are others, and there are many more. Suffice to say that legislative compliances affect the package and are therefore important.

Some of these topics are considered further in the chapter on Product Identification later in this book.

PACKAGING

If packaging is considered as the act or process of making into a package, here one examines the whole activity of canning and bottling and beer packaging and warehousing, and the importance is practically self-evident. If one considers the same six headings under packaging that form the areas under which the package itself was considered for importance, the first three are found to be of major importance to the act of making the package. These three are:

Fundamental
Technical
Financial

Fundamental

The act of packaging must place a liquid in a captive form inside a hollow container, so that the liquid becomes transportable, storable, stable and saleable. Out of this fundamental grows all the complex technology of packing and packaging beer, and all the facilities and equipment used in the brewery packing departments. Consideration of this technology forms the basis for many of the chapters in this book.

Technical

Technical importance is in the control of quality and purity of the product, so that during packaging and afterwards the product will have a consistent taste, proper shelf-life, low air, correct fills, perfect clarity, and all the other factors vital to keeping the product in top quality. The control of quality also extends to materials, handling of incoming materials, work in progress, and finished goods.

Technical importance also embraces all the engineering aspects of packaging—bottling operations, canning operations, the heart of packaging. Almost all of the technology of bottling and canning evolves around the unique characteristics of beer and its technical needs and limitation.

Beer must be handled so that the taste, appearance, carbonation and stability remain unchanged. The technology required to achieve this in terms of equipment and methods, and quality control, are the core of the act of packaging, and the core of this text-book.

Financial

The cost of the act of packaging divides into initial capital costs and continuing operating costs (excluding here the cost of packaging materials themselves). Capital investment is high in the beer packaging industry. Canning and bottling lines in 1980 in the U.S.A. cost approximately US$6 to 7 Million. Equated to the annual output of such a line, this is about US$8 per barrel investment cost. Operating costs in terms of people and energy are important, along with other costs, such as overhead. When deeply immersed in the technology of packages and packaging, one should not forget the importance of the costs involved of the many technical operations.

Legislative, Resource Conservation, and Marketing Considerations

It was stated that three factors in making packages were important, the fundamental, the technical and the financial. The further factors of legislative, marketing and resource conservation importance must not be overlooked. In the legislative area, safety and conformity to regulatory acts affect manufacturing. Compliance with hygiene and sanitation legislation is mandatory, and even if this were not the case, voluntary standards would be self-imposed by brewers for the protection of their quality products. Quality packaging is essential for good marketing. A badly presented package does not sell. Resources of energy must be conserved. Solid and liquid waste problems must be overcome. All these are areas of secondary, but still vital, important consideration that the brewer must take into account in packaging beer, and are considered in subsequent chapters.

SUMMARY

What then is the importance of packaging? The importance of packaging, that is the package itself and the act of making it, is co-equal to the importance of the product. One can't have one without the other, and both must be perfectly in harmony. The importance of packaging to the brewer is in these areas:

The Package

Fundamental—Transportation of a liquid to the consumer.

Technical—The preservation and protection of the product.

Financial—The cost of a package.

Marketing—The assistance towards product sale.

Resource Conservation—The suitability of the package in the total environment.

Legislative—The compliance with legislative statutes.

Packaging

Fundamental—The genesis of the whole technology of packing and packaging a liquid.

Technical—   The concern with preserving in a container a perishable and liquid food. The operations and engineering for achieving this.

Financial—   The capital cost of starting a packaging operation, and the continuing costs of operating it.

The total importance of packaging to the brewer is a complete amalgamation of all of these factors, covering the package and its production. The size and magnitude of this importance is tremendous and must not be underestimated. The world-wide growth of our industry is expected to continue, and it is in packaging that some of the most dramatic technological and productivity improvements will occur in the foreseeable future.

Understanding the importance of packaging will in turn lead to a better understanding of the wealth of knowledge in the chapters that follow in this book.

CHAPTER II

PACKAGING MANAGEMENT ORGANIZATION
BY CHRISTOPHER L. SPIRE

INTRODUCTION

Packaging today involves many varied but interrelated functions and operations. It is the purpose of this chapter to set forth how these activities relate to each other and how the personnel involved, especially the first line supervision, interact in an effective organization. Since some of our readers may have no background in beer packaging, it assumes no prior knowledge of the industry, and should prove especially helpful in providing the newcomer with a frame of reference.

Organizations are developed with the aim of providing effective control over the manufacturing process. It therefore becomes imperative that a discussion of the beer packaging plant organization be preceded by a description of this process. Beer is a malt, hopped, somewhat bitter, alcoholic beverage brewed by slow fermentation. The process to produce it, Figures 2-1 & 2-2, begins with the introduction of the basic raw materials in the brewhouse and concludes with the shipment of the finished goods by railcar or truck. This total view of the process is necessary for an understanding of the critical interractions between the packaging organization and those departments adjacent to it in the process flow.

PROCESS FLOW

The primary raw material in beer, barley malt, as well as cereal adjuncts are stored in grain bins or silos until ready for use. At the beginning of a typical process the malt is milled, weighed, and then added with treated water to the mash cooker. If an adjunct (normally corn or rice) is used, it is transferred from storage bins, weighed, and added to the cereal cooker along with treated water and some ground malt. Once the cereal cooker reaches a boiling temperature, the entire contents are transferred to the mash cooker and added to the malt and water already in the cooker. Once the starches are converted into fermentable sugars in the cooker, the mash is moved to the mash straining tank (lauter tub, mash filter, or strain master). Here the solid grain particles (spent grain) are removed and sold as animal feed. The remaining liquid (wort) flows to the brew kettle where hops and syrups are added once a boil has been achieved. The solid hop particles are next removed in a hop separator and then all suspended particles (trub) are allowed to separate out in the wort clarifier (hot wort tank). The wort is cooled to approximately 8-11° C as it

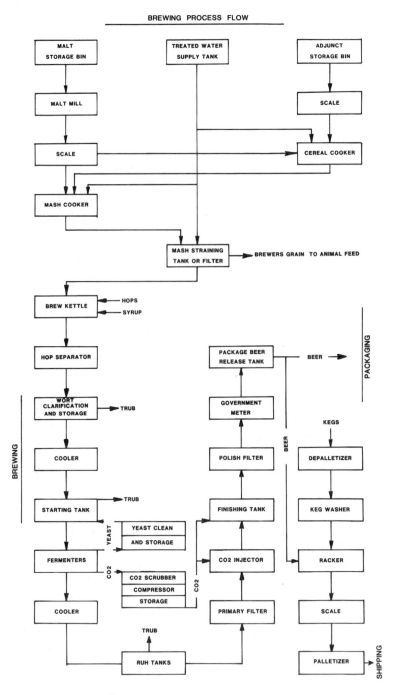

2-1. Brewing process flow.

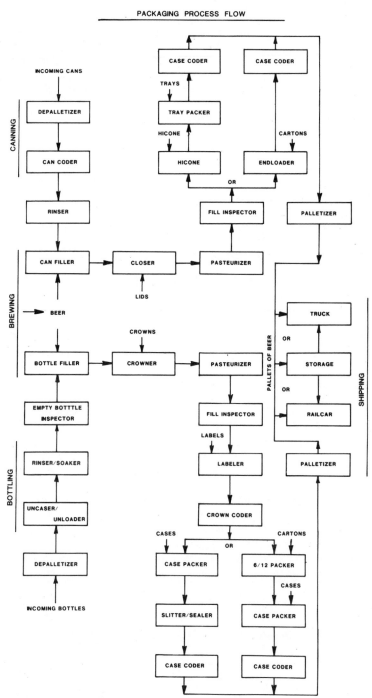

2-2. Packaging process flow.

flows to the starting tanks in the fermenting cellars or directly to the fermenters. Yeast is added at this point in the process and allowed to ferment the wort for 4–10 days. The yeast is then removed, cleaned, and stored for future use. CO_2 which is collected in the process of fermentation, is scrubbed, compressed, and also stored for future use. The beer is again cooled in transit to the ruh (lagering or aging) tanks. The beer remains in these cellars for up to 28 days which again permits some trub to settle out and be removed. The beer then goes through a primary filter and CO_2 injector prior to storage in finishing tanks. Based on demands from packaging and draught, the beer is again filtered, metered, and placed in tanks ready for release to the bottle, can, and draught lines.°

The draught operation begins with the depalletization of the empty kegs either by hand or machine. The kegs are washed both externally and internally and inspected. The kegs then move to the racker where they are filled with beer. The automatic rackers are normally followed by a scale. The final step in the operation is the repalletization of the kegs. From here the pallets of keg beer are transferred directly to waiting railcars and trucks or to a coldroom to wait for future shipment.

Empty cans arrive at the brewery palletized in bulk. They are placed into the depalletizer where tiers of cans are swept off the pallets and fed into the empty can conveyor system. In some companies the cans, while passing along the conveyor, go through a coder which marks the bottoms of the cans with a date/plant/line, etc. identification. Following this operation, the cans go through a rinser which, with water sprays, removes dust and any foreign material. The cans then travel to the filler and closing machine where the empty cans are filled with beer and then immediately sealed with a lid in a double seaming operation. Next comes the pasteurizer which, with hot water sprays, brings the beer up to pasteurization temperature (60° C) and maintains it there for a minimum of six (6) minutes. Each can is then checked for proper fill before proceeding to the packing operation. The most common package is the six pack which is placed in a tray of four six packs. Cans are also packed in 12- and 24-can cartons. Both trays and cartons are normally coded with the date/plant/line indentification, beer type, and special labeling as they are conveyed to the palletizer. Once palletized, the beer is taken directly to waiting railcars and trucks or placed in warehouse storage for future shipment.

Empty bottles arrive at the brewery palletized either in bulk or in the cases in which they will later be reshipped. Following depalletization, the bottles are removed from the cases, if required, at the uncaser (unloader) and then conveyed in mass to either a rinser or soaker. In the soaker, returnable bottles have the labels removed and are thoroughly washed with a caustic solution. In the rinser, non-returnable (new) bottles are merely sprayed with water to remove any dust or foreign particles. Following this operation the returnable bottles must be inspected either manually or by automatic bottle inspectors to insure they are clean and undamaged. The bottles are then filled and crowned. The pasteurization operation is identical to that for cans. Fill inspection can take place either prior to pasteurization or following. Next comes labeling, which is accomplished with a bank of labeling heads or 1-3 high

°For those wishing additional information, the above brewing operations are covered in detail in THE PRACTICAL BREWER published by MBAA (Madison, Wisconsin, 4th. Printing, 1981).

speed rotary labelers. In some operations the crown is then date coded. Following this, the bottle is packed in a 6- or 12-bottle carton and then repacked in the shipping case; or the carton is eliminated and the bottles are packed directly in the shipper. Some cases also require a machine to slit the top flaps from the side of the case and seal the case with adhesive. Similar to cans, most cases are then coded on their way to the palletizer. Once palletized, the bottle beer is treated the same as can beer in the shipping process.

PLANT MANAGEMENT

Although the process is basically the same in multi-plant and single plant operations, the reporting relationship of top management does vary. In a multi-plant operation, decentralization is required, due to communication network limitations which are magnified by the number of plants and the geographical separation between the plants and the corporate headquarters. The Plant Manager (General Manager or Resident Manager) has all functional departments directly under his control as shown in Figure 2-3. There can be exceptions, but this is normally limited to only one or two departments reporting to Corporate. In large plants there may be one or two Assistant Plant Managers. If two, one of these will usually have responsibility over operations to include Warehousing and Shipping, Maintenance, Packaging, Industrial Engineering, and Operations Control, and the other will have responsibility for administration, which can include Personnel (Industrial Relations), Accounting, Purchasing, and Public Relations. The Assistant Plant Manager assumes responsibility for the plant during the Plant Manager's absence and he is the prime interface between the corporate staff groups and the departments.

In a large single plant operation, as depicted in Figure 2-4, the opposite is normally the case. Department heads report to functionally corresponding Directors or Vice Presidents at the corporate level. However, in smaller companies many of these functions are combined under one Vice President, usually

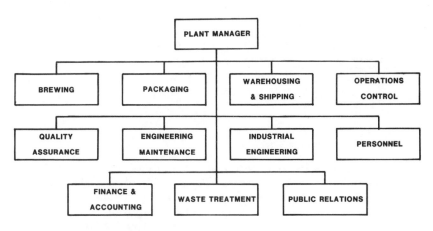

2-3. Multi-plant operation.

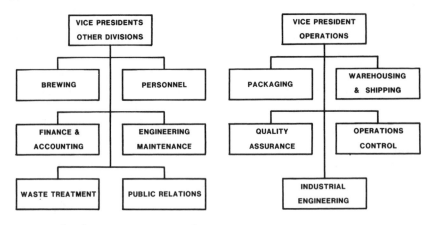

2-4. *Single plant operation in a large company.*

a Vice President of Production or Operations, as shown in Figure 2-5. Many functions, such as Personnel, etc., are not staffed at the plant level but are handled by a corporate staff group. However, below the department head level, the organizations are basically the same if not identical.

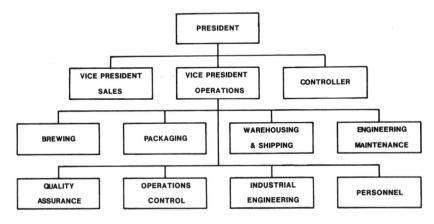

2-5. *Single plant operation in a small company.*

BREWING DEPARTMENT

Since the process begins with brewing, so will this discussion of the line departments. The Brewing Department is normally divided along geographical lines. The Brewhouse operation encompasses everything prior to fermenting. It is normally housed in one building and takes less than a day to complete one process or brew. A second subdivision is Fermenting, which includes yeast handling. These tanks are housed in a separate part of the plant, or in a separate building all together, refrigerated to 8-11° C. They can even be located outside the building enclosed in refrigerated jackets. The ruh (aging or lagering) tanks can fall within the same subdivision as Fermenting or a separate one. These tanks are geographically situated similar to the fermenting tanks. The final subdivision is Finishing which includes everything from primary filtration to package release. It is during this phase that the beer reaches proper carbonation and alcohol levels and is stabilized and clarified.

A Brewmaster (Brewing Manager) is in charge of the department with managers or superintendents over the subdivisions just discussed. Even though the Brewmaster may report to the Plant Manager, there is normally a strong tie to Corporate Brewing on product related problems and process changes.

The link between the Brewing and Packaging Departments is the package beer release cellars. This operation can come under either of the two departments. As the name implies, it is here that the final quality checks are made on the product prior to packaging. Often the government meters, which are utilized for tax accounting purposes, are located in these cellars. Communications between the two departments flow through this area. The Packaging Line Supervisor coordinates all beer changes with the Supervisor in this area. When a particular product begins to run low in the cellars, Packaging is notified by the cellars so appropriate changes can be made. Any product related quality problems when detected in one department, should be communicated to the other.

PACKAGING DEPARTMENT

A typical organization chart for a packaging operation in one of the larger breweries is shown in Figure 2-6. At the bottom of the figure are other titles that are commonly used. The Area Manager's responsibility is subdivided between bottle and can lines or geographically. It extends 24 hours a day, 7 days a week. The Superintendent has responsibility for an area on a particular shift. The Line Supervisor has responsibility for his line or unit during his shift. In some of the largest breweries, there is another level of management between the Superintendent and Line Supervisor. This Group Supervisor is responsible for a portion of the Superintendent's overall area. In smaller breweries the levels of management are reduced.

In most new brewery packaging line layouts the depalletizing and palletizing operations are separate from the main part of the line. They may be situated in a different part of the building, on a different floor, or even in a different building. As such, the Can Line Supervisor's responsibility usually extends from the conveyor bringing cans to the rinser to the conveyor taking cases from the packer. The crew consists of a filler operator, packer operator, a utility/relief person, and sometimes a pasteurizer discharge attendant. Responsibility for this line and crew involves all aspects of management—cost control, efficiency, employee relations, quality, safety, and sanitation. These will be discussed in detail later in the chapter.

The Bottle Line Supervisor's responsibility is similar to that above. It begins with the conveyor bringing cases of empty bottles to the uncaser and ends with the conveyor at the packer or sealer discharge. This crew includes operators on the uncaser, rinser/soaker, filler, labelers, and packers; a pasteurizer discharge attendant; bottle and label inspectors (in some operations); and a utility and relief person.

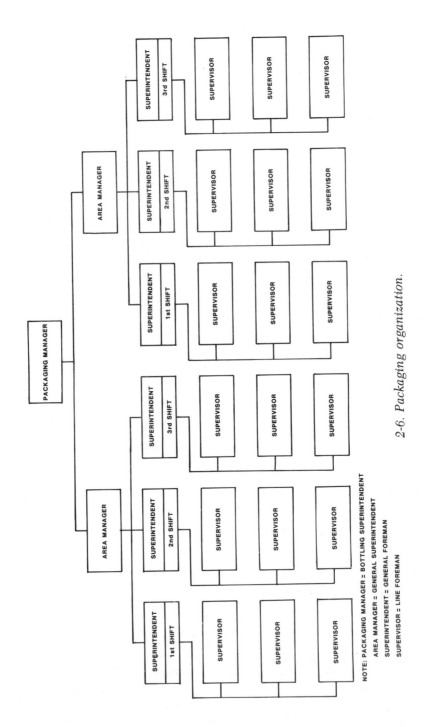

2-6. *Packaging organization.*

NOTE: PACKAGING MANAGER = BOTTLING SUPERINTENDENT
AREA MANAGER = GENERAL SUPERINTENDENT
SUPERINTENDENT = GENERAL FOREMAN
SUPERVISOR = LINE FOREMAN

The depalletizers and palletizers are normally all grouped together in one area or a few smaller areas. As such, they can be supervised by one or two Supervisors. These Supervisors can be part of the Packaging Department or Warehousing and Shipping. This determination may be based on the geographical location of the equipment, the method of manning the operation, or accountability implications. Regardless, the dividing line between this area and the line proper (normally somewhere in the conveyor system) must be clearly defined.

The draught operation can also fall into different departments for some of the same reasons. This includes Packaging, Warehousing and Shipping, and Brewing. The crewing on this operation varies depending on the amount of automation. The washer and rackers require operators as may the depalletizer and palletizer. In addition to the utility and relief operator, most operations also have keg inspectors.

WAREHOUSING AND SHIPPING DEPARTMENT

The packaging operation can only function efficiently if there is a steady flow of direct materials into the operation and of finished product out to Wholesalers. This is the responsibility of the Warehousing and Shipping Department. It is complicated by a limited storage capacity and yet mammoth material flow requirements.

The Warehousing and Shipping Department performs numerous functions and is often subdivided along those lines. They receive, unload, and store all direct materials and production supplies and then deliver them to the packaging lines when needed. This includes lids, crowns, labels, cartons, HiCone®, trays, cases, adhesives, and chemicals. Glass and cans are handled separately, since they are unloaded off the trucks and placed directly on the depalletizer infeeds or a staging area nearby. The supervisors' responsibility includes all aspects of warehousing to include storage, rotation, and accountability for both direct materials and finished product. They handle all returns from the Wholesalers (Distributors) by truck and railcar to include glass, pallets, cooperage and dunnage. Although the operation of the palletizers may fall under Packaging, the removal of the pallets of beer to the truck dock, rail dock, or storage is the responsibility of Shipping. It obviously does not stop here either, but encompasses the loading of the trucks and railcars. The dispatch function, which entails the control of all truck and rail movement within the brewery complex, often comes under their jurisdiction. Some of these functions may come under other departments such as direct material receiving under the Purchasing Department and dispatch under Operations Control.

Coordination between the Packaging Supervisor and Warehousing Supervisor is a daily occurrence. Material needs are communicated to insure a steady flow of direct materials. Package changes must be coordinated with the depalletizer and palletizer operation to insure the properly timed cut-off of one package and introduction of another. Material shortages between the depalletizer and the line and back-ups between the line and palletizer must be communicated so that the true cause can be identified and corrected. Shipping must be aware of major breakdowns on the packaging lines so that orders can be adjusted or delayed. Packaging must be informed of any material availability problems so that line schedules can be adjusted.

OPERATIONS CONTROL DEPARTMENT

The nerve center of the brewery is the Operations Control (Distribution) Department. This group plans, monitors, and controls the entire process from Brewhouse to Wholesaler. The process actually begins with the inventory programming and order service system. In many breweries today, this system is completely computerized. It maintains inventories on all wholesaler stock and processes orders to replenish that stock once it falls below minimum levels. All these orders are then matched to packaging line and bulk beer availability to determine a production schedule. Another function often performed by this department is the traffic function. It is their responsibility to control all truck and rail movement into and out of the brewery complex and to monitor and approve all freight, demurrage, and detention bills.

In order for Operations Control to properly monitor and control the process, they must receive timely information from Packaging on line performance as it affects the schedule. As a minimum, a recap of the actual production per package is provided to this department at the end of the shift. In addition, they must be alerted to any major breakdowns so that schedules can be adjusted and orders changed or delayed. This would also include required deviations due to bulk beer outages or material shortages.

QUALITY ASSURANCE DEPARTMENT

The quality of the product is actually controlled by the Packaging Department. Packaging should monitor the process and the product itself for any conditions outside specification. Quality Assurance (Quality Control) is responsible for assuring that Packaging is doing its job. Quality Assurance also performs certain inspections which require special instruments that are not available to packaging personnel.

The Quality Assurance Department performs many critical functions in the plant operation. One section monitors the beer throughout the brewing process particularly prior to its release to packaging. Another group may monitor the packaging process at the rinsers, fillers, pasteurizers, and filtecs. They perform package checks for proper fills, air content, CO_2 level, crowning, seaming, foreign material, leakage, labeling, coding, and carton/case defects. The Warehousing and Shipping operation is also monitored for proper stock rotation, fork truck damage to finished product, and proper truck and rail loading procedures. There may be a Material Testing Section which performs material acceptance testing and incoming material inspections on a random basis or when a problem is suspected. The Technical Service Section provides technical assistance to Packaging on material/equipment or beer/equipment related problems. The Quality Assurance Department can also monitor the state of sanitation in the plant and provides advice to the operating departments on particular sanitation problems such as pasteurizer treatment or filler sanitation. In some operations, they will even supervise some of the cleaning functions such as peripheral cleaning. If the pest control program is contracted outside, this department can monitor the contractor's performance in this area involving both rodent and insect control. They will also play a key role in the reprocess and repack operation. This includes the disposition of all beer placed on quality hold. Their role can vary from strictly inspection of reworked product to complete control and supervision of the program.

The Packaging Supervisor's responsibility toward the quality of the product parallels those of the Quality Assurance Department. Concern and attention in this area can greatly reduce the amount of finished product withheld from shipment.

The Supervisor should perform periodic checks on the packaging process. Checks on the bottle line should include the water pressure and spray alignment on the rinser; CO_2 pressure, beer level, and bottle handling on the filler; water pressure and alignment of the jetter (frequency and alignment of the ultrasonic knocker); sensitivity and operation of the empty bottle and fill inspection equipment; water temperature, cycle time, and spray header flow on the pasteurizer; glue tack and condition of the labeler; adhesive application and flap alignment on the carton maker; positioning of the containers in the packer; and the speeds of all equipment. Process checks on the can line are similar to those above on the rinser, filler, fill inspection equipment, pasteurizer, carton maker, and packer. In addition, the bubble breaker and undercover gasser CO_2 pressures should be monitored along with beer losses at the filler/closer.

Inspections of the product at each step in the process can also minimize large quality holds. The Packaging Supervisor should inspect for erratic fills, visual airs, and container damage after the filler/closer; leaking containers, foreign material, and bulged containers after pasteurization; label positioning and adhesion following labeling; the legibility and accuracy of all codes; the integrity and content following packing operations; and the pattern and pallet height at the palletizer.

The critical aspect of incoming material quality is machinability. For this reason, it is the Packaging Supervisor that is first to recognize problems of this type. Most common among these on bottle lines are excessive glass breakage, low crown torque, curling labels, and improperly scored cartons. On can lines, material defects include damaged cans, poor can lithography or coatings, defective tabs and lid rivets, defective HiCone®, and warped trays.

When defects are found—regardless of whether they involve the packaging process, the package itself, or the materials that comprise that package—the Packaging Supervisor immediately shuts down that part of the operation. The next step is to contact Quality Assurance and advise them of the problem. The product involved should be identified and isolated as much as possible. Finally, process deficiencies should be corrected and defective materials replaced.

Although Quality Assurance provides advice on sanitation, it is up to the Packaging Supervisor to accomplish those recommendations. Each operator must feel that his responsibility towards sanitation is just as important as operating the equipment. Sanitation and cleaning assignments should be assigned while the equipment is running, during minor and major breakdowns, and during scheduled sanitation periods. The Supervisor must insure that these assignments are performed at the appropriate times and utilizing the proper equipment and methods.

Of all the quality related functions performed by the Packaging Supervisor, the most important is to instill in his crew an awareness for quality and sanitation. A quality conscious crew will significantly reduce the amount of beer held for quality defects as well as substandard beer reaching the market. A crew conscious of sanitation will create fewer sanitation problems that require correction.

ENGINEERING-MAINTENANCE DEPARTMENT

The key to efficiency in the Beer Packaging Plant is teamwork between Packaging and Engineering-Maintenance. Since packaging personnel are around the equipment every minute that it operates, they are in the best position to determine what is contributing downtime to the line. It is then up to Maintenance to determine what corrective measures need to be taken. Both departments must then coordinate the scheduling of the equipment out of service, so the work can be accomplished.

In a large plant, the Engineering-Maintenance Department normally has 4–5 functional areas or subdivisions within the department. Brewery Maintenance provides support to the Brewing Department. The power plant and the facility itself come under the Utilities/Plant Maintenance Group. There is a separate subdivision for the maintenance of packaging lines plus all material handling equipment. Staff Engineering is normally centralized in one subdivision even though it supports the entire plant. Their functions include equipment installation, machinery modifications, and technical assistance on major problems. Some departments also have a planning-scheduling function which handles all engineering and maintenance work with the exception of emergency breakdowns. All the subdivisions come under the Plant Engineer (Chief Engineer). However, some companies are splitting off the Packaging Maintenance Group as a separate department in order to make it more responsive to the needs of the Packaging and Warehousing Departments.

The Packaging Supervisor's role with regard to packaging line efficiency involves a thorough understanding of how the equipment/line should operate and the effect the crew has on that operation. The equipment should be monitored for proper operation including checks with the operators. Repetitive problems should be identified and reported to Maintenance. The flow of packages on the line should be observed carefully to uncover bottlenecks. The speeds of all equipment on the line should be monitored because speeds both faster or slower than design can have a negative effect on output. Most of the equipment is designed to run in automatic for optimal throughput, but this also requires monitoring by the Supervisor. The use of equipment manuals can often speed up repair and diagnostic trouble-shooting, but this normally requires encouragement from supervision. The training of the crew in the proper operation of the equipment is also a function of the Supervisor. Involvement in line changeovers is necessary to insure completeness and timely startups. Writing up a maintenance work order is only part of the job. It must also include continuous follow up until work is accomplished. When breakdowns do occur, attempts should be made to bypass the problem area and minimize the length of the downtime. Finally, the Supervisor should insure the crew is efficiency conscious.

INDUSTRIAL ENGINEERING DEPARTMENT

The Industrial Engineering Department is involved in all aspects of the plant with emphasis on improved methods of operation. Often they handle projects which do not belong in the functional scope of another department. Typical functions that might be performed by this department include the development of plant layouts for both equipment and material. The development of labor standards, as well as material specifications, is often their responsibility. They perform method improvement studies and problem analysis on operational situations. Not only do they originate cost reduction studies but normally maintain the plant's cost improvement program. The justification of engineering projects and purchases is within their domain. They develop manpower utilization controls and reporting systems. Capability and capacity studies are frequent tasks. This also includes contingency studies such as rail versus truck shipments or packaging versus transshipping product. The development of computer applications for operational needs has now become a frequent project. The Industrial Engineering Department can be looked upon as the right hand of management to be applied as the need dictates.

PERSONNEL DEPARTMENT

The Personnel (Industrial Relations) Department provides support to line supervision in all people related activities. However, it usually is the Supervisor in packaging as well as other departments who is the primary representative of management and the company to the brewery worker.

The Personnel Department is also subdivided along functional lines. There is an Employment Section which administers the hiring process of both hourly and salaried employees. Labor Relations works with supervision on most union related matters. Formal technical and management development training is conducted by the Training Section. The Safety and Health Group provide expertise on safety related matters, administer the safety program, and furnish medical support. Security and fire prevention activities are also controlled by this department. The labor control function including manpower scheduling, vacation schedules, the absence control program, time cards, leave of absence, jury duty, and special assignments can be handled within the Personnel Department or within the individual line departments. Functions such as compensation and benefits are normally administered at Corporate.

The Packaging Supervisor's responsibilities parallel some of the functional areas just mentioned. As the critical link between the hourly employee and the Safety Department, the Supervisor should continuously inspect the work area for unsafe conditions. Inspections should insure that safety deficiencies are corrected to include employees not wearing the proper personal protective equipment. Since most accidents occur due to careless acts, any unsafe practices by people on the packaging lines should also be addressed. The investigation and reporting of all accidents is accomplished by the Supervisor in charge of the area. The responsibility also includes conducting safety training for the crew to instill in them a safety awareness which is critical to the success of the program.

In the area of employee relations, it is the Packaging Supervisor who actually implements company policy regarding the hourly work force. The Supervisor must be thoroughly familiar with the collective bargaining agreement and administer it correctly and consistently. Disciplinary actions should be appropriate for the offense and consistent with the practices of other areas in the plant. Grievances should be handled expeditiously and with the intent of solving the problem. The Supervisor should talk to each absent employee on return to work. For those with repetitive absences, the plant absence control program should be followed. The Supervisor provides assistance to employees on personal problems or advises them as to where they can receive help. This includes problems or questions on the Employee Benefits Program. Jobs should be assigned according to plant guidelines as should the scheduling of overtime. On-the-job training of the operators is controlled by the Supervisor as are assignments for formal training. Finally, the crew should be given any information pertinent to their job or their employment.

FINANCE AND ACCOUNTING DEPARTMENT

The Finance and Accounting Department under the Controller (Comptroller) provides support in all cost-related activities. Although the primary function in the plant is accounting, in many cases purchasing and information systems are also assigned to the department.

There are six functions in the accounting area which must be performed either in the plant or at corporate headquarters. Accounts Receivable processes all invoices for beer and other sale items such as spent grain, scrap cans and paper, etc. and credits for returns from Wholesalers (Distributors). Accounts Payable processes approved vendor invoices and credit memos. Cost Accounting monitors and reports on the performance of the plant and individual departments compared to the budget providing analysis where requested. Revenue Accounting handles the accounting and reporting required by Federal and State Beer Tax Bureaus. Payroll processes and generates paychecks for hourly and salaried personnel and handles inquiries on their computation. Inventory Control maintains accounting records for receipts, returns, usage, and inventories of all packaging materials and production and cleaning supplies.

The Purchasing Department is usually subdivided along functional lines. Direct Material Purchasing buys and/or schedules releases of materials used in the brewing and packaging process. Indirect Material Purchasing buys all items such as machine parts, tools, lubricants, cleaning supplies, production supplies, employee protective equipment, etc. Material Control coordinates the supply of direct materials between Purchasing and the user. The Storeroom controls the receipt, storage, issue, and accounting of all indirect materials with the exception of those ordered in such quantity that they are supplied directly to the production departments. The Storeroom is also responsible for reordering items based on a minimum/maximum inventory system.

The Information Systems Department manages the Data Processing and Records Sections. This includes the processing of all routine computerized reports, developing new reports and systems, and improving existing systems. They also maintain the official records of the plant to include the archives.

Of all departments, Packaging has the best opportunity to reduce operating costs. It is the most labor-intensive department per units produced. The cost of direct materials in the package far exceed those in the product. Even the bulk beer loss in Packaging approximates that in Brewing. It is logical then that the Packaging Supervisor's impact on cost control can be significant. For example, the line should be manned according to standard. When extra manning is required, it should be eliminated as soon as possible. When the line breaks down, the Supervisor should reassign the crew immediately. In order to reduce bulk beer losses, the Supervisor should work to eliminate beer leaks, minimize filler bowl dumps and the beer lost during a dump, obtain target fills, minimize filler spillage, and reduce line losses. Utility waste can also be reduced by eliminating leaks, utilizing only what's necessary, and shutting down during non-operating periods. The Supervisor can reduce direct material usage by minimizing line losses, salvaging cans and bottles in damaged cartons, checking Filtec® rejects, and reducing indiscriminate material waste by operators. Finally, the improvement of line efficiencies will reduce costs.

WASTE TREATMENT DEPARTMENT

Due to new regulations on environmental control in many states and provinces, the construction of new breweries has included the addition of waste treatment facilities. This has necessitated the development of a new field of knowledge in the brewery and a new operating department. This department has been placed under other departments such as Engineering, but often reports directly to the Plant Manager.

The primary function of the Waste Treatment Department is to collect all liquid effluent from the brewing and packaging process and treat it until it meets state requirements for discharge back into the local water system. The department also monitors the effluent and hydraulic loading from each area. With this information, programs can be developed to reduce the loading and in turn reduce costs and improve the efficiency of the entire operation.

Beer finding its way into the Waste Treatment Plant influent streams requires critical attention from management. It is essential to minimize and to control the points in the packaging operation which allow beer into the sewer. For example, all filling and closing machines can be provided with collection devices to bring the most concentrated products into one holding tank. Can and bottle de-filling devices are available to collect beer from short-filled containers or from beer returned to the brewery from mis-shipments. In all cases, it is absolutely essential to identify and to segregate these losses so that disposition other than the Waste Treatment Plant can be exercised. Such approachs permit: 1, reduction in waste and losses; 2, reduction of load in Water Treatment Plant; and 3, production of valuable by-products.

There are several cost effective approaches or combinations of approaches which may be considered. One alternative recognizes that there are technically and economically feasible processing methods and equipment available to recover the ethanol from waste streams and thereby add additional income from its sale as fuel. Beer solids, concentrated from the collected streams by the use of evaporators, can be added to spent grains, increasing its value.

A second alternative recognizes that there has been much work done by a few companies in some countries to re-process certain selected product streams for possible re-introduction into beer products upstream of the packaging operation. This technology is in its infancy and its use requires critical scrutiny to see that it meets corporate standards.

A third approach to useful disposition is the direct land application of collected beer streams. The cost effectiveness of this alternative depends largely upon the proximity of the brewery to suitable available acreage. Land application alternatives include irrigation, overhead sprinkling and other evaporative approaches.

Since the waste treatment process functions through a living organism, abrupt changes in the effluent (the organism's food) can have a very detrimental effect on the entire process. It is therefore, very important for the Packaging Supervisor to coordinate with the Waste Treatment Department when any abnormal discharges are required, particularly accidental discharges to the system.

PUBLIC RELATIONS DEPARTMENT

The Public Relations Department provides the link between the plant and the news media. Most often this function is performed at the Corporate Headquarters. However, on new plant start-ups, a Public Relations Section assigned directly to the plant can prove beneficial. Their purpose is to develop, clear, and process all information going to the new media. They can also build a good image of the Company in the local community as well as assist in the marketing effort in the local area.

CHAPTER III

THE HUMAN ELEMENT
BY A. BABB

INTRODUCTION

In today's business climate, there is an important dimension added to the art of managing and to the sciences of planning, designing, building and operating complex businesses that requires the addition of this chapter to a technically-oriented publication. This dimension is generally called "employee participation in management", and when this participation is directed as effectively and as efficiently as all other company resources, the results obtained can dramatically alter the image and fortunes of any corporation.

The people who individually and collectively make up an organization today require programs and processes which focus on improvement in the quality of work life. Therefore, it is incumbent upon responsible management to provide a style that encourages this environment. In the following chapters, the literally hundreds of years of combined experience, expertise, and know-how represented by the authors will serve the reader admirably as a technical storehouse of knowledge to be used in packaging operations. This chapter, in contrast, will present several elements in the development of a corporate strategy and management style based on people involvement and participation. The reader will gain an insight into utilizing what may well be the most effective resource in providing quality products and services at outstanding productivity levels.

MANAGEMENT ENVIRONMENT

Managing in the contemporary environment has proved shocking to many businessmen, and the United States provides a good example. The recognition that the rate of productivity improvement in the United States has slowed dramatically in the past few years has provided a major portion of this shock. Additionally disturbing is the news that both Europe and Japan have taken leadership roles in the productivity arena.

The American public in recent surveys holds the mistaken belief that industrial profits are exorbitant and that "management" is unjust and unfair. Individual behavior is often viewed as irresponsible and unethical. It is little wonder that board rooms across the United States are in a state of reflection.

As the management of responsible companies began to view these problems in a typically business, objective-oriented fashion, solutions came into focus. Business was not communicating its positive side. The American public could not relate to closed board room doors and tense, guarded statements issued to the press on a quarterly basis. It was perceived that this very limited amount of information or no information at all was negative information. Reaction by industry to solve this problem has been to create corporate or image advertisements and to tell about the good things that American business does on an on-going, daily basis. This approach is intended, in a word, to "humanize" corporate America; and it is working because many companies now report improvement in public opinion.

The next step in this humanizing process should have been an obvious one, but it has taken a long time to recognize, let alone implement. This step lies in the recognition that the people who comprise the companies help spread the word, both good and bad, about their companies. Their work is intricately interwoven into the fabric of their lives; and if their contributions individually and collectively are not realistically or adequately recognized, the quality of their work life suffers. This lack of a sense of unity can cause a corporation to stumble.

C. Jackson Grayson of the American Productivity Center sums up this philosophy well in his following statement:

"All people are at their best when they are essential members of an organization that challenges the human spirit, that inspires personal growth and development, that gets things done and that symbolizes only the highest standard of ethical and moral conduct—that's what quality of work life is all about."

It must be obvious that not all business managements fall readily into the categories of poor or excellent; however, so many can be so categorized that we must ask the question, "What is it that excellent companies are doing, and how are they doing it to gain such a favorable position?" To gain insight into some of their thinking, the evolution of employee participation in management needs to be examined. This style of management believes that, by using a participative or personal involvement style, an individual has a voice in his work environment; and, therefore, some say in his or her destiny. If management listens to its people, cost-effective ideas will emerge and a more quality-conscious, productive work force will result.

Nowhere else in the world has a participative style of management been more closely studied than in Japan. This approach, called a "Quality Circle" approach, was begun following World War II to help that country rebuild a war-torn economy. The idea and its expansion into Japan from the United States is generally credited to Dr. W. Edwards Demming. This style of management came into its own in the early 1960's when quality in Japanese goods was declared a national improvement priority. Management encouraged and supported voluntary meetings and activities to solve quality problems. Today, Japanese circles address not only quality problems, but safety issues, work procedures and practices. There are over 150,000 registered quality circles now active in Japanese industry.

The quality circle approach was first highly visible in the United States at Lockheed in the early 1970's, and there are now more than 1,800 companies that are known to be involved in a management style called "quality circle" or "employee involvement." For an example, Mr. Warde F. Wheaton of the Aerospace and Defense group, Honeywell, Inc. (December 14, 1981 *Industry Week*), points to his company as highly focused toward a worker with a whole new set of functions, motives and expectations. As people become more highly educated, they expect jobs with more diversity, flexibility, challenge; and, above all, they want to know that their ideas, input and what they do makes a difference, both to the company and to their own lives.

This example of industry recognition is repeated in the company philosophy and business approach taken by other widely-publicized and emulated companies. Notable among them are Hewlett-Packard, Dayton-Hudson Corporation and the Eli Lilly Company. A recent publication, entitled *Theory Z* by William G. Ouchi, highlights them in great detail as companies practicing a participative management style.

The portion of the work force in the United States represented by trade unions was approximately 20.9% in 1980 and declining (Dep't of Labor-Industry Week, Jan. 11, 1982), and the participative approach to problem identification and solving can be successful in this environment if the company and the union are on good working terms. There are several companies with successful programs, but it must be recognized that each of these efforts must be carefully structured due to contractual and legal constraints between unions and individual companies.

Not only is the industrial world engaging in this approach to business, but the approach to participative involvement has spread to service-oriented companies such as in the financial and culinary worlds. Many new restaurants, for example, are involving their people in deciding new approaches to provide improved service in addition to recognizably superior food.

Background investigation and reporting is documented in the works of well-known, capable management consultants and authors working in today's business and educational environment, and there are scores of valid examples. This chapter will not replay the work done by these people, but rather, it will present a business approach taken by one company practicing this philosophy.

The comprehensive process, which will be elaborated upon in detail, encompasses the fundamental goals of safety, quality, productivity and the quality of work life. The intent of this process is to gain commitment, responsibility and accountability at every organizational level in the achievement of these objectives and to recognize that in the most basic sense, employee involvement is the utilization of resources—time, material, people, technology and capital to optimally manage a business.

A Company's Example

It begins with a document produced by corporate management which sets forth the company's philosophy in doing business and defines corporate strategy as the company works toward its business purposes, goals and objectives. The systems approach to developing and reporting is generally used so that progress can be monitored and results can be measured. It is doubtful that a typical document exists, so the approach used by the Adolph Coors Company of Golden, Colorado is the example used in the following pages. Since this document forms the basis for the implementation of participative management, it is set forth in part here.

A STATEMENT OF CORPORATE PHILOSOPHY AND OBJECTIVES

Background and Philosophy

The company occupies a strong regional position in the U.S. brewing industry. This position has been achieved because product quality has been and will continue to be the major influencing factor in the marketplace. Products will be produced so that they will always be recognized as superior by the consuming public.

In addition to producing the highest quality beer, new, different products must be supplied to the increasingly segmented marketplace, and aggressive marketing of these products must take

place in order to maintain a position in the beer industry. In supporting the above, the business purpose of the company has three primary pursuits, as established by the Board of Directors:
1. Survive as a successful brewing company.
2. Assure that the employees share in the success of the company by providing job security and opportunity based on individual performance and achievement.
3. Assure that the company will always operate as a responsible corporate citizen.

Objectives

Survival as a viable competitor in the beer industry is central to this business purpose. A focus of the drive for survival is stated in the following objectives. These objectives are consistent with the overall corporate purpose and objectives and with competitive realities. They provide the specific measurable targets against which progress can be assessed, and they are so defined that achievement will assure survival.

Financial

We will strive to achieve a satisfactory return on net assets in the beer business with a combination of the following objectives:
1. Achieve a highly competitive cost of goods sold ratio to net sales.
2. Maintain low general and administrative costs on a per-barrel basis.
3. Manage assets to eliminate unnecessary investment.
4. Strive to maintain retail pricing at a level competitive in each product segment and geographical area.

Technology

We will maintain competitive advantage through technological developments as measured by improvements in product quality and facilities and equipment productivity.

Employee Relations

All policies and actions will be directed to the fulfillment of the company's commitment to personal respect, good pay and benefits, job security and job satisfaction for every employee.

Corporate Citizenship

We will continue to operate in total conformity to local, state and federal laws and on the highest ethical plane.

Group Implementation

Using this system, each major group of the company will continue to refine goals beneath the umbrella of the corporate philosophy, purpose and objectives. The Operations group document follows:

"The Operations group is organized to effectively design, construct, operate and maintain company facilities. In addition, the Technical Operations group is organized to provide technology and services to outside industry and businesses. Recognizably superior products and services will be provided at a practical low cost and in a professionally-managed, business team atmosphere. All efforts are directed towards the creation and continuation of a working environment based on employee participation, mutual trust, opportunity, challenge and fulfillment."

The implementation of this philosophy is guided by using the following goals and objectives:

Product Goals

1. SAFETY

Design and produce products which will be safe and wholesome to the consumer.

2. QUALITY

Provide the highest quality products, technology and services based on present standards, assuring superiority and preference at the consumer level.

Employee Goals

1. SAFETY

Promote a positive safety attitude which recognizes individual responsibility and achieves quantified targets. Design facilities which provide a safe working environment.

Management Development

Provide for self-renewal of the management organization by developing superior technical expertise and management skills.

Working Environment/Quality of Work Life

Create a working environment based on mutual trust which encourages employee participation at all levels and provides for personal growth and accomplishment, job satisfaction, recognition of individual performance and meaningful communications.

Financial Goals

1. PRODUCTIVITY/EFFICIENCY

Maximize the utilization of all corporate resources.

2. COST

Minimize costs consistent with operations goals.

3. BUSINESS DEVELOPMENT

Foster the development of profitable new business activities.

Community Goals

1. LEGAL COMPLIANCE

Comply with all local, state and federal laws.
2. ENVIRONMENT
   Ensure that the business decision-making process evaluates the external impact on society, along with economic considerations.
3. CORPORATE CITIZENSHIP
   Develop political and economic awareness. Participate in civic affairs.

IMPLEMENTATION OF PROGRAM

As each Operations division continues to work these overall goals into the departmental operating structure, additional objectives are quantified. The objectives are worked into action plans and, in most cases, become an integral part of the departmental management "pay-for-performance" plan. From supervisor up through division vice president, the pay-for-performance goals are documented and become the basis for subsequent performance reviews. Periodic departmental reports are issued in order to key on and keep abreast of progress toward achievement of the goals.

The employee goals of working environment/quality of work life will be examined in greater detail as illustrated in Figure 3-1. The pivotal point to be made here is that the philosophy is a pledge of mutual cooperation, trust and communication between management and employees. It requires that management will provide a safe working environment, competitive wages and benefits and that employee input, ideas and constructive criticism will be welcomed. By working together through one-on-one contacts and communication and with mutual trust and respect, there should be no need for third party representation to solve mutual problems. Employees are committed to attend work regularly and as scheduled, and to work safely with performance equal to abilities. Open and honest participation with constructive ideas and involvement will then achieve meaningful results for all. Each of the nine spokes of the quality of work life wheel is a segment of the overall philosophy.

Employee Involvement

There are two areas of this spoke which deserve special attention because they are designed to give the employees a greater voice in charting their own individual destiny, as well as having impact upon the direction of the company. One area is entitled "Employee Participation Meetings" (EPM). The groups which meet in these sessions are comprised of selected volunteer persons working in a geographical area under the direction of the area vice president, who also chairs the group. The group is comprised of people from the hourly work group and several levels of supervision (including an area departmental director) and support and staff groups who work in that area, for example, Purchasing and Maintenance. An Employee Relations representative generally attends in order that continuity between groups throughout the company is maintained. The group meets monthly and discusses topics of overall company interest or concern, reviews proposed policy or revisions to proposed policy, and in general, provides for management a sounding board and barometer of employee concern.

The collective thoughts of all these groups are funneled through a central committee made up of the EPM chairmen and becomes advisory to the Human Resources Department Vice President. This necessary input into company policy results in meaningful and representative policies for the company.

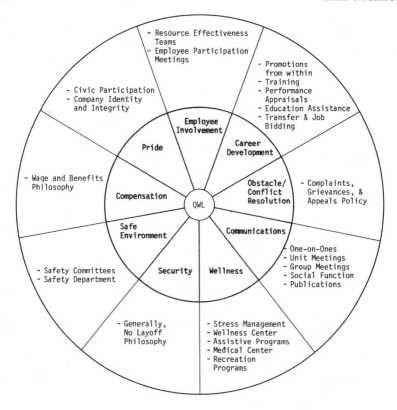

3-1. Coors employee relations philosophy

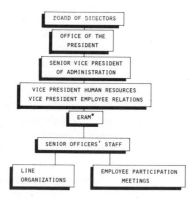

3-2. Coors policy approval process. °ERAM = employee relations advisory meeting.

Figure 3-2 illustrates the process of policy approval by the Board of Directors.

A second area of employee involvement is by participation in resource effectiveness. The resource effectiveness team concept is a blend of Japan's quality circle approach to problem solving and productivity, and of the unit meeting and line supervision approach. Objectives for both teams and management are as follows:

A. *Teams*
   1. Share with management the responsibility for improving quality, productivity and quality of work life by identifying, solving and preventing problems.
   2. Provide opportunity for individual growth through responsibility to the team as a member or leader. Group leadership skills can be developed, which will be recognized as potential management skills.
   3. Improve communications between management and employees about problem areas by team recommendations to management.
   4. Improve employee motivation and morale by increased employee participation in solving problems.

B. *Management*
   1. Share the responsibility for solutions to departmental problems with employees.
   2. Recognize team achievements by encouraging team presentations to management and by publicizing extraordinary team accomplishments.
   3. Promote mutual trust and respect through people-building philosophies demonstrated in the committed and supportive management recognition of the teams.

Teams operate on a low-key, bottom-up and participative, rather than a dictatorial, top-down approach. Participation is voluntary, open, and the entire team makes decisions for recommendation. The number of team members varies from six to twelve, and in most groups, the initial leader is a supervisor. Documentation of team progress and results is required, and members are paid for the meetings. A full-time coordinator has been provided to assist in starting and counseling the teams and to provide training for both team leaders and team members. Leader training skills include problem solving, communication, presentation and group leadership techniques. Member training is generally accomplished while the team is involved in solving its first problem as a way to keep interest high and demonstrate the applicability of the process.

There are allowable and non-allowable subject areas and projects defined for the teams. For example, the teams should feel free to work on solving problems in their own area relating to quality, productivity, area environmental concerns, waste or scrap reduction, communication and reporting alternatives, work simplification and unit performance measures. Some examples of problem areas not open to teams for resolution are areas of safety (these would be referred to safety committees), personal problems, personnel policies or compensation, wages and benefits discussions, which are covered elsewhere.

The ultimate success of this approach to employee involvement in problem solving within a work area lies in the commitment of management to actively listen and positively respond to the needs of the people.

Career Development

The point to be made with this segment of the philosophy is that a sincere

interest in each employee's career expectations and potential is not only expressed in company policy, but in the actions of the management. The job
bidding or transfer policy and philosophy is to encourage employees to find
the job within the company best suited to an individual's desires and/or
qualifications. In keeping with this philosophy, promotions, whenever possible,
will be made from within the corporate family.

To achieve this goal, each person must be aware of the job that they are
doing, as viewed by their supervisor. This is accomplished through periodic
performance evaluation and by reviewing progress toward the goals and objectives mutually agreed upon between the supervisor and the employee. If,
during the evaluation process, areas requiring additional skills development
or training are recognized, these needs are noted and a process is started to
rectify the needs. Those employees who see other jobs within the company
more to their liking are encouraged to take advantage of the educational
assistance program. The program provides for tuition reimbursement upon
the satisfactory completion of a course of study benefitting both the employee
and the company. This has resulted in many employees who have trained
and subsequently altered their careers within the company.

Obstacles/Conflicts/Resolutions

Just as the company has attempted to set objectives and goals in keeping
with its best intentions and according to the needs of its people, there are,
inevitably, those times when conflict will occur and opinions will differ. It is,
therefore, necessary to have in place a policy and a procedure to deal with
the differences of opinion and to protect both the rights of the individual and
the company. In an organization where there is third party representation,
conflicts usually can be ultimately resolved through an arbitration process. In
a company where there is no third party between the person supervised and
the supervisor, there are other alternatives to reach fair decisions.

There are two distinct categories into which conflicts fall. They are, on the
one hand, perceived injustices with the application of personnel policy or, on
the other hand, the perception that a policy is unjust. In the case of the
application of the policy, an employee who perceives that the corrective
discipline given by the supervision is unwarranted or unjust may appeal that
discipline to an appeal board. The decision of the board is final and binding
upon the company and the employee. The board is comprised of the vice
president of human relations or his designee, the employee's departmental
vice president or his designee, two persons chosen by the employee and a
fifth member chosen by unanimous agreement of the first four board members.
Deliberations are held among the five members, and they may call upon
anyone they choose to help reach a decision. As deliberations begin in a case,
the chairman outlines the policy, describes the action taken by the supervisor
and some alternatives available to the board. The action taken by supervision
can be reversed, altered or the original decision may be upheld. The board
is free to vote by secret ballot or to reach a consensus of opinion through
discussions. As this appeal system has evolved, supervision has become more
and more aware of its responsibility for honest and fair treatment and the
necessity to properly document previous work history.

If an employee perceives that a policy has been arbitrarily enforced or the
policy itself is perceived to be unjust, an approach called the "complaint

procedure" may be invoked. When this route is used, the complaint is first heard by the representative of the industrial relations department who renders an opinion. If the employee does not agree with this opinion, the complaint may be further processed to the Vice President of Employee Relations. In the event the employee still does not agree with the opinion given, the complaint may be taken to the office of the president where a final and binding decision will be made.

These options are determined by the employees to be fair and to be a viable route to resolve differences. It is, however, absolutely essential that the chain of command is involved in all disciplinary actions so that a determination of fairness can be made prior to the employee exercising the options outlined.

Communications

The inter-related activities referred to as "spokes" in the quality of work life wheel have a common thread which will allow the parts to work smoothly or, if not working well, will bring the process to a grinding halt. This common thread can be referred to as "communication" and consists of several parts. This need is not unique to any organization, but it is the cohesive force linking most organizations. Good communications begin with an understanding between a supervisor and the person supervised, which can only be developed if the supervisor and the supervised meet face to face periodically in what is termed a "one-to-one" meeting. Meetings of this type should be documented in an employee contact file, and the meetings should be away from the job environment in most cases. These meetings should cover the employee's personal concerns about the job environment or concerning a personal problem for which the supervisor may be in a position to offer assistance. This opportunity to build a working relationship and develop mutual understanding and trust is invaluable in the organization.

There are common information topics which are efficiently and more properly communicated to an entire work group through unit meetings. These needs are typically items involving safety, company work rules or general interest items involving company philosophy or the company's progress in the marketplace. Unit meetings most often will be conducted following the work shift for hourly employees, but can be held during working hours for salaried employees. The frequency of these meetings depends upon several factors; among them, timely or pertinent information availability or necessity, and the general mode of operation within the company. Meetings scheduled weekly are normal, but meetings on four to six-week intervals are not unusual.

Larger group meetings are usually reserved for communicating items of information that have far-reaching and general interest impact. The size of these meetings is usually governed by the available meeting and seating space. If questions and answers are needed, smaller group meetings are desirable and can be used effectively as an employee participation tool.

Although the practice is highly unusual in most companies, there is a growing awareness of the need for a supervisor to recognize on an away-from-the-job basis the accomplishments of his crew. This "pat on the back" recognition is accomplished by allowing the supervisor a once-each-year stipend to be used for an off-site social event. Some examples of these events are family picnics, after-shift early morning breakfasts, late evening pizza get-togethers, and in some cases, just an old-fashioned barbecue in the back yard. These events build good will and knit a crew together in a way not possible in the work-a-day world.

Written communications within an organization take many forms and are certainly a necessary and an effective way of communicating departmental, division or corporate information. The specific needs of a company must be analyzed in order to control the preparation and distribution costs involved. The printed word should be distributed on a "need-to-know" basis. For example, information to be disseminated through group or unit meetings should go to a distribution list comprised of departmental supervisors, the chain of command personnel and involved staff groups. Many general interest items can be communicated with publications mailed directly to the employee's home or through the organization's mail system. Special bulletins are, many times, necessary to supplement regular bulletin board postings which normally cover such things as job openings and awards, shift scheduling or reassignment and other general information news.

If an organization is to properly communicate its philosophy and get across the message that employees are important and contributing members to the organization, all of the approaches mentioned are truly important in that perception; for in every sense, actions speak louder than words.

Wellness

Wellness is to some an unfamiliar term, but its definition can be simply described as the opposite of illness. There is growing awareness that the medical community has been primarily geared to treat illness and not to promote the individual's total well-being in terms of physical and mental health. A look at the cost of health insurance plans will substantiate this position. There are, however, many programs in the industry which fall into the category of promoting wellness, even though they are not termed as such. Recreational programs which sponsor employees in sports, such as softball, bowling, trap shooting, archery, skiing, tennis and golf, are among those used in many companies to promote both physical well-being and mental relaxation. For those employees who are concerned with probably the most important factor in promoting wellness, that of maintaining a strong cardio-vascular system, a facility has been provided at this company with an indoor track, treadmills, exercise bicycles, rowing machines and other special physical fitness exercise equipment. This center is available to employees and their families and continues to be recognized as a major factor in reaching the company objective of the most physically-fit work force in the area.

There are a number of other employee assistance programs offered in keeping with this theme. Among them, a program to assist in the recognition and management of stress. Smoking cessation, alcohol use and abuse classes, nutritional awareness and other employee assistance programs focus on helping people manage and enjoy life.

Security

Those who compare Japanese and American business will usually give positive credit to the Japanese lifetime employment philosophy. Although one could argue the merits and demerits of this philosophy, one would be hard-pressed not to recognize the feeling of security that this approach to business brings to the employee. Today's cost of indoctrination and training the work force has given rise to this company's philosophy of retaining employees during seasonal, low volume conditions, a posture of generally no layoff. It has been determined that the short-term economic advantage gained in seasonal reduction of the work force is more than off-set by the increased costs in worker re-training and loss of morale. The employees working in this "no layoff" scenario are highly motivated, productive and display more pride in the quality of their work and their company.

Safe Environment

A safe working environment is the number one objective for operations. The design of a system to ensure this environment takes several forms. Quantified targets for accident frequency and severity, as well as lost time, first aid and doctor case targets are set for each operating division. Progress toward the goals is measured on a period basis, and audits are performed in conjunction with the safety department to pinpoint those areas which need attention. Those items which need attention are either referred to a safety committee which is comprised of supervision and employees, or to the chain of command for resolution. It is the recognition of safety as an attitude and the safe approach to a working environment which is key to the program. Through one-on-one contact, unit meetings and supervisory group involvement, each supervisor helps build this attitude in his unit and is subsequently held accountable for it through the pay-for-performance system. Several hours of training are required for both new and experienced supervisors throughout the year; and in each of these sessions, support from upper management is given. With this approach to safety, the improvement in accident records can be clearly remarkable; but the ultimate advantage is found in the absence of human suffering and pain.

Compensation

"All I want, boss, is a fair day's pay for a fair day's work!" How often have we, as managers, heard this common phrase. We all agree with it, but we all know that arriving at a mutual agreement on both counts, a fair day's work and a fair day's pay, becomes an arduous and difficult task. Certainly, good pay and good benefits for employees keep a company competitive in the labor market in the sense that top talent may always be attracted to the company. Primary to the development of this position is a company's stated policy on wages and benefits.

This philosophy states that the company will maintain a position which approximates the average of the local Selected Manufacturers Index (SMI) and the national market, but remaining equal to or above SMI. A yearly survey will be conducted to determine rates of pay, and the program will be administered by the Compensation department of the Employee Relations division. The benefits program, including vacations, retirement, self improvement courses, health assistance programs and paid absence from work for bona fide reasons will be available to *all* exempt and non-exempt employees and will be competitive with the area benefits programs. Additionally, for all job classifications, excellence in performance is encouraged by paying an additional wage to those who have demonstrated above-average capability in job performance. As previously stated, wages and benefits are subject to the obstacle/conflict resolution policy of the company and can be carried to the office of the president if inequities are perceived.

Company Pride

The whole of the parts of this approach to employee involvement and participation can be summed up by looking at the last spoke, which we call company pride. The company must be perceived by its employees as a good place to work and as being a responsible, contributing member of society. Since "the company" is its employees, the company's philosophy and actions must be reflected in the actions of employees. Participation in civic affairs, responsible, moral and ethical behavior as individual citizens of the community in which the employees reside and in the working environment all help in building mutual pride.

A department charged with improving the company's external image, promoting the free enterprise system, and developing political and economic awareness for all becomes essential and necessary. This department is a resource which employees may call upon as required to assist in building pride in the company.

SUMMARY

As responsible management continues to focus on the quality of work life for the people who constitute the company, a style of management will emerge. The style described in this quality of work life wheel is one of employee involvement and participation and we call the human element. By any name, a management style like this is one that recognizes human dignity and rights, and perceives the inestimable value that people will contribute to quality, productivity and profits, if given the opportunity to participate. The return on investment for all of this is the return on individual effort. Thus, the overall return on investment that management seeks will truly be linked to, and used synonymously for, a return on individuals and return on capital.

References:

1. Industry Week: January 11, 1982
2. Industry Week: December 14, 1981
3. Theory Z: William G. Ochi (Addison-Wesley 1981)

CHAPTER IV

MANAGEMENT REPORTING SYSTEMS

BY W.L. RAMMES

PURPOSE - GENERAL

Importance—Management reporting systems are required for accountability and control. Such systems should be designed to interface and present information in such a manner as to provide for:

1. Accounting input,
2. Operational control, and
3. Management/business decision making.

The base of any reporting and control system is measurement. "What you cannot measure, you cannot control" certainly applies to packaging, warehousing, and shipping systems.

Without responsive measurement and reporting, the control of packaging costs and future planning—for present or new packaging equipment, line design, and warehousing and shipping operations—cannot be acted upon with any degree of management confidence. In addition, accurate measurement and reporting is demanded in order to comply with regulatory and tax bodies.

Reporting systems and associated philosophies vary. It is the intent to limit this discussion to one such system on as general a basis as possible, in hopes that variations can be related and substituted.

Use—A management reporting system should be so designed and then used for:

1. Data presentation and subsequent reporting, and
2. Decision making.

Data must be collected and reported for both information purposes and for accounting purposes. However, a *management* reporting system must also lead to cost effective decision making. The system should be so designed that it can be readily used for operational control, operational changes, and investment alternatives. The reporting system must be based on accurate measurement, and must identify costs and point to problem areas.

Management reporting systems should be well integrated and data easily summarized. Detailed reporting for use at the line level is required, along with mechanisms to use that detailed data for summary level management reports. At the line (supervisor) level, reporting should be or should approach "real time". Decisions at this level take place as or right after events occur. Such "real time" reporting can be manual or automated and will be discussed later. Reporting at this level is at the lowest detail/cost level. This detail is later massaged and summarized for various plant and management personnel use. Further, the system should be able to compare similar operations for overall system control and alternate decision making.

How management uses information is obviously key in any business. Sound financial and operational control are the objectives of a well designed and integrated management information system.

STANDARDS

Throughout the following discussion, reference is made to standards. Standards are defined resource usage levels which represent expected performance. Standards therefore can be thought of as achievement levels or goals. Standards are the basic element of a management reporting and control system. Actual performance is measured against standard performance, and operating budgets for all direct resource usages should be developed using standards.

Standards are based on historical data, engineering studies, or a combination of both. Philosophies vary on how standards should be set and by whom. Whether done by the operating department or by a separate industrial engineering department, etc., the following points should be considered critical in establishing a standards program.

1. What are the standards to be used for? Ideally, standards should be used for controlling an operation and should be a basis for budgeting.
2. How realistic should the standards be? Standards should be realistic to the point that they can be achieved by a combination of good management practice and good worker performance.
3. Should standards contain an incentive to over-perform? This is an option of management and, if used, should be well understood by operating personnel. Also, considerable care must be taken when budgeting with standards that have built-in incentives. The financial implications of this type budgeting procedure must be well defined and recognized by senior management.

Again, philosophies vary on how standards are to be set and how they are to be used. It should be recognized, however, that standards established by professionals having experience in this field in combination with a sign-off by operating management should yield a system that will provide the basis for controlling costs.

OPERATIONAL MEASURES

Categories—In packaging operations, five basic resources are required to produce a finished package. They are:

Product—beer.

Materials—bottles, cans, cartons, other production supplies, etc.

Labor—production workers, bottlers, warehousemen, etc.

Energy/Utilities—electricity, fuel, water, etc.

Machines—packaging lines, fillers, crowners, packers, etc.

These resources combine to produce a *finished package*—cases of cans or bottles, half barrels, etc.

For accounting purposes, resources and their associated costs are subdivided into direct (activity related) and non-direct (period) costs. Many resources, other than those described above and falling into the category of non-direct costs, are required in packaging operations. Such items as salaries, maintenance labor and parts, and office expenses are but a few examples.

In order to limit this discussion, we will concentrate on the direct costs—those costs that vary with levels of production. Also the subject of packaging line utilization and efficiency will be examined, and the impact of efficiencies on costs will be discussed. Following the production cost discussion, we will look at warehousing and shipping reporting systems, and specifically look at information that is required for regulatory and tax bodies.

Direct costs are impacted by *price* and by *usage*. The effect of price on direct cost and the effect of usage on direct cost must each be understood and must be used separately for information and control purposes.

Price includes material prices, wage rates, energy/utility rates, etc. The responsibility for negotiating prices and controlling prices on a continuing basis may or may not fall within the packaging organization. Such is normally the responsibility of purchasing, industrial relations, and accounting personnel.

On the other hand, the control of resource *usage*—product, material, labor, energy, machines—is at the heart of a packaging reporting system. Obtaining the lowest and most efficient use of each resource, consistent with a defined level of quality, should be the goal around which a management reporting system is designed.

The use of each resource must be *defined, a goal or standard set,* and *actual usage reported* within specific time frames. Actual usage should be compared to defined (in some cases perfect) usage, or standard usage, or both. Examples are indicated for each major resource category.

Product—Beer

Beer released (transferred) from Brewing to the packaging area becomes a resource to the packaging operation. Accounting for this resource throughout the packaging operation is a major part of a packaging reporting and control system. Separate records of product flow by product type are necessary for regulatory reporting, but also can be used for product or process loss control.

1. *Defined Usage*

   Assuming no loss (perfect usage) and a standard 31 gallon barrel, 1 barrel of beer fills 13.7777 cases of 24/12 ounce bottles or cans.

2. *Goal or Standard Usage*

   Based on historical data or engineering studies, we know that losses occur during the packaging operation. This loss can be defined, and a goal or standard can thus be set. If, on the average, we lose .025 barrels for each barrel released to the packaging operation, then we can set a *standard loss* of 2.50% per barrel of beer released from Brewing.

3. *Actual Usage*

   Actual usage is based, for a specific time period, on the amount of beer released from Brewing and the amount of beer that was actually packaged. For example, assume for the month of January—

   7,425 barrels of beer released from Brewing
   100,000 cases of 24/12 ounce cans produced, which equates to 7,258 barrels of beer giving an actual loss of $(7,425 - 7,258) \div 7,425$ or 2.25%.

To summarize the above example:

Defined or perfect usage

0% Loss
(1 barrel = 13.7777 cases)

Standard Loss	2.50%
Actual Loss (for January)	2.25%

Since product loss is a *real* cost to the overall operation, importance should be placed on control and reduction of loss of this resource. When product is released from Brewing, it carries with it a cost of producing that product. If, for example, we assume a bulk product cost at the point of releasing of $10.00 per barrel, then using the above example, a loss of bulk product valued at $10.00 x (7,425 - 7,258) or $1,670 was experienced in the month of January.

Finer detail of product loss is defined and monitored in a good packaging operation. Product loss can be subdivided with those areas where losses are occurring, such as: bulk losses at the filler, filling losses, crowner/closer losses, line losses at the level inspectors, and warehouse losses.

Material—Examples of direct materials for packaging are:

Cans	Crowns
Bottles	Labels
Lids	Cartons

For a specific material, 12 ounce cans, the following can be developed:

1. *Defined Usage* (in this case, perfect usage)

   24 12-ounce cans per case are required; therefore, the defined usage is 24 cans.

2. *Goal or Standard Usage*

   Based on historical data or engineered study, we know that losses occur at various points and times on the packaging line, and that this loss can be defined. If we lose .10 can, on an average, for each case that is produced, then we can set a standard usage at

   24.10 cans per case, which

   says that 24.10 cans are required for each finished case of 24 cans.

3. *Actual Usage*

   Actual usage is based, for a specific time period, on the total number of cans supplied to the packaging line divided by the actual production of that packaging line. For example, assume for the month of January—

   100,000 cases of 24 - 12 ounce cans produced

   2,450,000 12 ounce cans supplied to the line giving an actual usage of 24.50 12 ounce cans per case.

To summarize the above example:

Defined or perfect usage	24.00 cans per case
Standard usage	24.10 cans per case
Actual usage (for January)	24.50 cans per case

This type of information can be developed for each specific material resource. With this information budgets can be developed and reporting systems designed to monitor and control costs. By applying price to the usage data, dollar variances can be calculated.

Using the above information, and assuming cans cost $.06 each, the following cost information can be developed:

2,450,000 cans used @ $.06 = $147,000 total cost of cans for January.

100,000 cases of 24 12-ounce cans were produced in January.

At 24 cans per case perfect usage

2,400,000 cans should have been used

50,000 more cans were used than perfect usage and at $.06 per can, a

($3,000) variance to perfect usage was generated.
Comparing to standard
at 24.10 cans per case standard usage
   2,410,000 cans were expected to be used
   40,000 more cans were used versus standard and
at $.06 per can, a
   ($2,400) variance to standard was generated.
See Table I for a sample report. Dollar variances for usage that exceeds
perfect or standard usage, that is an unfavorable dollar variance, can be
indicated with brackets ( ). Dollar variances based on usage below standard
would then be indicated without ( ). Use of this type information will give a
means for both identifying costs and controlling costs.

TABLE I
MATERIAL USAGE
JANUARY

| Description | Production Activity Cases | Usage-Cans/Cs. | | | Variance | |
		Perfect Usage	Standard Usage	Actual Usage	Versus Perfect Usage	Versus Standard Usage
12 oz. cans	100,000 cs	24.00	24.10	24.50	($3,000)	($2,400)

Labor—For production labor the following can be developed:
1. *Defined Usage*
   5 operators are required to operate a can line.
   Can line designed to produce 10,000 cases per 8 hour shift.
   Therefore, 40 manhours are required to produce 10,000 cases, or .0040
   manhours per case.
2. *Goal or Standard Usage*
   Based on historical data and engineered time standards, the following
   has been developed as a standard.
   9,500 cases per shift can be expected based upon historical data and
   engineered studies.
   5.5 operators are required (allowing for relief) based on engineered
   studies, or 44 manhours. Therefore, the standard allowance is .0046
   manhours per case.
3. *Actual Usage*
   Actual usage is based, for a specific time period, on the total number
   of manhours used to produce the actual cases of production. For example,
   assume for the month of January
      100,000 cases of 24 12-ounce cans produced
      440 manhours were used
      giving an actual usage of
      .0044 manhours per case
To summarize the above example:
Defined usage	.0040 manhours per case
Standard usage	.0046 manhours per case
Actual usage (for January)	.0044 manhours per case

As with the example on material, this type of labor information can be used for developing budgets and reporting systems. In this example, labor dollar rates can be applied and dollar variances calculated.

With the above data, and assuming a labor cost of $8.00 per hour, the following cost information can be developed.

440 manhours used @ $8.00 = $3,520 total labor cost for January
100,000 cases of 24 12-ounce cans were produced in January
at .0040 manhours per case defined usage
400 manhours should have been used
40 manhours more were used versus defined usage and at
$8.00 per manhour, a ($320) variance to defined usage was generated.
Compared to standard
At .0046 manhours per case
460 manhours should have been used
20 manhours less were used versus standard and at
$8.00 per manhour, a $160 variance to standard was generated. (This time a positive, no brackets, variance.)

See Table II for a sample report. Like the material illustration, this labor information will give a means for both identifying costs and controlling costs.

TABLE II
LABOR UTILIZATION
JANUARY

| Description | Production Activity Cases | Usage-Manhours/Cs. | | | Variance | |
		Perfect Usage	Standard Usage	Actual Usage	Versus Perfect Usage	Versus Standard Usage
Can Line Labor	100,000 cs	.0040	.0046	.0044	($320)	$160

Energy/Utilities—For energy/utilities, the following can be developed.
1. *Defined Usage*
   As an example, electricity—
   .150 kilowatt hours of electricity are required to produce 1 case of 24 12-ounce cans. This usage is based on both historical data and engineered study.
2. *Goal or Standard Usage*
   Same as above.
3. *Actual Usage*
   Actual usage is based, for a specific time period, on the total KWH used to produce the actual cases of production.
   For example, assume for the month of January
      100,000 cases of 24 12-ounce cans produced
      17,500 KWH were used
      giving an actual usage of
      .175 KWH per case
To summarize this example:
   Defined/Standard usage   .150 KWH per case
   Actual usage (for January)   .175 KWH per case

With this data, and assuming an electricity cost of $.05 per KWH, the following cost information can be developed.

17,500 KWH used @ $.05 = $875 total electricity cost for January.

100,000 cases of 24 12-ounce cans were produced in January.

At .150 KWH per case defined/standard usage

15,000 KWH should have been used

2,500 KWH more were used versus defined usage

and at $.05 per KWH, a

($125) variance to defined usage was generated.

See Table III for a sample report.

TABLE III
ENERGY USAGE - ELECTRICITY
JANUARY

| | | Usage-KWH/Cs. | | Variance |
| | Production Activity | Standard | Actual | Versus Standard |
Description	Cases	Usage	Usage	Usage
Electricity Can Line	100,000 cs	.150	.175	($125)

Similar data can be developed for each type energy/utility employed.

The information presented in these above three illustrations can be presented separately, i.e., all material on one report, all labor on another report, etc. An alternative would be to present information by package, i.e., all resource usage areas on one report for 24 12-ounce cans. See Table IV.

TABLE IV
RESOURCE USAGE - 12 OZ. CANS FINISHED PACKAGE
JANUARY

| | | Usage | | | Variance | |
| | Production Activity | | Standard | Actual | Versus Perfect | Versus Standard |
Description	Cases	Perfect Usage	Usage	Usage	Usage	Usage
12 Oz Cans	100,000 cs	24.00	24.10	24.50	($3,000)	($2,400)
Line Labor	100,000 cs	.0040	.0046	.0044	($ 320)	$ 160
Electricity	100,000 cs		.150	.175		($125)
					TOTAL	($2,365)

Standard or perfect usage rates can be used for budget preparation. By using a forecasted volume, usages can be extended by volume and price to calculate budget dollars by resource area and by package type.

Machines—Machines—fillers, labelers, packers, etc.—are purchased with capital dollars or are leased. How effectively the capital asset is employed should be a major part of a management reporting system.

Machine use is measured in terms of machine utilization and/or machine efficiency. There are various ways of calculating and reporting these two measures. Further, this subject is an important one in that the efficiency of machines and the overall efficiency of packaging lines does have a direct effect on the efficient use of the other four resources . . . product, material, labor and energy.

Overall efficiency of a packaging line can be measured in terms of actual output versus theoretical maximum output. Packaging line utilization can be measured in terms of actual operating time versus total available operating time.

Packaging line efficiency is affected by the efficiency of each component of the line. In order to adequately control and influence the efficiency of a packaging line, each component of that line must be monitored and its effect on the overall efficiency of the line determined. This can be done either manually or automatically through various automated monitoring devices, including computer controlled equipment with automated reporting enhancements.

The overall efficiency of a packaging line must be measured against a defined base. However, that base is complicated by the number and variety of separate pieces of equipment associated with that line. The design speed (or theoretical maximum output) of a packaging line should be based on the design speed of the slowest (or limiting) section or piece of equipment on that line. For most packaging lines, that piece of equipment is, by design, the filler. Therefore, the efficiency of a packaging line is measured against the design speed of the filler.

To look at a simplified example, assume a packaging line with a design speed of 1000 cans per minute. If that line is run continuously for 8 hours, the theoretical output of the line, in 24 12-ounce case equivalents, would be 20,000 cases. If the line *actually* produced 18,000 cases during a given 8 hour period, the efficiency of that line would be 18,000 ÷ 20,000 or 90%.

Obviously, the important item is not so much the 90% efficiency number, but rather the other 10%, i.e., the time and associated production loss due to equipment downtime. The efficiency reporting system, a key element in an overall management reporting system, must address not only line efficiencies, but also line downtime. Line downtime is the basis on which action is taken to improve line operations. See Table V for a sample efficiency report.

TABLE V
LINE EFFICIENCY

| Description | Production Cases | Minutes Operated | Lost Minutes | | | | | | Unit Efficiency |
			Depall.	Filler	Past.	Packers	Pall.	Total	
12 Oz. Cans	100,000	2,700	20	150	90	30	10	300	90%

Packaging line efficiencies, more than all other areas, have a direct effect on the efficiency and cost effectiveness of a plant operation. As a result of efficient line operations, material losses are minimized, therefore, material costs are less; occurrences of idled labor are lessened, therefore, labor costs are less; beer losses are minimized, therefore, product cost is less; and energy is utilized efficiently, therefore, energy costs are less. Further, the responsibilities of operators, supervisors, and maintenance personnel are made easier when packaging efficiency is high.

There are many alternatives and sophistications for reporting efficiency information. Time series graphing techniques which point to trends in efficiency levels is a very good tool, especially for upper management personnel, and particularly when multiple lines or multiple plants are involved. See Figure 4-1.

However the information is displayed, the most important benefit must be the resultant decisions which lead to improved operations.

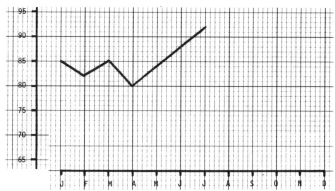

4-1. Efficiency graph

REPORTING SYSTEM INPUTS

There are many elements of input data that are required for packaging reporting systems. These elements are required not only to satisfy the needs of information and control systems, but must also feed information for accounting and state and federal reporting requirements.

Materials Reporting—Reporting of materials starts with the ordering process. Materials are ordered based on a projected production plan. Materials are received, may or may not be placed in inventory, and then used in the packaging process. Some materials are lost to scrap during the production process. A reporting system for materials, excluding the ordering process, should contain the following elements:

1. Material name/description
2. Material numbers
3. Amount received
4. Amount in inventory
5. Amount used

See Table VI. This information is used for both the accounting system and the control system. The quantity used, in this case 2,450,000 cans, is the input to the control system discussed earlier. Inventories of packaging materials must be taken, in most instances at a minimum of at least monthly, and reconciliations made for accounting purposes.

Labor Reporting—Reporting of labor is based on hours. Labor hour reporting is input into both a payroll system and a control system. Labor is scheduled

TABLE VI
MATERIAL REPORTING
JANUARY

Material Description	Material Number	Amount Received	Beginning Inventory	Ending Inventory	Amount Used
12 Oz. Cans	100100	2,400,000	250,000	200,000	2,450,000

for specific work elements and for specific time periods. Labor hours can be either reported automatically, via time clocks, manually via foreman record keeping, or both. Normally both automatic and manual reporting is done for not only a system of checks and balances, but also for accurate recording of hours worked for various job functions. A reporting system for labor should contain the following elements:

1. Employees' name and number
2. Job description or assignment
3. Hours worked

See Table VII. The hours worked in this case is the input to the control system. An employee may work at more than one job in a given eight hour period. It is important that the system be designed so that a record is made of the number of hours worked at each position.

TABLE VII
LABOR REPORTING

Employee Name	Employee Number	Job Assignment	Hours Worked
Doe, John	D100	Filler Operator	6
		Fork Truck Driver	2

Energy/Utilities Reporting—Energy and utility usage is usually determined via meter readings and actual billings. How accurate and detailed reporting of these resources are is based on the amount of metering available. As energy becomes more expensive, the control of this resource becomes increasingly important. The number of meters required must be balanced against the value received. However, in order to have a management information system that both details costs to the individual package type and leads to adequate controls, the amount of metering is an important consideration. If metering allows energy usage measurement at the packaging line level, then meter readings over defined periods allow for input into the control system as discussed earlier. If, however, metering is limited to input to the total plant only, then a system of distributing energy costs to individual packaging lines and individual packages must be devised. Normally, these distributions are based on engineering studies which take into account the amount of equipment requiring energy and the amount of energy required by piece of equipment.

Machine Efficiency/Utilization Reporting—Packaging line efficiency reporting can take many forms and can be manual, automatic, or both. The success and accuracy of a reporting system depends on accurate input and follow-up. Even though an automated system may be more accurate than a manual system, the manual system which requires the packaging line supervisor to record downtime may be more successful in that the individual is more aware of downtime and its effect on the line. Means should be sought that integrate both automatic and manual systems, take advantage of both, and lead to decision making and action that improves the operation of the line.

The main focus of a packaging line efficiency reporting system is on line downtime. Downtime should be recorded for each major piece of equipment or area, a reason given for the downtime, along with what action was or is required to correct the downtime cause. Depending upon the design of the packaging line and the amount and location of accumulation built into the line, downtime of specific pieces of equipment may or may not affect the output of the line at any one point in time. The output of the line is only affected when the filler stops. However, this does not diminish the importance of downtime on all pieces of equipment, as each piece of equipment is a link in the packaging line that can affect the output.

Downtime of a piece of equipment or area exists if:

1. Prime exists, i.e., the package or product is available for processing.
2. Equipment or areas downstream are ready or waiting to accept the package or product.
3. This piece of equipment or this area is not processing the package or product.

The packaging line should be divided by major piece of equipment or area. As an example, for a bottle line:

1. Unstacker
2. Empty Bottle Case Delivery System
3. Uncaser
4. Rinser/Soaker
5. Empty Bottle Conveyor/Bottle Inspection
6. Filler
7. Crowner
8. Full Bottle Conveyors/Bottle Inspection, Fill Level
9. Pasteurizer
10. Late Side Full Bottle Conveyors
11. Labelers
12. Packers
13. Slitter/Sealer
14. Full Case Delivery Belt
15. Palletizer

Again, as an example, for a can line:

1. Bulk Can Conveying System
2. Bulk Can Depalletizer
3. Empty Can Conveyors
4. Rinsers
5. Filler
6. Closer
7. Pasteurizer
8. Full Can Inspection

9. Full Can Conveyors
10. Packer
11. Full Case Delivery Belt
12. Palletizer

Other areas of downtime that should be recorded include line changeovers, downtime due to other than mechanical reasons, such as material shortages, major power outages, etc.

Automated downtime monitoring assures two important measures—frequency and duration of downtimes. Manual reporting, on the other hand, will not be as precise regarding frequencies and durations; however, it will afford reasons for downtime and will lead to actionable decisions regarding correction of downtime causes. Again, a well integrated system, consisting of both types of reporting, is the best alternative.

One method of tracking and reporting downtime is through a log kept by the packaging line foreman. The foreman's log, in addition to recording downtime and downtime reasons, also can be the input document for other measures, particularly quality related items, such as beer temperatures, airs, CO_2, pasteurizer temperatures, etc., and production related items such as beer meter readings and case counts.

Figure 4-2 is a sample foreman's log. Downtime is recorded by major piece of equipment or area, reasons for downtime are explained, and action taken or action required is indicated. On the back side, Figure 4-3, are other line checks that may be required to keep adequate records of the line operations.

	HOUR	1	2	3	4	5	6	7	8
	CASES	2000	2500						
	TOTAL	2000	4500						

	TIME	REASON		ACTION REQUIRED			
20	9:35	PALLET MAGAZINE JAMMED		CONVEYOR CHAIN & SPROCKET REALIGNED			

(DOWNTIME MINUTES — columns: BCC SYSTEM, BC DEPAL., MT CAN CONV., RINSERS, FILLERS, CLOSER, PASTEURIZER, FULL CAN INSP., FULL CAN CONV., PACKER, FULL CASE CONV., PALLETIZER)

4-2. Foreman's log

The foreman's log acts not only as a history of line performance, but also as an action oriented document that should lead to correcting line performance deficiencies or elimination of downtime causes. Downtime causes and resultant action required can impact many departments, e.g., maintenance, quality control, purchasing, etc. The foreman's log can be the input to a maintenance schedule, can alert quality control to problem areas, and advise purchasing of material quality or scheduling problems. This log, or a summary of such, should be the focal point in production-maintenance meetings.

	CASE COUNTER 1	CASE COUNTER 2	BEER METER
END			
START			
TOTAL			

	FILLER COUNTER PRESSURE	BEER OUT TEMPERATURE

TIME	FILLER SPEED	FILL CHECK	AIR CHECK	COUNTER PRESSURE	BEER LEVEL	INSPECTORS	PAST. TEMP.	CAN CODE	LIDS	CARTON CODE

4-3. Reverse side of foreman's log

As with any reporting system, the most important factor is follow-up. This report is key to an effective management system. Without proper follow-up, and feed-back to the foreman, the effectiveness of the system is lost.

In addition to the foreman's log, a production schedule is normally given to the foreman indicating what product and package is to be produced and in what quantities. Actual production is entered on this schedule, along with beer meter readings, and this becomes the input to accounting. See Figure 4-4. Beer meter readings and case counts are important in that they are the inputs for state and federal regulatory and tax reports.

Date		Line		Time Sent		By	
Quantity Scheduled	Product	Container	Stock Number	Actual Production	Case Counter Reading	Beer Meter Reading

4-4. Production Schedule.

Following the production process, finished package goods are warehoused and then shipped. Formalized inventory procedures and reporting, along with accurate shipping documents are required. After product comes off the packaging line and is palletized, it is stored, for varying lengths of time, in the warehouse. Through periodic inventories, product is counted and verified against production and shipment records. Again, as with packaging lines, warehousing records can be either manual, automated, or a combination of both. Included in warehousing procedures can be sophisticated stock location and inventory automated systems. Such systems keep track of product locations, product age, and inventories, and can be tied directly to stock movement and shipment records. Order generation and ship orders are required to schedule shipping operations. The degree of sophistication of such systems is dependent on the size of the operation and the multiplicity of products. Further warehouse and shipping controls include checking of truck and rail loads, along with truck and rail seals for security reasons. Actual shipments, by customer, are required for accounting purposes and formalized records must be maintained.

Data processing operations, whether manual or automated, receive data from packaging and shipping operations and transform this information into output reports. As with other systems, the size and sophistication of data processing services is dependent on the size of the operation. Multi-plant, multi-line, multi-package operations require highly automated systems versus a one-plant, one line operation. Data Processing outputs are used for accounting purposes, information systems, and control systems.

OUTPUT REPORTS

Output reports should be designed either for accounting purposes or for management information/control purposes. In some cases, a report may satisfy both needs; normally, however, accounting reports are more detailed out of necessity and therefore may not be in a format easily used by management for operational control. Also, measures for control purposes are not always transferable to bottom line financial information. For example, a production line operating at a 90% efficiency level may not mean much to a financial analyst, even though high efficiency levels favorably impact bottom line results.

Materials—Using the information as indicated in Table I, output reports can be developed that track material usage. Because materials, certainly in packaging operations, make up the largest component of cost, it is important that adequate systems are in-place to control this resource. Dollars variances can be tracked as well as usage of individual packaging material items. Figure 4-5 is an example of a time series graph of 12 ounce can usage. By plotting usage around perfect usage or standard usage, it is readily apparent how the usage of this resource is being controlled. Also, dollar variances can be reported on for set time intervals. For example, as illustrated in Table VIII, both monthly and year-to-date dollar variances are indicated for a number of packaging material items.

As with all components of cost, responsive follow-up using the management information system is a must. Follow-up should occur down through the various levels of management, and causes for variances or out-of-control conditions explained at the lowest detail level. This will then "close the loop" of a good control system.

Labor—Beyond labor reporting for payroll purposes, output reports can be designed to measure the productive use of this resource.

Labor efficiency is the measure of the use of labor versus standard. This

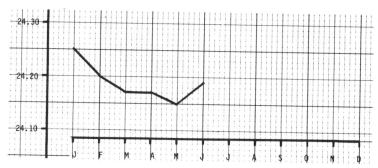

4-5. *12 oz. can usage.*

TABLE VIII
MATERIAL VARIANCES

Description	Month Variance Versus		Year-to-Date Variance Versus	
	Perfect Usage	Standard Usage	Perfect Usage	Standard Usage
12 Oz. Cans	($ 500)	$1,000	($2,000)	$ 500
Lids	($4,000)	($3,000)	($1,500)	($1,200)
Cartons	($ 10)	$1,300	($ 80)	$1,600
TOTAL	($4,510)	($ 700)	($3,580)	$ 900

TABLE IX
LABOR EFFICIENCY

Description	Production Activity Cases	Standard Hours	Actual Hours	Dollar Variance	Efficiency Versus Standard
Can Line Labor	100,000	460	440	$160	105%

can also be related to in dollar variances, both shown as an example in Table IX.

An additional measure, which allows the tracking of labor usage, is based on the amount of labor used to produce a barrel of beer. This can be expressed in barrels per manhour or other similar measures. By monitoring trends, it is readily apparent whether labor efficiency is being achieved.

Obviously, many items affect labor efficiency, the most apparent being line efficiencies in the packaging area. However, the effective use of labor in warehousing operations, shipping operations, etc., can also be monitored on a barrel per manhour basis.

Overtime costs are an additional measure of the effective use of labor. Overtime dollars relative to budget, or overtime dollars on a per barrel basis, are just two means of tracking this expense.

Energy and Utilities—As previously mentioned, energy and utilities are becoming an ever increasing percentage of production costs. Reporting systems that track energy usages, such as oil and gas measured in BTU's, electricity measured in KWH, and water and sewer costs, are becoming more and more important. Figures 4-6 and 4-7 are time series graphs indicating fuel and electricity usages. Similar type information can be developed and monitored for water and for sewer.

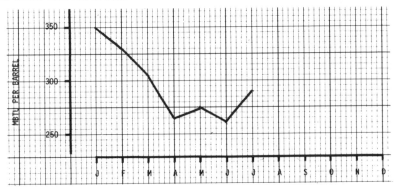

4-6. Fuel usage

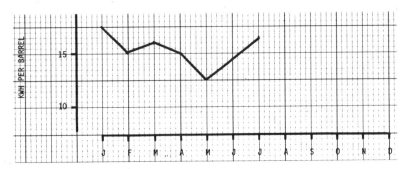

4-7. Electricity usage

Sewer costs can be reported in terms of flow, BOD, etc. The degree to which these usages and costs are monitored is obviously going to be determined based upon their cost impact. These are, however, real components of production costs and systems should be developed to monitor and report their associated impact.

Machines—Because of the importance of packaging line efficiencies on most other production costs, this one area can give management a definite feel for the trend in overall operations and costs. Table V showed a sample line efficiency report. Numerous types of tables and graphs can be made using the information presented on this report. One such report can be a simple time series plotting line efficiency as was seen in Figure 4-1. Other measures can involve cases per shift, barrels per shift, barrels per hour, etc. Any means that remain consistent and measure efficiency against a predetermined base should suffice. The measurement chosen is normally chosen by management based on a management style and emphasis. For any measurement and control system to be effective, it must be understood by not only all management levels but also by the production workers and machine operators.

Beer Metering and Finished Package Accounting—In the United States, specific information is required and must be filed with governmental bodies. Two such reports are the Brewers Monthly Report of Operations and a Beer Tax Return required by the Department of the Treasury—Bureau of Alcohol, Tobacco and Firearms. See Figures 4-8 and 4-9. Both of these reports require that detailed records be maintained in all areas of the plant. Bulk beer is metered through approved meters, and detailed accounting of production, consumage, returns, laboratory samples, shipments, etc. is made. Such accountability requires strict procedures.

Warehousing and shipping reports generally are accounting records and such information as inventory levels, shipments, returns, etc. should be constantly monitored at the plant level. Every effort should be made to assure the accuracy of these records, and to maintain in operating order all meters and case counters.

In Canada, brewers are required to maintain detailed daily records of beer production, movement and shipment. Federal Excise Duty is computed daily on the final count of filled packages going to warehouse. Fills are monitored to ensure correct payment. A Federal Sales Tax is applied to beer shipped for sale and each Provincial Government levies its own taxes, although the basis for these varies from province to province.

Complete records must be kept and available for Excise inspection, of the disposal of all beer produced including shipments, returns, destruction of beer unfit for sale, consumption and normal production losses. The Canadian Excise has never formally approved the use of meters for official purposes of duty calculation, but they may be used for internal record keeping. Gauged tanks are used to determine volumes.

Multi-Plant Operations—Reports are required by corporate level management when dealing with a multi-plant system. When designing such a system, it is best to view reporting output requirements in terms of a pyramid-type system. As reporting moves through various levels of management, by necessity detailed reporting becomes more and more aggregated. For example, a corporate level manager with a multi-plant operation needs to first look at an overall efficiency number for a given plant rather than the efficiency of each line at that particular plant. Only on an exception basis should he need to look at each line at a given plant. See Table X. An important aspect, however, in this type management reporting is the need for all levels of management to understand the system and have access to the lowest level of detail when required.

To follow this same logic, dollar variances can be aggregated up to one number for a given plant. This number is made up of variances of each resource item, from 12 ounce can usage to overall material, from labor for a filler operator to overall plant labor, etc., until an overall plant variance number is generated. See Table XI. Each level of management will determine what aggregate level best suits his needs from both an information and control standpoint.

BREWERY *(Name and Address)*

DEPARTMENT OF THE TREASURY
BUREAU OF ALCOHOL, TOBACCO, AND FIREARMS

BREWER'S MONTHLY REPORT OF OPERATIONS

DATE *(MONTH AND YEAR)*

INSTRUCTIONS

1. Prepare this form in duplicate. Send the original to the Regional Director, Bureau of Alcohol, Tobacco and Firearms, by the tenth day after the end of the month for which submitted. Keep the duplicate at the brewery readily available for inspection by ATF officers.

2. Make entries from Form 2051, Record of Brewery Operations, or from authorized substitute records.

3. Report beer in terms of barrels of 31 gallons carried to the third decimal place; report cereal beverage in whole barrels only.

4. If the quantity of beer previously reported on a Form 103 is affected by adjustments made on a tax return, Form 2034, adjust the current Form 103 by interlining plus or minus entries on appropriate lines in columns (c) and (e) of Part I. Do not interline plus or minus entries in the totals in column (f) or in the totals on lines 14 and 35; instead, such totals should be the net total of the entries and adjustments in the applicable lines and columns. Fully explain adjusting entries in the space for "Remarks."

5. Shortages of keg and case beer reported in Part I, line 30, columns (c) and (e), must be fully explained in either Part IV, or in a separate signed statement submitted with this report. Failure to satisfactorily explain shortages of case or keg beer may result in the assessment of taxes applicable to these shortages.

6. Report material in pounds and in the appropriate general classification, as: malt and malt products, corn and corn products, rice and rice products, wheat and wheat products, barley and barley products, sorghum grain and sorghum grain products, sugar and sirups, and hops. Quantities of hop extracts in pounds and their equivalents in pounds of hops shall be reported as two separate items.

7. If wort or wort concentrate received from another brewery or from a pilot brewing plant is used in the production of beer or cereal beverage, report on a separate line in an unused column of Part II the quantity and balling of the wort or wort concentrate used. Also report on the same separate line in the appropriate columns the quantities of the various materials used in originally producing the quantity of wort or wort concentrate reported used.

PART 1 — BEER SUMMARY (IN TERMS OF BARRELS)

ITEM	CELLAR OPERATIONS (a)	RACKING OPERATIONS		BOTTLING OPERATIONS		TOTALS (f)
		BULK (b)	KEG BEER (c)	BULK (d)	CASE BEER (e)	
1. ON HAND FIRST OF MONTH						
2. PRODUCED						
3. WATER/LIQUIDS ADDED IN CELLARS						
4. RECEIVED FROM RACKING AND BOTTLING OPERATIONS						
5. REC'D FROM OTHER BREWERIES AND FROM PILOT BREWING PLANTS						
6. RECEIVED FROM CELLARS						
7. RECEIVED-BEER RETURNED TO BREWERY AFTER REMOVAL THEREFROM						
8. REC'D-BEER RETURNED TO BREWERY AFTER REMOVAL FROM ANOTHER BREWERY						
9. RACKED						
10. BOTTLED						
11. OVERAGES *(INVENTORY)*						
12.						
13.						
14. TOTALS						
15. REMOVED FOR CONSUMPTION OR SALE						
16. REMOVED FREE OF TAX FOR EXPORT						
17. REMOVED AS SUPPLIES *(VESSELS, ETC.)*						
18. REMOVED-USE IN RESEARCH DEVELOPMENT OR TESTING						
19. TRANSFERRED TO OTHER BREWERIES AND TO PILOT BREWING PLANTS						
20. CONSUMED ON PREMISES						
21. TRANSFERRED FOR RACKING						
22. TRANSFERRED FOR BOTTLING						
23. RETURNED TO CELLARS						
24. RACKED						
25. BOTTLED						
26. LABORATORY SAMPLES						
27. DESTROYED UNDER SUPERVISION						
28. DESTROYED WITHOUT SUPERVISION						
29. RECORDED LOSSES *(INCLUDING THEFT)*						
30. SHORTAGES *(INVENTORY)* *(See Instruction No. 5)*						
31.						
32.						
33.						
34. ON HAND END OF MONTH						
35. TOTALS						

4-8. U. S. Brewer's Monthly Report of Operations

DEPARTMENT OF THE TREASURY — BUREAU OF ALCOHOL, TOBACCO AND FIREARMS **BEER TAX RETURN** *(Prepare in quadruplicate — See instructions on back)*	1. SERIAL NUMBER *(Begin with "1" Jan. 1 each year)*

2. PERIOD COVERED *(Time, month, day and year)[1]*		3. FORM OF PAYMENT	
From	To	☐ CHECK ☐ MONEY ORDER ☐ OTHER *(Specify)*	

4. EMPLOYER IDENTIFICATION NUMBER	5. AMOUNT OF PAYMENT	NOTE: PLEASE MAKE CHECKS OR MONEY ORDERS PAYABLE TO THE INTERNAL REVENUE SERVICE

6. RETURN COVERS ☐ PREPAYMENT ☐ PERIOD INDICATED	*(Show Employer Identification Number on all checks or money orders)*

7. NAME AND ADDRESS *(Begin one space below dots)*	Internal Revenue Service Use Only

TAX	$	
PENALTY		
INTEREST		
TOTAL	$	

RECAPITULATION OF TAX *(Before making entries 1 through 5, fill in applicable schedules)*

1. TOTAL TAX *(line 10 A col. (c) plus line 10 B col. (c))*	$
2. ADJUSTMENTS INCREASING TAX *(From line 17)*	
3. GROSS TAX *(Total of lines 1 and 2)*	
4. ADJUSTMENTS DECREASING TAX *(From line 24)*	
5. TAX TO BE PAID WITH THIS RETURN	$
(Line 3 minus line 4) (Includes $ _____ net interest paid)[2]	

Under penalties of perjury I declare that I have examined this return, including accompanying explanations, statements, schedules, and forms, and to the best of my knowledge and belief, it is true, correct and complete, and includes all transactions and tax liabilities required by law or regulations to be reported.

SIGNATURE	TITLE	DATE

SCHEDULE A. — BEER TAX *(Based on barrels of 31 gallons)*

CHARACTER OF TAXPAYMENT *(a)*	TOTAL BARRELS *(b) (3 decimal places)*	AMOUNT OF TAX *(c)*
6. KEG BEER FOR TAXPAYMENT *(From line 42, col. (c))*		
7. BOTTLED BEER FOR TAXPAYMENT *(From line 42, col. (d))*		
8. TOTAL REMOVALS		
9. RETURNS TO BREWERY *(From line 42, col. (e))*		
10. NET REMOVALS AND AMOUNT OF TAX FOR THE PERIOD		
A. NET REMOVALS *(line 8 minus line 9)* AND AMOUNT OF TAX AT $9.00 PER BARREL		$
B. NET REMOVALS *(line 8 minus line 9)* AND AMOUNT OF TAX AT $7.00 PER BARREL *(for qualified brewers/maximum allowance 60,000 barrels per calendar year or proportioned amount)[3]*		$
NET REMOVALS AT $7.00 PER BARREL FROM JANUARY 1 OF CURRENT YEAR TO THE END OF THE CURRENT TAX PERIOD *maximum 60,000 barrels or proportioned amount)[3]*		

SCHEDULE B. — ADJUSTMENTS INCREASING AMOUNT DUE *(See instructions)*

EXPLANATION OF INDIVIDUAL ERRORS OR TRANSACTIONS *(a)*	TOTAL BARRELS *(b) (3 decimal places)*	AMOUNT OF ADJUSTMENTS	
		(c) TAX	*(d) INTEREST*
12.		$	$
13.			
14.			
15.			
16. TOTAL BEER AND AMOUNT OF ADJUSTMENTS		$	$
17. TOTAL TAX AND INTEREST ADJUSTMENTS *(Column (c) plus column (d))*			$

[1]/Time need be shown only where brewer uses a business day other than a calendar day *(See 27 CFR 245.5).*
[2]/Subtract interest in line 23, column (d) from interest in line 16, col. (d) and enter net interest paid with this return, if any.
[3]/Entry shall be made only by brewers qualified for reduced tax rate *(See 27 CFR 245.110 a and 245.110 c).*

ATF F 2034 (5130.7) (2-77)   EDITION OF 11/76 MAY BE USED

4-9. U. S. Beer Tax Return

Other Reports—There are other reports that flow through the packaging department that provide operating supervision valuable information.

1. Those from Quality Assurance cover both packaging materials and product quality. The first category may help avoid operating problems while

TABLE X
PLANT EFFICIENCIES

Plant X	92%
Plant Y	87%
Plant Z	96%

LINE EFFICIENCIES BY PLANT

PLANT X		PLANT Y		PLANT Z	
Line 1	90%	Line 1	91%	Line 1	97%
Line 2	96%	Line 2	75%	Line 2	96%
Line 3	87%	Line 3	84%		
		Line 4	97%		

TABLE XI
PLANT VARIANCE REPORT

	Month Variance Versus		Year-To-Date Versus	
Material Usage	**Perfect Usage**	**Standard Usage**	**Perfect Usage**	**Standard Usage**
12 Oz Cans	($ 500)	$1,000	($2,000)	$ 500
Lids	.	.	.	.
Cartons	.	.	.	.
12 Oz NR Bottles	.	.	.	.
.	.	.	.	.
.	.	.	.	.
.	.	.	.	.
Total Material Usage	($6,000)	($2,000)	($8,000)	$1,000
Labor Efficiency				
Can Line Labor	($ 320)	($ 760)	($1,400)	($1,200)
Bottle Line Labor	.	.	.	.
.	.	.	.	.
.	.	.	.	.
Total Labor	.	.	.	.
Energy/Utility Usage				
.	.	.	.	.
.	.	.	.	.
Total Energy/Utility Usage	.	.	.	.
TOTAL PLANT	($8,000)	$4,000	($7,000)	$3,000

those in the second, that of product or packaging quality, are an assessment of packaging performance. One important report is the Consumer Complaint Report which is, in effect, an assessment of packaging performance by the customer and deserves close attention at all levels. These reports are covered in greater detail in Chapter XXII.

2. Safety Reports involving both Accident Reports originating at the supervisory level and the subsequent Safety Investigation Reports provide feedback bearing on the well-being of personnel. Such reports are covered in detail in Chapter XXI.

3. Maintenance Reports cover a variety of subjects important to operating personnel. For example, a Work Request to repair or adjust a piece of equipment can originate with line supervision. A Maintenance Report covering the work done not only provides information to supervision not present during the actual maintenance but it is also part of the historical file on that item of equipment. Additional information on this subject can be found in Chapter XXV, Maintenance and Lubrication.

RESPONSE - FOLLOW-UP

As has been stated throughout this discussion, and no matter what type of information/reporting system is employed, the system cannot be effective unless constant follow-up and feedback is the rule. Supervisor's logs should lead to shift action, or daily action, or both. Daily and weekly production/ maintenance/quality control meetings are required to respond to apparent problem areas in the production process. By reviewing logs, graphs, and cost information, management must assure that the proper response and emphasis is properly directed. This type of effort must be made at all management levels. A follow-up system should be devised that measures actions and monitors progress. Finally, the next round of management reports will indicate if actions taken have worked. A properly designed and implemented management information system should provide the vehicle to control packaging operations.

Equally important to short-term response and follow-up is mid- and long-term planning. A well designed information and control system can provide essential information for future line design, plant design and equipment evaluation and selection. Models can be developed that can predict plant costs which can be used for decisions regarding plant expansions and new sites.

To summarize what was stated at the beginning of this work, the purpose of a good management reporting system is accountability and control. The system must both provide operational control and serve as an input to management/business decision making. Reporting systems and philosophies vary based on the needs and styles of corporate management. The system described herein was used to illustrate the basic principles in any management reporting system. How management uses information is key in any business. A well developed and well utilized management reporting system will both control costs in the near term and provide the basis for long term planning.

REFERENCE FOR ADDITIONAL READING

"Isolating Controllable Budget Variances", A.L. Leith *MBAA Technical Quarterly*, Vol. 15, Pg 87-93, 1978

CHAPTER V

PACKAGING DEPARTMENT LAYOUT

BY DONALD R. SITTNER AND
WILLIAM G. SPARGO

INTRODUCTION

The design elements of the total beer packaging and shipping operation must be recognized as the key ingredients for good packaging line layouts and successful performance of brewery packaging lines. Brewing the finest quality products is the first part of the total picture, with efficient packaging line layout being the second part, each complementing the other, for a totally successful operation. Specifically, producing the packages on an efficient packaging line is as significant as packaging the product in attractive containers and packages for sales and marketing.

An efficient brewing and packaging operation starts with an efficient site plan layout of the brewing, packaging, utilities, roadways, rail tracks and other support facilities. Of particular concern is the relationship between the brewing and packaging operations. Figure 5-1 shows a plot plan with the buildings numbered. The names of the buildings are shown on the right hand side of the illustration.

Figure 5-2 shows a typical site plan with the various buildings shown. Note the Brew House, Stock House and Utilities. Adjacent to these facilities is the Packaging operation. This integrated arrangement is beneficial from the standpoint of providing a satisfactory design for the filtered beer lines supplying the bottle and can fillers and keg rackers as well as the routing of utility lines.

SHIPPING & RECEIVING

Packaged beer is shipped by both truck and railroad as shown on Figure 5-3. For this reason it is necessary to provide a good design for both railroad and truck loading and unloading at the plant. Locating the facilities on the property must include suitable switching of the rail cars and suitable roadways for truck movement with minimum interference with rail switching.

Note the main plant entrance is shown on the lower part of Figure 5-4. This is to be used for visitors, office workers, and brewery workers, in addition to truck traffic for receiving and shipping. Another entrance can be provided for Construction personnel and vehicles.

The site plan also demonstrates how building location is arranged to provide for easy expansion of any of the areas without disturbing the central areas, such as the entrance, security building, administration, or employee lunch areas. The expansion of the stock houses would take place by expanding to the lower portion of the figure. The same would be true for the brew house. Neither would impact the packaging and shipping operation.

60

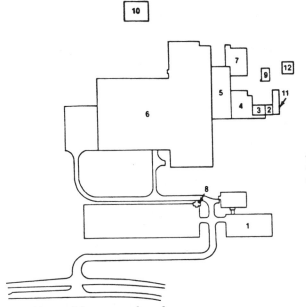

1. ADMINISTRATION
2. GRAINS HANDLING
3. BREW HOUSE
4. STOCKHOUSE I
5. STOCKHOUSE II
6. BEER PACKAGING &
   SHIPPING
7. UTILITIES
8. SECURITY
9. CHIP STORAGE
10. YARD BUILDING
11. TRACK SHED
12. GRAINS DRYING

5-1. Typical brewery plot plan.

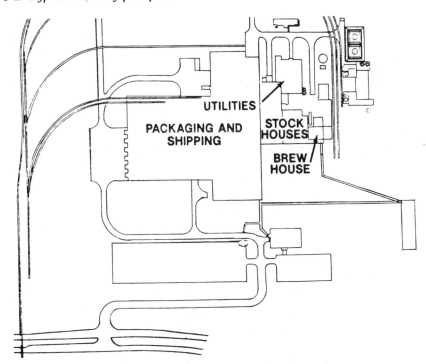

5-2. Typical brewery site plan illustrating buildings adjacent to Packaging & Shipping in detail.

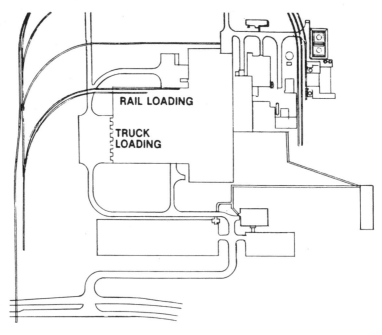

5-3. Site plan showing rail and truck loading layout.

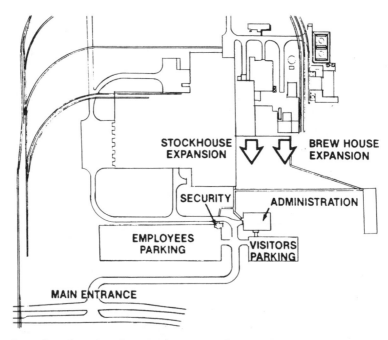

5-4. Site plan showing plant entrances, parking and an expansion proposal.

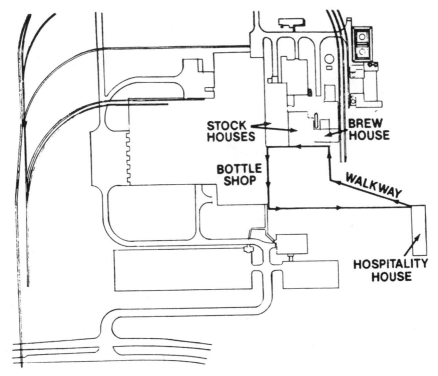

5-5. Plot plan showing visitor facilities and a tour routing proposal.

Note in the lower right hand corner of Figure 5-5, the location of the hospitality house. This is the building visitors would enter to take a tour of the brewery. The visitor tour could include walking from the hospitality house across an elevated walkway to the brewhouse and stock house. As the walking tour continues, visitors could leave the stock house and enter the beer packaging and shipping building, and walk along a gallery which would enable them to observe the operation of the bottle and can lines. As the visitors would complete their tour, they could walk from the bottle shop back to the hospitality house by means of an exit ramp and outside walkway.

Note at the lower right of Figure 5-6, the visitor and office personnel parking lot adjacent to the administration building, and to the left, the employee parking lot. Employees enter through a plant security building at the corner of the employee parking lot.

Figure 5-7 shows what is referred to as a key plan. This shows the general arrangement of the beer packaging and shipping operation including bottle, can and keg packaging lines within the packaging and shipping area. The packaging lines shown include two can lines to the left in the upper portion of the picture and two bottle lines to the right in the upper portion of the picture. As indicated previously, the packaging operation is designed to be expandable, and generally, expansion of additional can lines would be to the

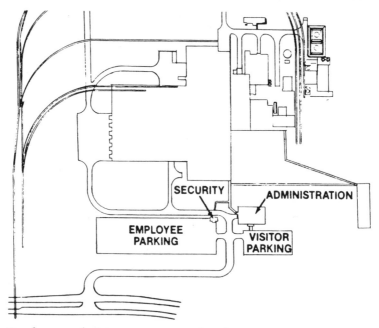

5-6. *Employee and visitor entrance and parking.*

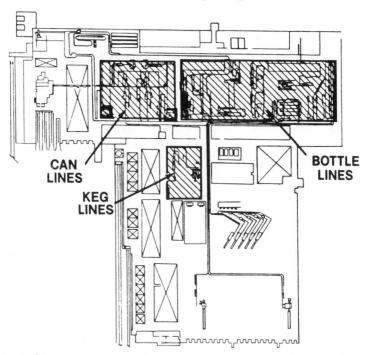

5-7. *Typical Brewery key plan showing arrangement of Packaging & Shipping areas.*

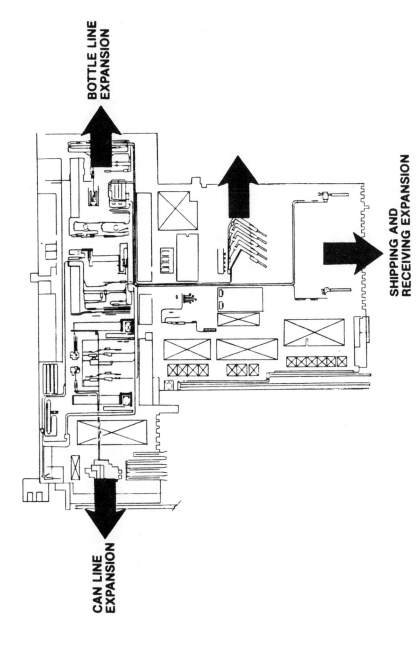

5-8. *Expansion plan for can & bottle lines and warehouse areas.*

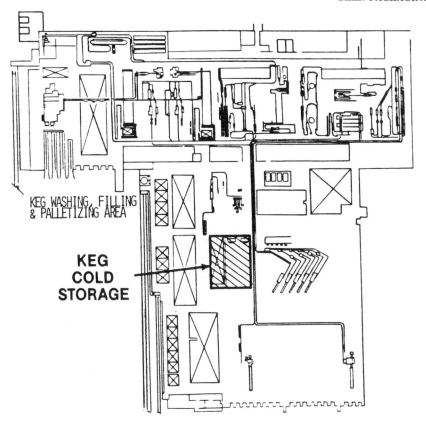

KEG WASHING, FILLING
& PALLETIZING AREA

**KEG
COLD
STORAGE**

5-9. Typical Draught beer layout with keg cold storage room.

left and expansion of additional bottle lines would be to the right. Expansion of the shipping and receiving areas, including the full goods warehousing operation, would be in the lower portion as shown in Figure 5-8.

Note in the center of Figure 5-9 the keg washing, filling and palletizing operation, with the draft beer cold storage room for storage of the filled kegs prior to shipping.

Figure 5-10 shows an overall view of the beer packaging and shipping operation as it would look after an expansion. The expanded operation, as shown, is approximately twice the capacity of the facility prior to the expansion.

Referring again to the overall layout of the operation prior to expansion, it can be seen that the truck dock area at the lower part of Figure 5-11 is used for receiving and shipping by trucks. This includes the receipt of returnable bottles, as well as new non-returnable bottles, and provides for shipping of filled cases of returnable bottles, non-returnable bottles, cans and filled kegs. To the left of the truck dock area in the lower left hand corner of the building, are railroad tracks which provide for rail receiving and shipping (unloading and loading). In the upper left are located five truck docks for miscellaneous

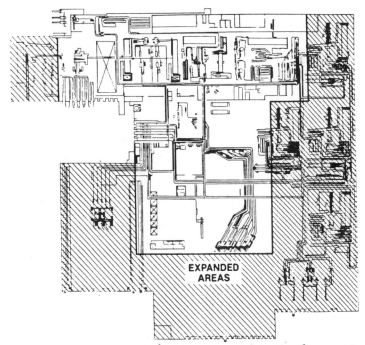

5-10. *View of brewery expanded to approximately twice the capacity.*

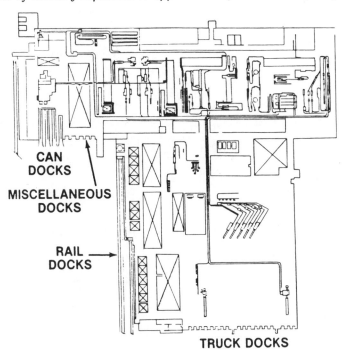

5-11. *Arrangement of receiving and shipping docks for both truck and rail.*

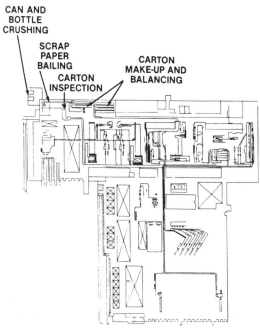

5-12. *Layout of scrap packaging material disposal and returnable carton handling areas.*

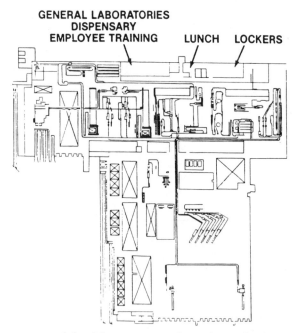

5-13. *Layout proposal for laboratories and employee facilities.*

material receiving and to the left of the miscellaneous receiving docks are located additional docks for the receipt of empty cans. In the extreme upper left hand corner of Figure 5-12 are located the can shredder and bottle crusher for disposing of unusable scrap bottles and cans. Across the upper portion of Figure 5-12, from left to right, are the scrap paper baling operation, the returnable bottle carton inspection and salvaging operations and the carton make-up and balancing operation. To the right of the carton balancing area, shown in Figure 15-13, at floor level, are located general laboratories, medical dispensary, employee training facilities, lunch room and locker facilities. Shown on Figure 5-14 is the second floor above the general laboratory facilities, where offices for resident plant engineering personnel can be provided. Above the locker facilities to the right of the general laboratory is a visitor viewing gallery from which visitors may observe the bottle and can line operations.

**RESIDENT PLANT   VISITOR VIEWING
ENGINEERING   GALLERY**

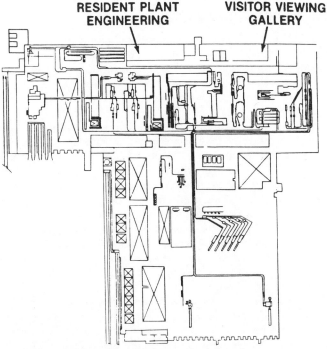

5-14. Second floor layout showing provisions for plant engineering offices and tour facilities for efficient utilization of space.

TYPES OF PACKAGING LINES

As mentioned previously, beer is packaged in cans, non-returnable bottles, returnable bottles and kegs.

Generally, can lines are capable of producing only cans. There is sufficient difference between the containers, and there is sufficient volume of production required, that a separate packaging line design has been developed for can production. There are a few convertible bottle and can lines; however, an examination of these so called convertible lines indicates that they are actually two complete packaging lines, a bottle line and a can line, with the exception of the pasteurizer and the feed and discharge conveyors.

A second type packaging line that is very popular is the non-returnable bottle line. This type bottle line produces throw away bottles which are received from the glass bottle manufacturing plant. At the brewery they are rinsed, filled, pasteurized, labeled and packed and are then shipped and sold. After the consumer drinks the product, the glass bottle is either recycled through a recycling center back to the glass bottle manufacturing plant, or is discarded as trash and buried in a sanitary land fill.

Perhaps the most traditional type of bottle line is that which produces returnable bottles. About 35 years ago all bottled beer was produced in returnable bottles. Returnable bottle lines are considerably more expensive than non-returnable bottle lines and operate at slower speeds and with less efficiency.

GENERAL DESIGN PARAMETERS

Line layouts are developed according to guidelines applicable to particular circumstances. In many cases, it is necessary to provide a new packaging line in an existing building with many design constraints such as available floor space, headroom, floor loading capacity, size, location and spacing of building columns, relative location of related operations, i.e. receiving and depalletizing of containers, etc.

Assuming there are no such apparent building limitations, there should be judicious consideration of floor space when layouts are developed to avoid unnecessary "waste" of space, or cannibalization of space required for other needs such as full case storage, order make-up, etc. A basic requirement is to determine the sales and marketing requirements for particular containers and packaging requirements. This would include not only can line vs. bottle line, but also if it is to be a returnable or non-returnable bottle, if multipacks are required and what types—for example, 6-packs, 8-packs, 12-packs, basket carriers vs. wrap-around or film wrapped packs. Sales and Marketing requirements must be determined early since the size, speed and cost of the line depends on the sales and marketing needs as well as the ability of the company to finance the project.

When the volume of packages to be produced by the new line has been decided, and the proposed line speed determined, then design concepts and system designs can be worked out to enable floor space requirements, conveyor types and lengths between equipment items, and many other considerations can be determined. The actual layout work can now commence.

Packaging line layouts are usually "U" type or "in line" (reference Figure 5-15) or a variation of these two basic types (reference Figure 5-16). Line layouts must conform to building constraints. Available space may not be wide enough or long enough to accommodate a strict "U" or "in line" configuration.

If there are no building constraints, then personal preferences may influence the layout. A "U" or "C" type layout may be preferred if the prevailing philosophy requires the line foreman to see both the "early" side and the "late" side of the line from a particular location.

Straight through rotary labeler layouts may cost less, but parallel type labeler feed and discharge conveyors may be preferred. This enables an operator to see and clear infeed conveyor combiner jams in minimum time, inspect for

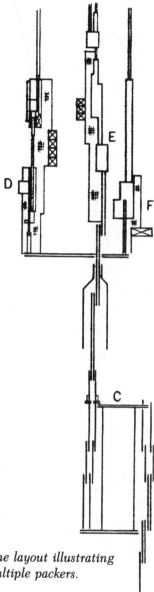

A - Filler
B - Seamer
C - Pasteurizer
D - Six Can Packer
E - Twelve Can Packer
F - Twenty-Four Loose
     Can Packer

5-15. Typical in-line layout illustrating a can line with multiple packers.

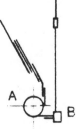

properly labeled bottles as well as feed labels to the label basket, all from the same general location.

An "in line" line layout may minimize corner turns or curved conveyors, but may require a longer layout, and may hinder operators and line supervisors from being able to watch the entire line operation and product flow.

A "U" type layout of the bottle filler and level detectors may be preferred for low fills to be rejected near the filler operator. The "U" type layout may also be of more benefit to operators, supervisors, and maintenance personnel in analyzing and determining solutions to problems that are occurring on the line.

Type of equipment also influences line layout. The type of uncaser, labelers, and packers together with their feed and discharge conveyor requirements dictates the amount of square footage (length by width) of floor space for those parts of the line. This can prevent a strict "in-line" or "U" type layout, and a compromise layout results that is generally biased by the philosophies and experiences of the different engineering and operating departments.

Proper footage of conveyors should be provided which should include "accumulation" as required. Accumulation may be provided before the filler to maintain continuous filler operation to compensate for uncasing, depalletizing, washing, rinsing or conveying jams. Likewise, accumulation after the filler is intended to help keep the filler running when short duration backups are caused by palletizing, packaging, labeling or conveying problems.

Other possible considerations include: accessibility of the various operations, surveillance by operating supervision, maintenance accessibility (to replace long shafts, etc.), fork truck accessibility to supply and/or remove materials, etc.

TYPICAL 12 OUNCE CAN LINE

For the discussion concerning a typical 12-ounce can line, refer to the key plan layout drawing on Figure 5-11. In the upper left hand corner of this drawing are can receiving docks.

Trucks with powered conveyor beds back up to these docks with their rear doors opened and then load-blocking materials are removed. The truck conveyors are energized, as are the conveyors within the packaging plant, and the entire truck load of pallets of empty cans is discharged in slightly over two minutes. The loads within the truck trailers consist of two rows of pallets, with layers of empty cans stacked on the pallets. As the load is discharged from the truck trailers and enters into the packaging building, the two rows of pallet loads of empty cans are separated by means of skewed conveyors. The resulting two rows of bulk pallet loads of cans move forward on individual accumulating conveyors until the trailer is empty.

After the trailer is empty, it is removed from the can receiving dock. The trailer can be moved to another dock which is used for loading the empty can trailers with pallets, separator sheets, etc., for return to the can making plants.

Pallet loads of empty cans that have been unloaded from the trailer are located within the packaging plant on individual accumulating conveyors. These conveyors supply the cans to a transfer car which is used to transfer

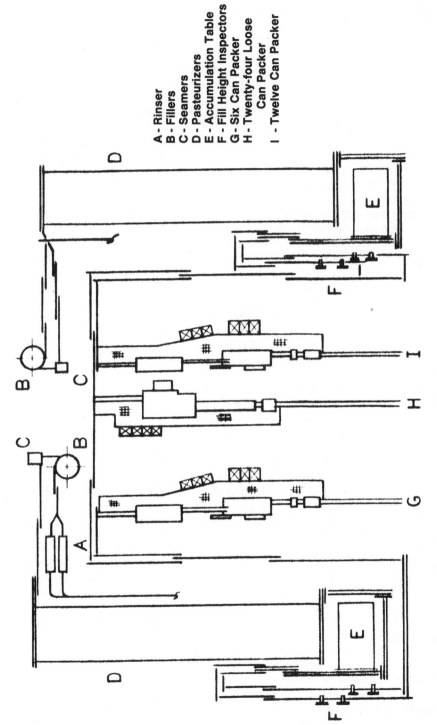

A - Rinser
B - Fillers
C - Seamers
D - Pasteurizers
E - Accumulation Table
F - Fill Height Inspectors
G - Six Can Packer
H - Twenty-four Loose
Can Packer
I - Twelve Can Packer

5-16. Typical 12-oz. can line layouts that use multiple packers.

pallet loads of cans from a particular receiving conveyor system, to the infeed conveyor of a particular bulk can depalletizer.

After an individual pallet load of empty cans is transferred to the infeed conveyor of a bulk can depalletizer, it advances to an "unwrap station". At this location an operator removes the straps and top frame, and permits the pallet load of cans to advance to the bulk can depalletizer. Plastic straps are used to secure the load of cans to the pallet, including the wood top frame.

After the plastic straps are removed from the pallet load of empty cans, the straps are fed into a scrap chopper, which chops them into small pieces that are accumulated in a hopper for recycling. The layers of empty cans include approximately 389 cans per layer, and there are approximately 21 layers of cans per pallet load.

The bulk can depalletizer basically consists of two parts. The first part pertains only to the handling of pallets and pallet loads of empty cans, while the second part pertains to the handling of the empty cans. As a bulk pallet load of empty cans enters the bulk can depalletizer, it advances into what is referred to as a hoist bin. Usually, bulk can depalletizers will have a pair of doors that open to permit the pallet load to enter the hoist bin, and close after the pallet load has moved into position within the hoist bin. The primary function of these doors is to straighten the load if the load is leaning backwards.

When the load has reached its position within the hoist bin, it is elevated until the top layer is slightly above the mesh belt that receives the layer of cans from the hoist bin. When the pallet elevator has stopped, a sweep bar assembly is actuated which pushes the layer of cans off the separator sheet and onto a mesh belt at which time another assembly with suction cups removes the separator sheet and deposits it in a paper stacker. This sequence of events continues until all layers of cans have been "depalletized" and all separator sheets are stacked in the paper stacker. The empty pallet is then discharged to a pallet stacker, and a new pallet load of empty cans is brought into the hoist bin.

The empty cans are moved by the mesh belt, discharged onto a conveyor and directed to a single filing device.

Single-filing devices for cans are available in several different styles. One type consists of a waterfall in which the cans are transferred from a horizontal surface, in which the can is upright, to a lower horizontal surface, in which the can is lying on its side. The cans are single-filed with this so-called waterfall type single-filer, as they move through what is referred to as a blender, after which the cans usually pass through a twist and are uprighted.

Another type of single-filer consists of a horizontal round rotating disc. Single-filers of this type have been used for can single filing for lines for varying speeds. These single-filers usually measure at least 4 feet in diameter and are available in 4, 5, and 6 feet diameters.

A third type of single-filer consists of a series of table-top conveyor chains that transport the cans through a combining section and works on the principle of accelerating cans to provide spaces, then reducing the distance between the guide rails to combine the cans.

Another approach to empty can handling is one of transporting the cans from the wide mesh belt of the depalletizer, to another conveyor about 12"-15" wide of either table-top conveyor chain, or other types of conveyors. If the can single-filing is done at the depalletizer, then single-width conveyors are provided from the single-filers to the empty can rinsers, which are located near the can-fillers. If the cans are conveyed on wide conveyors (12″-15″ wide), a single-filer is located just before the cans are delivered to the empty can rinsers.

All cans should be coded to provide control in the brewery and insure quality control and rotation with the wholesaler/retailer. There are various types of can coders available ranging from flexographic to electrostatic. Can coders may be installed in the empty can system, in which case empty cans are coded or they may be installed after the cans have been filled. Filled can coding will be referred to later in this chapter. If electrostatic coders are used, coding empty cans avoids the possibility of water on the cans.

Empty can rinsers are available either as powered rinsers, or gravity rinsers. Most brewers currently use gravity rinsers. The conveyors from the bulk can depalletizers to the rinsers are elevated, and the rinsers are installed on a decline between the elevated empty can conveyor system and the can filler infeed conveyor system, which is located near floor level. Empty can rinsers are rated according to the speed of satisfactory foreign matter removal, and the amount of rinse water retained in the container after the drain section. Electrical controls associated with gravity can rinsers should maintain a prime of cans passing through the rinsers. Unless this is done, cans will tend to pass through gravity-type rinsers with excess velocity, minimizing the amount of time exposed to the rinsing operation. This can result in foreign matter not being removed from the cans.

CAN FILLER AND SEAMER

At the inlet of the can filler, cans are either held back by a locking device, or, when the device is released, permitted to move into the can filler infeed.

The infeed usually consists of a timing screw (worm) and an infeed star. The infeed star and guide place the empty cans onto the filler platforms.

After the can is positioned on the platform, it is centered by a device that is part of the filling valve assembly. CO_2 is admitted to the empty can until it is counterpressured, at which point beer is admitted to the empty can. As the beer fills the can, it encounters a float ball which seats against a rubber tube which, in turn, causes the filling operation to stop. At this point the pressure in the head space of the can is relieved, permitting the can to be removed from the filling valve. The can is discharged onto a transfer conveyor chain which transports it to the seamer. As cans are being transported from the filler to the seamer, they pass under devices referred to as bubble-breakers. These devices emit CO_2 in minute streams that break large bubbles on the surface of the beer. These large bubbles are usually created in the initial part of the beer filling operation and contain quantities of air which can cause oxidation of the product.

As the can enters the seamer, it is exposed to an undercover gasser, a device that emits CO_2 in a predetermined pattern that purges air from the head space of the cans. As the can is passing through the undercover gasser, it receives a lid, or "end", and the combination lid and can are then transferred to the seaming head where the edges of the lid and the flange of the can are rolled over to form an interlocking seam. After the seam has been formed, the can is removed from the seaming chuck assemblies, and the can is discharged onto a table top conveyor chain.

As the cans leave the seamer, they are conveyed on single-width table-top conveyor chain past a push-off table, the purpose of which is to absorb cans (accumulation) when a backup or jam occurs to prevent cans from backing up into the seamer itself. After the cans pass the push-off table, they will usually pass through a twist and be inverted. Cans are conveyed from single-width high-speed table-top chain, in steps, to wider, slower conveyors to reduce the speed of the cans by the time they enter the pasteurizer. On the multi-width conveyor between the seamer and the pasteurizer a spray tunnel is mounted for rinsing beer off the cans. This prevents beer from getting into the pasteurizer and causing microbiological growth. The water used for the full can rinsing is normally recycled from the empty can rinser.

The common practice is for filled cans to be inverted as they pass through the pasteurizer in order to detect bad seams. Pressure inside the cans is increased in the pasteurizer which forces beer out of cans with bad seams, causing low fills. The pasteurizers commonly used by most brewers are generally referred to as tunnel pasteurizers. These may either be single-deck or double-deck and may have a conveying surface consisting of carriers attached to carrying chains, or the conveying bed may be a walking beam. As the cans are conveyed through the tunnel pasteurizer, the spray temperatures heat the product to a minimum of 140° for a period sufficient to prevent any further activity by either yeast or any microbiological items that may have been present. After the product has been held at this elevated temperature for a specific period of time, the pasteurizer then cools the beer to an acceptable temperature for storage that prolongs shelf life.

After cans leave the pasteurizer, they are normally transported on wide conveyors to an accumulation table provided to absorb short packer stops without causing the pasteurizer, filler and seamer to stop. After the accumulation table, the cans are divided into two smaller widths of massed cans which are then single-filed and passed through two sets of series level-detectors. The majority of the can fill-level inspectors today utilize a radioactive isotope-produced beam and a detector which can determine the difference between a column of liquid and the absence of liquid. Cans with liquid present at the elevation of the beam are permitted to pass and go on to the packers. Cans in which a space is detected are rejected by a high-speed, short-stroke air cylinder-operated ram. These cans are bumped off of the can conveyor onto a sloping table where they are checked, and if determined to be good, placed back onto the conveyor, or, if confirmed to be low fills, are then destroyed.

After the cans have passed through the level detectors, they are inverted by another twist. The cans are now upright with the lid on top and are transported on a common conveyor providing two or three lanes of cans. Some distance prior to the packer, a space is provided to enable the lanes of cans to be balanced with respect to each other. This is necessary because can dividing for fill height inspection after the pasteurizer was only approximately equal, and it is possible that one lane may have more cans than the other. This would cause a backup condition which would shut down the level detectors and the conveyors back to and including the divider, and ultimately, the filler-seamer. The lanes of cans are then fed to the Hi-Cone six-can packer, which is most common to all brewers.

The Hi-Cone six-can packer will group six cans together and apply the plastic six-pack carrier to the group of cans. The Hi-Cone packer includes a turner-diverter which turns the six-packs and/or divides them into two rows prior to being supplies to a tray-packer. This packer groups 4/6 can packs and loads them onto a corrugated tray which is then glued. At the discharge of the tray-packer the ends of the trays are coded by a random flexographic coder after which the cartons are turned 90° and transported by carton conveyor to a palletizer at a remote location.

TYPICAL 12 OUNCE N.R. BOTTLE LINE

Figure 5-17 shows a typical non-returnable bottle line that was designed to handle various sizes of bottles, including 7-ounce, 8-ounce, and various 12-ounce bottles. A bottle line that must have the capability of handling various sizes of containers is less efficient than a single purpose line. It handles the various small volume production packages to enable other production lines to be available for the popular bottles that need large production runs, thereby maintaining better line efficiencies.

The non-returnable bottle line actually starts with the carton depalletizer which is located near the truck receiving docks. A fork truck removes pallet loads of cartons with empty bottles from the truck and places these pallet loads on the infeed conveyor of the carton depalletizer. The pallet loads feed into the magazine, or chamber, and are elevated into the suction head which holds the top layer. This is the most common design for high speed lines. With the upper layer secured in the vacuum head, the remainder of the pallet load is lowered a short distance. The vacuum head deposits the layer of cartons on a roller conveyor or a stripper plate. In both cases, the cartons are then supplied to a carton-orienting and single-filing device which feeds the cartons into the carton conveyor system that transports them to the packaging line itself. Some brewers may use bulk glass systems. The operation is similar to the bulk can systems prior to the can fillers.

The cartons are transported by a carton conveyor system to an uncaser which removes the bottles from the cartons. The bottles are transported on bottle conveyor to the empty bottle rinsers. The empty cartons are transported by carton conveyor from the uncaser to a balancing area for either storage or transportation to bottle packers.

The empty bottle rinsers referred to are in-line rinsers or twist rinsers. In these rinsers, bottles are pushed through a twist which inverts the bottles and passes them over nozzles which spray water into the interior of the bottles. Bottles then pass through what is referred to as a drain section to permit proper drainage of the water used for rinsing. After the drain section, the bottles are turned right side up and discharged onto a table-top conveyor chain and transported to a bottle filler.

The bottle filling operation is the most significant operation of the bottle line. The bottle filling operation will be discussed in detail in another Chapter.

As the bottles leave the filler/crowner they are transferred from a single lane bottle conveyor at the crowner discharge star to wide conveyors that reduce bottle velocity and increase bottle stability. Bottles are then conveyed in mass, divided by two combiners, and single-filed for filled-bottle inspection. The filled bottle level inspectors can be obtained with either photoelectric

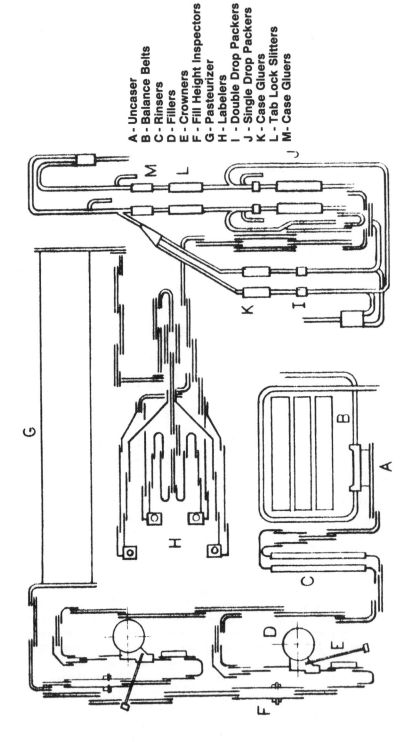

A - Uncaser
B - Balance Belts
C - Rinsers
D - Fillers
E - Crowners
F - Fill Height Inspectors
G - Pasteurizer
H - Labelers
I - Double Drop Packers
J - Single Drop Packers
K - Case Gluers
L - Tab Lock Slitters
M - Case Gluers

5-17. *Typical 12-oz. non-returnable bottle line that produces multiple NR bottles and packages.*

detection or radioactive isotope detection. The most prevalent current models are of the radioactive isotope type. These also have the capability of detecting level in bottles even if located after the labelers.

After the bottles leave the fill height inspectors, they are usually transported to the tunnel pasteurizer. After the pasteurizer, good design practice provides an accumulation table. Accumulated bottles keep the pasteurizer running in the event that the labelers are not taking the bottles away as fast as the pasteurizer is discharging them. After the accumulation table, bottles are supplied through a bottle conveyor system that divides the bottles as required to two, three or four labelers shown in the key plan on Figure 5-17. The labelers shown are rotary style labelers. These labelers have the capability of applying 360° wrap around labels as well as 180° body and neck labels. These labelers provide the complete versatility needed on packaging lines for the constantly changing requirements in the marketplace.

After the labelers, bottles are conveyed to the packers. Cartons with bottles leave the packers and pass through full-case inspectors, after which the cartons are transported through tack flap slitters and gluers. The cartons are conveyed through an open flap detector and then to a palletizer.

12-OUNCE RETURNABLE BOTTLE LINE

A 12-ounce returnable bottle line is shown on Figure 5-18. As with non-returnable bottles, pallet loads of cartons with returnable bottles are also un-loaded from trucks by a fork truck and placed on the infeed conveyor to a carton depalletizer. Here, the cartons are depalletized and then conveyed to the uncaser. The uncaser uncases the returnable bottles and discharges them onto the bottle conveyor that transports the returnable bottles to the infeed load table of a soaker (bottle washer). The soaker empties the bottles of any extraneous liquid and immerses them in hot caustic solutions to remove labels and clean and sterilize the bottles. The bottles are rinsed with fresh city water and discharged onto bottle conveyor to be transported through empty-bottle inspectors. These machines are capable of detecting foreign objects or liquids. After the bottles leave the empty bottle inspectors, they are transported to the bottle filler which is the same type of unit as used for non-returnable bottles. After leaving the filler/crowner, bottles are conveyed through fill height level inspectors and into a tunnel pasteurizer.

After the pasteurizer, bottles are conveyed to an accumulation table and the labelers after which the returnable bottles are conveyed to the packers. Additional packer operators are usually required because of the design of the returnable bottle carton. The cartons used have either four flaps or two flaps.

After the packers, the cartons are combined and conveyed to flap closing guides and sealed or locked. The returnable line can also have the capability of running a non-returnable bottle. The same line equipment used to process returnable bottles can also be used for non-returnables. After the labelers, non-returnable bottles can be diverted to a 6-bottle wraparound packer. The 6-bottle packages are divided and supplied to packers which pack four 6-packs to a tray or tack flap carton. When tack flap cartons are run, they are transported from the packer to a tack flap slitter and then to the carton sealing machine.

After cartons have passed through the sealing machine, they are transported

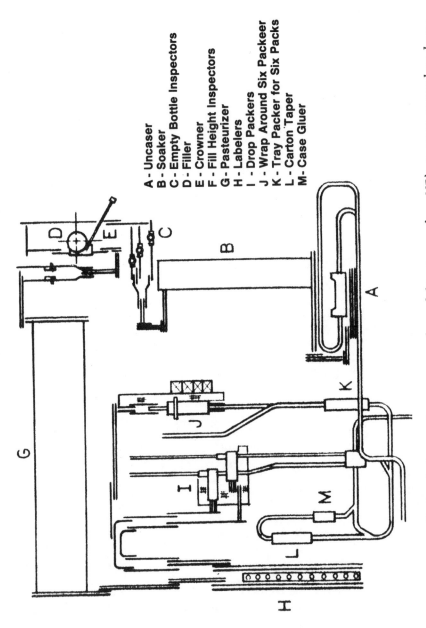

A - Uncaser
B - Soaker
C - Empty Bottle Inspectors
D - Filler
E - Crowner
F - Fill Height Inspectors
G - Pasteurizer
H - Labelers
I - Drop Packers
J - Wrap Around Six Packeer
K - Tray Packer for Six Packs
L - Carton Taper
M - Case Gluer

5-18. Typical 12-oz. returnable bottle line with wrap around capability to produce NR's in wrap around packages.

by carton conveyor through open flap detectors and then to a palletizer.

PALLETIZERS

After leaving the packaging lines as good cartons of cans and bottles, the cartons are conveyed to the warehouse where the palletizers are located. The conveying system consists of a series of belts and accumulation conveyors. The accumulation should be sized to absorb 3 to 5 minutes of downtime on the palletizer before a backup shuts down the packers. The 3 to 5 minutes is based on a typical jam condition on the palletizers, and the length of time required to clear the condition and put the palletizer back into operation. Obviously, higher line speeds will require longer runs of conveyor to provide the jam clearing time.

Spare palletizer capacity is also an item that has to be addressed based on the reliability that a brewery has experienced with its selection of a particular brand of palletizer. A common rule of thumb has been one (1) spare for 3 to 4 operating palletizers. Hand palletizing is impractical with the new high speed lines, unless a situation occurs that leaves no alternative to get a needed product into the market. Determination of spare capacity must be justified against line inefficiency, product loss, and initial expenditure of capital dollars.

GENERAL CONSTRUCTION—FLOORS

It is essential that existing floors, and new poured floors, be checked and provided with sufficient structural capability to support the operating weights of the machines. The bottle washer in particular will require special treatment because the operating weight includes the machine, water and caustic solution, and bottles, and it is probably the heaviest piece of equipment on a packaging line.

Consideration must be given to the type of floor surface to be provided. This will include quarry tile, acid-proof pavers, epoxy coatings, concrete, or a combination of these items. Quarry tile or acid-proof pavers are usually used in the areas of the bottle washer, filler, labelers and packers.

Safety should be considered in selecting the materials and determining the design for the floor. Abrasive grit can be obtained in quarry tile, acid-proof pavers or it can be broadcast and lightly troweled for either epoxy or concrete surfaces.

Floor slopes should be provided to drain water, beer or other liquids to floor drains or trench drains. Floor slopes should be provided between 3/16 inch per foot and 5/16 inch per foot to enable proper drainage and avoid puddles which are both unsafe and unsanitary.

Finished floors in breweries must be virtually non-porous and non-absorbent to prevent the accumulation of the product in cracks, crevices or pores with resulting odor and mold growth.

GENERAL CONSTRUCTION—UTILITY SUPPLY LINES

Generally, piping and conduit can be routed to packaging equipment from above or from below.

Overhead supply lines have the advantage of simplifying floor construction and facilitating cleaning. If not properly designed, overhead supply lines can be unattractive. Properly arranged and grouped overhead supply lines can present a satisfactory appearance and provide for minimum maintenance and maximum accessibility.

Utility supply lines from below can be acceptable if installed on the ceiling of a lower floor and grouped lines brought through the floor slab and properly sealed against leakage.

Utility supply lines imbedded in the floor (other than sewer lines) are not recommended. Such design can result in corrosion, deterioration, and prohibitive future repair and relocation costs as well as providing spaces in which mold and bacteria can form and grow.

SUMMARY

An efficient, high speed packaging line requires investigations, considerations, and consultations in many areas. The design starts with overall plant layout and feasibility studies and ends with start-up, debugging, and punch listing the line to bring it up to operating standards.

Inputs from Operations, Maintenance, Safety, Industrial Engineering, Cost Reduction, and Brewing Departments to Corporate Engineering are vitally important. Unless this input is obtained, the result could be the repeat of prior mistakes and not taking advantage of suggestions that could lead to improvements for new lines.

A packaging line represents a considerable share of the overall plant cost. In a new installation, for example, a can line rated at 1800 to 2000 cans per minute represents a $4 to $5 million equipment cost investment, and a returnable bottle line producing 1000 to 1200 12 oz. bottles per minute $7 to $8 million. Clearly, such an investment warrants the utmost care in the planning stage. Indeed, the results of such planning will determine, to a large degree, the subsequent operating costs of the department.

Section II: Bottling Operations

CHAPTER VI

BOTTLES—
MANUFACTURE & STANDARDS
BY WILLIAM A. MOLL

I. HISTORY OF GLASS

Origin of Glass

The first glass on the face of the earth was from natural phenomena, the majority from volcanic action. Prehistoric man discovered this material would hold a sharp edge and could be broken and shaped into tools and weapons. Ancient artifacts also have revealed that glass was utilized for jewelry and ornamental purposes.

The origin of man-made glass is recorded by both history and legend. History dates the first man-made glass back to about 5,000 B.C.

By legend, Phoenician sailors are credited for the discovery. The stories generally follow the line: sailors in preparing their evening meal built a fire on a sandy beach and supported their cooking vessel with blocks of natron from their cargo. (Natron is hydrated native sodium carbonate and was used in ancient times for embalming and as a cleansing agent.) In the morning, the sailors found the natron and sand had combined and melted, forming glass.

First Containers

This man-made glass was first used as a glaze on pottery. Later containers were formed by casting the glass or by repeated dipping of a paste form into molten glass. The containers were used for cosmetics and ointments. They were highly prized and often buried in tombs. Today, examples of these containers are on display in many museums around the world.

Blown Containers

A major development occurred around 300 B.C. with the invention of the blow pipe. This brought about several rapid interrelated events. Containers could be made at a faster rate, thus they came into more common use. New types of containers were possible which could be sealed air tight with plugs and wax coating. Merchants then were able to ship oils, wine, honey and other products on long sea voyages to other countries. Not only did the use of glass containers spread, but the craft of glass making itself spread, with the center moving from the Egyptian area to Greece.

The conquests of the Roman Empire brought the center of glass making to Rome from which it spread to Western Europe. During the Crusades, near the end of the 11th century, Venice became the new center for glass. The trade became highly secretive and guarded. Despite the fact that penalties, including death, were imposed for tradesmen leaving the area or transporting glass articles to other countries, glass making did spread through Europe and on to England.

Development of Glass Industry in America

Glass container manufacturing was the first industry in America. The first glass making operation began in Jamestown, Virginia, in 1608. About ten years later, glass factories started in Plymouth, Massachusetts, and one in Salem, Mass., started about 1632.

The first glass factory in America considered successful was founded in 1739 by the German immigrant, Caspar Wistar, and was situated in Salem Country, New Jersey. He produced drinking glasses, bowls, jars and bottles. Wistar glass pieces can be viewed in museums today.

Development of Automation

Toward the end of the 19th century, semi-automatic process for press and blow and blow and blow principles of glass container forming were being developed in England and America. It was not until 1903 that the first fully automatic glass forming machine appeared, a vacuum and blow process invented by Michael Owens.

6-1. Owens process glass forming machine

Suction Process

The Owens process was a rotary machine based on a completely new principle of filling the blank mold by dipping the open end into a pot of molten glass and sucking the glass into the mold by vacuum. For the next 20 to 25 years, this automatic process dominated the glass container market.

Gob Fed Process

Development of the gob feeder brought fully automatic press and blow and blow and blow forming process into operation around 1925. A number of different gob fed forming machines were developed, among them, Hartford-Empire Individual Section (I.S.), Lynch and Miller.

6-2. IS process glass forming machine

At the present time, in United States, individual section, gob fed, blow and blow process is the most universally employed manufacturing operation for beer bottles. Press and blow process is also utilized for the manufacture of beer bottles.

II. GLASS AS A MATERIAL

Composition

Glass is truly a remarkable material. It is produced from the most abundant and universally available materials on earth. For the manufacture of glass containers, the major ingredients are sand, soda ash, and lime. A typical batch composition would be:

Sand - SiO_2 - Silica	72%
Soda Ash - Na_2CO_3 - Sodium Carbonate	14%
Lime - Ca_2CO_3 - Calcium Carbonate	12%
Stabilizers - Al_2O_3 - Alumina	2%

    Feldspar
    Blast Furnace Slag
Colorant or Decolorant Material
    Iron Sulfide - Amber
    Iron Chromite - Emerald Green

Cullet

An important factor, particularly in today's ecologically aware society, is that glass is recyclable. Cullet, crushed reused glass, is a part of every raw material batch.

Characteristics of Glass

Glass is virtually chemically inert. It will neither add to nor take from the taste or purity of the product it holds. It is impermissible. It will not allow gas to pass through it, either in or out. It will not corrode.

The theoretical strength of glass exceeds one million psi tensile.[1] Glass fibers prepared under highly controlled conditions and tested under controlled atmosphere have exhibited strength values of 500,000 psi.

Glass breaks only under tensile load. The compressive strength of glass is so great that even under compressive forces, breakage origins occur in an area under tension due to deformation creating bending stress.

Strength and Fracture Characteristics of Glass

The strength of container glass is directly related to the condition of the surface. The phenomenon is often referred to as "surface flaw sensitive". Microscopic abrasions or discontinuities become stress concentrators and reduce the theoretical strength significantly.

For undamaged blown glass containers, a fair design value for tensile strength would be 12,000 psi. After normal handling through the manufacturing process and brewery operation a realistic strength value for design analysis purpose would be 6,000 psi.[2]

The advertising slogan used by one of the major house paint manufacturers, "save the surface, and save all" describes glass strength accurrately.

In addition to glass breaking only under tensile stress, the fractures resulting follow very definite rules:

1. The fracture originates at a point on a surface, not within the glasswall.
2. The fracture propagates 90° to the applied major force.
3. The fractures have a definite response to the forces producing them, developing predictable patterns associated with given forces, i.e., internal pressure, impact, thermal shock, etc.
4. The stresses developed by more than one force acting simultaneously is equal to the vector sum of the individual stresses.
5. The fracture can stop and restart.
6. Fractures never cross one another.

Influence on Container Design

In addition to being the basic rules for the science of glass fracture analysis, the above facts provide a basis to develop design parameters for a glass container, by taking into consideration the forces encountered in the normal life of a given container.

For the purpose of this publication, we will consider only the design parameters for a beer bottle. By the nature of the product involved the primary concern must be internal hydrostatic pressure forces.

The design shape most resistant to internal pressure force is the sphere, as it distributes the stress developed uniformly over its entire surface. However, this design is not suitable to meet the needs of a commercial beer container.

[1]Preston, F.W.: Bul Amer. Cerm. Soc., Feb. 1939
[2]American Glass Research

The next best design is a cylinder with semi-spherical ends, but it will not stand up for processing and still needs a means to fill and empty the container. We now arrive at the best practical shape for a beer container—a cylindrical body, a radius at the heel blending into a bearing surface radius with the inward domed bottom closing the end. On the other end, a shoulder radius blends into either a spherical or conical shape to a cylindrical neck to which is formed a shape capable of attaching a closing device.

Through this exercise, it is established, the design of a glass container which must withstand internal hydrostatic pressure will be cylindrical.

Through both experimental testing and theoretical analysis, it has been established that the cylindrical section glass container under internal hydrostatic pressure force develops stresses following the boiler formula.[3]

$$S_t = \frac{PD}{2t}$$

The circumferential tensile stress =

$$\frac{\text{the internal pressure (psi) x the inside diameter (inch.)}}{2 \text{ x the wall thickness (inch.)}}$$

The longitudinal tensile stress =

$$\frac{\text{circumferential stress}}{2}$$

To further develop the parameters for beer bottle design, the following factors can be employed:

Practical tensile strength including safety factor = 4,000 psi.

Maximum internal pressure expected = 100 psi developed by 3.8 gas volumes at 150°F (CO_2 content of beer and maximum pasteurization temperature)

Diameter (for purpose of illustration) = 2.75 in.

$$4,000 = \frac{100 \times 2.75}{2t}$$

$$t = \frac{100 \times 2.75}{8,000}$$

$$t = .034''$$

Thus for design purpose, the minimum thickness for the cylindrical body should be .034".

For sections other than straight cylinders, such as heel and shoulder contours, label indent features, and bottom areas, the calculation of stress becomes much more complex.

[3]Teague, J.M., Jr. & Blau, H.H.; *Jour. Am. Cerm. Soc.* Vol 39, No 7 July 1956 pp 229-252

In actual design studies, the inter-relationship of design factors and stresses developed by impact, vertical load, thermal shock as well as internal pressure, or any combination of these forces, can only be dealt with by the use of computer programs where theory has been combined with the empirical results obtained from research. For this reason, the use of modern computer technology has become almost a necessity in the most effective design of beer containers.

Protective Coatings

The Glass Industry, in an effort to better capture the original high strength of a glass container and to prevent a deterioration of this strength has developed "protective surface treatments".

Permanent surface treatments are not suitable for use with returnable bottles due to reactions with materials in the soaker-washers. The "hot-end" materials are acted upon by the caustic washing chemicals and develop an iridescence. The "cold end" materials are acted upon by products of digested labels and develop an objectionable film.

Surface treatments for returnable bottles are most often mono sodium stearate base and are water soluble.

For non-returnable beer and beverage containers, most are two step applications resulting in what is referred to as a "permanent type treatment".

"Hot End Treatment"

Newly formed hot bottles are subjected to an atmosphere of vaporized metallic compound which reacts with the glass surface by chemical bonding resulting in a primer which provides permanency to the "cold end" treatment.

"Cold End Treatment"

The second step of the protective coating is applied after the cooling section of the annealing lehr usually at a bottle temperature about 300°F. The material most often used is an emulsion of polyethylene; however, other materials such as beeswax, oleic acid, etc. are sometimes employed. The purpose of the second coating is to give lubricity to the container surface for preventing abrasions or other surface damage from bottle-to-bottle or bottle-to-guide rail contact during the normal handling on conveying lines and through processing equipment.

Surface Protection, A Factor of Bottle Handling

In addition to protective coatings to preserve the strength of a glass container, it is equally important to construct conveyor guiderails and bottle handling parts on processing equipment of nonmetallic material to minimize the chance of damaging the glass surface.

Lines should be inspected periodically for protruding bolt heads or misaligned guiderails which could cause small bruises upon contact.

Conveyor speeds should not be excessive. Well balanced conveyor speeds not only aid bottle handling, but excessive speeds can be a source of damage to the bearing surface of the bottle, as well as a factor to wear on the chain itself. Further comments on this subject will appear in the section on line performance.

III. MODERN GLASS MANUFACTURING

Batching

The mixture of materials for the manufacture of glass containers is not a continuous flow operation; it is prepared in unit "batches". For this reason, the structure where the "batch" is prepared is generally referred to as the "batch house". Physically, it can be a large single structure containing the complete operation of raw material storage, batch gathering, control, weighing, mixing and conveying to the furnace, or a series of individual storage silos with a system for collection and carrying to the weighing and mixing area.

Major raw materials are delivered by covered hopper rail cars or truck trailers to the glass plant. They are then transferred to the storage bins or silos by bucket elevators, belt conveyors, screw conveyors, pneumatic conveying systems, gravity, or any combination of these systems. It is important to keep materials separate to prevent contamination of one material by another.

Preparation of a batch in modern plants is completely automated or computerized and occurs on a demand basis from a sensor on the mixed batch storage bin feeding the batch charger at the furnace melter. The materials are collected and weighed individually, though most often accumulatively, in very precise scale systems to very close tolerance.

Next to weighing, mixing is a very important process, as complete homogeneity of the batch is necessary to produce quality glass. Mixers are generally equipped with mixing blades and/or baffles to promote the mixing action as the drum rotates. Mixing time is also an important factor. Often water is introduced during the mixing cycle both to control dust and to aid in preventing segregation of the batch during conveying to and being fed into the furnace.

Cullet is added to the batch usually at the time of discharge from the mixer as the batch is being conveyed to the furnace. It is important that the cullet be of the same color and basic composition as the glass to be melted, that is, the source of cullet should be glass containers and not heat-resistant borosilicate glass or window glass. The cullet must also be free of contamination, metal bottle caps, tramp metal scraps and clay refractory pieces in particular.

Melting

Continuous regenerative type furnaces are the most commonly used for melting container glass. They can be fired with either natural gas or fuel oil, and most are equipped with duo-systems to utilize either. There are two basic types of regenerative furnaces, the "side port" and the "end port". Electric melting furnaces are also utilized in glass container manufacturing.

Side Port Furnaces

Large furnaces, greater than 400 feet^2 melting area, are usually side port design. Side port furnaces are so designated relative to the direction of firing and the position of the regenerators in relation to the melter.

The side port furnace consists of three connected structures. The center structure contains the melter and the refiner which have a connecting channel through their bottom, called the throat. The regenerators, which are huge heat exchangers and contain a checker pattern of layer upon layer of special fire brick, are positioned on each side of the melter and are connected to the melter by structures called ports.

The fuel and air mixture is introduced in the ports for firing across the bed of glass in the melter and the exhaust gases are exited out the ports on the other side of the melter. The hot gases are channeled through the checker

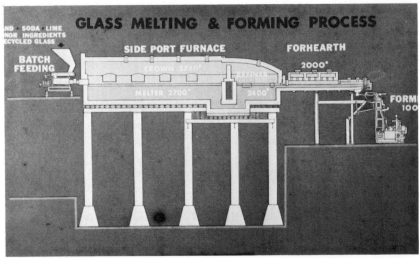

6-3. *Glass melting and forming machine*

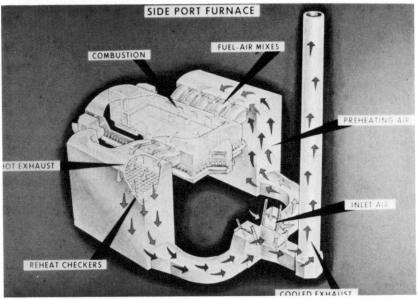

6-4. *Side port furnace*

work of brick in the regenerator and give up much of their heat before continuing out the stack.

The air for firing is pre-heated as it is brought in through the bottom of the previously heated regenerator and channeled to the port for introduction

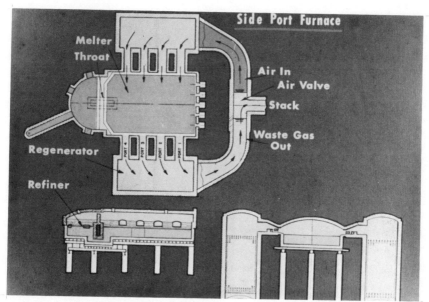

6-5. *Side port furnace*

with the fuel. The firing cycle in the ports connecting the melter and regenerators is reversed from side to side on about 30 minute cycles, and the regenerators change functions from extracting and storing heat from the waste gas to releasing heat to the incoming combustion air.

In a side port furnace, the raw materials are introduced through openings in the backwall of the melter by the use of batch chargers. Most furnaces have a structure called the "dog house" protruding from the backwall in such a manner that chargers can be placed on the two opposing diagonal sides; and by regulating the feed of the chargers, they control the pattern of the blanket of unmelted batch covering the bed of molten glass. The blanket will usually cover ⅓ to ½ of the back area of the melter. The temperature of the molten glass in the melter will be in the range of 2700°F to 2800°F.

The molten glass moves through the throat from the bottom of the front of the melter to the refiner. In this chamber the glass is conditioned for desired uniform temperatures and release of dissolved glasses to remove seeds and blisters. The refiner will have an alcove connecting to a forehearth and feeder for each forming machine to which it will supply glass.

The molten glass is cooled and conditioned for equalization of temperature throughout the stream in the channel as it moves to the feeder spout.

End Port Furnace

Smaller furnaces, less than 400 feet^2 melting area, are usually of end port design. The end port furnace consists of two structures, the regenerator behind the melter with two connecting ports.

The regenerator is divided vertically from front to back by a wall positioned between the two ports. Incoming combustion air is preheated as it comes up the one side of the regenerator, combines with the fuel in the port and fires

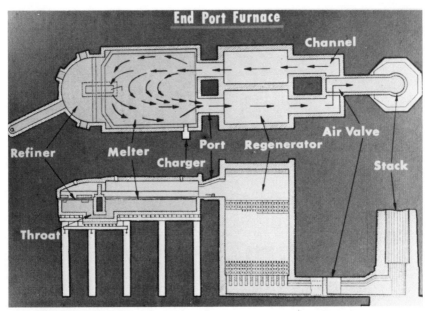

6-6. End Port furnace

in a horse shoe pattern in the melter. The exhaust gases exit out the other port and heat the checker work of brick in the other half of the refiner as they continue to the stack.

There may be just one batch charger at the rear corner of the melter or on some larger units a second charger on the other rear corner.

The rest of the operation of the end port furnace is the same as that of the side port furnace. Furnace instrumentation has become highly sophisticated including computerization. One of the most important features to control is glass level in the melter and refiner, as it affects the head of glass at the feeder and has a direct bearing on the gobbing operation.

Electric Melting

Even though glass is an insulator in its solid state, it will conduct electricity when hot and in the viscous state. All-electric glass melting furnaces came into successful use in Europe in the 1920's.

When the hydro-electric power programs were being developed in the Tennessee Valley and on the rivers in the far western states, it appeared there would be an inexpensive source of power giving an advantage for electric glass melting furnaces in America.

There is a cost advantage in the construction of the furnace itself in that all that is required is the melter. There is no need for regenerators or stack systems. As a result, the electric furnace requires less building space than a fuel fired furnace.

The electrodes for electric heat are molybdenum rods which are immersed into the molten glass either from the lower sidewall of the melter or directly up through the bottom. This accounts for another advantage because the heat from the electric power is liberated within the glass itself.

Under use, the electric furnace has no crown and the batch is distributed over the complete area of the bed of molten glass. Generally, there will be a crust of unmelted batch about 6 inches deep over the total melter area. This acts as an insulator and holds the heat within the molten glass.

The rest of the operation of the electric furnace would be similar to that of the fuel fired furnaces.

In recent years, the cost of electric power in America has increased at such a rate that electric glass melting furnaces have been at a disadvantage. Further expansion of the use of electric furnaces is unlikely unless there is a technological break-through in the development of low cost electric power.

Glass Conditioning

The glass melting process, regardless of the type furnace or energy source, is designed ideally to supply a definite tonnage of glass per 24 hour period. It would then be desirable to have the total pull from all forming machines on that furnace equal the ideal and each individual machine pulling the same quantity at a constant rate. However, due to production scheduling needs for different size bottles which are produced at different speeds and the possibility of different characteristics of the machines themselves, number of sections, double gob, triple gob, etc., the ideal conditions never exist.

It thus becomes necessary to condition the glass for each individual machine's requirements. This is accomplished in the channel between the furnace refiner chamber and the machine feeder. This channel is divided into two sections, one for changing the temperature of the incoming glass, referred to as the "cooling section"—somewhat a misnomer, in that at times it is necessary to heat the glass and there is always some flame at the burners even when cooling wind is applied.

Gob Feeder

The bowl of the gob feeder, or spout, is an integral part of the forehearth section.

The essential parts of the gob feeder are: a revolving tube, a reciprocating plunger or needle, an orifice ring and immediately below the orifice a set of shear blades.

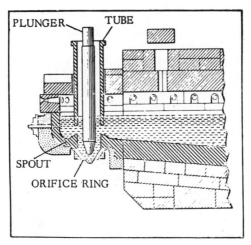

6-7. Gob feeder

It is at this point where the forming operation of the bottle itself has its beginning. By the setting and timing of the feeder and shears, the weight and shape of the gob is controlled.

The gob feeder should deliver a glass gob so shaped that it will enter the blank mold without excessive mold contact, distortion or reshaping of the glass.

Referring to figure 6-7, the tube is adjustable in height above the spout and controls the rate of glass flow. It is the main adjustment for gob weight. The setting of the tube is also interrelated to the glass temperature.

The plunger is adjustable in height above the orifice, and in length and acceleration of the reciprocating motion or stroke. It is the main control, along with differential timing, to define the shape of the gob. Another factor is the shape of the end of the plunger. A pointed end produces a pointed gob and a rounded end produces a shorter more blunt gob.

The shears are adjustable in position below the orifice, in rate of cut and its phase in relation to the action of the plunger. Both the action of its plunger and of the shears are controlled by separate cams.

The differential between the timing of the plunger stroke and the shear cut is the most important factor influencing gob shape. No delay between the full downward stroke of the plunger and the shear action results in a short, compact gob, while the longer the delay as the plunger moves upward, the longer and thinner the gob shape.

The orifice diameter determines the initial diameter of the gob and is selected in relationship to the weight of the desired gob and the machine speed of the operation.

At this point, the gob could be fed to either blow and blow, press and blow, or a press only forming operation to produce a container.

Bottle Nomenclature

Before continuing with the forming of the bottle, the terms associated with the various parts should be explained.

The top of the bottle where it is capped is called the "finish". When glass containers were hand blown, after the main body and neck was formed, the shape was broken off from the blow pipe and went to the "finishing operation" where the container was hand "finished", usually shaped to be corked. Even though the finish is the first part of the bottle formed by all automatic glass machines, the name remains.

Most other names are obvious such as neck, shoulder, body, heel and bottom. Parting lines are actually mold seams evident in the surface of the bottle. Often a second seam parallelling the vertical mold seam is visible and it is formed by the blank mold.

The radius at the bottom of the neck and the top of the shoulder is called the "base neck", but often is referred to as only the "base". This term is sometimes confused with the bottom section of the bottle. The bottom section consists of the heel, the toe-in, the bearing surface and the push-up area or center bottom.

Forming Operation

At this time in United States the majority of all beer bottles are produced on I.S. or Individual Section type machines. (See Figure 6-2) The sections are independent of one another and may be inactivated for adjustment, change

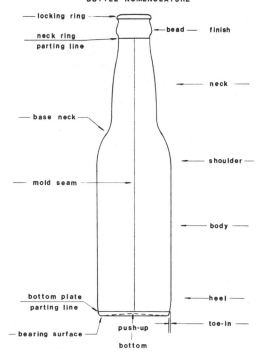

6-8. Bottle nomenclature

of equipment or repair without affecting the other sections of the machine. Each section is actually a complete bottle manufacturing unit.

The sections can be fitted with single, double or triple cavity mold equipment to produce 1, 2 or 3 bottles during one cycle of the section. Very small bottles, not beer containers, have also been produced using quadruple cavity mold.

Machines can be made with varying number of cavities, with most modern beer bottle producing machines being either 8 or 10 sections.

Blow and Blow Operation

The mold equipment required to dress one section of an I.S. machine for blow and blow operation is shown in Figure 6-9 and the complete cycle of the section to produce a bottle is shown in Figure 6-10.

The gob of glass is delivered from the feeder to the blank mold by way of a collection scoop and delivery chutes. The gob drops through a guide funnel into the blank mold which is in the inverted position. (1) As soon as the gob clears the funnel, the baffle swings over positioning on top of the funnel, and air is applied to settle the gob into the finish. The plunger is up in place forming the complete finish as well as the void to later start blowing a shape. (2) The funnel and baffle swing aside, during which time the partially shaped gob reheats. (3) Almost immediately, the baffle swings back seating itself on the "bottom" of the blank and completing the blank cavity. The plunger

6-9. Blow and blow mold equipment

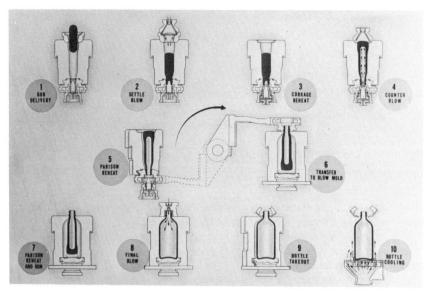

6-10. Functional Diagram for Blow and blow operation

retracts and blow air completes the parison shape. (4) The baffle swings away, the blank mold opens and the glass parison is held in an inverted position by the neck ring. (5) The neck ring arm pivots 180° in a vertical plane, positioning the parison within the closing bottle mold. (6) Just as the bottle mold closes the neck ring is parted releasing the parison to the proper position in the mold. The neck ring arm pivots back to its original position below the inverted blank to begin another cycle, and the parison is allowed to reheat and run or elongate. (7) A blow head now swings into position over the finish, seating itself on top of the bottle mold and compressed air blows the bottle to its final shape. (8) The bottle mold opens leaving the completed hot bottle standing on the bottom plate of the mold. At the same time a takeout tong closes around the neck of the bottle under the finish. (9) The take out transfers the bottle out of the mold to a position over the deadplate which has openings for cooling air. The bottle is released from the take-out tongs and stays on the deadplate momentarily for additional cooling. (10) The bottle is then swept off the deadplate onto the machine conveyor.

Looking closely at Figure 6-11, it is possible to see bottles being held by the take-out tongs, bottles on the deadplate and bottles on the machine conveyor.

6-11. Take out sequence for IS process

Press and Blow Operation

Press and blow operation to produce wide mouth containers on the I.S. machine was developed in the late 1930's. The manufacture of narrow neck containers, including beer bottles, has been developed only in recent years and the complete disclosure of the various methods have been proprietary.

The difference between the Press and Blow operation and the Blow and Blow operation is that the parison is pressed to shape by a plunger that fills the complete void in the parison replacing the settle blow and counter blow operations.

The gob is delivered through a funnel to the blank mold in the same manner as blow and blow operation (1); however, the funnel swings away immediately and the baffle positions on the blank, sealing the end and completing the parison shape. At the same time, the plunger starts its penetration. (2) In step

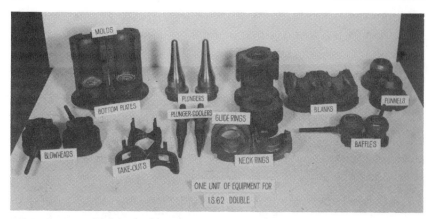

6-12. Press and blow mold equipment

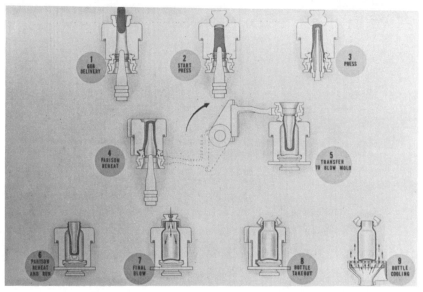

6-13. Functional diagram for Press and blow operation

3, the plunger completes the press cycle. Note the internal plunger cooling tube in the cut away view Figure 6-13 (3). The plunger then retracts, the blank mold opens and the parison held by the neck ring inverts to the bottle mold. (4) The rest of the cycle is the same as blow and blow.

The importance of good bottle handling practices starts immediately after the bottle leaves the mold. The vulnerability to strength reduction from abuse to the surface of the glass is especially true in its newly formed high temperature condition. Proper bottle spacing must be maintained to prevent bottle-to-bottle contact. Uneven conveyor transfer points across deadplates and conveyors should be avoided and guides or mechanical transfer aids should be free of sharp protrusions and avoid bare metal contact. Proper bottle spacing should be maintained until the bottle has been cooled to handling temperature at the end of the annealing lehr.

Mold Equipment

For the blow and blow operation, the blank cavity design has the greatest influence on the distribution of glass and general make-up of the finished bottle. The design of the blank is dictated by the design of the bottle to be formed, the weight of glass specified for the bottle and the machine speed in bottles-per-minute (BPM) expected production. The design of the tip which presses the finish and starts the void in the parison also has a degree of influence on the distribution of glass in the parison. In very recent years, much of the blank cavity design calculation has been computerized. Due to many inter-related variables in glass forming, actual results for new items cannot always be anticipated; therefore, samples are manufactured from unit molds (the equipment required to dress one section of the forming machine). If the results are not satisfactory, redesign can be determined before a full set of equipment is manufactured.

It has possibly become evident that the manufacturing of glass containers deals for the most part with the science of heat transfer. The glass is melted at approximately 2800°F, refined at 2400°F, conditioned to 2100°F, the gob enters the blank mold at 1850°F-2000°F and the completed bottle is set out on the machine conveyor at 950°F. This last step extracts about 1000°F of heat in just a matter of seconds. It is understandable that exterior mold design, amount of metal in the mold, the presence or lack of fins or grooves on the mold and the manner in which and the amount of cooling wind applied are also important variables to be considered.

Annealing

Another phenomenon which occurs as a result of the rapid transfer of heat and the mechanics of blowing the bottle is the creation of both thermal and mechanically induced stresses in the newly formed bottle. To relieve the stresses, the newly formed bottles are put through an annealing process.

Annealing lehrs are huge oven-like structures and vary from 6′ to 10′ wide and 80′ to 120′ long. They can be either gas fired or electrically heated. As the bottles enter the annealing lehr from the forming machine the bottle temperature is increased to 1050°-1100°F and held for a short period of time. At this temperature, all stress is relieved. Since glass breaks only from tensile stress, it is desirable to set a controlled temper with the outside surface skin in slight compression. The bottles are cooled at a predetermined rate to set this temper.

Once the temper is set, it will not change unless the bottle is again taken up to over 1050°F and all stress removed.

As mentioned earlier in this chapter, "hot end" surface treatment is applied to the bottle on the conveyor from the forming machine to the lehr. The "cold-end" surface treatment is applied near the end of the cooling section of the lehr. The surface treatment protects the glass from strength reduction abuse, and provides lubricity to the surface which aids in line mobility not only through the glass manufacturing conveying, inspection, and packing operation but for the useful life of the container.

Bottle Inspection—Quality Control

Quality control is an all encompassing term. In glass bottle manufacturing, it actually starts with review of the bottle design itself, the design of the mold equipment, and carries on throughout the complete manufacturing process from receipt of raw materials to the loading of delivery trucks.

Hot End Bottle Inspection

The inspection of the bottle itself starts at the forming machine. The operator maintains surveillance over weight variation. This not only has a direct bearing on the performance of the forming operation, but also the bottle make-up and capacity control.

The machine operator will also check "set outs", that is samples from each mold cavity operating, for dimensional characteristics. These will usually include all critical finish dimensions, height, maximum body diameter, off-perpendicular, and off-level finish. Most of these measurements are performed with "go-no-go" limit type gauges. Random bottles are broken to observe glass distribution for areas of minimum thickness and uniformity.

Cold End Bottle Inspection

Methods and programs for the inspection of glass bottles will not only differ from company to company but to some degree right down to individual manufacturing lines, depending on the type of bottle being manufactured and its particular critical requirements based on end use.

In past years, the bottles were manually picked up from the side or end of the lehr, visually inspected for defects and hand packed into the cartons. Statistical sampling inspection based on Mil Std 105D was usually employed as the main tool for quality control, by accepting the lot, or rejecting it for reinspection. In more recent years, the bottles are transferred from the lehrs to conveying systems, defect detection is accomplished by electronic and mechanical inspection equipment and the bottles are automatically case packed or built into bulk loads.

To meet the high performance requirements of today's market, the inspection concept for glass containers has shifted from one of controlling quality by selection in the cold end to process control at the forming machine.

Rounds of bottles (bottles from each mold cavity on the forming machine) are taken from the lehr, inspected for visual defects and measured for dimensional specifications. If a cavity or cavities are found defective or out of specification, a recheck of those cavities is conducted. If the recheck confirms that the condition continues to exist, the cavity will be discarded until the condition is corrected. The discarding of the cavity is accomplished either manually or, more often, automatically.

The true function of the inspection at the side of the lehr is to develop information regarding quality appaisal by cavity operating for feed back to the hot-end for decision making concerning machine adjustment, mold equipment replacement etc. The purpose is to maintain a higher level of quality while at the same time reducing the amount of bottles discarded for poor quality.

Defect Detection

Detection and discard of the more critical defects is now conducted by automatic equipment. These machines, through optical scanners, will detect checks (cracks through the glass surface) in the finish area which could cause leakage of filled product or breakage and checks in the heel and bottom which could be a source of breakage. Other scanners view the sealing surface of the finish to detect irregularities which could effect sealing. Mechanical equipment subjects the bottles to squeezing forces which simulate stresses developed by impact and cause substandard strength bottles to break, discarding the fragments.

Still other mechanical equipment plug gauges the opening of the finish to assure proper clearance for bottle filling equipment. Often, at the same time, a sealing head positions on the finish and low air pressure is injected as another means to detect conditions which potentially would not seal when capped.

Very recently, electronic equipment has been developed to scan the sidewall area of the bottle for detection of certain defects. This equipment utilizes TV camera pick up with a mini-computer to analyze the input.

As a part of the process control concept, information from the automatic defect detection equipment reject meters must also be communicated to the forming machine operators. On-line visual inspection light plate stations are generally also maintained following the automatic gauging section and ahead of the automatic case packer.

Physical Testing

As yet, some tests do not lend themself to continuous or automatic performance and are conducted on an assigned frequency basis. In addition, actual measurements for dimensional checks conducted at the forming machine or lehr with "go-no-go" gauges are desirable to establish trends for individual cavities and ranges within the total set. The same is also true for bottle weight and capacity.

Internal Pressure Testing

For beer bottles, one of the more important tests conducted is internal hydrostatic pressure resistance. The standards for this test are established by A.S.T.M. and the test is accepted by U.S.B.A.

The ramp pressure tester developed and built by American Glass Research, Inc. is an approved test unit widely adopted by the glass industry.

Bottles to be tested are filled to overflow with water. The bottles are held around the neck, under the finish. A sealing head is clamped in place over the finish, and by pushing a "start" button internal pressure is developed within the bottle at a constant rate until either the bottle breaks or the predetermined terminating test level is reached. The tester can be set to terminate at a chosen "pass level" or to the maximum of the equipment or bottle failure, which ever occurs first.

The accepted pass level for N.R. beer bottles is 150 psi and for trade return bottles 175 psi.

One of the most important steps in conducting the internal pressure test is to analyze all low level, pass level and below, breakage fragments for location of the origin of failure and assignable cause. This information is reported to the forming machine operator to aid in the action to be taken for correction.

In addition to the routine frequency of "pass level" testing, it is a good practice to conduct at least one test per 8-hour shift of a complete round of bottles to destruction (or maximum level of the test equipment) to observe overall average and individual cavity strength trends.

6-15. Thermal shock testing machine (Courtesy American Glass Research, Inc.

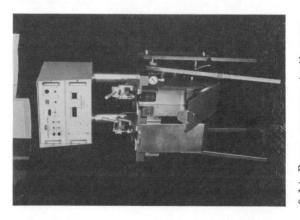

6-14. Ramp pressure testing machine (Courtesy American Glass Research, Inc.

Thermal Shock Testing

The other physical test with standards established by A.S.T.M. is resistance to rapid temperature changes or thermal shock.

When a glass container is subjected to rapid temperature change it is the surface which is chilled which develops tensile stress. Taking into consideration another factor associated with the strength characteristic of a narrow neck glass container, the inside glasswall of the container will exhibit approximately 50% greater tensile strength than the outside surface, due to the fact it has been protected from all surface abuse and has been contacted only by compressed air when formed, it is the outside surface which is subjected to the chilling condition.

A hot bath-to-cold bath immersion test will subject the outside surface of the bottle to the most severe thermal shock condition it can encounter. The thermal shock test equipment designed and built by American Glass Research, Inc. meets the A.S.T.M. requirements for this test. .

The test equipment consists of two large tanks which are filled with water. Both tanks have circulating systems and temperature controls. The one tank has a heating system and the other tank a cooling system. The cold water temperature is maintained at 70°F, the standard base, and the hot water temperature is adjusted to obtain the desired differential. The standard for beer bottles is 75°F differential.

A round of bottles is placed in the divided cell wire or expanded metal enclosed basket, and a top of the same construction is clamped over the bottles. When the test cycle is started, the basket transfers into the hot water tank and the bottles fill with the hot water. The basket with the bottles remains in the "hot tank" for 5 minutes while the water is vigorously circulated around the bottles to bring the glass temperature to total equilibrium with the temperature of the water.

The basket then transfers to the "cold tank" subjecting the bottles to the pre-set level of thermal shock. The basket remains in the cold tank for 30 seconds, as it is the initial shock which develops the highest stress. As the temperature difference between inside and outside glasswall reduces, the amount of stress also reduces. .

The basket then returns to the inspection and load position and the bottles are inspected for fractures. If breakage is encountered, it is important to diagnose the origin and cause of failure. This information is communicated to the machine operator to aid in determining the corrective action necessary.

When a failure below the accepted standard is experienced in either the internal pressure or the thermal shock test, immediately additional bottles from the same mold cavity are retested to determine if the failure was just a random occurrence or if there is an existing recurring problem with that particular cavity. If additional breakage is experienced in the re-test, the offending cavity or cavities are discarded from the production until the cause of failure has been corrected; and the bottles packed between the time of failure and the last conducted satisfactory test are held up from shipment until an audit test can be conducted to determine the points where the condition causing the breakage began and the questionable bottles discarded.

Statistical Sampling Inspection

At one time, statistical sampling inspection of packed ware was the main tool for quality control in most glass container manufacturing plants. Utilizing plans from Mil. Std. 105, lots were inspected and either accepted for shipment or rejected to be completely reinspected. Due to the significantly increased speed of beer packaging lines and the inter-related more strict performance requirements, this method of control is neither technically nor economically viable. However, statistical sampling inspection is still a very important part of the overall quality assurance program, in that it is the means to determine if the rest of the system is in control.

Is the process itself in control? Is the lehr inspection detecting defective conditions and providing proper feed-back to the forming operation? Is the automatic defect detecting equipment rejecting those conditions intended? If lots are rejected or if the process average of the rejected lots shows an increase, there is an immediate indication that a portion of the system is not functioning and usually points out the area requiring attention.

Packaging - Warehousing - Delivery

Packaging today has become almost completely automated, including case packing, bulk load building, palletizing, pallet strapping, and shrink or stretch wrapping. While this automation has eliminated some of the "human error" conditions of the operations, there are still features that require attention.

Automatic case packers should have non-metalic material covering the leading edges of the divider lanes and either coated or complete non-metalic drop guide fingers to prevent surface damage to the bottles.

Unit loads, both bulk and palletized cartons, should be centered on the pallet and if any overhang does exist, it should be an equal amount on all four sides, for good stability to the load and to prevent damage to the bottles or cartons.

Strapping tension on bulk loads must be sufficient to hold the load securely and compensate for the compression of bottom units in warehouse storage, but not so tight as to promote deep indentation of the bottle into the tier sheet.

Load Identification

Some brewing companies specify the manner in which individual cartons and unit loads are coded to identify supplier, plant location, manufacturing unit and date of production. If it is not specified, it should still be a part of the standard operating procedures. While one purpose of coding is inventory control, the most important use is for identification when there is a need for problem investigation.

Good Manufacturing Practices

The F.D.A. regulations, Title 21, Part 128, specify Good Manufacturing Practices for industries engaged in the manufacturing, processing, packing or holding of human food. Brewery operations are covered by these regulations.

The glass container manufacturing operation does not fall under the provisions of the regulations; however, it must be recognized that as a supplier to an operation that is governed, they must be cognizant of the regulation and responsive to the needs of the brewer.

In addition to maintaining monitored good housekeeping programs, it is advisable to contract with a reputable pest control firm for scheduled services.

IV. STANDARDS FOR BEER BOTTLES

There are many reasons why standards for bottles are a necessity: they may come from many different suppliers; they may be used on different styles of processing equipment; they may be reused by a different processor than the original purchaser; and above all, they must fit other components such as closures, labels, packs and cartons that make up the ultimate unit. All this makes it desirable to have the interests of both the supplier and the processor coordinated through industry associations that arrive at standards acceptable to each.

Glass Packaging Institute

G.P.I. is an association providing services which are of mutual interest to member glass container manufacturers. Among the many subcommittees within the group are container design, finish design, and testing procedures. One of the primary responsibilities of these committees is to coordinate the standards and specifications within the glass container industry with manufacturers of related components or processing equipment and the users of glass containers.

United States Brewers Association

The U.S.B.A. is the brewing industry's counterpart to the glass industry's G.P.I. The U.S.B.A. maintains sub-committees on bottles and on closures. In addition, associate members from the supplying industries are invited to be representatives on the particular committee to aid in the coordination of activities and concerns which are of mutual interest.

The sub-committee on bottles publishes "Recommended Brewing Industry Beer and Ale Bottle Purchase Specifications". These specifications are coordinated with GPI specifications and standards.

American Society For Testing And Materials

The American Society for Testing and Materials (A.S.T.M.) is an international, nonprofit, technical, scientific and education society which operates through more than 105 main technical committees. The committees function in prescribed fields under regulations that ensure balanced representation among producers, consumers, and general interest participants.

A.S.T.M. is the recognized authority in the United States on standards for material, testing procedures for materials and manufactured articles and criteria for the equipment with which the tests are to be conducted. Four of the important standards which apply to brewery containers are:

C-224 Standard Method of Sampling Glass Containers
C-148 Standard Method of Polariscopic Examination of Glass Containers
C-147 Standard Method of Internal Pressure Test on Glass Containers
C-149 Standard Method of Thermal Shock Test on Glass Containers

Performance The Key

The ultimate evaluation of any package is how it performs on the processing line and out in the trade. Evaluation of performance is a useful tool to both the vendor and the processor.

It has been general experience that, with exception to qualifying new packages or a new supplier, statistical sample incoming acceptance inspection does not fulfill the purpose intended and does not justify the cost of the program. To provide any degree of reliability of meeting the desired brewery line performance levels and still allow a reasonable vendor risk, it requires extremely high sample sizes. With today's timed deliveries and high speed processing lines there is insufficient time between the arrival of the load and the requirements of the production line to conduct the inspection and arrive at a decision.

If the inspection has not yet arrived at a decision, but production requirements and unloading dock space dictate using the load, the program loses a lot of its creditability. This is not to imply that there should not be some form of quality evaluation.

Vendor Rating programs based strongly on performance evaluation by random work sample inspections is advisable and has been found to be of mutual benefit to both the supplier and the brewery. Usually the evaluations consist of random observations recording occurrences of bottle breakage at the filler, crowner and pasteurizer discharge. Observation for leaking bottles is also conducted at the pasteurizer discharge. Breakage or leaker rates are usually expressed in units per 10,000 bottles processed.

These observations not only rate the vendor performance, but can also detect a developing line-related problem if trends for all suppliers increase at the same operation or if a particular line experiences different performance than other lines observed processing the same mix of bottles.

To attain the most benefit from performance evaluations they must be reviewed periodically with the bottle supplier. Ideally a monthly review will allow action to be taken before an unfavorable trend becomes a serious problem. Reviews any less frequent than quarterly only report past history and do little to reverse the start of an unfavorable trend.

Problem Investigation

If a processing line problem is encountered—breakage, leakers, etc.—a few samples illustrating the condition are of far more help in analyzing the problem than cases of unprocessed bottles. In the case of breakage, as many of the fragments as can be collected should be saved. Bottom plate sections are particularly important to establish if the problem is cavity oriented or general.

If a problem is cavity oriented, it is highly probable that the problem is bottle related. Bottle related problems can be due to a physical condition between the bottles from that particular mold cavity and some element of the processing line resulting in selective situation causing one cavity to be more vulnerable to a severe or unusual stress than other cavities, even though all are entirely functional containers. The other possibility is a defective condition related to a particular cavity. If the problem is quite general, it is more likely to be equipment related.

If breakage involves a few large pieces with an apparent similar pattern, indicating a low energy failure, the bottle was either highly defective or badly damaged. On the other hand, if there is a great amount of fragmentation, it is the indication of a high energy failure, usually brought about by an excessive force.

As stated in the section on the IS machine, each forming section is actually an independent bottle-producing unit by itself. For this reason the occurrence of a defective condition is more often associated with a bottle produced from a single mold cavity or cavities operating on a single section rather than multiple cavities across the machine.

Based on the above and the nature of the inspection procedures, defective conditions do not usually exist over prolonged periods of time. Therefore, if a problem thought to be associated with a bottle defect is encountered, the following steps are recommended until the supplier's technical representative can investigate:

1. Save samples illustrating the problem.
2. Discontinue feeding the line with bottles from the suspect production period.
3. By checking production code on the carton, supply the line with bottles from a different shift, different production date, different machine position or different supplier.
4. If the condition continues, the problem is probably associated with the filling line itself and an investigation should continue in that direction.
5. If the condition is corrected, isolate the remainder of the suspect production and review with the supplier's technical representative. By simple pallet-by-pallet audit the extent of duration of the condition or presence of the questionable cavities can be determined.

Line Performance A Function Of Equipment

To fully enjoy the capabilities of processing equipment to accept the normal variation in dimensional characteristics of a glass bottle, the first important step is for newly designed equipment to be built with the knowledge of the specification tolerances related to the item to be processed. The equipment manufacturer should be provided a bottle print with all dimensions and tolerances, not just a case of sample bottles which may represent only a small range of the total allowed tolerance.

Equipment set-up and periodic adjustment checks should be conducted with metal dummy bottles formed to maximum specified diameters and minimum height tolerances. The compensation in most equipment will then allow proper operation throughout the normal range of specification tolerances. By setting the line with so-called "ideal bottle samples", you may be robbing yourself of the full potential of the equipment.

Processing Line Stability

One of the more favorable features of glass as a packaging material is that it can be formed in a very wide variety of shapes and designs, allowing great marketing appeal. However, the designs most appealing to the marketing group may not produce the optimum production conditions in the actual packaging operation.

As bottling line operating speeds have increased, particularly approaching and exceeding 1,000 bottles per minute, bottle handling conditions arose which had not been a serious problem at lower operating speeds. These adverse bottle handling conditions can be improved from several directions—bottle stability, line operation and line layout.

At line speeds below 800 BPM with the short stubby bottle designs in popular use a few years ago there was not the awareness concerning bottle stability. With the marketing change to taller, more distinctive design bottles being adapted at the same time brewery processing speeds were being dramatically increased the subject of bottle stability came to the surface. To put the subject in simple terms, bottle stability as related to design is an inter-relationship between bottle-to-bottle contact position, height-to-bearing surface diameter ratio, and vertical distribution of glass weight.

What was previously thought to be the ultimate, though not practically attainable, completely uniform distribution of glass from a functional strength point of view and economics of glass weight to bottle capacity did not always produce the most stable container. Concentrating on placement of glass, within the ability of the forming process, to the lower portion of the bottle will aid in improving stability. To achieve this, taller, smaller diameter designs may require a greater glass weight to capacity ratio than shorter, larger diameter designs.

Stability—A Function Of Line Operation

Much can be accomplished through line adjustment to successfully process even the more unique bottle designs. Conveyor speeds should be balanced to prevent sudden acceleration or deceleration. Excessive conveyor speeds causing the chain to run faster than the bottle movement should be avoided. Transfer from conveyor to conveyor or across dead plates should be even or slightly stepped down in the direction of movement, never stepped upward.

Bottles should be kept in contact with one another as much as possible to avoid large voids. This can be accomplished through setting of limit switches and providing adequate accumulation area to accommodate momentary equipment stoppage and to assure a continuous supply of bottles to each part of the operation.

For single filing on infeed to a power drive, guide rails should be set no less than 1/16″ greater than maximum bottle diameter and no greater than ⅛″ wider than maximum bottle diameter. This will allow proper alignment, freedom to move but restriction from nesting.

Stability VS. Mobility

Although directly related, the terms stability and mobility differ. Poor mobility can contribute to poor stability. The opposite is not a direct relationship. Mobility from the bottle view point is dependent mostly upon good permanent surface treatment. From the line operation it is a function of proper conveyor soap lubrication.

Other Bottle Design Features

Due to the versatility of glass and its ability to be blown into unlimited shapes and designs, often lettering or logo decorations are incorporated as part of the package. Care must be taken to position the blown decoration to prevent glass to glass contact between adjacent bottles. This will prevent bruising or chipping of the raised portion which would be detrimental to both the strength and visual appearance of the bottle. Positioning of the design should also avoid areas of bottle control such as twist rinser guide rails, especially for the inverted position, and crowner neck guides. Ideal equipment adjustment cannot be achieved if aligned with an interrupted design pattern.

Label indents provide protection to the label, both immediately after it is applied and vulnerable to repositioning or sticking to the label on an adjacent bottle and also from scuffing. However, label indent bottles require more careful location of guides, particularly in a twist rinser, to prevent vertical motion causing the heel of one bottle to move into the indent of the next bottle. This action not only affects line mobility, but can result in surface damage to the contact areas.

Due to the nature of the design, a bottle with label indent will develop higher vertical load stresses than a straight-sided bottle under the same crowner load. If the surface is damaged to create a stress concentrator, the strength may be reduced to the point of experiencing crowner failures.

Bottles—Manufacture And Standards

Glass is a remarkable material. It is one of the oldest materials utilized by man, and yet there are mysteries associated with its structure and related strength attributes that are still to be discovered.

Bottle manufacturing was the first industrial development in America. The advances in technology have been enormous, and yet some of the basic concepts have not changed much since the days of hand blown operation.

Standards to which glass bottles perform today were considered completely impractical and impossible just a few years ago, and yet we know greater processing speeds and the performance requirements necessary are just around the corner. Glass containers are one of the most ancient packages, and yet remain today at the fore-front of the Packaging Industry.

REFERENCES

1. PHILLIPS, C.I. *Glass: The Miracle Maker* Pitman Publishing Corp., Chicago, Ill., 1941
2. PRESTON, F.W. Bottle Breakage—Cause and Types of Fractures *The Bulletin of the American Ceramic Society* February, 1939
3. HOLSCHER, H.H. Feeding and Forming *Handbook of Glass Manufacture, Vol. I* Ogden Publishing Co. Third Printing 1961
4. TEAGUE, J.M., JR.Investigations of Stress in Glass Bottles Under Internal Hydrostatic Pressure *The Journal of the American Ceramic Society* Vol. 39, No. 7 July, 1956
5. Refractories, Glass and Other Ceramic Materials, Part 13, American Society for Testing Materials, Philadelphia, Pa.

CHAPTER VII

BOTTLE WASHING
BY J.L. KAPPELE AND
L.M. LAISHLEY

INTRODUCTION

In major geographical areas of the world, such as South America, Europe, Japan, Mexico, Canada, Australia, Africa, etc. (unlike the United States where approximately 80% of the beer sold is in non-returnable containers), the returnable bottle is still the prime container. Since bottle washing is a key element in the returnable bottle cycle, this important subject warrants treatment in some detail.

While the use of non-returnable containers in the brewing industry is increasing world-wide, the returnable bottle will very likely retain its present dominant position for a number of reasons:

—in a typical market, the largest single element of the cost of beer sold in non-returnable containers is the cost of the container. In small well-organized and predominantly "deposit" bottle markets, the cost-effect of the container itself is negligible. In such markets, the added costs of bottle collection and return, plus the reprocessing costs at the brewery, are much less than the comparable cost of non-returnable containers.

—in contrast to the U.S.A., many of the world's domestic markets are relatively small geographically, and are served efficiently by breweries in the small to medium size range, e.g.: up to 3 million hl annual production. These plants serve specific major population centres and their distribution patterns facilitate the organization of complementary systems for bottle return. The relatively small size of these operations as compared to those in the U.S.A., dictates much higher costs in the purchase or manufacture of non-returnable containers, thus creating an even greater spread between returnable and non-returnable total package cost.

—ecological considerations will continue to have importance in many market areas, pricing non-returnable containers very unfavourably or eliminating them altogether.

There are some negative aspects to the use of the returnable bottle, which should be recognized:

—bottle scuffing and corresponding deterioration in container appearance will take place in busy markets where bottle returns exceed 85%. Under these circumstances it is not unusual for a large proportion of the bottles to make 20 to 40 trips before disappearing from the "float". Considerable work is currently in progress world-wide on various approaches to eliminate this serious problem, e.g. coatings, scuffrings, modulated speed control on packaging lines, scuffed bottle detectors, etc.

—container standardization increases the efficiency of a returnable bottle

110

system, but limits the variety, type and style of package offered to the consumer. This can become a serious marketing drawback.

—in spite of a high-quality bottle washing operation and subsequent electronic and/or visual inspection, a small number of unsatisfactory bottles can reach the market and give rise to consumer complaints.

—the processing of returnable bottles in the brewery is considerably more labour intensive than is the case for non-returnable containers.

In spite of these drawbacks, it appears that the returnable bottle will remain the dominant container for many years to come in most of the world's beer markets. Bottle washing will therefore continue to be a matter of great importance to the brewing industry at large.

This chapter deals with the subject by starting with a discussion of the basic principles involved, and how these principles are followed in the various operating functions of a typical bottle washer.

The next section of the chapter describes in some detail, the chemical composition and other characteristics of typical bottle washer solutions and describes some of the chemical reactions obtained with certain of the soil elements encountered in bottle washing.

The main section of the chapter deals with bottle washing equipment and its operation. This includes handling and storage of returnable bottles, uncasing, bottle conveying, washer loading, washer types and construction, washer operating procedures, maintenance procedures and cleaning procedures, washer trouble shooting, and the safety aspects of washer operation. A description of empty bottle inspection is also included in this section.

The final section covers the economics of bottle washer operation and describes the main items contributing to the total cost of operating a bottle washer. Various approaches to operating cost reduction are suggested, including solution reclaim and re-use. The section concludes with a description of typical reclaim systems and their operation.

BASIC PRINCIPLES AND FUNCTIONS OF A BOTTLE WASHER

Basic Principles of Bottle Washing

The objective of the bottle washer is to clean and to remove labels from soiled returnable bottles. This task is achieved when physically and biologically clean bottles are discharged from the rinser.

Non-returnable bottles do not need to be processed through the bottle washer; a simple rinsing device is sufficient to prepare the bottles for the filling operation.

Several factors determine the cleaning effect:

—The design of the bottle washer.
—The condition of the returnable bottles.
—The composition of the bottle washing solution.
—The temperature of the solution.
—The submersion or contact time.
—The quality of the water.

In the following, each factor will be commented upon.

Typical Bottle Washer Operation

Basically, bottle washers are designed to facilitate the following sequence of operation:

a) the bottles are subjected to an internal and external pre-rinse with water in order to remove loose soil and foreign material

b) the bottles are alternately immersed and drained by passing them through a series of isolated tanks, each containing large quantities of washing solutions. Mechanical agitation of the solution and jetting creates a shearing action which aids in separating soil elements and labels from the bottles, and dispersing both in the solution

c) the fouled washing solution is drained from the bottles as they pass from one tank to another.

d) the bottles are rinsed free from the washing solution

The Conditions Of the Returnable Bottles

Soiled returnable bottles fall into four categories:[1]

a) "Normal trade returns" make up the bulk of the bottles coming back to the brewery. These are bottles which make the round trip to the brewery to the trade and back again in less than 2 months time.

b) "Storage bottles" are bottles which were kept in warehouses, basements, garages etc., for longer periods. These bottles are more difficult to clean than normal trade returns.

c) "Ditch bottles" are characterized by heavy accumulation of soil along the interior of one side wall as a result of lying on the side in outdoor locations for extended periods of time. The soil may be dried mud, sand, mould and algae or any combination thereof. Ditch bottles are normally collected by salvage operators and can return to the plant in single or multiple deliveries involving significant quantities. Under these circumstances they should be segregated and washed separately at the end of a production run when special attention can be given to the washing operation.

d) Uncleanable bottles which have substances such as tar, paint, plaster or weld splatter attached to the glass surface. These soils are insoluble in normal bottle washing solutions and the bottles can therefore not be cleaned. These bottles should be discarded before loading the bottle washer.

Composition Of The Washing Solution

Bottle washing solutions are made up using caustic soda (NaOH) and additives; the total is thoroughly mixed with water to prescribed solution strengths. The chemical effect of the washing solution is related to its ability to disperse soil which is attached to the bottle surface and to avoid redeposition. Good wetting and rinsing properties of the washing solution are essential for obtaining the desired cleaning effect. Cleaning power varies with the concentration of the solution and the operating temperature. A rule of thumb states that the same germicidal effect can be obtained either by raising the temperature by 10°F (5.5°C) or by increasing the strength of the solution by 50%. However, it should be cautioned that the application of this rule may only be valid within a narrow range.

Selection of high caustic concentrations will ensure the desired germicidal effect but also:

—produce excessive pulp and fibres from paper labels

—etch bottles

—may require the installation of neutralizing units to meet local effluent specifications.

—concentrations over 5% may lead to waste due to carryover.

Temperature Of The Solution

Higher temperatures of the washing solutions will accelerate the cleaning process. High temperatures are also necessary to obtain sterility so the adjustment of temperatures is quite important. If the bottles are subjected to an excessive temperature change, breakage due to "thermal shock" can occur. The temperature differential between compartments should not exceed 56°C (100°F) on the up-leg and 23°C (40°F) on the down-leg. Even at these limits some breakage may occur due to thermal shock which produces a characteristic crack extending completely around the base and often up the side wall of a bottle.

Hot soak temperatures make the vapor zone very hot and this can cause the contamination to bake on if the bottle washer is stopped for a long period. High temperatures also tend to cause fast drying of the bottles in the vapor zone, which may result in an alkaline dry-on in the absence of wetting agent.

Submersion Or Contact Time

The longer the contact time, the greater is the cleaning effect; however, prolonged contact time should be avoided because of the corrosive attack of caustic soda solutions on glass. Under those conditions beer bottles may acquire a cloudy appearance.

"Total time" refers to the number of minutes required for a bottle to complete passage through the washer from loading to unloading. The "submersion time" (also called soaking time) constitutes the time a bottle is submerged in the caustic solutions and does not include the time used for rinsing or for bottle transfer from one compartment to the next. On the other hand, "contact time" refers to the time during which a bottle is subjected to the action of the caustic solution which would be equal to submersion time, plus the time spent in transfer from one solution compartment to another. It should be noted that the Canadian standard of accepted practice is a minimum of twenty minutes of submersion time.

As a bottle travels in and out of hot caustic soak compartments, its soiled surface is subjected to two separate and distinct cleaning mechanisms. One is time-dependent, the soaking sequence, the second is time-independent, the filling and emptying sequence. The first mechanism is related solely to the time the bottles are submerged in hot caustic. The second, time-independent mechanism is related to the number of times the bottles are filled and emptied. The phenomenon has been described by Jennings[2] as Dupre's effect which in turn depends upon the number of times an air-liquid interface sweeps across a soiled glass surface. For example, in a single compartment washer, a bottle would have two interfaces, i.e. one filling and one emptying; a three compartment washer would have six interfaces. Barry-Wehmiller Co. conducted lab tests designed to simulate bottle cleaning processes. The results indicated that for equal soaking time (6-9 minute range) a three compartment washer can remove twice as much soil as a single compartment machine. From the above it becomes clear that washing machines cannot be judged solely on soak time.

The Quality Of The Water

In bottle washing the degree of water hardness plays a crucial part. In North America water hardness is expressed as mg $CaCO_3$ per liter despite the fact that a variety of cations (Ca^{++} and Mg^{++}) and anions (SO_4^{--}, Cl^-, NO_3^-) may be present.

"Temporary hardness" is due to the presence of bicarbonate such as $Ca(HCO_3)_2$ and $Mg(HCO_3)_2$ and can be partly removed by boiling. In contrast "permanent hardness" results from the presence of sulphates of calcium and magnesium and boiling has no substantial effect on their concentration.

Hard water causes scaling in the bottle washer and reduces the efficiency of the washing solution. In the rinser section hard water can plug the spray nozzles and lead to undesirable spotting on cleaned bottles. Temporary hardness is also of concern in the rinser as the sodium hydroxide carry-over reacts with calcium bicarbonate to form the precipitating calcium carbonate.

Good results have been obtained by adding polyphosphates to the rinse water. These compounds combine (sequester) with calcium and magnesium ions and stay in suspension.

The removal of scale producing ions from the rinse water is also very often practiced. The most commonly used water softener is a bed of sodium zeolite resins which exchanges sodium ions for scale-forming ions of calcium and magnesium.

Regeneration is achieved by treating the exhausted resin with 10% brine solution. During this process the calcium and magnesium ions are replaced by sodium ions.

Basic Functions of a Bottle Washer

The soiled bottles are mechanically loaded into carrier chains with pockets from which they are discharged after completion of the cleaning cycle. When loading and discharge take place at the same end, the washer is a "single-end machine". More common, however, are "double-end machines" where loading and discharge takes place on separate ends. One end machines need only one operator, double-end machines require two operators but allow a more hygienic operation. Machine arrangements are also available in double-end machines permitting loading and unloading to take place at different floor elevations.

Pretreatment or Prerinse

Before the bottles are subjected to the main cleaning process they are pretreated with warm water or mild caustic. This is done to flush out liquid residues, to remove excessive soil and to attemperate the bottles for the following soak in hot caustic. Good pretreatment also reduces contamination of the next compartment.

Two variations may be encountered: presoaking or prejetting. Presoaking reduces breakage due to thermal shock, allows heat recovery and does not require the installation of additional pumps. In contrast prejetting removes excessive soil more effectively and makes it easier to control undesired development of microorganisms in the pretreatment stage.

Main Cleaning

After pretreatment the bottles travel automatically into the section of the washer where the main cleaning process takes place. Hot alkaline solutions soften and dissolve label adhesives and disperse soil residues and microbial contaminants. This is accomplished by alternately soaking and jetting the bottles with washing solutions in several compartments. Although the make-up of aluminum foil labels differs substantially from paper labels, the removal times are very similar for both label types (recently introduced "metallized paper labels" appear to take longer). It is desirable to separate the labels as quickly as possible from the washing solution to avoid disintegration of the label into minute pulp fibers which plug jets and filters. Paddle agitators are normally employed to aid label removal.

Label separators form an integral part of bottle washers; they are designed to provide a continuous label removal while the machine is in production. Without label separators the life cycle of the washing solution would be greatly reduced.

Final Rinse

All machines have a final rinse stage for removing the alkaline bottle washing compounds from the glass surface and to temper the bottles prior to the filler. This section of the washer consists of undershot jets and overhead sprays which first apply dilute caustic and then fresh water to the bottles to remove the last traces of soil and residual detergent. At the end of the washing process the bottles are drained and automatically discharged from the pockets to a conveyor.

BOTTLE WASHING SOLUTIONS

In bottle washing the detersive system consists of three major elements:
—the bottles
—the soil or dirt which is attached to the bottles and
—the washing solution
In this section we will deal only with the latter, the washing solution.

Properties of Bottle Washing Solutions

The basic requirements of the solution are that it lowers the adhesion of the soil to the glass surface and that it keeps the unwanted foreign matter in suspension for easy rinsing. Close inspection of these basic requirements reveals that the washing solution must comprise the following:

Germicidal Properties

The ability of a solution to destroy harmful microorganisms depends on its composition, on the temperature and the submersion time. Many states have enacted laws governing the strength of bottle washing solutions and it is to the brewer's advantage to acquaint himself with the regulation. It may be useful to quote the minimum requirements for obtaining a sterile bottle as recommended by the National Soft Drink Association. (Formerly called American Bottlers of Carbonated Beverages).

"Unclean bottles shall be exposed to a 3% solution of which not less than 60% is caustic (NaOH) for a period of not less than 5 minutes at a temperature of not less than 55°C (130°F) or to an equivalent cleansing and sterilizing process".

Germicidal equivalents to the above recommendations may be obtained by a multitude of combinations of time, concentration and temperature; Table I depicts such equivalents to achieve 99.9% germicidal efficiency.

Wetting or Penetrating Properties

The ease with which the bottle surface can be wetted is an important property of the washing solution. This property permits the solution to contact the entire soiled surface and to penetrate deposits of dirt, residue and foreign material in the bottle; it does so by reducing both the surface tension of the liquid and its interfacial tension with the glass. Surfactants is a commonly used word to describe these surface active agents.

TABLE I
GERMICIDAL EQUIVALENTS*
REQUIRED CONCENTRATION (in %) of NaOH AT VARIOUS TEMPERATURES

TIME	TEMP. 110°F. (43°C)	120°F (49°C)	130°F (54°C)	140°F (60°C)	150°F (66°C)	160°F (71°C)
1 Min	11.8	7.9	5.3	3.5	2.4	1.6
3 Min	6.4	4.3	2.9	1.9	1.3	0.9
5 Min	4.8	3.2	2.2	1.4	1.0	0.6
7 Min	4.0	2.7	1.8	1.2	0.8	0.5
9 Min	3.5	2.3	1.6	1.0	0.7	0.5
11 Min	3.1	2.1	1.4	0.9	0.6	0.4
13 Min	2.8	1.9	1.3	0.8	0.6	0.4
15 Min	2.6	1.7	1.2	0.8	0.5	0.3

* According to National Soft Drink Association

Good wetting properties are important for the rapid removal of both paper and foil labels in large pieces. Speedy label removal reduces label breakdown into pulp and fibers, which are more difficult to remove from the washing solutions.

Rinsing Properties

During the rinsing process all soil and detergent residues must be removed from the bottles; a detergent with good rinsing properties will facilitate this operation. It should not be expected that the rinser removes materials which remain strongly attached to bottles. It is the major function of the soaking compartments and the jet-rinse sections to break the soil-glass bond. Good rinsing properties will promote drainage and reduce the quantity of caustic carry-over from compartment to compartment resulting in savings in caustic consumption.

Sequestering Properties

A sequestering or chelating agent is a chemical compound which can combine with metal ions in solution to form water-soluble complex ions. In bottle washing it is primarily the calcium, iron, aluminum and magnesium ions that require sequestration.

The formation of Ca^{++} and Mg^{++} chelates in the washing solution is necessary to prevent the deposition of insoluble calcium and magnesium salts which form an unsightly film on bottles and which produce a heavy scale on carrier chains, pockets, and tanks. Scale can also interfere with heat transfer, plug nozzles and increase the physical load on the machine. Also, scale on the carrier chain and pockets acts as a porous sponge, increasing the alkali carry-over from compartment to compartment.

Deflocculating or Dispersing Properties

The above property of a washing solution will aid the process of dispersing by keeping colloidal particles in suspension.

Emulsifying Properties

Emulsification is the suspension of particles within a second liquid phase. In bottle washing, this property aids in the removal of oil films from surfaces.

Anti-Corrosion Properties

A good washing solution protects the soaker/rinser against corrosion.

Anti-Foaming Properties

Excessive foaming reduces the effectiveness of the cleaning process. Adhesive soils are primarily responsible for foam formation in the soaker because they combine with caustic to form "soaps". Foam depressants are frequently added to the soaker solution to make it more effective.

Lubricating Properties

A properly designed washing solution should also lubricate the exposed drives and parts in the soaker.

Dissolving and Neutralizing Properties

Washing solutions must be able to solubilize some soils and to neutralize acid residues.

Solubility

Maintaining the optimum concentration of the washing compounds is important. Complete solubility is a prerequisite for this undertaking.

Economy

Operating costs should be kept as low as possible without jeopardizing quality. It is indeed a technical challenge to design a bottle washing solution which balances these two basic requirements.

Ingredients of Bottle Washing Solutions

Unfortunately, there is no single compound available which possesses all of the above properties. It is therefore necessary to combine several chemicals to obtain a washing solution which meets most of the mentioned requirements. In the following the main bottle-washing compounds and ingredients will be described.

Caustic Soda

Sodium hydroxide, as it is called chemically, is a strong alkali and it is the principal ingredient of almost all bottle-washing solutions. It is usually shipped as a liquid in 50% concentration and when diluted with water an evolution of heat takes place.

Caustic soda is most economical to use and has excellent germicidal qualities. In solution it is a powerful solvent which readily peptizes soil and saponifies oils and fats. However, it does have several drawbacks and limitations:

—It contributes to scale formation.
—It has poor rinsability, and if caustic were used alone carry-over between tanks would be excessive.
—It foams under high pressure.
—It will promote scuffing and etching of bottles if used in high concentrations.
—It also reduces labels to pulp when used in high concentrations on low wet strength labels.

Because of these drawbacks caustic additives or improvers are needed to obtain an effective washing solution. Brewing companies either add the necessary ingredients to the caustic or purchase already blended bottlewashing compounds.

Sequestrants

To prevent scale formation sequestrants are added to the caustic solution. The most frequently used sequestrants are gluconates, glucoheptonates, polyphosphates and in recent years organophosphonates. Ethylenediaminetetraacetic acid (EDTA) is also used, although primarily in conjunction with phosphates.

The properties of various sequestering agents determine their effectiveness in bottlewashing formulations. The sugar acids (gluconic, glucoheptonic) are added to the soaker compartments at sequestration levels to control Ca^{++},

Mg^{++} and other metals. However, when diluted to threshold levels during alkaline and fresh water rinse stages they fail to prevent scale formation.

The inorganic polyphosphates are effective scale inhibitors during the fresh water rinse. They are ineffective, however, as scale inhibitors in the alkaline rinse stage. Also, they hydrolyze in hot caustic solutions and convert to orthophosphates forming insoluble Ca^{++} and Mg^{++} salts which precipitate. The phosphonates are effective sequestrants and soil deflocculants like the inorganic polyphosphates. But unlike the polyphosphates, they are hydrolytically stable in hot caustic solutions and thus prevent precipitate formation at all washing stages. In addition, they are effective threshold agents in the alkaline as well as in the fresh water rinse.

Surfactants

Surface active or wetting agents may be employed in small quantities (1% to 5% of caustic). They are complex chemical molecules with a hydrophilic or a hydrophobic part; most commonly used are non-ionic defoaming surfactants; both are characterized by good dispersing, emulsifying, wetting and rinsing properties.

Foam depressants

Silicones are not used very often as foam depressents in bottle washing solutions. Modern surfactants are designed to include defoaming qualities.

Formulated Premixes

The key to a correctly formulated premix is obtaining the correct blend of detergent ingredients, in order to effect all the cleaning steps which are necessary without overuse of any ingredient. This is not an easy task: not only do the conditions for bottlewashing differ widely from one operation to another, but even within the same soaker operation conditions change as the soil load within the soaker increases until it is finally dumped, or the washer solution recycled.

The individual components required in a soaker detergent have all been mentioned: alkali, sequesterants, wetting agents, soil suspending agents, defoamers etc. The correct choice of the ratio of each ingredient for any particular soaker requires expertise which can best be provided by the specialized chemical supply companies. Obtaining this correct balance of ingredients is important for if the amount of one ingredient is too low, the quality of the washed product might suffer, the machine might scale or foam, or the bottles be improperly cleaned. Overuse of any of the ingredients leads not only to unnecessary costs, but also has more subtle effects. Excessive use of caustic or sequesterants can lead to bottle etching, excess defoamers can result in residual films.

Formulated bottlewashing compounds are always more expensive than the individual components on a direct weight basis. However, the costs in using site-prepared washing formulations which are not carefully balanced can very often exceed the apparent advantage of purchasing each ingredient separately. Such costs include extra labour and overhead to blend materials, plus raw material and finished product storage costs. In addition, the blending of individual detergent components in a bottleshop can be a time-consuming and potentially hazardous practice.

Custom blended formulations are supplied by chemical specialty companies to be used in the full range of bottlewashing equipment, and for all conditions of water quality, temperatures, etc. Representatives of these companies are able to provide use/cost effectiveness analyses to demonstrate the most efficient product and concentration for any particular situation.

Aluminum Foil Label Removal

Aluminum foil labels differ considerably from paper labels so the process of their removal warrants special attention. Foil labels are manufactured from aluminum foil, approximately 0.003″ (0.08 mm), laminated to paper. The paper is bonded to the aluminum foil either with paraffin wax or with an adhesive. Paraffin-wax bonded labels are preferred for returnable bottles because they separate easily in hot caustic and thus reduce consumption of washing solution.

Label removal is an important aspect in bottle washing, and in effectiveness depends primarily on:

—temperature of the washing solution
—soaking time
—concentration of the washing solution
—type of label
—type of glue.

Different types of labels respond differently to these conditions. The caustic soda solution simultaneously disintegrates the inks, dissolves the aluminum, the bonding agent and the glue by which the label was attached to the bottle.

Specially designed inks are used in conjunction with foil labels to visually indicate the distinctive feature of the product; such inks contain titanium oxide (TiO_2) and carbon blacks as colouring media. The ink pigments are usually insoluble and a large portion will settle to the bottom of the compartments; however, occasionally, the suspended ink particles will float to the surface of the washing solution and become lodged on the inner surface of the bottles. Such bottles exhibit unsightly "ink spots".

When aluminum reacts with sodium hydroxide free hydrogen gas is produced. Assuming 100% foil labelled bottles, approximately 17–27 cubic feet/minute of hydrogen gas is generated in a bottle washer that processes 1400 bottles per minute. When hydrogen is combined with dry air in certain proportions it will explode if ignited by a spark or flame. Since hydrogen is lighter than air, the danger area is above the level of the washing solution. In order to avoid accidents, the best rule to follow when aluminum labels are involved is to vent all bottle washers on top and to keep open flames and open electrical switches below the level of the solution.

The other reaction product, sodium aluminate, is formed at the expense of NaOH. This depletion occurs in addition to the caustic consumed for cleaning and sterilizing. In the presence of water sodium aluminate undergoes hydrolysis to produce aluminum hydroxide and sodium hydroxide.

The equation represents an equilibrium with the reaction proceeding in both directions. Initially, the main force of the reaction is to the right but as the concentration of $Al(OH)_3$ and NaOH increases the reaction slows down.

Sodium aluminate and soluble silicates (from bottles and fillers in paper labels) form a sodium-aluminum-silicate compound which is insoluble and believed to be the main constituent of the hard, siliceous scale found on heater coils. It is important that washing solutions contain ingredients that prevent settling of these silica producing compounds.

BOTTLE WASHING EQUIPMENT AND OPERATION

Bottle Washing—Preparatory
Handling of Returned Bottles

Ideally, a bottling facility processing empty bottle returns would operate with the returns matching production requirements on a FIFO (first in/first out) basis, with a minimum time lag between the customer and the final cleaning process. However, because of seasonal or other imbalances in returns, on-site or remote empty goods storage may be required, which in effect will age the returns and which will result in increasing the difficulty in providing a properly washed and sanitized bottle. This storage time is in addition to the time the empty bottle was in the customer's hands.

During the storage period, any residual liquid left in the bottle will tend to evaporate and concentrate leaving a perfect medium for the formation of yeasts, moulds and other growths. Unfortunately extended periods of time will permit this growth to completely dry out and form hard crusts which then become even more difficult to remove.

Historical data from the individual operating plants will usually be sufficient to determine how the excess returns can be managed. In most instances, it will only be necessary to rotate the returns to ensure that a maximum pre-determined storage time is not exceeded. Other conditions, such as climate, seasonality or type of returns, may dictate prewashing prior to storage in order to reduce insect infestation, future cleaning requirements, rejects and customer complaints. Since this process results in additional costs due to a duplication of all functions (except labeling) between uncasing and packing, the economics of this procedure must be weighed very carefully.

Included in the returns will be "uncleanable" bottles which will exceed the cleaning ability of even the best bottle washers. These bottles are contaminated with substances which are insoluble in the normal bottle washing solutions. Because of possible contamination of the cleaning solution, these bottles should be removed prior to the bottle washer. In many instances because of high uncasing speeds and mass bottle transfer, it is impossible to identify uncleanable bottles prior to the bottle washer, and therefore it is important that the soaker discharge operator and/or the electronic bottle inspectors identify and remove the bottles prior to bottle filling. Bottles removed at this stage should be examined for either destruction or recycling.

Uncasing

In most new bottling lines the uncasing system is designed with enough capacity to provide between 115 and 125% of the filler capacity (100% base). The type and size of the uncasing system will ultimately be determined by the bottling line capacity, type of case in use and most certainly by other similar installations in the bottleshop. Depending on the marketing area served, it is conceivable to receive returns in any or all of the following types of cases:

—Plastic Retripper
—Corrugated Retripper (Shell with Sleeve)
—Gaylord Retripper
—Trays
—Corrugated or Boxboard one-way carton or multi-cartons
—End load or wrap-around cartons

Each of these bottle cases has certain peculiarities which may dictate the type of uncasing system needed. Cartons with top flaps require flap control and/or flap removal and also usually require additional upstream equipment and operating labour.

It can be expected in any returnable bottle market, that a portion of the returned bottles will be classified as foreign and that they must be removed, destroyed or repacked for reshipment and credit. The extent of the problem will dictate whether or not the foreign bottles can be removed by hand (by operators) prior to machine uncasing, or sorted in a bottle sorting and repacking system after uncasing. Variations in bottle diameter and height can play havoc on any type of uncaser, causing equipment damage and missed bottles. This eventually translates to reduced efficiency and increased glass shrinkage. Foreign bottles which do not match the dimensional limits of the bottle washer lane guides or pockets will eventually cause bottle washer stops due to jamming and safety stop protection. For this reason it is important that sufficient equipment (sorting) or inspection be instituted to ensure that improper bottles do not reach the soaker load portion of the bottle washer.

In actual practice, most of the bottle cases previously mentioned lend themselves to conventional uncasing using either air actuated cups or mechanical devices to grip the neck of the bottle and remove it from the case. Other styles of uncasing are referred to in the next section. Bottles are then transferred to a table or bottle conveying system for eventual feed to the bottle washer.

Types of Uncasers

Continuous Inline: Opened cases are fed into this type of machine in single file for removal of bottles with overhead grippers. This type of machine falls into two categories:

- —Indexed Head—where the machine has a specific number of heads arranged in the same pattern as the bottles in the incoming case and attached to a continuously rotating endless chain drive. Indexing of all cases is necessary on this machine. A typical example of this type of machine is the IAC High Speed Uncaser.
- —Continuous Uninterrupted—this type of machine has a continuous uninterrupted row of fingers which move over the bottles. Case feed to this type of machine can be random and does not require indexing because the continuous rotating drive chain contains an endless belt of gripper fingers. The Jones-Model HSU Uncaser—is a typical example of this type of machine.

Reciprocating or Batch: This type of machine normally works on a reciprocating basis uncasing more than one case per uncasing cycle. The reciprocating cycle can be defined as the time it takes for the carriage with the uncasing heads to start from a rest position over the cases, lower itself to engage the bottles, lift the bottles to the table or bottle conveyor and then return itself to the rest position.

Depending on the design, it is possible to have a single row machine with the ability to pick up to seven cases per cycle, or a multi-row reciprocating machine which could uncase a complete pallet layer of up to ten cases simultaneously. Case indexing and the positive location of each case beneath the uncasing head is an absolute necessity for proper operation of this style of uncaser. Operating speeds or capacities are effectively increased by designing the carton feed and empty carton discharge to function during the time the uncased bottles clear the case and the uncaser carriage returns empty after depositing the bottles on the table or bottle conveyor. An example of the many manufacturers of this type of machine is the Holstein and Kappert GARANT Uncaser, shown in Figure 7-1.

Case Unloader: This type of machine is most commonly used for new glass in cases, where cases are received at the machine inverted. The top unsealed flaps are then on the bottom while the empty bottles are in an upright position in the case. The weight of the bottles then opens the inner flaps and the bottles drop the length of the inner flaps on to an unloading belt. The empty case is raised by an incline and is lifted off the bottles. This process is also used in uncasing locations where the bottoms of the cases are sawed off and the bottles are removed from the case in the same manner.

7-1. Typical Reciprocatory Uncaser (Courtesy of Holstein and Kappert Co.)

Bottom Saw: These machines are used in conjunction with end load or wrap-around type cartons, where the bottles are packed tightly without partitions making overhead withdrawal impractical. After cutting the bottom of the case off, the bottles are separated in much the same manner as in the case unloader example, item C above. Typical of this type of machine is the WMF Saw Uncaser manufactured by the Western Metal Fabricators, Lethbridge, Alberta.

Uncaser Design: As previously stated, the uncaser design will vary, depending on the type of bottle, type of case and material handling system which is prevalent at any specific location. A wide range of equipment is available from a number of manufacturers to meet both the capacity and design requirements for any specific situation.

Uncaser Operation

Regardless of the equipment chosen there will be random instances in which the machine will fail to retrieve some or many bottles. This normally is caused by the condition of the returns or when the bottles are not centered beneath the cups or fingers. As a result, missed bottles will not accompany the empty case to scrap, case washing (plastic) or storage, as the case may be, unless there is some means of bottle retrieval. The choice of either manual inspection and removal or mechanically inverted case cleaner removal will depend on the system and economics of the particular plant. By maintaining a record of this type of deficiency, Plant Operations will be able to assess the uncaser performance and the necessary maintenance requirements. The removal of foreign bottles, damaged bottles and crowns prior to the operation will improve uncaser performance.

Empty Carton Handling

(a) Single Trip: Single trip cartons are usually the easiest to contend with. After either removing missed bottles and/or trash and possible partition salvage, the case is usually routed to by-products recovery, baled and then sold in the recycle paper market.

(b) Retrippers: Whether the case is cardboard or plastic, the case exiting the uncaser must be inspected, culled or cleaned prior to re-use. It should also be pointed out that there could be a time lag of up to 60 minutes between the uncasing and case packing functions, which will impose a warehousing problem for cases processed during that period. Designs and layouts must include adequate space allotment to store the empty retripper cases awaiting packing.

(c) Partition Salvage: Depending on the economics, sanitation, space limitations, etc., the advisability of operating a partition salvage operation will have to be reviewed on an individual basis. Operating data from plants operating such a system show partition recovery rates up to 90%.

Bottle Conveying System—Uncaser to Soaker Load

This system plays an important role in maintaining continuous bottle washer operations. The system must be designed to eliminate fallen bottles and to provide a continuous supply of bottles to the soaker load table. Sufficient surge capacity should be built into the system to accommodate short uncaser stops. Generally, two minutes' accumulation at maximum soaker speed would be considered an absolute minimum to provide the necessary flow of uninterrupted bottles.

Scuffing of returnable bottles has become a major concern to most companies utilizing this type of container from the standpoint of appearance and customer acceptance. Scuffed bottle tests have revealed that a major portion of damage occurs on this section of the bottle conveying system where the bottles are dry, dirty and subject to significant bottle to bottle abrasion. Considerable thought must, therefore, be given to the design of this bottle transport/accumulation system to minimize scuffed bottle conditions.

Prewetting

To assist the conventional bottle washing operation, it is also possible to provide additional prewetting time by spraying or cascading rinse water from either the pasteurizer or the soaker, (water which would normally be destined for the sewer), over the bottles, after they leave the uncasing station. This operation will effectively add prewetting time equivalent to the conveyor system accumulation time and will add to the effectiveness of the bottle washing process.

Bottle Washer Load

The washer load operator located at the unscrambler table portion of the load table, ensures that all bottles exiting the bottle conveying system are upright and are devoid of crowns or other defects which would adversely impair the cleaning operation. Once on the table, the bottles are divided into a number of single file bottle lines to match each bottle carrier pocket across the width of the washer. To accomplish this, the combined action of multiple table chains, ploughs, oscillating deflectors and lane guides are required. Because of the significant number of bottle deflecting devices on the table, there is a definite tendency to cause fallen bottles, and for that reason it is usually advisable to run with a full table at all times. Depending on the degrees of sophistication, an automatic control system can be installed to maintain bottle "prime" or it can be left to a start/stop table operation actuated by the operator. The design of the bottle deflector system is important to the operation of the table, since excessive pressure can cause bottles to break and/or overturn in the lanes or alternately reduce the bottle supply to a section of the washer infeed causing starvation and/or fallen bottles.

Variable speed table chains will greatly assist in optimizing bottle handling and bottle pressure. The load table mechanism takes the bottles from the individual lanes and moves each bottle in the row gently and securely into each carrier pocket across the width of the bottle washer.

If for any reason a bottle, or a row of bottles, does not index properly into the carrier pocket and causes a jam, most machines are equipped with a safety device which will stop both the pusher mechanism and the bottle washer, indicating a washer load safety trip. This type of fault normally requires the washer infeed operator to manually correct the fault and remove the obstruction. Following this corrective action, the operator must reset the bottle pusher mechanism which will then clear the safety trip and allow the bottle washer to be restarted. From a control standpoint, this operational area can play an important role in the monitoring of bottle line performance. By utilizing a computer-assisted monitoring system, simple on/off clocks or filling in a simple operating form (by the washer infeed operator) operating management can receive pertinent downtime records to administer the entire bottle infeed/uncasing operation. A typical manual control form covering the washer load area is shown for reference, Figure 7-2.

SOAKER LOADING REPORT   Date:

SHIFT		MACHINE			START		FINISH		
MACHINE STOPS (MIN.)		1/4	1/2	3/4	1	2		MAJOR STOPS	TOTAL
MECHANICAL									
POCKET STOPS									
BROKEN GLASS									
FLIPPING BOTTLES									
MISC., BOTTLE SUPPLY									
BOTTLE SHOP									

CLOCK START –   CLOCK FINISH –

7-2. Bottle Washer Loading Position Report Form

Description and Design of a Typical Bottle Washer
Bottle Washer Types

Although bottle washers are manufactured in a number of countries throughout the world, the basic design and operation of the various machines offered follow the same general guiding principles as described earlier. The differences usually relate to the degree of emphasis given rather than to some radical departure from the recognized principles of bottle washing.

In view of the fact that a number of the mechanical functions performed in a bottle washer are reasonably complex, e.g.: bottle loading and unloading, synchronizing spray movement with bottle movement, machine mechanical protection, label removal etc., there is tremendous scope for variation in the mechanical design approaches which can be used. The evaluation and selection of one machine over another depends on the user's acceptance of a particular design approach and machine configuration as being most suitable for his particular needs and operational conditions. In North and South America, Australia, Japan, and Africa, the modular-designed multi-tank machines seem to find general acceptance. In Europe and some other parts of the world, the compact and very efficient single tank machines are often used.

Another point of difference in machine design is the location of the bottle infeed and discharge positions. On "single-ended" machines, the bottle infeed is usually arranged below the bottle discharge. On "double-ended" machines, the infeed and discharge are located on opposite ends of the washer. A further variation on "double-ended" machines occurs when the infeed and discharge positions on the machine are located at different floor elevations.

In single tank machines, the lower portion of the machine contains the bottle infeed, the pre-rinse and pre-soak section, and the main soaking tank. The soaking tank is arranged in a horizontal configuration and provides for several submerged horizontal "passes" of the carriers through the tank before drainage of solution from the bottles takes place. The upper portion of the machine contains the post-soak drainage section, followed by a series of independent spray-rinse sections providing both internal and external caustic rinsing. The last spray-rinse section operates with fresh water. This is followed by a water drain section after which the bottles are discharged from the machine directly above the bottle infeed.

The single tank concept permits the design of a very compact and highly energy- and water-efficient bottle washer.

In the modular-designed multi-tank double-ended machines popular in North America, see Figure 7-3, the bottom of the machine is an open channel which accommodates the bottle carriers and chain, returning empty from the bottle discharge to the bottle infeed position. The upper or main body of the machine contains the various soaking, caustic-jetting and spray-rinse compartments. The carrier chain passes through the various compartments in a serpentine configuration, with the bottles draining back into each compartment prior to moving on into the succeeding compartment.

In the modular concept, a user may select the number of compartments, as well as the height of compartments, in order to provide the required amount of submerged soaking time and the number of fill-empty cycles desired in the soaking process.

The overall machine process step sequence can vary considerably in the modular design concept. A typical sequence might be as follows: bottle infeed, pre-rinse sprays, warm pre-soak compartments, several soaking compartments with compartment temperatures and caustic concentrations increasing until the required maximums are reached, a pulsating caustic internal jetting compartment, "post-soak" compartments, a recirculated water section with internal and external sprays, a final fresh water rinse spray section, a drain section followed by bottle discharge.

A typical machine currently in service would be 40 pockets wide and have 7 to 9 compartments including one caustic jetting compartment and one rinse section, all of which would provide an output of 1800BPM and a total soak

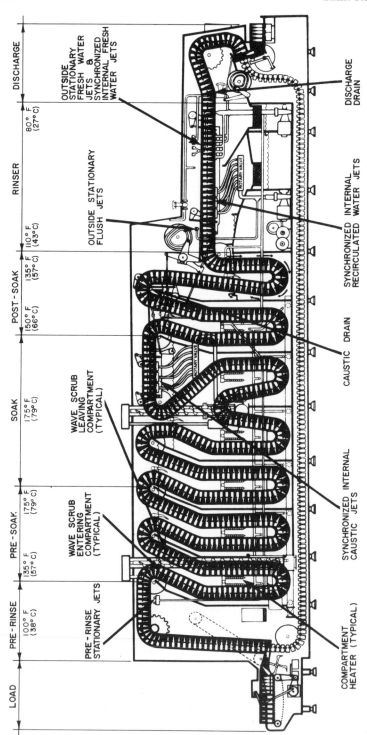

LOAD | PRE-RINSE 100° F (38° C) | PRE-SOAK 135° F (57° C) | PRE-SOAK 175° F (79° C) | SOAK 175° F (79° C) | POST-SOAK 150° F (66° C) / 135° F (57° C) / 110° F (43° C) | RINSER 80° F (27° C) | DISCHARGE

PRE-RINSE STATIONARY JETS

WAVE SCRUB ENTERING COMPARTMENT (TYPICAL)

WAVE SCRUB LEAVING COMPARTMENT (TYPICAL)

OUTSIDE STATIONARY FLUSH JETS

OUTSIDE STATIONARY FRESH WATER JETS & SYNCHRONIZED INTERNAL FRESH WATER JETS

DISCHARGE DRAIN

SYNCHRONIZED INTERNAL WATER JETS

SYNCHRONIZED RECIRCULATED WATER JETS

CAUSTIC DRAIN

SYNCHRONIZED INTERNAL CAUSTIC JETS

COMPARTMENT HEATER (TYPICAL)

ROTARY VALVE

7-3. Multi Tank Modular Design Bottle Washer (Courtesy of Barry-Wehmiller Co.)

time of 20 to 30 minutes.

Bottle Washer Components

The following information is based primarily on North American bottle washer construction, and is given mainly to highlight some of the design and operational considerations which must be taken into account in the manufacture of a bottle washer.

Tank: the tank essentially forms the main frame or "body" of the machine, to which all other components and operating systems are attached. The tank is a fabricated steel structure divided into sections according to the compartment requirements for a particular machine. The tank is supported clear of the floor and the empty carriers and carrier chain return from the discharge to the infeed positions in a channel provided at the bottom of the tank structure.

Bottle transport: each bottle is supported in a "pocket" which carries the bottle through the entire washer sequence of operations. Pockets can be plastic or steel, with steel currently preferred in North America. The pockets are constructed in rows, currently up to 40 pockets wide on standard machines, and the total "row-assembly" of pockets is referred to as a "carrier". The individual carriers are supported at each end by the carrier chain, which must follow the serpentine path through the machine. The carrier chain in effect supports a continuous series of carriers throughout its length, and the whole assembly of carriers on chain as installed in the machine, is often referred to as the "carrier blanket".

In spite of its length and rugged service, the carrier chain is a precision item, and must be installed and operated with great care. The empty return carriers and chain run in a special support track located in the channel at the bottom of the tank structure. To reduce the required force and wear associated with moving this massive assembly, the return tracks are provided with a built-in lubrication system.

The carrier chain hangs loose in each compartment guided by brackets attached to the tank sidewalls. The loose suspension is accomplished by driving both the infeed and discharge ends of the chain in each compartment at the top. Bottles are kept in the carriers through the use of deflectors, which take the form of bars and troughs also supported from the compartment sidewalls.

Bottles are fed into the carriers at the washer infeed position by means of a rotary loading mechanism, which in turn is supplied with bottles by the load table. (See Figure 7-4) The load table operates to place a bottle from each loading lane into curved bottle guides arranged to correspond with each pocket in the carrier. The rotary loader picks up the bottles in the vertical position, and propels them up the curved bottle guides where they gradually assume a horizontal position ready to enter the carrier pockets at the appropriate instant. Pusher cams synchronized with the travel of the carrier chain propel the bottles into the carrier pockets.

Bottles are unloaded from the carriers at the washer discharge position by means of a cam arrangement which accepts them from the carriers and lowers them gently onto the discharge table (See Figure 7-5). To make this possible, the carrier chain is routed to the discharge position with the carriers positioned so the bottles are in an upright position. As the carrier approaches the discharge, a deflector is provided to support the bottles. The deflector is arranged so the bottles gradually drop away from the pockets until finally they are supported on the lobe of the discharge cam. After they are lowered onto the discharge

7-4. *Bottle Washer Loading Position*

7-5. *Bottle Washer Discharge Position*

table the cam continues to rotate, and its profile moves the bottles away to provide clearance for the next row of bottles to come down onto the discharge table.

Synchronized Sprays: this technique is used in bottle washers where internal jetting is to be provided in addition to submerged compartment soaking. In the hot sections of the machine, the synchronized sprays consist of pulsating jets of hot caustic. In the rinse section, the sprays utilize hot recirculated water for pre-rinse and warm fresh water for the final rinse.

The motion of the carriers is continuous throughout the entire machine, and any system for internal spraying must take this into account. One way that internal hydraulic spraying can be accomplished is by synchronizing the movement of the spray heads so they are exactly in registration with the open necks of the moving bottles while the pulsating spray action is in progress. In order to register the sprays with the bottles, the sprays are mounted on a moving rack. The rack moves under the action of a cam which causes the rack to rise and engage the bottles, and then moves it in synchronism with the bottle carriers for the greater part of its forward stroke. The rack then falls away from the bottles and makes its return stroke at a rapid rate, in order to be ready for the next cycle. Hot caustic under pulsating pressure is supplied to the spray racks through rubber hoses. The bottle mouths are aligned with the spray nozzles by means of centering cups attached to the rack assembly.

Heating System: each compartment is provided with one or two heat exchangers, often supplied in a multiple pipe single-pass arrangement. Individual temperature control for each compartment is accomplished through the use of a liquid-filled direct-acting temperature controller. The normal heating medium is saturated steam, but high temperature hot water systems have also been used. A steam header is mounted on the machine for its full length, with an isolating valve on the connection to each compartment. When the washer is operating normally, the heaviest heating demand occurs on the load end compartments, which must raise the bottles, carriers and chain to the maximum operating temperature. In the remaining compartments, heating is required to take care of heat losses only to maintain the required operating temperatures.

Main Drive Assembly: the design of the drive system must take into consideration the large machine size and the high inertia associated with the carrier blanket, plus the various mechanical sub-systems powered from the main drive, e.g.: paddle agitators, load and discharge assemblies, etc. The drive system in a typical design consists of a constant-speed induction motor, a variable speed drive, a special controlled-action clutch and brake assembly, and the main speed reducer unit.

The motor is coupled to the variable speed drive unit, which permits speed adjustment of the washer in relation to the speed of the overall bottling line operation. The variable speed drive in turn is coupled to the clutch-brake input shaft. The clutch-brake assembly is controlled by a special power supply which regulates the torque transmitted to the main gear reducer unit, in accordance with a pre-determined operating sequence. In a typical starting sequence, the drive motor starts and comes up to full speed at no load. At this point the clutch gradually increases the torque applied to the washer mechanical drive system. This procedure eliminates starting shocks both on the machine and on the electrical supply. After a time delay to allow the washer to come up to speed, the clutch controller regulates the output torque to a much lower level, providing the mechanical drive system with an additional measure of protection. On stopping, the clutch instantly disconnects from the motor and variable speed drive, and at the same time the brake is energized on a progressive basis bringing the washer to a smooth controlled stop. On reaching full stop the brake locks the mechanical drive, preventing any further motion until a new start is initiated.

Label Removal: in a multi-tank machine, the majority of the labels will become free of the bottles in the first two or three compartments, and the remaining hard-to-remove labels will be distributed through the succeeding compartments. The objective is to free the labels from the bottles as early in the machine sequence as possible, so the labels will remain relatively intact, making label separation from the compartment solution a much easier task. Each compartment is provided with a paddle agitator which creates a bi-directional wave action at and under the top surface of the solution. This wave action forces the solution back and forth through the carrier pockets as the carriers enter and leave the compartment, flushing the labels out of the pockets and into the main body of the compartment solution.

Each compartment is provided with a solution discharge and solution return valve, both of which are automatically controlled in a step program sequence. An external pump which serves several compartments, circulates the solution carrying the labels and pulp through a liquid-solid separation unit mounted on the side of the washer. Separation units can take a number of forms, with travelling screens and vertical screw-extractors both commonly used. The separation units are designed to deliver a stream of label pulp, as dry as possible, into a receiving conveyor or floor hopper. After passing through the separation unit, the solution enters the circulating pump suction and is then delivered back to the same compartment via the compartment solution return valve. A system of piping and nozzles is provided inside the compartment to create a solution circulation pattern which will convey the labels and label pulp away from the carriers and toward the discharge valve.

The automatic program control allows one compartment at a time to be connected to the separation circuit for an appropriate length of time found from experience to provide good label removal from the compartment.

Operation And Maintenance
Preparation of Operating Procedures

Well written and detailed formal operating procedures are a pre-requisite to any successful bottle washer operation. They are needed to provide continuity of operation, operational control and basic data for supervisory and operating training. To provide the necessary operating and maintenance systems, the operations and maintenance departments must collaborate on the preparation of these operating procedures. This should ensure proper operation while producing acceptable bottles at the minimum labour, material, utility and maintenance costs.

There is a need to collect all relevant technical design criteria including any peculiarities of the bottle washer. This information usually forms the basis for the required operating and control documents used for determining efficiency, water consumption, solution consumption and reclaim. Having this information in one document centralizes all the basic data needed to cross-check the operational data collected from the various control reports. It is suggested that the manufacturer's published operating and maintenance manual be used as the basis, adapting those sections which are pertinent to the actual operation. The information should include the following:

—*Bottle Washer Equipment Data*
   Design Details (Bottle type and dimension limits)
   Equipment Number (Plant)
   Manufacturer and Model number
   Operating Speed (Design and maximum)
   Submerged Soak Time (Minutes-design)
   Travel Time through Soaker and Rinser (Minutes)
—*Compartment Details* (For each compartment)
   Compartment Name and Number
   Capacity (Volume)
   Control Temperature
   Solution Concentration (Including upper and lower control limits)
—*Spray Details* (For each location)
   Identification
   Location and Number of Spray Headers
   Capacity (Volume)
   Pressure
—*Label Removal Equipment Details*
   Location
   Sequencing (If programmed)
   Capacity (Volume processed in a given period of time)
—*Bottle Washer Solutions*
   The details outlined here would specify the solution components, percentages and any special considerations with regard to solution make-up.

Typical Operating Considerations

In addition to containing basic machine data, the operating procedure manual should fully describe all details pertaining to operation, cleaning and maintenance of the bottlewasher. While exact details will, of course, vary from one machine to another, and from one bottleshop to another, all manuals should include the following basic categories:

1) Machine startup/shutdown procedures.
2) Cleaning (Daily/Weekly)
3) Solution Management Procedures (including daily operational checks)
4) Maintenance (Running)

The following general guidelines apply to each category:

1) Machine Startup/Shutdown Procedures

Startup: Any formal procedures developed for the operation usually focus on utilities (steam, water, air, etc.), and ensuring that these various components are operational in advance of the shift start-up time. Steam demands can be excessive at start-up due to the nature of the temperature control equipment, and possibly require some manual intervention until temperatures come under control. Well in advance of start-up (approximately one hour), all pumps and conveyors should be turned on to ensure proper operation. All compartment temperatures should be checked to ensure that they are in control and at the proper settings. General monitoring of the temperatures should continue until the bottle washer has been completely filled with bottles at which time the heating demands should stabilize. The levels in all tanks should be checked along with the operation of any agitators and sprays.

Shutdown: the shutdown of the bottle washer will involve such basic items as turning off:

—all soaker and rinser controls;

—main steam supply;

—any associated conveyors;

—air and water as necessary;

—and the clearing of all bottles from the rinser discharge.

2) *Cleaning—Daily:* The following list of items would form the basis for a daily bottle washer cleaning procedure. Further details may be obtained from the Cleaning and Sanitation chapter under Soaker/Rinser Cleaning.

—Use low pressure hose to wash down load table, infeed conveyor and rotary infeed.

—Clean screens in the pre-rinse area.

—While soakers are operating, visually check all caustic sprays and hoses in the recirculating, reclaim and fresh water sections to locate plugged nozzles and defective hoses. Replace or correct as required.

—Clean spray racks nightly. (Plugged nozzles will usually lead to an increased reject rate.)

—Clean any compartment screens.

—Open and clean any drip pans over bottle discharge

—Hose and clean the entire discharge assembly, including the discharge conveyors. Some cleaning agents may be incorporated into the cleaning and washdown procedure to sanitize or improve cleaning. Utilization of high pressure—low volume cleaning units is recommended.

—Avoid direct hosing of electrical motors and electrical components.

—Normally, the final post soak tank (water) should be dumped daily to avoid cleaning solution carryover.

—The need to dump or partially dump a first post soak tank will depend on the tank and the amount of solution carryover to that tank. Again, experience and operating hours will dictate the requirements, and this is referred to later in the chapter.

—The need to add a sanitizer to the rinse water (reclaimed) prior to start-up will be dependent on prevailing biological norms for that plant.

—To maintain proper housekeeping, some efforts must be made to remove any caustic from the outside walls or top of the bottle washer, by washing with water. Remove excess grease by wiping or solvent cleaning.

Cleaning—Weekly

—Complete the recommended daily cycle.

—Drain, clean and refill any compartment scheduled on the check list.

—Remove spray manifolds, clean and/or replace. From an operating and maintenance standpoint, it is usually more desirable to have spare spray headers to replace the ones in use. This permits proper maintenance and cleaning of the used spray headers on a controlled basis, allowing standardization of the spray header maintenance replacement service.

—Dump any compartment listed on the cleaning schedule.

—Descaling—this procedure is outlined in the Cleaning and Sanitization chapter.

3) *Solution Management Procedures*

All efforts made to produce a high quality beer can be negated if that product is put into unclean bottles. It is therefore crucial that completely clean and commercially sterile bottles are discharged from the bottle washer. Constant control of the temperature and the composition of the washing solution must be carried out to assure that the desired cleaning effect is achieved.

Bottles exposed to the hot caustic solution in the Soaker compartment become sterile; however, reinfection in the rinse water compartment or while passing through the rinsing station is commonly experienced. Routine examinations of the caustic concentration and of the biological contamination of the rinse water is therefore an essential part of the total quality control program in beer packaging.

There are three aspects to the effective management of the washing solution and the contents of the rinse section compartments.

Preparing fresh solution.

Maintenance of the strengths of the various compartments of the solution while in the washer; this includes checks on the build-up of organics and aluminates.

Removal of the solution for reprocessing outside the washer or dumping to sewer as necessary.

Most bottleshops use prepared washing compounds which are received in liquid form, usually at a concentration of 50% by weight. Very little use has been made of solid or flake compounds in recent years and for details of preparation of solution from these forms the reader is advised to consult the supplier or the book "Bottling and Canning of Beer" by Ruff and Becker.[3]

Liquid caustic or compound is stored in tanks, normally inside to avoid the necessity for heating, because 50% caustic will solidify below 15°C (59°F). It is then transferred by gravity or pump through a batch-type totalizing meter to a mixing pit or tank in order to make up batches of intermediate strength solution, typically 20–25% by weight. The exact quantities required for dilution can be determined with the assistance of the compound supplier. When charging a compartment in the bottlewasher, water is first used to partially fill the compartment, then the correct volume of intermediate strength solution, and finally a topping up of water or reclaimed solution is added to bring the level up if necessary to the working level.

As far as the specification for solution strength in the compartments is concerned, because of wide variations in machine design (European vs. North American), bottle return conditions and label removal systems, it is almost impossible to specify an ideal solution concentration.

Traditionally European machines are run at lower percentage levels of solution in the area of 1.5% to 2.5% concentration, whereas the North American norm is on the higher side ranging up to 4.5% to 5.0% alkalinity. In-plant testing and the measurement of cleaning results will usually dictate the concentrations and limits needed for any particular bottleshop.

Maintaining the effectiveness of the solution in the washer usually involves adding fresh intermediate strength solution. Although the compartment concentration may have to be checked a number of times each day, addition of fresh solution is not normally required more than once a shift. Addition of fresh intermediate strength solution will also be required if the compartment has been partially refilled with reclaimed solution after being cleaned out.

In both cases a nomograph should be used to determine the required volume of intermediate strength solution. Addition is best undertaken while steam is being supplied to the compartment or some other form of agitation in order to minimize stratification and encourage good mixing.

Methods For Testing Soaker Solutions

Two approaches are used to test washing solutions: one is based on a differential titration, the other is based on the measurement of electrical conductivity. A brief summary of the two methods is outlined below. The reader is advised to consult other references such as (3) to learn more details about these methods.

Differential Titration

This method is most useful as it allows the determination of free causticity, sodium aluminate and total alkalinity side by side. The foregoing is achieved by titrating the soaker solution with sulphuric acid to the phenolphthalein end point to determine the free caustic after the carbonates have been precipitated with barium chloride. After this dermination the remaining aluminate is hydrolysed by addition of sodium fluoride and further titration yields the amount of sodium aluminate. Total alkalinity is determined by the quantity of acid consumed without the addition of barium chloride.

Electrical Conductivity

Solution controllers which are based on conductivity are frequently used to monitor caustic concentration. Some models are designed to transfer liquid caustic automatically from the storage tank into the soaker compartment. The units use a temperature-compensated probe to sense the caustic concentration.

The conductivity instrument has certain limitations which must be recognized. While sodium hydroxide has a specific conductance, so do other electrolytes which may be present in the solution. For instance, sodium aluminate has about one-tenth the conductivity of NaOH. The conductivity of the solution reflects therefore the conductance of all ingredients and some caution has to be applied when the results are interpreted. However, the conductivity instrument provides a very rapid method for determining solution concentration.

Regular inspection of the contents of the rinse section is also important to determine if carryover of washing solution is occurring or if there is biological contamination of the rinse water. Examples of tests for the rinse section are as follows:

Method For Testing Residual Alkali in Bottles

Alkaline reaction in bottles indicates excessive caustic carry-over and/or inadequate rinsing. Tests for determining it are very simple and involve the addition of a small amount of water and indicator such as phenolphthalein.

Biological Examination of Empty Bottles

Bottles can become contaminated with micro-organisms in the rinser section of the bottle washer. The recommended method for examining such a contamination is based on the plating technique. A measured quantity of sterile water is added to a bottle exiting the rinser and closing it with a stopper previously soaked in alcohol. An aliquot portion of the water is then transferred onto a solid medium in a petri dish (plate). After incubating the inoculated medium under standardized conditions visible colonies develop from single cells. By counting the colonies an indication of the number of organisms originally present can be obtained.

In order to keep the number of micro-organisms in the rinser section at a minimum a level of 1 to 5 mg chlorine per liter of water is maintained. The desired chlorine level is obtained by the addition of a hypochlorite compound to the water. The concentration of chlorine in the rinse water can be determined by means of the "Ortho-Tolidine comparator kit" which is available from chemical supply houses.

Draining Soak and Rinse Compartments

There is no universally accepted standard which governs how often the soaking compartments should be cleaned. Each plant must establish criteria which suit their particular mode of operation and conditions. The type of maintenance, water condition, bottle condition, label removal system, etc., will greatly influence the need to change solution and/or dump compartments. In the interests of material and manpower savings, this process should be kept to a minimum and should be based on quantifiable measures such as:

—Cleaning effectiveness—measured either biologically or by percent rejects.

—Label particles and solid contamination—which can be identified visually or again by empty bottle reject percentage.

—Adverse effect on mechanical components—which can be measured in downtime or recurring mechanical problems.

If the label removal system operation and sequence is satisfactory and bottle breakage due to thermal shock is not a problem, the frequency of draining soak compartments becomes a function only of the buildup of fine suspended paper fibres, insoluble organics from glues and dirt and aluminates, the latter from aluminum foil labels if present.

Provided the strength of the bottlewashing solution is maintained by addition of concentrated solution from time to time, the compartment contents need only be emptied when the buildup of aluminates and solids is such that severe precipitation is starting to occur in the compartment, and operation will be affected.

For relatively clean bottles with exclusively paper labels the number of bottles which can be washed before the first or second compartments have to be drained can be as high as 250,000 bottles per m^3 of total soak volume. (1,000 bottles/gallon). However, where aluminum foil labels are used almost exclusively, and with a proportion of 'ditch' or 'basement' bottles, the solution may have to be changed after only 25,000 bottles throughput/m^3 total soak volume (100 bottles/gallon).

Obviously there is a wide variation according to conditions and practical experimentation is encouraged. An example of such experimentation has been performed and reported by Leipner.[4]

Where large quantities of bottles with aluminum foil labels are washed, some plants have based their decision to drain compartments on a predetermined limit of percent sodium aluminate, often 2-3%. However, there is some evidence that concentrations in excess of this figure will not affect washing since the aluminates can precipitate out with other solids at the bottom of the compartment.

In summary, as long as the bottle washer discharges clean and sterile bottles and there is no interference to the mechanical or heat transfer components there is generally no need to sewer or clean the soaker solution.

In any case, a schedule for changing the solution in soak compartments must be drawn up based on time, but with consideration if possible for numbers of bottles that have been washed.

Bottleshops with multiple lines and bottle washers may for the purposes of manpower scheduling and cleaning control, be required to set up formal planned cleaning schedules identifying the specific work to be carried out on a daily basis. A sample of a simple control sheet (Figure 7-6) is shown for reference.

BOTTLE WASHER CLEANING SCHEDULE MONTH OF:

		N°	FIRST WEEK M T W T F	SECOND WEEK M T W T F	THIRD WEEK M T W T F	FOURTH WEEK M T W T F
SOAKER	COMPARTMENT	1				
		2				
		3				
		4				
		5				
		6				
		7				
		8				
		9				
N° ___		10				
SPRAYS HEADS	FIRST RINSE					
	FINAL RINSE					
	N° 5					
	N° 8					
PULP HOPPERS REMOVED	CHECK N°					

7-6. *Bottle Washer Cleaning Schedule Form*

Whatever the interval chosen for cleaning soak compartments, it is desirable that the spent solution be transferred to a caustic reclaim system, so that even premature draining will not result in unnecessary losses. Such a system is described in the economics section of the chapter.

The rinse section water compartments, unless they contain usable concentrations of solution, are normally drained to sewer daily, immediately after bottling operations have ceased.

4) Maintenance

Running maintenance on the bottle washer normally involves lubrication of the moving parts such as drive chains, bearings, gear boxes and the main carrier chain. The maintenance department is usually charged with this responsibility which must be carried out on a regular pre-determined basis. Costs and individual plant practices will determine whether the grease lubrication function is accomplished with an automatic mechanical lubrication system or if it is done manually.

The main carrier chain will require a soap lubrication system which in most plants will be tied into the main soap system supplying the bottle conveyor. Because of the cost of replacing main carrier chains, it is recommended that a check of the carrier chain lubrication system be conducted on a daily basis and be included on the operational log.

From a preventive maintenance standpoint, it should be standard procedure to check the slack in any compartment which has been dumped and cleaned prior to recharging.

No attempt will be made in this chapter to define preventive maintenance requirements or regularly scheduled overhaul programs. Any unusual behaviour of the machine should be investigated and corrected immediately to avoid future damage and downtime. Continuous stops initiated by the machinery safety devices is an early warning signal for necessary adjustment and maintenance help.

Bottlewasher Performance

The relative success of the afore mentioned procedures in producing a clean bottle must be measured. The commonly accepted method is to monitor the reject ratio at empty bottle inspection. It is generally agreed that this ratio should not exceed one bottle per thousand, or 0.1%. This figure represents cleanable bottles that fail to be cleaned and should not include other classes of bottles such as false rejects, broken, uncleanable or liquid-filled, in the calculation. Any rate in excess of this figure indicates a malfunction of the cleaning process which requires trouble shooting and remedial action.

Trouble Shooting

Although the design and operations of bottle washers may vary from one manufacturer to another, there are in fact many problems or direct similarities which can be analyzed as the probable cause and corrected in the same manner, see Table II.

Health and Safety

The chemical reaction of the aluminum portion of foil labels with the bottle cleaning solution will produce hydrogen gas as noted before. This gas can collect at the top of the bottle washer or escape into the bottleshop and collect at high points of the ceiling. Since there are wide explosive limits with hydrogen it is usually advisable to provide a positive venting system to remove the gases generated. This system should also be designed to remove other vapour and fumes emanating from the hot bottle washing solution. This is especially true in bottleshops which have low overhead clearance and minimal plant air changes.

Bottle washing solutions must be handled with great respect and therefore, it is mandatory that proper procedures and safety gear be provided for anyone assigned to solution make-up, bottle washer cleaning or subject to contact with soaker solution. Proper safety eyewash and overhead shower facilities should be provided at strategic locations adjacent to the bottle washer.

Empty Bottle Inspection

The presence of uncleanable or damaged bottles, the possibility of random washer malfunctions or the improper management of washer solutions can result in the appearance of improperly washed, improperly emptied or other forms of unacceptable bottles at the washer discharge. Consequently, it is mandatory to carry out some form of empty bottle inspection prior to filling.

Such inspection usually takes place in two stages:

(a) at the washer discharge, and

(b) at specific inspection stations, either manual-visual or electronic.

TABLE II
TROUBLE SHOOTING GUIDE

	Dirty Bottles	Caustic Carryover	Cloudy Bottles	Label Carryover	Bottle Breakage
HEADERS					
Pre Rinse—pressure/plugged/alignment	X				X
Hydro-Rinse—pressure/plugged/alignment	X				X
Final Rinse—pressure/plugged/alignment	X	X		X	X
Overhead Sprays	X	X		X	
Centering cups—damaged or missing	X				
SOLUTION/WATER					
Low solution concentration	X			X	
High solution concentration		X	X	X	
Solution buildup in Fresh Water Tank		X			
Wetting Agent	X	X			
Chelating Agent			X		
Hard Water			X		
High sodium aluminate	X				
TEMPERATURE					
Low solution temperature	X				
High solution temperature			X		
Excessive temperature differences (Thermal shock)					X
MISCELLANEOUS					
Low solution levels	X			X	
High solution levels		X			
Screens plugged	X			X	
Machine speed (reduced soak time)			X		
Long stoppages			X		
Excessive venting			X		
Bottles—long storage	X				
Bottles—uncleanable	X				
Label removal system	X			X	
Agitators (compartment)	X			X	
Scale on carriers (solution carryover)		X			

The washer discharge operator can provide a fairly continuous monitoring of the outside surface condition of the overall mass of bottles being discharged, and also has the opportunity to pick out the more obvious unacceptable bottles.

By reporting specific changes in the condition of bottles at the washer discharge, e.g.: cloudy bottles, label carryover, caustic carryover, excessive breakage, etc. the discharge operator can initiate early troubleshooting and correction of the washer operation.

The mass transfer of bottles from the washer discharge is subsequently broken down into multiple lanes which provide for single-file transfer of the bottles through the second stage inspection stations. In the case of manned-visual inspection, each single file transfer lane will have a conveying speed in the range of 100 to 150 bottles per minute, i.e.: a 600 BPM bottling line would require a minimum of 4 inspection lanes. The actual inspection on each lane is carried out by an operator who scans the bottle sidewalls and bottoms against an illuminated diffusion screen located on the opposite side of the conveyor. Conveyor guiderails are normally omitted at the inspection station. The operator removes defective bottles and, depending on the nature of the defect, puts them into a cullet bin for scrap or into a crate for eventual recycle through the washer. The range of attention span for good visual inspection is between 15 and 30 minutes, which dictates frequent rotation of visual inspectors to other jobs on the bottling line.

In the case of electronic inspection, each single file lane will have a conveying speed commensurate with the inspection capacity of the electronic empty bottle inspection machine (EBI) being used. Current-generation EBI's are rated in the 600 to 800 + BPM range so, in general, a minimum of two inspection lanes are required to service most modern bottling lines. In view of the tremendous importance of reliable accurate empty bottle inspection and the need to maintain bottling line operating efficiency at high levels, it is common practice to equip each inspection lane with two EBI's in series. This arrangement increases inspection reliability and accuracy, and at the same time provides a back-up machine always "on-line".

EBI's are available from several manufacturers, and over the years many variations in machine arrangement have appeared. The most common configuration in machines currently offered is a power-assisted or bottle-pressure propelled "starwheel" which carries the stream of bottles in a single sweep, off the infeed conveyor, through the inspection position and back onto the discharge conveyor. The starwheel also carries the rejection mechanism which, when activated by the inspection apparatus, directs a reject bottle away from the discharge conveyor onto a holding table or a separate reject-bottle conveyor. A typical arrangement for this type of EBI is shown in Figure 7-7.

A number of different approaches are used in the design of the inspection apparatus by the various manufacturers, but in most machines being offered today, only the bottom of the bottle and possibly a very small portion of the bottom sidewall are subject to inspection for dirt or foreign objects. A typical inspection method involves the use of a stationary light source placed under the bottom and bottom sidewall area, and the pattern of light transmitted upward to the inspector through the neck of the bottle is modified if dirt or a foreign object is present in the field of view. Sophisticated optical arrangements coupled with "state of the art" electronics form the basis for highly reliable and very accurate detection systems. Most EBI's also offer supplementary detection options which include residual liquid, broken necks, damaged crown finish, etc. Another available and very important feature is the provision of counters to record total bottles processed and total rejects. This data can be fed to an internal micro-processor for the determination of a running "rejection rate" which can be compared to the desired pre-set standard. Variances beyond certain tolerance levels will trigger an alarm.

The performance of EBI's in service must be monitored on a routine basis, and specific operating procedures must be established and rigorously followed, if the optimum utilization of the machine's capability is to be obtained. These procedures fall into two categories:

(a) routine checks to insure that all the various detection channels are functioning properly and that the sensitivity and other operating adjustments are set at suitable levels to satisfy the objectives of the routine check;

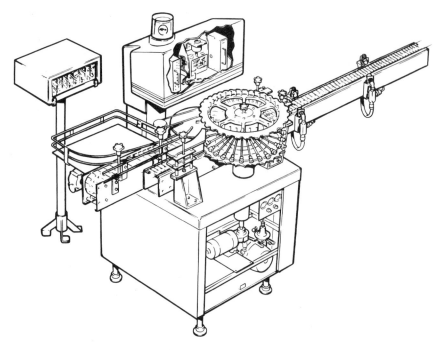

7-7. Electronic Empty Bottle Inspector (Courtesy of Industrial Dynamics International Inc.)

(b) statistical or long-range checks to insure that the overall machine operation is sufficiently fine-tuned to provide the level of inspection required to meet the quality control objectives established for the type of glass being run on the line.

The routine check procedure usually involves an inspection of (and if necessary wiping off) the light source elements, plus the passing of sample reject bottles through the machine. The sample bottles are suitably identified so they can be easily separated from the production bottle stream. Sample or "test" bottles are usually prepared by the quality control group, and include a small (3mm) square piece of opaque black tape placed in a specific location on the inside bottom of the bottle. These will activate the various zones or detection channels as appropriate for the particular machine's optical and electronic systems. Test bottles are also prepared for other detection features such as plugged necks, residual liquid, broken necks, damaged crown finish, etc. Normally the EBI manufacturer establishes an outline specification for the preparation of test bottles for his machine, and suggests a procedure for their use.

The statistical or long-range checks are extremely important in that they enable the operator to evaluate the machine's overall performance which in turn can be related to foreign object or other bottle complaints received from the trade. Statistical checks involve the recording and comparative analysis of data relating to total number of bottles inspected, "true" rejects obtained (i.e.: bottles having dirt, foreign objects or other unacceptable features) and "false" rejects obtained (i.e.: bottles which when examined have no unacceptable features insofar as the consumer is concerned, but which were rejected for some other reason, e.g.: glass imperfections, thickness variations, colour streaks, mold marks, or conveyor lubricant bubbles adhering to the bottom, etc.) This data must be carefully collected, recorded, analyzed and plotted on an "ongoing" basis. Various statistical techniques can be used involving false reject rate, true/false reject ratio, total rejects, number of trade complaints, etc. Current "state-of-the-art" EBI's can operate to provide highly reliable and very accurate detection. The problem in production is to determine what the acceptable level of false rejects can be, and still provide a good bottling line operating efficiency. Since the generation of false rejects is related directly to the quality of the glass and to some degree production conditions in effect on the line, the detection sensitivity of the EBI's must be adjusted as high as possible and at the same time not exceed the acceptable false reject rate. Typical false reject rates are 1/1000, 1.5/1000, 2/1000 etc. Bottle washer performance is judged on the true reject rate, and as covered previously, an acceptable rate is 1/1000.

All EBI manufacturers provide manuals which cover recommended operating procedures for their machines in great detail. An interesting paper providing general technical coverage of this subject has been prepared by Flood.[5]

BOTTLEWASHING ECONOMICS

Operating Costs

The purpose of this section is to identify and place in perspective the various economic factors related to bottlewashing. The rinsing of non-returnable bottles is a relatively simple procedure which has little or no economic implication other than treated or non-treated water use. The main thrust of this section is therefore directed to the economics of washing the returnable bottle.

Many of the costs associated with bottlewashing were until recently almost insignificant, but rapidly rising costs of fuel, electricity, maintenance, labour and caustic has demanded that more attention be given to each of these aspects of bottlewashing. Operating expenses such as these must be analyzed from an efficiency standpoint, in order to determine the appropriate level of ongoing monitoring and control. The operating cost of the bottlewasher can be broken down into various components as shown in Figure 7-8. For the purposes of illustration the example chosen is a typical 1000 bpm (bottle per minute) bottlewasher operating on a two shift basis for 4000 hours a year. Costs are approximate for 1982 and are typical for North American locations.

In addition to those outlined in Figure 7-8 there can be other semi-hidden cost factors which are dependent on local conditions and operating practices. In many locations the high pH of bottlewasher effluent requires correction to meet municipal sewer discharge requirements. For example, if a sulphuric acid neutralization system is used, the neutralization material costs can be up to one tenth of the bottlewashing compound costs. Another semi-hidden cost can be associated with label pulp disposal where landfill deposit regulations and surcharges recognize causticity and moisture content.

It can readily be seen that bottlewashing has a significant cost which warrants special attention and control. An examination of Figure 7-8 will reveal that

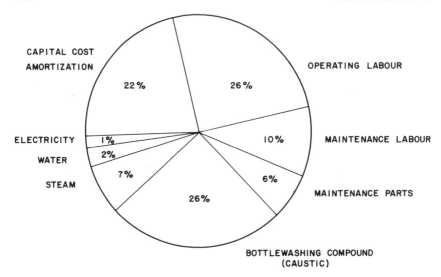

7-8. Relative Cost of Operating a Typical 1000 bpm Bottle Washer

1. Based on 2 shift operation (4000 hr/yr) the total 1982 cost range is $500,000 to 600,000 per year, or about $130 to $150 per operating hour
2. Amortization over 10 years
3. Wages include benefits, 2 operators required
4. Maintenance includes annual overhauls
5. Compound is pre-mixed caustic type, aluminum foil labels considered.

36% of the total operating cost is represented by the consumables: compound, steam, water and electricity.

Bottlewashing Compound Consumption

This occurs as follows:

—by physical carryover on the bottles, chains and pockets from the soaking compartments into the rinse section.

—by chemical reaction with dirt, glue and the aluminum of foil labels, if used.

—by losses during compartment cleanout and label removal.

Chemical reaction, label removal and cleanout losses range between 10 and 50% of the total caustic used in the bottlewasher. The combination of dirty bottles, aluminum foil labels, and an inefficient label removal or caustic reclaim system will position a bottle washing operation at the high end of the range. Since carryover losses are mainly related to the physical arrangement and design of the machine, cost saving efforts must be directed at reducing the chemical reaction, label removal and cleanout losses. Carryover losses can be controlled by the use of wetting agents as a part of the bottlewashing compound formulation. The strength of the wetting agent should be checked at regular intervals and supplemented when depletion is evident. Carryover will also increase if porous scale formations are allowed to build up on the chain, carriers and pockets.

Steam Consumption

The approximate steam distribution to the machine is as follows: 55% to heat the bottle pockets (assuming they are of metal construction) and chain, 25% to heat the bottles themselves and 20% to cover heat losses from the machine to the surrounding bottleshop. It is interesting to note that internal heat loss of the machine is greater than the external heat loss plus the heat input to the bottles. Note that when condensate from the bottle washer compartment heating coils is returned to the boiler, some form of pH monitoring device and alarm should be included in the condensate return piping.

Water Consumption

Water is used in mixing soaking compartment solutions, in bottle rinsing and for cooling the bottles to the appropriate exit temperature. The first two items are directly related to machine operation, and are more or less fixed for a given machine and performance objective. Water use directed at achieving a particular bottle exit temperature can result in summer-winter consumption variations as high as 3 to 1. The subject of bottle exit temperature is covered in some detail later.

Many bottlewashers have steam and water savings features incorporated in their basic design. As a result, the machine operating manuals are often an excellent source of information and recommendations for operating procedures which can reduce water and steam consumption. The following are typical of the various economy features included in modern bottle washers:

Water Control Valves: Most bottlewashers have automatic water control valves, which make sure that the water flows only to the rinse section jetting when it will serve some useful purpose. Such a valve on the main rinse section supply can be connected to the main drive mechanism to shut off the supply when the drive is disengaged.

A second valve, usually cam-operated, can be connected to shut off the undersprays when they are not directly under a bottle mouth. An alteration to the function of either of these valves can result in greatly increased water consumption. On older machines, the retro-fitting of such features could substantially reduce overall water consumption.

Recirculated Water Section: The recirculated water section usually consists of a pump and sprays both under and over the bottles, located immediately adjacent to the final fresh water sprays. Spray piping and spray nozzles must be fully operational and clean, as otherwise more fresh water will have to be admitted to rinse the bottles properly. Some form of cartridge or basket type water filter is often fitted in the line to the sprays and this should be regularly checked.

Pre-rinse Feature: On some machines the pumped recirculated water is also supplied to the infeed end of the machine via a tee on the pump discharge piping. This water is delivered via a heat exchange coil to the prerinse spray headers which are situated at the machine infeed, immediately ahead of the first soak compartment. The heat exchange or "tempering" coil is located in the "post-soak" compartment and heats the water on its way to the pre-rinse spray headers. The pre-rinse feature is very important for several reasons: First, loose dirt is removed from the bottles before they come into contact with the first caustic soak compartment thereby reducing caustic consumption and resulting in a cleaner compartment. Secondly, wetting of the bottles cancels out the effect of dragout or carryover from the first compartment so that the level is maintained. Thirdly, tempering of cold bottles in winter by the warmed recirculated water minimizes thermal shock and breakage as the bottles enter the first soak compartment. Finally, steam consumption is reduced because the heat removed from the carrier chain pockets and bottles in the post-soak compartment and the rinse section, is transferred back to the chain and incoming bottles. This substantially reduces that portion of the steam which goes towards heating the carrier chain and pockets.

A side benefit of the prerinse feature is that the post soak compartment is cooled by the tempering coil therefore preventing thermal carryover into the rinse section. This minimizes the amount of fresh cold water which must be added to the rinse section to cool the bottles.

Reclaim Water Section: This section is basically similar to the recirculated water section, but is supplied by overflow from that section. Proper operation of all the sprays is essential; otherwise poor bottle cooling and rinsing will occur, resulting in excessive use of cold fresh water in the final rinse section.

Mention has been made of these features because many operators are not familiar with their purpose, and significant steam and water saving will result through their proper adjustment and operation.

Some Important Operating Considerations

The following items should receive concerted attention if high quality bottle washing is to be achieved at the lowest possible cost.

Standby/Preheat Procedures

It is well worthwhile to carry out practical tests in order to determine how long it takes the bottlewasher to reach operating temperature when starting up after a weekend or an off-shift. If the steam control valves and traps are in good working condition, standard warm up times can be determined and the operating procedure written in such a way that the bottlewasher does not remain heated for any longer than necessary prior to the start of bottling.

Liaison will be required with the boiler room personnel during these tests to insure that warm-up steam demands do not impose loads which require startup of additional boiler capacity.

Efficient Label Removal

The efficiency and speed of removal of any label removal system has other implications than just determining the cleanliness of the washed bottle. The more rapidly the labels are removed from the caustic, the less degradation of the fibre occurs, resulting in less depletion of caustic strength and hence savings in caustic. Secondly, less degradation of labels reduces the chance of fine pulp carryover into the rinse section, minimizing nozzle blockage and hence optimizing fresh water use. Thirdly, the less pulping of labels that occurs, the less caustic will be lost through absorption as the label solids are disposed of.

It therefore follows that keeping the label removal system clean and well maintained has a positive effect on caustic and water costs.

Cleaning of Spray Nozzles

Blocked spray nozzles whether on overhead or undersprays will obviously lead to poor rinsing and hence traces of caustic on the bottles. Unfortunately, the remedy is often to increase water flow into the rinse section via the water fill valves in order to dilute the rinse section and reduce the problem. The more effective rinsing and most economical use of water will be achieved when the spray nozzles are kept rigorously clean.

Minimizing Solution Dumping

Unplanned maintenance inside soak compartments is particularly wasteful because it often involves the dumping of the caustic in the compartment concerned. Being unplanned, there is often no temporary storage tankage available to receive the caustic, and it must be sewered. The percentage of caustic lost due to such causes can be high, particularly if the scheduled interval for cleanout of compartments is normally long. The exercise of some foresight and the recognition and diagnosis of operating problems will often eliminate the need for unplanned solution dumping.

Bottle Exit Temperatures

Excessive water consumption will result, particularly in summer, if bottles are brought out of the bottlewasher cooler than really required for an acceptable filling operation. There is some case for arguing whether there is any advantage in bringing out bottles at a surface temperature less than ambient bottleshop temperature, particularly if large accumulation is involved between bottlewasher and filler.

TABLE III
FRESH WATER FLOW (litres per sec)

Fresh Water Temp.	2°C	10°C	15°C	18°C
For Bottle Exit Temp. of 20°C	4.7	5.9	7.9	9.8
For Bottle Exit Temp. of 25°C	3.8	4.5	5.4	6.4

Table III should help illustrate the importance of specifying the maximum acceptable bottle exit temperature. Shown is the theoretically derived flowrate of water required to achieve the cooling effect on the bottles. Since efficient rinsing can normally be achieved with fresh water flows of 3.8L s (60 USGPM) or less, dependent on local conditions, flowrates above this in the table represent excesses for cooling purposes only. Actual flowrates will obviously vary according to bottlewasher size, container type, etc. but the relationship between fresh water temperature and bottle exit temperature will be similar.

Other Utility Conservation Techniques

Rinse Section Refrigeration: In some situations with extremely high water costs and high incoming water temperatures, mechanical refrigeration equipment can give a return on investment when used to cool the final rinse section water. In this way fresh water is provided sufficient only for an efficient rinse of the bottles; the cooling effect is provided by the refrigeration system. The economics require detailed analysis in each case. At the present time, North American energy and water costs are such that there would not be an acceptable return on investment in mechanical refrigeration for the final rinse section water.

Solenoid Valves—Rinse Section Fill Valves: it may be that, despite all efforts to control water use in the rinse section, control of caustic levels and/or rinse section temperature will require the fill valves or other lines to be left on. In this case, addition of solenoid valves interlocked to the soaker drive will limit water use when the machine is not discharging bottles.

Lowering of Soak Temperature: Steam savings of about 1½% /°C (0.9%/°F) can be achieved if the soak temperature can be lowered while still providing a satisfactory clean container. The soak temperature could be higher than necessary if a gradual shift in return bottle cleanliness has occurred or if better washing compounds are being used or considered than those available when the original soak temperature was specified. In the washer used as an example in Figure 7-8, lowering the soak temperature by 5°C (9°F) could have approximately $2500 per year at 1982 costs.

Insulation of Machine: The insulation of bottlewashers by applying panels to the outside of the soak compartments has been considered in recent years to reduce heat loss. There is merit in reducing heat loss during design and construction of bottlewashers, but the retrofitting of washable insulation panels on existing machines is still not an attractive investment for the bottler at 1982 fuel prices. It will be some time before the problems of sanitation, maintenance accessibility etc. associated with insulation in this application can be ignored in the interest of fuel savings. Although the application of two inches of insulation over the entire bottlewasher could reduce heat loss by over 80%, the effect on the total steam consumption will be not much more than 15%.

Caustic Reclaim

The term caustic reclaim is used to describe the variety of processes which may be used to extend the life of caustic bottlewashing compounds, and normally refers to processes outside the bottlewasher and label separation devices. Spent caustic soda poses a disposal problem and in high concentrations even of short duration can cause operating problems at waste treatment plants. Almost all municipalities or districts have pH ranges specified in effluent discharge bylaws, compliance with which is mandatory. Allowance for violation of pH limits is not normally negotiable or subject to a surcharge, as is typical with other waste treatment parameters. Caustic reclaim systems, which minimize the frequency and amount of discharge of caustic soda are normally justified primarily on this requirement to comply with bylaws. Reduced caustic consumption which may result is an added benefit but depends upon the type of labels used, return bottle cleanliness etc.

It must be emphasized that the task of caustic reclamation will be minimized if the bottle labels are removed intact without pulping and are extracted from the caustic solution as quickly as possible while the bottlewasher is running. A system which results in minimum label destruction is desirable in this case. It is then important to minimize losses of free caustic liquid with the pulp and this can be achieved by use of a label press to ensure that the labels are disposed of in a dry state, with less than 80% moisture if possible. The liquid recovered can then be added to the spent caustic inventory.

Processing Spent Solution

Processing spent washing solution generally only involves removal of the insoluble fractions of aluminates, organics and, of course, the paper fibre. It is found that concentrations of 2–2½% aluminates may be tolerated since excesses will precipitate out by gravity. Caustic reclaim therefore often involves a sedimentation process and final topping up of strength before the solution is returned to the bottlewasher. Since the sedimentation process takes time, as much tankage as is affordable is recommended. In this way unplanned maintenance involving opening of compartments can be accommodated without having to sewer the solution.

A typical system is shown in Figure 7-9. Spent caustic is drained according to schedule into large tanks after passing through a vibrating 80 mesh screen to catch large pieces of labels and other solids. These solids should be passed through the label press and disposed of with the main label disposal. The liquid fraction from the press flows into the reclaim tank, where liquid from the pressed labels has also been directed during the normal label removal operation.

The reclaim tanks themselves act as decant vessels with the solids settling to the bottom. A minimum of 12 hours undisturbed settling is recommended for good results. If tankage is severely limited or if time is not available, the

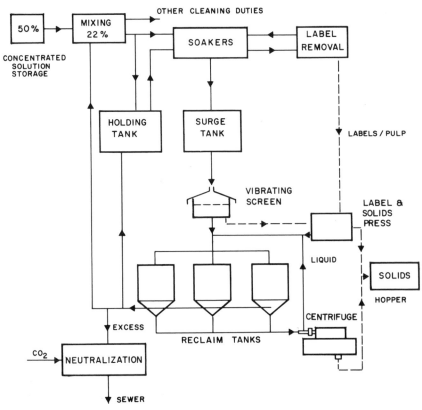

7-9. Caustic Reclaim System Flow Diagram

use of a decanter-type centrifuge can provide similar results instantaneously. It is interesting to note that experiments show that the time factor is the only marked advantage of the centrifuge over gravity settling. Clarified solution is then pumped from the top of the reclaim tank often via a floating suction arm to a holding tank where it is brought up to strength by adding fresh solution. It is then ready for return to a cleaned compartment in a bottlewasher.

The solids which accumulate in the reclaim tank bottom can be allowed to build up in level until settling and drawoff are affected, and this period may be two weeks. The challenge is then to remove the solids from the tank bottom with a minimum of liquid losses to sewer. The simplest method involves emptying the tank of clear solution down to the interface between the two layers, then hosing out the tank bottoms to sewer, but caustic losses can be very high. A much better operation results from the use of a decanter centrifuge to draw off the tank bottoms even while the tank is full. For this purpose a conical bottom tank with a minimum 30° slope from horizontal has been found to be most suitable. The clear solution is returned to the tank and the solids are sent to bulk container disposal to join the labels and screened solids. Readers may also be interested in a more detailed description of a typical system by Arbour.[6]

A fully developed caustic reclaim system will acquire surpluses of solution over a period of time due to the fact that liquid losses have been minimized and yet fresh solution has been added to maintain strength. Surpluses should then be used to dilute fresh concentrated solution rather than using fresh water whenever making up batches of intermediate strength solution. Some breweries have also experimented with using surplus reclaimed bottleshop solution as a dilution base for concentrated brewhouse cleaning solution.

Nevertheless, after all possible ways of utilizing the reclaimed solution have been looked at, there may still be a surplus. This must usually be sewered as concentration by evaporation or other means is likely not to be cost effective or suitable, unless a continuous large surplus is available. Surplus solution disposed of via the sewer should be drained slowly over a long period of time or batch neutralized as described briefly in the next section.

Neutralization of Effluent

Neutralization of excess solution is prudent prior to discharge to the sewer unless it can be assured that controlled draining over a period of time will not cause the main effluent from the plant to be in violation of local pH limits.

a. *Batch Treatment*

Batch neutralization has been accomplished using carbon dioxide gas either with a submerged diffuser/mixer, or with a recirculating pump and pipe mounted injector. It may also be convenient to neutralize spent brewhouse solution in the same vessel at the same time. Since a 3500 gallon tank of 3% strength surplus solution can cost over $100 to neutralize if purchased CO_2 is used, it can be cost effective for breweries to recover impure or waste counterpressure CO_2 for the purpose, if pure collected CO_2 is in short supply.

b. *In-Line Effluent Neutralization*

It may be that in some locations even if measures are taken to ensure batch neutralization of spent solution, pH limits are still exceeded due to carryover in the rinse section of the bottlewasher. This is quite possible in areas of very low water hardness where the buffering capacity is minimal.

Assuming all measures have been taken to minimize the physical carryover (such as removal of scale, use of wetting agents etc.), neutralization of the entire brewery effluent may be required. This can be achieved in a below-ground sump or an above-ground tank.

Three different materials are used in breweries for in-line effluent neutralization. All methods require adequate mixing and efficient control to be successful.

—*Concentrated Acid:* Sulphuric acid of around 93% strength is the most easily available and lowest cost concentrated acid available in North America. Some handling and storage precautions are required, and accurate metering into the effluent is essential. A check should be made to ensure that final sulphate levels in the effluent will be acceptable. Annual acid costs for a 1,000,000 hL brewery (100% bottles washed) for neutralizing the effluent could be $15–30,000.

—*Carbon Dioxide:* Complete pH control systems are available which utilize pure or near-pure carbon dioxide, including a diffuser/mixer suitable for sump or tank mounting. However, the availability of low cost CO_2 is of prime importance as the annual neutralizing supply and material cost for the 1,000,000 hL brewery using exclusively purchased CO_2 could be $40–50,000. Use of collected and purified fermentation CO_2 will cut this cost by 3–4 times if available, and if exhausted counter-pressure or impure fermentation gas is used the cost is negligible. The capital cost of equipment to recover impure CO_2 varies greatly according to the layout of the brewery, and justification has to be made on a case-by-case basis.

—*Boiler Flue Gas:* Boiler flue gas contains about 8–10% CO_2 and has been used to neutralize effluent, with a number of installations in Germany, and fewer in North America. The capital cost of such installations is very high, but this could in some instances be tolerated if sulphuric acid is only available at high cost (as is the case in Germany) or if sulphuric acid cannot be used due to unusually severe sulphate restrictions in the final effluent.

A more detailed review of neutralization methods is given by Lom.[7] Whichever method is used, neutralization of brewery effluent is a costly business. The installed capital cost can be particularly high if extensive rearrangement of sewers or construction of sumps is required. Every attempt should be made to minimize the loss of caustic bottlewashing solution, and to control discharges so that a steady pH profile is maintained, thus ensuring that installation of pH control equipment is not required prematurely.

CHAPTER SUMMARY

The returnable bottle is well-established in the majority of domestic beer markets throughout the world. In spite of the market appeal and convenience of the many non-returnable containers available today, the basic economics of the returnable bottle in these established markets will ensure that it will remain a dominant container in the brewing industry for many years to come. Bottle washing, the key element in the returnable bottle cycle, will therefore continue to be a subject of prime importance to the brewing industry.

While the fundamental principles of bottle washing have remained unchanged, great strides have been made in developing high-speed and efficient bottle washers. Many different machine arrangements are available to accommodate the different operating conditions encountered in various parts of the world. Concerted industry efforts have also resulted in improving the performance of bottle washing solutions, and complex multi-element products with custom formulations to suit varying conditions are now available.

Sophisticated bottle washers and washing solutions require equally sophisticated systems and procedures for their operational management.

ACKNOWLEDGEMENTS

The authors wish to thank M.J.W. Hancock and E.A. Pfisterer of Molson Breweries of Canada, for their assistance and co-operation in the preparation of a substantial portion of the material included in this chapter.

The authors also gratefully acknowledge the assistance and resource material provided by Diversey Canada Ltd., and the Barry-Wehmiller Company of St. Louis, Missouri.

REFERENCES

1. DUNCAN, D.G. *Brew. Digest*, Vol.57, No.2 29-33 (1982)
2. JENNINGS, W.G. *MBAA Tech. Quart.*, Vol.2 160-164 (1963)
3. RUFF, D.G. and BECKER, K. *Bottling and Canning of Beer*, Chapter 3,4 and 12, Siebel Publishing Co. Chicago, 1955
4. LEIPNER, W. *Brew. Digest*, Vol.50, No.10 48-54 (1975)
5. FLOOD, D.T. Industrial Dynamics Co. Ltd. Technical Note (July, 1980)
6. ARBOUR, R.G. *MBAA Tech. Quart.*, Vol.16, No.2 73-78 (1979)
7. LOM, T. *MBAA Tech. Quart.*, Vol.14, No.1 50-58 (1977)

CHAPTER VIII

BOTTLE FILLING AND CLOSING

BY W.G. SPARGO

Filling Operations

Introduction

The bottle filler is the key piece of equipment on the entire bottle line. The significance of the filler cannot be overemphasized because the performance of the line and the quality of the finished package is directly dependent upon the filling operation.

The design and operation of all equipment before the filler is planned to provide a continuous supply of bottles to the filler. As long as the filler is running, it should be provided with a bottle for every filling station. The design and operation of the bottle line after the filler is also based on the filler output so as to enable the filler to discharge a filled and crowned bottle from each filling station without interruption. Thus, the entire line before the filler is planned to provide an abundant bottle supply and the entire line after the filler is planned to take the bottles away at least as fast as they are filled and crowned.

Optimum line efficiency thus occurs when the filler is permitted to run every minute of the shift (or other time period) and when the filler produces satisfactorily filled and crowned bottles every minute of the shift. This assumes that the filler is running at the maximum speed for which it and the entire line are designed and/or set. Needless to say, optimum line efficiency also requires good bottles, no bottle breakage and no equipment malfunction or breakdown that would adversely affect the filling operation.

There is another very important item that is absolutely essential to a satisfactory bottle filling operation, and that is a properly designed beer supply that not only supplies sufficient quantity of beer but also delivers the beer to the filler at the proper rate of flow compatible with all conditions of the bottle filling operation from start-stop to continuous operation for extended runs. The beer supply must also preserve the integrity of the beer by maintaining proper beer temperature, at least minimum CO_2 equilibrium pressure, but not excess pressure, and must maintain the instantaneous rates of flow without exceeding suitable velocity to prevent product punishment and possible damage.

We will first discuss in a general way this miracle machine, the filler itself, and later on deal with the various facets of the filling operation.

Bottle Fillers—General

Bottle fillers can be as small as a stationary single filling valve laboratory filler or as large as designers and manufacturers decide for them to be. Fillers have been built that have more than 160 filling valves and with speed capability in excess of 1400 bottles per minute.

Generally, bottle fillers are rotary machines. Fillers have been built to rotate

149

either clockwise or counter clockwise. The majority of the bottle fillers in the United States are clockwise with the empty bottles entering the filler from the left, when viewed from the operating position. Smaller (and slower) fillers, such as 40- and 50-valve machines, may or may not have a timing screw to index bottles into the infeed star. Usually 60-valve, and larger, fillers are provided with timing screws (infeed worms), although with larger fillers, other devices, such as half pocket chains, have been introduced. A device for stopping the flow of bottles is usually provided at the infeed of the timing screw. Actuation of this device stops the flow of bottles to the filler and permits clearing the filler of bottles for a backup and shut down condition.

Bottle fillers all perform the same basic functions, namely indexing empty bottles, transferring them to the filler platforms, counter-pressuring the bottles and filling them with beer. After the actual bottle filling, the bottles are transferred from the filler platforms to the crowner and during the transfer, the beer is caused to foam and force the air out of the head space of the bottle just prior to the actual crowning of the bottles. Some fillers have an additional feature, that of pre-evacuating the bottle before it is counter-pressured.

While the basics of the bottle filling operation are the same for all fillers, the "hardware" differs with different manufacturers' designs.

All fillers have a "bowl" or similar device to receive beer from the beer supply line and distribute the product to the various valves. Filler bowls vary from relatively small "center bowls" to torus (doughnut) shape "ring bowls" to a separate bowl remote from the filler. Most bowls have level detection devices that signal beer control valves and or supply pumps. Filler bowls usually have pressurized gas in the bowl above the level of the beer. At least one type filler uses an annular ring type chamber to distribute beer to the valves. This chamber is completely filled with product and does not have gas in the chamber. Some fillers require CO_2 in the bowl above, and in contact with, the beer while others claim similar performance with either CO_2 or compressed air.

Filling concepts, valves and assemblies are also quite varied. There are two basic concepts, (1) fill to a level and (2) displacement filling. Filling to a level can be achieved by either long tubes that convey the beer to the lower part of the bottle with the gas from the bottle being vented out a separate passage of the tube or the vent tube concept in which beer enters along the inside of the bottle and the gas is vented out a "vent tube" in the center of the container until beer covers the tip of the tube. Filling by displacement is achieved by entirely filling the bottle through a tube with dimensions determined by the desired displacement.

Scope of Filling Operation

To provide a satisfactory bottle filling operation, the design must include a satisfactory design for the bottle conveyor system from, and including, the bottle rinser to the filler as well as a satisfactory design of the bottle conveyor system from the crowner to and including the pasteurizer or, if no pasteurizer, the next main packaging machine such as the labelers. It also includes the beer supply system with the release tanks and their gas supply, tank outlets and related items, as well as the actual beer line and fittings from the release tanks to the filler bowl, and the beer measuring device (optional).

The importance of the release system is to supply the fine product, which has been brewed and aged, without any degradation of the product.

When the beer has been delivered to the filler intact, it must then be distributed throughout the bowl to the valves, and into the bottles without significant loss of any of the fine properties inherent to the product and with minimum beer loss.

Importance of Filling Operation

The bottle filling operation handles the product and the clean empty bottles, places the product in the bottles, removes headspace air from the filled bottles and crowns the bottles, and must do this at required high speeds without adverse effect on the product, using bottles and crowns from various manufacturers and with minimum product loss. The bottle filler is often times referred to as the "key" piece of equipment on the line and is used as the basis to determine the design of the "early side" of the line for feeding bottles to the filler and the design of the "late side" of the entire line after the filler. Line speed is, therefore, determined by filler speed and line efficiency is based on this speed.

The fine quality and characteristics of the beer resulting from the brewing operation can either be preserved or partially lost depending upon the filling operation. The quality of the filling operation is determined primarily by the O_2 pickup and CO_2 loss during the filling and crowning operation.

Beer Supply

For the filler to produce satisfactorily filled bottles, it must first receive the beer in a satisfactory condition. The standard method used for the majority of bottle fillers in the United States fills beer at a temperature of between 32°F and 37°F. A filling in the finished beer release tank and release lines should not be allowed to fall below 12 to 13 psig or the CO_2 in the beer will be released from the solution.

To maintain proper carbonation of the beer, the beer pressure in the release tank must be maintained at a minimum of 12 to 13 psig by pressurizing the tank head space, preferably, with CO_2. To prevent a drop in pressure at the tank outlet, the outlet fitting must be properly sized for the desired flow rate so that the velocity does not exceed 7½ feet per second. A suitable vortex breaker at the drain outlet may also be used to prevent a vortex from forming, and drawing CO_2 into the line with the beer.

The beer line and fittings should be selected to correspond to the expected flow rate of beer through the system. Beer should not be subjected to velocities over 7½ feet per second and should not have to negotiate right angle turns (as experienced in pipe tees, etc.). For all changes in direction, large radius elbows should be used. The only place beer should normally be allowed to flow in excess of 7½ feet per second is in the beer control valve before the filler. Because of the special design of these valves, the high velocity at this one point does not damage the beer as long as the pressure drop across the valve is not excessive.

Measurement of Beer Delivery

Measuring the quantity of beer delivered to the bottle filler is necessary not only for company and tax records but also to monitor and control beer losses. Beer to the filler can be measured in basically two different ways:

1. Release tanks.

With the known capacity of the release tank and the use of a graduated sight glass on the tank, the volume of beer released to the filler can be determined and recorded.

2. In-line meter.

A meter may be placed in the release line to the filler. A turbine meter can be used, but a magnetic meter is better suited for beer since there are no moving parts to wear and it offers the most cleanable design. Magnetic flow meters are very accurate when properly calibrated. One absolute requirement for accurate metering with a "mag" meter is maintaining the supply line packed with solid liquid. There must also be a sufficient length of straight pipe before and after the meter to assure good laminar flow. "Stringy beer" has had CO_2 released from the beer and cannot be accurately metered by a "mag" meter.

A magnetic flow meter can be calibrated by using a turbine meter in line with the magnetic flow meter. The use of turbine meters for normal operation at high speeds is not recommended.

Beer Supply to Filler

Basically, there are several types of beer supply systems:

1. "Gravity" with tank bunging pressure on beer and with beer supply control valve.
2. "Gravity" with special release pressure on beer and with beer supply control valve.
3. Centrifugal pump with beer supply control valve.
4. Positive displacement pump.
5. Loop Manifold.

System No. 1 is the simplest system. CO_2 gas is supplied to the tank head space above the beer at 12 to 15 psig. This prevents CO_2 from escaping from the beer without adding carbonation to the beer. With properly designed tank outlets and properly sized beer lines, the pressure at the low pressure point of the supply line should be at least 1 psig greater than the equilibrium pressure to maintain the carbonation in solution. With this system sufficient pressure will exist at the beer control (flow modulating) valve for maximum flow required by the filler. This system is the simplest design and is the simplest to operate and control.

The "gravity" with special release pressure is normally used on systems where the hydrostatic head from the tank to the filler is not sufficient to provide proper operating pressure at the beer control valve during filler startup or normal running. This "dual pressure system" uses normal bunging pressure of 12-15 psig when the tank is not supplying beer to the filler, and a higher pressure is used when the system is ready for the filler to run. This higher pressure is set high enough to provide the necessary driving force for proper flow through the beer control valve to the bowl.

A pump is used when the static head caused by tank bunging pressure is too low for proper beer control valve and filler operation and a dual pressure system is not desired or cannot be used.

If a centrifugal pump is sized properly to match the filler speed, the pump will run continuously while the filler is stopped for short periods of time (one minute or less) without overheating or damaging the beer.

If a positive displacement pump is used, it must receive a signal from the filler level control telling it when to run and stop.

With any of these release systems, except the positive displacement system, a level control valve just prior to the filler must be used to keep the beer inside the filler bowl at the correct level and the beer in the supply line must always be kept at a point above the equilibrium pressure even during startup and running.

The loop or Manifold System is a method often used to deliver beer to several fillers in one Packaging Building. This Manifold System consists of a stainless steel pipe loop adequately sized to supply the full requirements of the various fillers in the Building plus a 10 or 15% return through a smaller pipe line.

A large centrifugal pump with a fluid drive is used to transfer the beer through the manifold. As the demand for beer changes the fluid clutch responds to a signal from a pressure control, which is set to maintain a pressure approximately 25 to 30 PSI above the maximum counter pressure of the filler bowls.

The small quantity of excess beer that returns, passes through a cooler and then through a pressure control valve into the suction side of the main pump.

A small (jockey) pump is also incorporated in the system. This pump is sized to circulate the beer at the manifold return rate when the manifold is not in use, i.e., the weekends. This pump keeps the beer in the manifold packed and cold at a reduced energy level.

Each filler location has a drop leg with a block valve and control valve, which receives a signal from the filler liquid level control, plus appropriate fittings desired by the operating department such as a sight glass, drain valves, sampling ports and thermometer.

It is very important that proper procedures be used to initially supply the beer to the filler. The drop leg from the manifold should be supplied with a venting device at the highest point and the entire line from the manifold to the filler should be filled with water prior to the opening of the beer block valve.

Every effort should be made to keep the manifold free of air and gas. A bleeder should be installed at the highest point in the manifold. This bleeder should be opened on a periodic basis.

The beer control valve at the base of each filler will close automatically when it receives a signal from the manifold low pressure system caused by either an electrical or mechanical failure. The automatic closing of the valves will maintain the manifold in a packed condition.

All beer lines should be well insulated.

Bottle Supply to Filler

As stated previously, line efficiency is based on the filler. It is necessary to maintain a constant supply of bottles to the filler. As fillers become larger, and faster, the bottle feed system must supply bottles at greater speed. One problem is starting and accelerating the stationary bottles when the filler gate is first opened. Because of this, most high speed fillers have a multispeed drive which allows for a slow start and smooth acceleration.

Bottle Indexing Devices

With proper bottle supply, bottles are then indexed and transferred to the filler platforms. Bottle flow immediately prior to the filler is normally controlled by a start/stop device such as a gate or metering star. The gate or other device does not regulate the speed of the bottle flow, but only releases, or stops, the flow of bottles to the filler. An indexing device is located after the gate and receives bottles in a back-to-back manner. This device is normally a timing screw (infeed worm). The pitch of the screw gradually changes to the pitch of the next downstream device, usually a transfer star, and the bottles are accurately transferred to this device at the spacing (pitch) required by the filling valves. The star wheel then places the bottles onto the filler platforms. At this point a guide strips the bottles from the star wheel and positions them against a bottle back rest and/or under a centering bell. As the bottle platform is raised, the centering bell contacts and centers the bottle and allows the bell to slide up the tube.

Bottle Filling Machines

Production model bottle fillers are rotary machines with the number of valves determined by the manufacturer according to the filling speed of the valves and the speed range planned for the particular model filler.

Fillers are available from some manufacturers as clockwise machines only. Other manufacturers offer bottle fillers as either clockwise or counter clockwise machines. Different arrangements of feed conveyors with bottle combiners as well as arrangements of the crowner discharge conveyor are also available.

The conventional arrangement, see Figure 8-1, includes a clockwise filler

8-1. *Crown 120/30 Beer Filler which has 120 filling valves and 30 crowning heads and is rated at 1400 12-oz. bottles per minute. (Courtesy Crown Cork & Seal Company, Inc.)*

with the bottle supply entering from the left and the filled and crowned bottle discharge either to the right (straight through) or to the rear of the crowner.

The importance of proper handling of the beer to the filler bowl is very often underestimated. For all bottles to be properly filled, the beer level and bowl pressure must remain constant.

Filler Bowls

Filler bowls come in two basic types, torus or center. Torus bowls, sometimes referred to as either ring or donut bowls, usually have relatively small cross sections. (Figure 8-2) This type of bowl usually has from four to eight radial pipes to distribute beer from the supply line manifold to the bowl. Distributor tubing from the bowl to the valves is not needed, since the valves are mounted either in the bottom of the bowl or attached to the outside of the bowl. Ring bowls produce a standing wave in the bowl when the filler is rotating and filling. Also, centrifugal force raises the beer level at the outside of the bowl and lowers it at the inside of the bowl. Because of the standing wave and centrifugal force effect, beer level is difficult to control. If a float is used, it will pass through this standing wave. If multiple dip tubes or conductivity sensors are used, the system should be set up to measure the low point rather than the high point of the wave in order to maintain level when running, and prevent overfilling of the bowl when the filler is not filling bottles. Because of the large amount of surface area on top of the beer in a ring bowl, CO_2 should be used for counter-pressure to prevent excess air pickup.

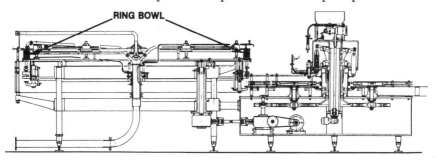

RING BOWL

8-2. Ring bowl filler.

Center bowls, Figure 8-3, have no standing wave. Centrifugal force exerted on the beer by rotation, attempts to cause the level of the beer in the center of the bowl to become lower and the beer level at the outside of the bowl to rise. Because of this, the beer level detecting device should be placed at the intersection of the horizontal level when the filler is not running and the sloping surface of the beer when the filler is running. At this intersection in the bowl the beer level remains constant. When a center bowl design is used, the already small surface area of beer that is in contact with the counter-pressure gas can be further reduced by the use of a float that reduces the contact surface to the peripheral space between the outside of the float and the inside of the bowl. This float is to serve no purpose during the filling process other than minimizing the surface area of the beer in contact with the gas in the bowl.

If the filler has a center bowl, the beer supply line to the bowl is normally through a rotary joint in the center of the bottom of the bowl. If the filler

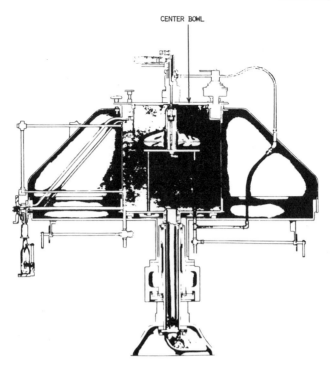

CENTER BOWL

8-3. Center bowl filler.

has a ring bowl design, the beer supply line is normally connected to a rotating manifold with rotating joint and delivered by equally spaced distribution pipes to the bowl as mentioned previously.

Bowl pressure is maintained by a gas pressure regulating and/or relieving valve.

The beer level in the bowl is maintained by either a float, conductivity probes or differential pressure tubes.

With the float method, the float usually opens and closes a port as it rises and lowers. The CO_2 or air flowing through this port is then restricted and causes an increase in pressure. This changing pressure controls either a beer flow control valve or starts and stops a pump.

With the conductivity probe method, when the beer level rises or lowers, an electric signal is either initiated or discontinued. The signal is used to regulate a beer flow control valve or pump.

The two dip tube method to measure differential pressure utilizes one short tube and one long tube entering the filler bowl. One tube ends in the head space of the bowl. The other tube extends to a point near the bottom of the bowl. By forcing a small amount of CO_2 through the dip tubes, the pressure differential between the two tubes can be measured, and a signal produced to control the beer control valve or pump.

Filler Tubes

Different filler manufacturers utilize different designs of filling valves and

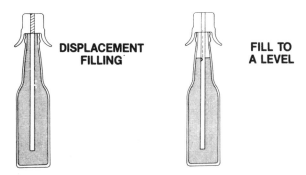

8-4. Two basic types of bottle filling.

tubes. Primarily, filling tubes fill either by tube displacement or to a level.

When filling by tube displacement, (Figure 8-4a) bottles are filled completely. When the bottles are lowered from the filling tubes, the amount of beer remaining in the bottle should be the stated volume for that size bottle. Beer level variations in the bottles are primarily the result of variations of the volumes (overflow capacities) of the bottles.

With one system for filling to a level, Figure 8-4b, there are two passages in the filling tube. The large passage is for the beer to pass through to the bottom of the bottle. As the beer level rises in the bottles, the displaced gas escapes through the smaller passage in the tube. When fill level covers the vent passage opening, gas can no longer escape through this vent causing beer to stop filling the bottle.

With another system of filling to a level, beer enters the bottles along the inside wall surface of the bottles. Gas escapes through a "vent tube" which is a small diameter tube with the lower opening of the tube at an elevation in the bottles that stops gas escape, and beer entry, when the proper fill has been obtained.

The filling valve assembly itself has multiple passages to control preevacuation (in some fillers), counter-pressuring, vent gas escape from the bottles and thereby control filling, and bottle headspace pressure. Some fillers control the passages by valves. In other fillers one multi-position valve is used, while in still other fillers multiple single valves are used.

Filling

Once the bottles are on the platforms and raised into position, the filling process begins. For some fillers, the first step in the process is preevacuation. With this process, a partial vacuum is drawn on each bottle.

The next step, whether or not pre-evacuation is used, is counter-pressuring of the bottle. (See Figure 8-5) This step provides pressure inside the bottle sufficient to preserve the product carbonation, that is, to keep the gas pressure in contact with the beer above the equilibrium point during filling such that CO_2 will not be released from the beer. The counter pressure gas can be either CO_2 or air.

After the counter-pressure is established, the filler valve (or valves) are repositioned to the filling mode, opening both the beer supply to the filling tube and the vent passages. As the beer enters the bottle through the tube, the counter-pressure gas in the bottle is displaced through the vent passage

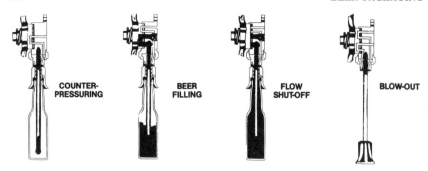

8-5. *Beer filling sequence.*

to either the bowl, a vent chamber, or to atmosphere. During the filling operation, some beer enters the vent line or passage. After filling, the vent line must be purged to provide a clean passage for venting for the next bottle.

After filling, the beer flow is stopped by stopping the gas escaping from the bottles and repositioning the filler valve. If all of the adjustments are made properly, the bottle will reach the desired fill point immediately before the beer shut off cam. After closing all of the passages to the bottles, some fillers use a bottle head space pressure relief (SNIFT). This is the release of pressure from the bottle before breaking the seal with the valve and centering bell. This pressure release produces a calmer beer upon leaving the filler.

The last operation is purging the vent passage. This is used to blow out any beer from the vent passage. This must be done after each bottle is filled to keep the vent passages clean and dry to prevent adverse effect on the next fill.

After filling, the bottle is removed from the filling tube and is discharged from the filler to the crowner via a star wheel or a half pocket transfer chain. The beer foamer is installed in the transfer area.

Bottle Headspace Air Evacuation

Once the bottle has been filled and has been lowered from the filling tube and bottle finish centering device (bell), it is necessary to eliminate air from the headspace in the bottle. This air must be evacuated before crowning to prevent oxidation of the beer. This is done by one of three methods; a bottle knocker, an ultrasonic foamer, or a water jetter.

Bottle knockers are used on relatively slow speed bottle fillers. This device employs a metal rod with an adjustable spring. The knocker is cocked as each bottle passes and the knocker strikes the following bottle. This causes the beer to foam and expel the air from the headspace of the bottles.

The ultrasonic foamer utilizes an ultrasonic generator and a transducer with a stainless steel shoe which contacts the bottles while they are still on the filler. The vibration of the transducer shoe causes the beer to foam and expel the gas from the headspace of the bottle. This method is an improvement over the bottle knocker because it is capable of higher speeds without causing bottle breakage. Out-of-round bottles and glass thickness variations can cause inconsistency of beer foaming action.

Another beer foaming device especially beneficial for high speed bottle fillers is a water jetter. This system employs a high pressure, sterilized source of water which is delivered to a fine solid stream nozzle. Only a few micro liters of water enter each bottle, but the high pressure used creates an effective beer foaming action. When the nozzle is attached to an adjustable arm, the distance from the point of jetting to the crowner can be varied. This enables accurate control of the amount of foaming, permitting minimum beer loss.

Bottle Filler Drives

Bottle fillers and crowners are driven primarily by hydraulic or AC or DC electric drive motors. Each have advantages and disadvantages and each installation must be evaluated from the standpoint of the features that are important to that particular installation.

Hydraulic Drives
A. Possible advantages of hydraulic drives are:
    1. Simple constant speed electric motors can be used to drive the hydraulic pump.
    2. The pump drive can remain running even when the filler is idling or stopped.
    3. The pump and speed control assembly can be in a remote location relatively free from beer and water.
    4. Various speeds, acceleration, deceleration, torque limits, etc. can all be controlled.
    5. Maximum torque at zero rpm can be obtained.
B. Possible disadvantages of hydraulic drives are:
    1. Personnel may not be familiar with hydraulics. An electro hydraulic system may require greater time to diagnose and correct problems.
    2. Oil leaks and/or oil spills.
    3. May require water cooling.

Electric Drives

There are several types of electric drive systems including single or two speed AC, AC with soft start, AC with frequency inverter, DC, Eddy current clutch drive units, and wound rotor recovery drives. These drives can be furnished as totally enclosed fan cooled units, however, the Eddy current drive must be water cooled when totally enclosed.

Comments regarding the electric drives are:
A. The AC with frequency inverter appears to have many advantages.
    1. It uses a standard AC induction motor which, when totally enclosed and fan cooled, can be located in the filler base.
    2. The inverter can regulate speed, acceleration, deceleration, and torque limits.
    3. Although it has only one type of system (electrical), a qualified electrician is needed for proper adjustment and maintenance of the unit.
B. Of the other types of electrical drives, the single or two speed, AC with or without soft start, are not electrically speed adjustable. (They can be and are mechanically adjustable, at least for slower speed fillers.)
C. DC provides the flexibility of an AC inverter drive, but requires more maintenance.
D. The Eddy current clutch drive system provides the flexibility of a hydraulic system since the motor runs at a constant speed while the Eddy current clutch controls the drive output. The major disadvantage is that to be totally enclosed, it must be water cooled.

BOTTLE CROWNING

After filling, the bottles must be crowned. Because of the foaming action required to evacuate the air from the headspace, the time from the point of jetting to the crown application must remain constant for a particular foamer setting. When the bottle reaches the crowner it is located on a platform directly below a crowner head. As the crowner rotates, the crowner head is lowered and the crown is pressed down onto the crown ring or threaded finish of the bottle and the crown skirt is crimped to the proper crimp dimension. This occurs by forcing a tapered throat down over the crown after it has been positioned on the bottle. The standard crown ring diameter is 1.050″. The amount of crimp is controlled by adjusting the depth that the tapered throat is forced down over the crown.

Bottle Crowners

The many manufacturers of bottle crowners provide a variety of crowner concepts and component arrangements.

The crowner dial is a rotating device that feeds individual crowns in single lines, and supplies them into a rectifier chute. The single filing device may be either vertical or horizontal. When located vertically, a large amount of crowns are placed in the hopper in contact with the dial. As the dial rotates, the crowns are supplied into a vertical chute. When the dial is horizontal, only two to three layers of crowns are required in the hopper.

The crowner dial feeds the rectifying chute (or tube). The purpose of this device is to take the crowns that are received from the crown dial and orient them so that they are all in one plane facing one direction. Rectifier chutes come primarily in two designs; tube and flat.

The crown chute extends from the rectifier chute or tube down to the crowner assembly platforms or plungers. In some cases the crown chute delivers the crowns directly to the crowner platform. In other cases the crowns are delivered via an intermediate transfer wheel to the underside of magnetic crown plunger assemblies. Crowners can be equipped with either single or dual crown chutes. With single crown chutes, a "no crown" detection device on the crown chute usually sounds an alarm and can also shut off the bottle flow to the filler. With a dual chute system, when a jam occurs in the primary chute an alarm may be sounded and the secondary chute activated.

Many crowners employ a crown platform to receive and position the crown below the throat. The platform can either be solid or floating (compensating platforms). Long neck bottles, such as the standard returnable export shape bottle, permit the use of a solid platform. Short neck bottles with a high shoulder require compensating platforms which permit the crowner throat to lower and crimp the crown even though the high shoulder prevents further travel of the platform. This compensating type of platform is more costly and difficult to maintain but is necessary for many crowners.

The bottles, after being delivered to the crowner via star wheel or tangential half pocket transfer chain, must be centered under the crowner heads. This is accomplished by half pocket back rests or well designed plastic stars. After the bottles are placed into the pockets, the crowner head starts to descend onto the bottles. With some crowners, a centering device centers the bottle to assure proper crowning. After this, the crown contacts the crown ring of the bottle and the throat is forced down over the crown, crimping the skirt to the proper "crimp" as discussed previously.

FILLER CLEANING AND SANITIZING

Beer is a food product, and must be handled and packaged in a sanitary manner. The parts of the filler which come in direct contact with the beer must be kept free of bacteria or any other foreign material, such as lubricants, etc. Filling operations for bottle lines without pasteurizers require that the filler be kept asceptically clean. This requires continuous spraying of the filling tubes, valves and bells with fresh water and/or other cleaning and sanitizing measures determined to be necessary.

On all fillers, the filler bowl, valves, tubes and beer supply and distribution lines must be periodically cleaned. This is most easily done with a CIP (Clean In Place) system in which a suitable cleaning solution is circulated through the various passages, lines, valves, and (in some cases) bottles, through to the beer supply line. By proper sizing of the beer flow passages and the CIP system, effective velocities can be obtained to clean the components without causing damage. After cleaning has been completed, the cleaning solution must be drained and the system thoroughly rinsed with a fresh water flush.

Ultrasonic cleaning of tubes is an efficient method. The tubes are removed from the adapters, and put into stainless steel mesh baskets and immersed into a solution of bio-degradable detergent and water at 140°F in an ultrasonic bath machine for 20 to 30 minutes, then removed and rinsed in clear water for approximately 15 minutes. The tubes are then reassembled with the adapters and are ready for the bottle filler.

PRECAUTIONS

When the beer foaming device on a filler has been set to create sufficient foam to assure proper headspace air evacuation with minimum beer loss it performs efficiently only at that particular filler speed. Consequently the filler should not be stopped with bottles in the filler, or between the filler and the crowner, as this will adversely affect the fill level, air content in the bottle and beer loss. It is essential that bottle backups and/or jams are detected far enough in advance so that the filler and crowner can be cleared out at a normal running speed to assure a proper fill of all bottles.

Beer Loss

Bottle filling beer losses range between 2½% and 4% and are a function of design, maintenance and adjustment of the filling equipment (such as the pull down cams, etc.) and adjustment of the foaming devices prior to crowning the bottle. Generally, bottle filling beer losses are higher than can filling beer losses because beer is caused to foam to expel air from the bottle headspace before crowning.

Contaminants

Contaminants, such as litho dust from crowns, carton fibres and airborne or "drop in" type foreign matter, can be reduced by protective shields placed over the open tops of the bottles on the conveyer from the bottle washer or rinser to the filler infeed and by installation of a vacuum dust collecting device on the crowner dial and chute entrance. Glass enclosures can be eliminated by proper adjustment of the bottle centering devices on the filler and crowner and immediate replacement of bent or broken filler tubes.

MAINTENANCE AND TROUBLE-SHOOTING

As with all precision machinery, expert maintenance, lubrication and repair are absolutely necessary for satisfactory performance. Manufacturers' instruction manuals must be followed closely and vendors' service engineers and technicians should be questioned thoroughly to maintain proper operation. Normal maintenance consists of cleaning and sanitizing, minor adjustment and repair, and lubrication, all of which can normally be accomplished during shift changes, lunch breaks, etc. Troubleshooting is necessary to correct operating problems, whether common or infrequent, which prevent proper operation of the filling machine. Each brand of filling machine is different from its competitors, yet all fillers are sufficiently similar that the following troubleshooting guide will be of value.

1. Analyze Carefully. Do not jump to conclusions. No two problems or defects are identical; therefore, each one requires careful and persistent analysis. Do not solve symptoms, solve the "Problem".
2. Follow a Logical Sequence. Haphazard adjustments may waste time and could be injurious to the equipment.
3. Do One Step at a Time. If the adjustment does not correct the problem, restore the original condition before making a different adjustment.

TROUBLESHOOTING GUIDE

SYMPTOM	CAUSE	SOLUTION
1. BOTTLE FILL		
A. Overfilling	1. Damaged or incorrect gasket.	a. Replace gasket.
	2. Snift &/or shutoff incorrect.	a. Tighten or replace gaskets and shut off cams or valves.
	3. Vacuum snift leads (if equipped).	a. Tighten or replace O-ring.
	4. Bottle damage.	a. Check infeed, tubes, centering devices.
	5. Screen damaged.	a. Replace screen, check vent tube installation.
	6. Valves leaks.	a. Install O-ring or gasket correctly, tighten valve, replace valve disc.
	7. Vent tube not seated.	a. Install properly.
	8. Guide off center.	a. Install properly.
	9. Short vent tube.	a. Replace.
	10. Incorrect filling tube.	a. Replace.
B. Underfill	1. Vent tube bent.	a. Replace vent tube. (Be sure bottle infeed handling and positioning are correct.)
	2. Spreader damaged.	a. Replace spreader. (Be sure bottle positioning at infeed is correct.)
	3. Nozzle damaged.	a. Replace nozzle.
	4. Screen damaged or dirty.	a. Replace screen. (Be sure vent tube installation is correct.)
	5. Bowl level low.	a. Set bowl level correctly with float.
		b. Be sure pressure valve setting is correct.
	6. Valve lever too low.	a. Loosen clampscrew and adjust lever.
	7. Neutral cam too high.	a. Lower neutral cam.
	8. Vent tube too long.	a. Replace with correct length vent tube.
	9. Sealing rubber worn or cut.	a. Replace sealing rubber.
	10. Vacuum system not working.	a. Be sure cam position is correct.
		b. Be sure the vacuum hole is not plugged.
	11. Valve sticking.	a. Replace valve.
	12. Filling tube wrong dia or length.	a. Replace.
	13. Shut off cam incorrect.	a. Check cam and valve lever.
	14. Filler speed too great.	a. Adjust speed of filler.
C. No fill.	1. Bottle damaged.	a. Replace bottle. Check infeed timing and alignment.
	2. Centering tulip rubber damaged.	a. Replace rubber.

SYMPTOM	CAUSE	SOLUTION
	3. Vacuum valve stuck open.	a. Be sure valve is clean.
	4. Snift valve stuck open.	a. Be sure snift valve is clean.
		b. Check for broken spring.
	5. Valve sticking.	a. Remove bent top assembly. (This indicates installation problem.)
	6. Valve spring broken.	a. Replace spring.
	7. Tulip rubber not seated on nozzle.	a. Align tulip correctly.
		b. Be sure tulip spring pressure is correct.
	8. Vent tube nipple loose.	a. Replace valve.
	9. Cam missing, broken valve.	a. Check and replace as required.
	10. No beer supply.	a. Check sight glass and beer trip cam.
	11. Malfunction of valve trip plunger.	a. Check air connection.
		b. Check plunger mounting.
		c. Check piston.
	12. Valve trip sensing.	a. Not opening up valves. (Check sensor under filler or wand sensor mounted on the outside, whichever is used.)
D. Heavy foaming while bottle leaves filler.	1. Vacuum pump not working.	a. Be sure vacuum pump is operating correctly.
	2. Three-way valve positioned incorrectly.	a. Be sure to return valve to operating position after cleaning.
	3. Vacuum too low.	a. Look for vacuum system leaks. Tighten connections.
	4. Product too warm.	a. After prolonged stoppage, it may be necessary to increase product pressure in filler.
	5. Filler pressure too low. (Counterpressure)	a. Be sure pressure controller and pressure valve are set correctly.
	6. Bottles not clean.	a. Foreign substance can react with product.
	7. Bowl level too high.	a. Check float orifice for damage. Repair/replace if necessary.
	8. Vacuum valves not operating.	a. Be sure the vacuum cam is correctly located.
	9. Stirrup pressure too low.	a. Check panel gauge and adjust.
	10. Changing tanks in cellar.	a. Air pockets. Bleed product until it looks clear in the sight glass.
	11. Foamer set too high.	a. Adjust for less foaming.
E. High air in bottles.	1. High air may be in product entering filler.	a. Check air in product entering filler.
	2. Vacuum too low.	a. Be sure vacuum system is operating correctly.
	3. Too little foam as bottle enters crowner.	a. Be sure foam jetter is clean and positioned properly.
		b. Increase jetter pressure.
	4. Bottle underfilled.	a. Too little liquid allows larger percentage of air reading. Check length of vent tubes.
	5. Bottle transfer not smooth.	a. Sloshing of liquid does not allow good foaming. Be sure bottle guide is properly positioned.
	6. Product too cold.	a. Check temperature.
	7. Snift cam worn or not properly adjusted.	a. Replace or adjust cam.
	8. Speed too fast, not allowing time for foam to rise.	a. Reduce speed.
	9. Jetter pump malfunction.	a. Check for water leaks or bad diaphragm. Tighten water connections and replace diaphragm.

2. BOWL LIQUID LEVEL

SYMPTOM	CAUSE	SOLUTION
A. High bowl level.	1. Damaged orifice on float.	a. Replace orifice insert.
	2. Gas pressure too low.	a. Adjust regulator to provide sufficient gas supply.
	3. Exhaust float does not close orifice.	a. Float may be stuck in down position. Replace float.
		b. Float may be leaking. Repair/replace/tighten.
	4. Excessive product pressure.	a. Be sure pressure valve and controller are properly set.
	5. Gas not entering bowl.	a. Broken gas hose. Repair/replace.
		b. Plugged center column.
	6. Float not adjusted.	a. Remove float and readjust correctly.
	7. Gasket and butterflies leaking.	a. Replace gasket.
	8. Cleaning valves open, cause CO_2 loss.	a. Close valves. Be sure beverage control valve, pressure controller and pressure transmitter are properly set.
	9. Differential pressure cell not adjusted.	a. Check air pressures, connections, etc.
B. Low bowl level.	1. Float not adjusted correctly.	a. Remove float and readjust correctly.
	2. Product valve not operating.	a. Check air supply to instrument's controller; must operate correctly.
	3. High CO_2 bowl pressure.	a. Be sure float cap is open for venting during startup.
	4. No beer from cellars.	a. Check with line supervisor.
	5. Differential Pressure cell not adjusted.	a. Check pressures, connections, etc.

SYMPTOM		CAUSE		SOLUTION
C. Erratic bowl level.	1.	Pressure controller not adjusted.	a.	Be sure pressure system is operating properly.
	2.	Vent cap not clean.	a.	Wash.
	3.	Sporadic hanging up of product float in open or closed position.	a.	Clean or replace valve linkage.
	4.	Differential pressure cell.	a.	inspect and adjust
3. BOTTLE HANDLING				
A. Breakage at bottle stop.	1.	Bottle stop positioned incorrectly.	a.	Adjust bottle stop.
	2.	Rail positioned incorrectly.	a.	Be sure the rail distance from bottle stop is correct.
	3.	Bottle stop pressure incorrect.	a.	Adjust pressure regulator.
B. Breakage at infeed worm.	1.	Infeed worm not properly timed.	a.	Time worm with infeed star.
	2.	Infeed worm rail (back-plate) loose.	a.	Broken spring on rail. Replace spring.
			b.	Rail too tight on swivel shafts. Loosen rail.
	3.	Bottle not fed smoothly into infeed worm.	a.	Conveyor may have glass under belt. Remove glass.
			b.	Wear strips may be worn. Replace wear strips.
	4.	Conveyor speed too slow.	a.	Be sure infeed conveyor is properly adjusted.
	5.	Infeed worm damaged.	a.	Replace worm.
	6.	Tipped bottles.	a.	Check soap lines. Check reason for tipping.
	7.	Bottles out of spec.	a.	Change bottle lot.
	8.	Wrong infeed worm.	a.	Replace worm.
C. Breakage at infeed star.	1.	Star not timed with infeed worm.	a.	Time worm with infeed star.
	2.	Wear plates not proper height.	a.	Replace plates periodically.
			b.	Watch for bent plate. Replace bent plates.
			c.	Check for worn lift cylinder rollers.
	3.	Screw head protruding.	a.	Be sure screw heads are flush with wear pads.
	4.	Star pocket vs. bottle guide clearance insufficient.	a.	Check for oversize bottles.
			b.	Bottle guide casing loose and shifted. Adjust.
			c.	Be sure star and bottle guide are the correct size for bottle being run on filler.
	5.	Star not timed with life cylinders.	a.	Be sure star is timed to cylinders.
	6.	Lift cylinders too high.	a.	Pull-down cam worn. Contact factory representative.
	7.	Burrs on infeed worm.	a.	File off, cut off or replace.
D. Breakage at filler discharge.	1.	Filler not timed.	a.	Time pocket chain to bowl using in-motion timer.
	2.	Wear plates incorrect height.	a.	Periodically replace wear plates.
			b.	Look for bent plate.
	3.	Chain pockets vs. guide clearance is insufficient.	a.	Check for oversize bottles. Use correct size bottles.
			b.	Bottle guide loose and shifted. Adjust.
	4.	Bad centering tulips. (Bottles hanging in tulips at discharge.)	a.	Check tulips. Replace bad tulips.
			b.	Check for oversized bottles.
	5.	Bottles out of spec.	a.	Change bottle lot.
	6.	Take-off guide not correctly aligned.	a.	Align take-off guide.
E. Breakage at crowner entry.	1.	Crowner too low.	a.	Adjust crowner height correctly.
	2.	Bottle guide clearance insufficient.	a.	Check for oversize bottles. Use correct size bottles.
			b.	Be sure bottle guide is correct for bottle being run on filler.
	3.	Dead plate too high.	a.	Lower dead plate.
F. Breakage in crowner.	1.	Crowner too low.	a.	Adjust crowner height.
	2.	Crown throats incorrect size.	a.	Install proper crown throats.
	3.	Crown platform bored too small.	a.	Be sure crown platform allows free entry of bottle and does not permit crown to fall through hole.
	4.	Worn or broken pressure foot.	a.	Periodically replace pressure feet.
	5.	Broken springs.	a.	Replace springs periodically.
	6.	Bottle size out of spec.	a.	Check bottle tolerances.
	7.	Crown pads worn.	a.	Replace pads periodically.
	8.	Crowner not timed.	a.	Time crowner with crowner chain sprocket.
G. Breakage at crowner exit.	1.	Bottles lifted by crown platforms.	a.	Replace broken spring.
	2.	Insufficient clearance between pockets and bottle guides.	a.	Be sure bottle dimension is correct.
	3.	Worn crowner pads.	a.	Replace pads.
	4.	Wear plate too low.	a.	Raise wear plate.
H. Crowns not holding in platform.	1.	Magnets not holding.	a.	Be sure magnets are properly located in platform.
	2.	Platform hole too large.	a.	Be sure platform hole allows bottle to fit through, but does not allow crown to fall through.
	3.	Crown wiper not adjusted.	a.	Adjust wiper.
			b.	Be sure wiper spring tension is correct.

SYMPTOM	CAUSE	SOLUTION

4. UNCROWNED BOTTLES

SYMPTOM	CAUSE	SOLUTION
A. Crowns not fed to chute.	1. Crowner selector disc incorrect clearance.	a. Adjust selector disc to allow crowns to enter chute freely, yet not double up and cause blockage.
	2. Bent crown enters chute.	a. Clear the chute.
	3. Pocket formed in crown hopper.	a. Reduce weight of crowns in hopper.
	4. Crowns hanging on rim at selector disc.	a. Check for protrusions on crown rim.
	5. No air on top vent way.	a. Be sure crowner air supply is adequate.
	6. Crowner dusty.	a. Wash with water.
B. Crowns not moving freely.	1. Chute shunt not properly dimensioned.	a. Be sure chute shunt has only one crown thickness opening.
	2. Crown disc worn.	a. Replace disc periodically. Disc must have free movement.
	3. Crown chute worn.	a. Plastic parts can become worn by sharp crown edges. Replace crown chute.
	4. No air on bottom vent way.	a. Be sure crowner air supply is adequate.
	5. Bent crowns entering chute.	a. Be sure there are no bolt protrusions in hopper.
		b. Check for overloaded magnetic belt.
	6. Crowner dusty.	a. Wash with water.
C. Crown will not exit chute.	1. Exit positioned too high or too low.	a. Adjust crown chute exit properly.
	2. Air connection plate rough.	a. Repair/replace.
	3. Air connection plate bent incorrectly.	a. Repair/replace.
	4. Crown head twisted.	a. Be sure crown heads are properly aligned.
	5. Insufficient air pressure.	a. Adjust.
	6. Bent crown in bottom of chute.	a. Check incoming crowns to filler. Remove bent crowns.
	7. Crowner element too low.	a. Check head, roller and locking bolt. Adjust.
D. Crowns not holding in platform.	1. Magnets not holding.	a. Be sure magnets are properly located in platform.
	2. Platform hole too large.	a. Be sure platform hole allows bottle to fit through, but does not allow crown to fall through.
	3. Crown wiper not adjusted.	a. Adjust wiper.
		b. Be sure wiper spring tension is correct.
	4. Chute too far from platform.	a. Adjust to correct position.

SUMMARY

The basic principles of a bottle filling operation include the beer supply from the release (bright, filtered or finished) beer tanks to the filler bowl (or distribution pipes or chamber) to and through the valves and tubes into the bottles, all according to the proper velocity and pressure-temperature-CO_2 solubility relationship necessary to preserve the integrity of the beer.

The above applies to all types of bottle fillers, whether center bowl type, ring bowl type or remote bowl. It also applies to "fill to level" type bottle filling designs, whether by vent tube type filler or level type long tube filler or "displacement" filling.

Thus, low velocity beer flow, well designed passages and minimum restrictions are all necessary to minimize turbulence and agitation of the product. In addition, the pressure on the product from the release tank to and including the counterpressure in the bottle must be sufficient to retain the CO_2 "in solution" in the beer. The rate of the counterpressure gas being released from the bottle must be controlled and it controls the rate that the beer enters the bottle, thereby minimizing agitation and preventing CO_2 from being released from solution with resulting excess foaming, low CO_2 contents and low fills.

There are advantages and disadvantages of both long vs. short tube fillers, as well as center bowl vs. ring bowl designs.

Short (vent) tube fillers usually require pre-evacuation of the bottles to achieve low air contents in finished packages. They do, however, minimize the possibility of chipped crown finishes. Some valve designs require mounting in a chamber filled with product, such as a ring bowl, although center bowl and flooded ring bowls (or annular chambers) might enable less air pickup in the filling operation. Two-speed filling of the bottles also minimizes air pickup in the bottles and can provide increased overall speed of filling.

Thus there are advantages and disadvantages to different designs; experience, personal preferences and the economics of a particular installation are factors which also help determine which design is best suited.

CHAPTER IX

BOTTLE CLOSURES
BY J.F. EVERETT

HISTORY

Closures for beer bottles evolved from the natural cork stopper through several hundred "patented closures" to the present day plastic-lined crown. Space does not permit a detailed description of all these closures. It is a fascinating history; the following are some highlights of that history.[1]

Cork, from the outer bark of the cork oak (Quercus suber), was for centuries the primary source of stoppers for many kinds of vessels, including those containing beer. Cork bark (the outer layer) is stripped from mature trees; after boiling, cleaning and drying, it is ready to be processed into dozens of useful products, including cork stoppers.

While cork stoppers were effective closures, the need for a closure that could be applied faster and be manufactured more uniformly became the spur for inventors to perfect such closures. It was the late 19th century and machines were being invented to produce all manner of commercial articles and replace much of the tedium of manual labor. Among these new machines were those designed to fill and cap bottles.

The Codd patented bottle stopper (1873), the Hutchinson stopper (ca. 1879), the "Lightning" stopper, and the "Loop Seal" (Wm. Painter, 1885), were but a few of the myriad bottle stoppers in use during the late 19th and early 20th centuries. All these stoppers sealed the bottle inside the neck, i.e. plugged the bottle opening. At that time all glass bottles were hand blown and the bottles' openings were not particularly uniform. Hence, the stopper had to accommodate some of the dimensional deficiencies in hand-blown ware.

In 1903, Michael J. Owens succeeded in developing a fully automatic machine for making glass jars and bottles. This invention made possible low-cost containers of uniform size, capacity and finish; it was now possible to consider other means of sealing the bottle opening.

CROWNS

When Patent No. 468,226 was issued to William Painter on February 2, 1892, there were few contenders left who could compete with the simplicity and efficiency of the "crown closure". Painter's closure had corrugations formed in the skirt of the crown and was lined with a natural cork disc. Subsequently, paraffined linoleum discs were used; ultimately cork composition discs were developed which could withstand the rigors of pasteurizing. Later, "spots" (discs) of varnished paper, Vinylite, tinfoil and aluminum foil

---

[1]For a more complete history, see Nurnberg, John J., "Crowns, The Complete Story", 4th ed., 1967.

were adhered to the surface of the cork composition discs to prevent beer (or other beverages) from leaching undesirable components of the cork composition disc that could affect the taste of the bottled product.

Between 1906 and 1909, Samuel C. Bond designed and patented a closure akin to the familiar crown closure except it had no corrugations in the skirt. It was, at first, lined with a natural cork disc; later a composition cork disc replaced the natural cork disc. A machine applied the closure to the bottle finish; in the process, the machine formed corrugations in the closure.

With the refinement of the crown closure, standardization of bottle finishes and improvements in bottling equipment, filling and sealing beer bottles became quite efficient.

During World War II, the cork forests of the western Mediterranean shores were ravaged by extensive stripping of the bark needed for life jackets, insulation and other materials for the war effort. As a result, the price of good quality cork rose steadily as its availability declined. However, the infant plastic industry, spawned by the war, took hold in the United States and soon plastic materials were available that showed promise as cork substitutes. Polyethylene, elastomers, and vinyl polymers were among those investigated as substitutes for cork composition. Early in 1955, the Bond Crown division of Continental Can Company introduced the first commercial, solid, molded polyvinyl chloride lined crown.

Along with the introduction of plastic linings in crowns came changes in the dimensions (primarily, overall height) of the crown shell. Cork-lined crowns were greater in overall height because the cork composition discs were almost one-tenth of an inch thick. Thinner cork composition discs were commercially available in mid-1950's and these prompted dimensional changes in the crown shell that carried over to the plastic-lined crown.

Finally, plastic-lined crowns all but eliminated the familiar cork-composition lined crowns by the mid- to late-1960's.

In 1966, the Armstrong Cork Company introduced a crown closure that could be removed from the bottle finish without the aid of the familiar bottle opener. This crown was dimensionally identical with contemporary crowns but was made of thinner, softer metal. It was lined with a foamed PVC sealing ring that had lubricant incorporated in it to facilitate removal from the bottle finish. Along with the "Turn-Off" crown, a special four-lead threaded finish was developed to which the crown was applied and from which it could be unscrewed by hand. Its development exemplified the then infant "convenience packaging" trend.

Other "convenience closures" came to be used in the brewery: the "Roll-On" aluminum cap, "pull-tab" aluminum caps and all-plastic closures are a few examples of "convenience closures". More about them later.

Crown Manufacture

Manufacture of the crown, basically, consists of coating and lithographing sheets of metal; crown shells are punched from the decorated metal; the shells are lined with plastic gaskets (almost universally plasticized PVC), inspected, counted and packaged for shipment.

Crown Metal

The steel used in the manufacture of crowns is a low metalloid steel, designated Type MR. The metal is single-reduced to gage then electrolytically coated with either tin or chromium/chromium oxide. Raw, uncoated steel (black plate) will rust rapidly without the presence of these metallic coatings.

The thickness of steel produced for tin mill products is expressed in pounds per base box; this expression of gage can be translated into inches. The usual gages of metal used in crown manufacture are 80, 90 or 95 lbs./base box. Those weights of metal translate into 0.0088″, 0.0099″ and 0.0105″ ± 10%, respectively (see Table 9-1).

TABLE 1
Nominal Base Weight—Theoretical Thickness and Thickness Tolerances

Nominal Weight, lb/Base Box	Theoretical Thickness, in.	Thickness Tolerances, Over and Under, in.
75	0.0083	0.0008
80	0.0088	0.0009
85	0.0094	0.0009
90	0.0099	0.0010
95	0.0105	0.0011

Besides the gage of the metal, there is the matter of metal hardness. After the steel has been cold-rolled to gage, it is necessary to relieve the stresses in the steel as well as to heat treat it to proper softness required for punching and forming the crown shells. The process is known as annealing. The results of annealing can be measured with an instrument called the Rockwell Superficial Hardness Tester.

Tin mill products used in the manufacture of crowns are annealed to one of two tempers: T-3 or T-4. Tempers of tin mill products can range from T-1 to T-6; the higher the number, the harder the metal. Each temper designation has a range of values for that temper. In the case of T-3, the aim range is 54-60; for T-4, the range is 58-64 (see Table 9-2). These numbers are read from the dial gage on the Rockwell Hardness Tester when the specimen is checked for hardness.

The gage and hardness of metal used for pry-off crowns (i.e. those used on G.P.I.[2] 600 series finishes) is usually 90 or 95 lb./base box, tempers T-3 or T-4. Metal used for "Turn-Off" crowns is thinner and softer, 80 lb./base box; T-3 is generally specified although 90 lb./base box, T-3 metal has been used for "Turn-Off" crowns.

Since uncoated steel (black plate) would rust quite rapidly, metallic coatings are applied to the steel to prevent this. Tin has been used in this capacity for many years. At first, the sheets of steel were dipped into a bath of molten tin to accomplish this. Modern practice is to accomplish the same result with an electrolytically deposited coating of tin. The amount of tin deposited on the steel is also measured in lb./base box. The most widely used tin coating weight for crowns is ¼ lb./base box. This means that ¼ lb. of tin is coated on both sides of the sheet over an area equivalent to 62,720 sq. in. (a base box is equivalent to 112 sheets, 14″ x 20″).

Tinplate is available in two forms: bright tinplate and matte tin-plate. Bright tinplate has a bright, lustrous surface achieved by remelting the electrolytically deposited tin at carefully controlled temperatures, then allowing it to cool to form the mirror-like surface. Matte tinplate has a "satin" appearance, not as

[2]Glass Packaging Institute

TABLE 2
Temper Designations Single-Reduced Tin Mill Products Box Annealed

Temper Designation	Aim Rockwell Hardness Range, HR30T[a]	Characteristic	Examples of Usage
T-1	49 ± 3	Soft for drawing.	Drawn requirements, nozzles, spouts, closures.
T-2	53 ± 3	Moderate drawing.	Rings and plugs, pie pans, closures, shallow-drawn and specialized can parts.
T-3	57 ± 3	Shallow drawing general purpose with fair degree of stiffness to minimize flutings.	Can ends and bodies, large-diameter closures, crown caps.
T-4	61 ± 3	General purpose where increased stiffness desired.	Can ends and bodies, crown caps.
T-5	65 ± 3	Stiffness, rephosphorized steel used for hardness to resist buckling.	Can ends and bodies, moderately or noncorrosive packs.

Temper Designations Single-Reduced Tin Mill Products Continuously Annealed

Temper Designation	Aim Rockwell Hardness Range, HR30T[a]	Characteristic	Examples of Usage
T-4-CA	61 ± 3	Moderate forming. Fair degree of stiffness.	Closures, can ends and bodies.
T-5-CA	65 ± 3	Increased stiffness to resist buckling.	Can ends and bodies.

[a]These ranges are based on the use of the diamond anvil.

lustrous as bright plate. It is the surface that results from the electrolytic deposition of tin on steel.

The volatility of tin prices and the wide swings in its availability prompted a search for an alternative to tin. The result of this worldwide search was "tin-free steel". Very thin coatings of chromium and chromium oxide are electrolytically deposited on the steel to produce either a fairly shiny surface or a matte surface, according to the customer's preference. Chromium/chromium oxide coating thickness is expressed in mg./sq. foot. Chromium is applied at a minimum weight of 5.0 mg./sq. ft.; the chromium oxide coating ranges from 0.75 to 2.0 mg./sq. foot.

The finished, coated coils of tinplate (or tin-free steel) are coated with a very thin film of lubricant to aid in the handling of the sheets in the manufacturing operations. Materials used for this purpose include butyl stearate, dioctyl sebacate and acetyl tributyl citrate.

The metal is manufactured in coil form in the steel mill but must be cut into sheets to enable the crown manufacturer to use it. The sheets may be cut to an approximate size in the mill, then trimmed to close tolerances by the crown manufacturer. The mills can also cut sheets to close tolerances, thus eliminating this operation for the crown manufacturer. The sheets must not only be cut to very precise dimensions, but they must be square at the corners. If this is not done within the allowable tolerances, it will have serious consequences in the decorating and punching operations of crown manufacture.

Crown Production

The crown manufacturing process begins with application of coatings to the metal sheets. In the case of tinplate, size (primer) coating is roller-coated to at least one side of the sheet—the side that is to be lithographed with the decoration. If this were not done, the decoration would not adhere well to the bare tinplate surface. The surface of chromium oxide film on tin-free steel is such that lithographing inks and coatings adhere rather well without the benefit of size coatings.

Coatings are applied to the side of the metal which will become the inside of the crown. These coatings serve two purposes: they protect the metal and prevent direct contact of the product (beer) with the metal which would cause an "iron pick-up" taste. Coatings inside the crown also provide a surface that lining materials will adhere to quite tenaciously. The coatings used inside crowns are generally vinyls or modified thermosetting vinyls, formulated to provide minimal flavor that could be extracted from, or transferred to, the beer.

The coatings and inks used in the coating and lithography operations are "cured" by passing the coated (decorated) sheets through long, temperature controlled ovens. Each coating or decorating operation has its own temperature specifications to achieve optimum "cure" of the coating material or decorating inks used in the process. The temperatures used for the decorating process vary for each material, but they are usually in the range of 300° to 400°F.

The process by which crowns are decorated is technically described as offset lithography. The inks used in this printing process are described as "conventional inks", i.e., inks which require some heat to "set" or harden them. Recently, inks have become available which are "set" or hardened by the use of ultra-violet light. Besides the colorants in the ink, these inks contain photo-polymers. Photo-polymers, along with "activators", form larger polymer chains, resulting in film formation when exposed to intense ultra-violet sources. The ultra-violet sources are usually quartz lamps using mercury vapor as the U.V. source. The use of U.V. curable inks allows the crown manufacturer to eliminate at least one pass through the gas- or oil-fired ovens normally used to cure "conventional" inks.

Inks used in the crown metal decorating process use pigments, dyes or "lakes" to achieve the specified color. Some of these pigments, notably lead chromate and lead molybdate, have been used to prepare specific colors (e.g. red, yellow, some greens and blues). Concern over dust generated during hoppering of the crowns and the potential for lead-containing crown dust to contaminate bottled product, caused crown manufacturers to seek so-called "lead-free" inks to replace those formulated with lead-based pigments. While these inks are not literally lead free, they do not contain any lead-based pigments. Any lead found in these "lead-free" inks is minimal (generally less than 300 ppm) and is a result of unavoidable contamination of the ubiquitous metal.

When the coating and decorating operations are complete, the sheets of metal are ready for the punch press where the crown shells will be produced. The punch presses are double-acting, i.e., in one stroke the press performs two operations: blanking and forming. The punch press may have 16 to 27 complete sets of tools, so with each stroke of the press, a like number of crown shells are produced.

Briefly, the punch press operates this way. A set of punch press tools contains a punch and die, inside of which are housed a ram and former, respectively. As the press closes, the punch and die cut a disc of metal from the sheet. The disc is held between the punch and the former; the ram, housed inside the punch, descends and pushes the disc of metal into the former to produce the familiar shape of the crown shell.

During this operation (punching) the crown shells are checked regularly for dimensional characteristics; this is to assure mobility in high-speed crowning operations.

The crown shells are conveyed to the assembly operation where the sealing gasket is placed in the shell. The material most widely used for lining crown shells is a plasticized PVC in the form of a plastisol (a thick paste) or a dry blend (powder or powder converted to pellet). Other ingredients mixed with the PVC resin are plasticizer(s), anti-oxidants, stabilizers, and if required, foaming agent(s), lubricant(s), and colors. For plastisols, very fine, powdered PVC resin is blended with the other ingredients in a low intensity mixer to make the plastisol (paste). A much coarser, porous PVC powder is blended with the other ingredients in a high intensity mixer to make the dry blend which can be used as a powder or converted to pellets.

PVC formulations destined for pry-off crowns usually have little or no lubricant added to the liner formulation; those destined for "Turn-Off" crowns must have some kind of lubricant system added to the formulation to facilitate removal of the crimped crown from the bottle finish by hand.

Plastisol paste is metered, under pressure, by nozzles or "guns" to make one of three types of lined crowns.

(a) Spin-lined crown has a drop of plastisol placed in the center of the shell. The shell is spun at high speed to move the plastisol to the corner radius and side walls of the shell. The lined shell enters an oven for liner polymerization and foaming.

(b) A sealing ring or bead of plastisol paste is put (at a certain diameter) in the shell by turning the shell one revolution. The lined shell enters an oven for liner polymerization and, if desired, foaming.

(c) A molded lined crown has a metered amount of hot plastisol placed in the center of the shell; then, a molding punch, under heat and pressure, shapes the liner. Final polymerization can occur during the molding operation or the crowns can enter a small oven for final polymerization and, if desired, foaming. (See Figure 9-1.)

The dry blend powder (or dry-blend converted to random sized pellets) is used to make molded lined crowns only. The dry blend powder or pellets are fed into an electrically heated extruder. A screw conveys the material through the extruder where it is melted, completely polymerized and forced through an orifice in a continuous manner. A rapidly revolving knife in front of the extruder cuts off a very precise amount of extrudate and places the pellet (after a 180-degree turn) into a rapidly moving, induction heated, crown shell.

9-1. Crown liner patterns: a, W. H. Hutchinson; b, H-C Industries; c, Kerr Glass; d, Crown Cork & Seal; and e, Zapata Industries.

If the liner is to be a foamed liner, it will start puffing as soon as the plastic exits from the extruder orifice, and it will be completely foamed as the crown enters the molding station. The molding punches are warm and are kept from becoming too hot by cooling water that flows through the inside of the punches. When the crowns exit from the molding turret, the liners are completely cured and no further curing is required.

The lined, cured crown is discharged onto a conveyor belt for cooling and inspection. From the inspection belt the crowns enter counter bowls, that feed them very rapidly, single file, through electronic eyes that count the crowns as they enter the crown cartons. This inspection (either visual or mechanical) and counting operation is common to all crown manufacturing.

Crowns are usually packaged in 70 gross containers. The container is a double-wall corrugated box fitted with top and bottom pads (sheets of paper) and, if specified by the customer, a polyethylene bag (liner) to further protect the crowns from dust and dirt. Boxes can be individually sealed with tape, water-based adhesives or hot-melt adhesives.

The individual boxes are palletized, strapped, shrink-wrapped or stretch-wrapped, according to the crown manufacturer's choice or the customer's specification.

Crown Shell Dimensions

Crowns delivered to the customer's plant must perform in a way that contributes to production efficiency. The first evidence of good quality in crowns is the efficiency with which they move through the crown hoppering and feeding system. The crown shell dimensions and profile must be within specification if this part of the filling/crowning operation is to proceed efficiently. Over the years, as crown liners changed from cork composition to plastic materials, the height of the crown shell changed to accommodate the thinner

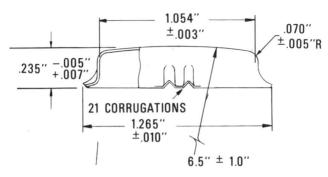

9-2. Crown shell dimension (1980). (Courtesy USBA)

plastic liners. Otherwise, the other dimensions have remained quite constant. The USBA[3] crown shell dimensions shown in Figure 9-2 represent the current industry specification. The gage shown in Figure 9-3 is used to determine if the crown Shell is within the USBA height and diameter specifications.

Crown Liner Specifications

As in any manufacturing process, there are standards of quality for the product. Although the crown shell dimensions have been standardized, each crown manufacturer establishes dimensional parameters for the particular liner configuration produced. The guidelines used in determining sealing ring configuration and dimensions are the G.P.I. finish specifications.

Crown Testing

Sealing performance of the crown is measured by laboratory tests as well as performance on the bottling line.

One test for sealing performance is described in the U.S.B.A. Closure Specification Manual, Appendices 2A & 2C. The test requires filled packages to be submerged in a hot water bath (120-140°F) for 24 hours. The test bottles are checked from time to time during the course of the test for evidence of leakage—bubbles of CO_2 escaping from beneath the crown. At the conclusion of the test the test packages are cooled, then checked for CO_2. This test can be used for bottles sealed with either pry-off or turn-off crowns. Since the test requires so much time, a modification of this test is used by some brewers. In this modified version, the bottles are submerged in a hot water bath (140-160°F) for one to two hours. The bottles are observed periodically for signs of leakage. An occasional bubble coming from a bottle(s) is normal and is no cause for concern. If bubbles emanate from the crown skirt in a steady stream, then the bottle and crown should be examined for evidence of the cause of leakage, including the crowning operation.

In all of these tests, of course, control packages must be used to establish the data base. Control packages are not subjected to the test conditions except for the time factor. Control packages may be checked for CO_2 fresh off the filling line (or pasteurizer discharge); another group of filled bottles from the same part of the production run, as the test bottles, can be held at room

[3]"Brewing Industry Recommended Closure Purchase Specification", U.S.B.A., Inc., Issued January, 1978.

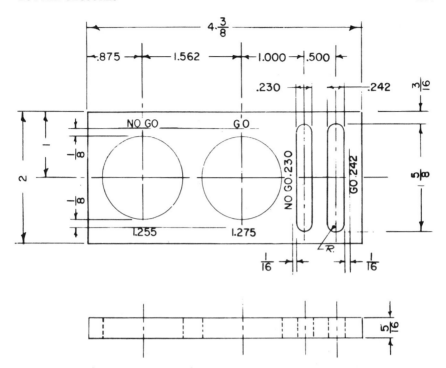

9-3. *Crown dimension gauge for 0.235" crown. (Courtesy USBA)*
*Note: Steel stamp nom. hole and slot widths, "GO" & "NO-GO" as shown
in 3/32" high characters prior to anodizing. Tolerance on gauge holes and
slot widths +.0005 prior to anodizing. Gauge holes and slots to be within
.005 of true position. Break all sharp edges and remove all burrs. MTL—
hardened aluminum-anodized. Inspect frequently for wear.*

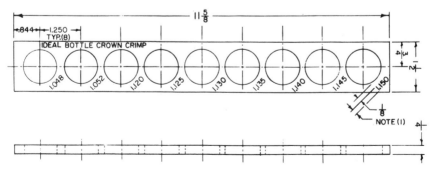

9-4. *Nine hole Ideal Bottle Crown Crimp Gauge. (Courtesy USBA)*

temperature for the duration of the test period, then checked for CO_2 retention.

Crown Crimp

When the crown is applied to a bottle, the consequences of application can be measured by a crimp gage (Figure 9-4). This gage simply measures the O.D. of the crimped shell. In the course of applying a crown to a bottle finish, the crowner must accomplish a certain amount of mechanical deformation of the crown shell in order to properly attach it to the bottle finish and effect a seal. Crimp diameter is measured by using a gage, made of metal, which has two or more accurately dimensioned holes machined in it. Crimp gages may take several forms. It may have only two holes—the maximum and minimum specified crimp. More often, it is a multiple-hole gage, with the hole sizes ranging from 1.125″ to 1.150″ in 0.005″ increments. Gages of this type can be used in production, quality control and maintenance.

The range of acceptable crimp diameters for crowns is generally between 1.125″ no-go- to 1.135″ go. This means that the gage hole that is 1.125″ diameter will not fit over the skirt of the crimped crown; the 1.135″ diameter hole will fit (slide over) the skirt of·the crimped crown. If a 1.135″ ring gage hole will not go over the crimped crown, but a 1.140″ ring gage will, this is also satisfactory and will not cause leakage. However, as soon as convenient, the crowner should be brought into recommendation specifications.

When the crowner throat begins to act on the flutes (corrugations) of the crown (a pry-off crown in this instance), the force is translated into leverage at the bend (turnover angle) in the crown skirt. This force pushes the turnover angle under the locking ring, using it as a fulcrum. The skirt of the crown is reduced in diameter in the process; this reduction in diameter is the crimp diameter measured by the gage(s) described above.

During the application of a turn-off crown, however, the crown throat contacts the corrugations and literally straightens the panels (and the corrugations) as they are coined around the threads of the bottle finish. As a consequence of this re-forming of the crown skirt, the crimp diameter of the turn-off crown will be smaller by about 0.005″ than the crimp diameter of the pry-off crown.

While crimp diameter is one measure of the correct application of the crown, it is by no means a measure of the ultimate sealing performance of the crown. For example, a crown may have a "correct" crimp diameter but be slightly cocked during application and adversely affect the seal. If this is the case, then corrective action needs to be taken.

Removal Torque

Turn-off crowns must be readily removed by hand. To measure this feature, a torquemeter is employed. Figures 9-5 and 9-6 illustrate two types used. The most widely used is the Owens-Illinois Model 25 which has a range of 0–25 in.-lbs. The scale on the meter is divided into ½ in.-lbs increments. The bottle is placed inside the adjustable posts on the table of meter and tightened in position by the knob on the side of the table. The turn-off crown can then be grasped by the bare hand or a suitable rubber grip can be used to assist in gripping the crown. The crown is rotated counter-clockwise in a steady twisting motion until the crown starts to unscrew from the finish; this usually coincides with a maximum torque reading on the scale.

The Owens-Illinois torquemeter can be equipped with a "follower" for the

9-6. Kerr Torquemeter.

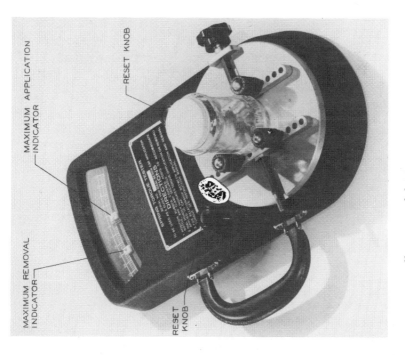

9-5. Owens-Illinois Model 25 Torquemeter.

pointer on the meter as an aid in reading the maximum torque registered. A few notes of caution: When measuring the removal torque, a smooth, steady turning motion must be employed, otherwise, the needle will "bounce" and push the follower past the actual maximum value.

To use the Kerr torquemeter, the crowned bottle must be placed on a flat, firm surface. The torquemeter, fitted with the proper, rubber-lined chuck is then placed on top of the crown. With the torquemeter held vertically, the handle is turned in a counterclockwise motion. When the maximum torque needed to loosen the crown is reached, the follower on the dial face will indicate the torque. After each measurement, the follower is re-set to the zero mark, on the dial face.

Technique will vary from operator to operator; one may turn the crown at a faster rate than another. To account for any operator differences, all torque data should be initialed so sets of data compiled by more than one operator can be compared (analyzed) for such differences.

Very high removal torques (i.e., in excess of 10-11 in.-lbs.) can be accounted for as a consequence of a number of circumstances. The bottle finish may be cracked; in this instance it is easily sensed as soon as the crown is twisted and the test should be stopped immediately to prevent injury.

The bottle finish may have extrusions of glass at the vertical parting line that will scrape against the inside of the crown shell as the crown is being removed. This will cause the removal torque to be higher than usual. These extrusions need only to be extended 2-4 mils beyond the "E" wall of the finish to produce this result.

If the horizontal parting line between the guide ring and the neck ring tools becomes worn, it too will produce glass extrusions (protusions) at the site of the parting line. In this case, the initial removal torque of the crown will be normal (5-10 in.-lbs.), then increase quite suddenly as the crimped crown skirt encounters the protrusions.

In both the situations described (extrusions at the neck ring parting line and at the parting line of the guide ring and neck ring) evidence of the scraping action of the protrusions can be seen when the crown is removed. The evidence is bright, shiny metal inside the crown skirt where the coating has been scraped away down to bare metal.

Still another factor that can affect removal torques is the hot-end coating applied to the glass containers. Hot-end coatings should be applied to the bottles so the contact areas of the bottle (i.e. where one bottle would contact the other) are covered; there should be minimal "overspray" of the coating at the neck and finish. This requires some rather careful control and sometimes is almost unavoidable because of the size or geometry of the bottle. Excessive hot-end coating can be detected rather easily on amber ware as the glass exhibits a "gunmetal" or bluish hue. Visual detection of excess hot-end coating on flint glass is not as easy. In any event, the amount of hot-end coating on or near the finish can be rather accurately measured with a special instrument designed and marketed by AGR (American Glass Research). As a guide, hot-end coating applied in excess of 20 CTU's (Coating Thickness Units) is considered to be the onset of excess coating.

Excessive hot-end coating can increase the removal torque to 1 to 2 in.-lbs. on the average. High removal torque resulting from hot-end coating can be a matter of degree. In that case, it may be best to conduct tests with one or two other sources of competitive ware to provide a comparison of data. In addition to this comparison, the AGR coating meter should be used to compare hot-end coating levels on the ware being tested.

Another phenomenon that affects removal torque is dried beer solids that become trapped between the crown skirt and the bottle finish. When the bottles are filled then transferred to the crowner, some device—a mechanical "knocker", high pressure water jet or ultra-sonic energy—causes the beer in the bottle to foam and displace the air in the headspace of the bottle. Since the crown is applied as the beer is foaming out of the bottle, there is a distinct possibility that foam will be trapped between the crown and the bottle finish. Some of the foam will drain from the crown; some will be washed or diluted as the bottle travels through the pasteurizer. To insure removal of the beer foam immediately after crowning, bottles can be sent through a spray system on the conveyor line that directs streams of water up and under the crown skirt (Figure 9-7). If this is not done, there is a possibility that some beer foam will remain. When it dries, it forms a strong bond between the crown skirt and the bottle. The adhesive power of dried beer solids is unbelievably strong! If present in sufficient quantity, it can make crown removal, by hand, virtually impossible without some mechanical assistance.

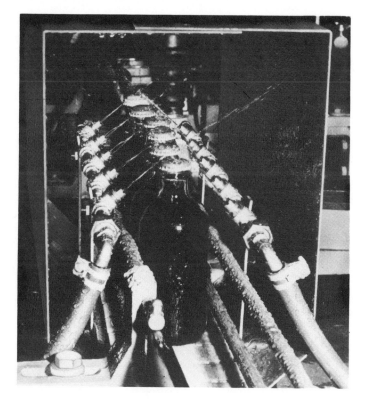

9-7. Spray Tunnel. (Courtesy Kerr Glass Mfg. Co.)

While hot-end coatings can cause higher than normal removal torques, cold-end coatings may cause another phenomenon—"crown back-off". Cold-end coatings are sprayed on bottles shortly after they emerge from the annealing lehr. Their purpose is to provide a lubricated glass surface which will enhance mobility of bottles on the filling line. The temperature of the bottles as they emerge from the lehr, and the amount of spray directed at the bottles—particularly when the spray is near the finish—can be the ingredients that may subsequently cause "crown back-off". If, when the bottles emerge from the lehr the surface temperature is high enough, i.e., exceeds the softening point of the solid ingredient(s) in the cold-end coating, the material will tend to spread and form a more or less continuous coating on the glass surface. When this ware is sent through the filling line, bottles coming from the crowner discharge will be sealed correctly and the crimp will be within specification; but, when the bottles emerge from the pasteurizer, a percentage of them will exhibit a "high foam collar" or actually have beer foam oozing from beneath the crown skirt. Examination of bottles exhibiting these characteristics will reveal the crown has apparently "backed off" and, in fact, if the crown is turned clockwise, it is possible to turn it back (tighten) on the threaded finish and seal the bottle. Re-tightening the crown must be done immediately, at the pasteurizer discharge, before the beer (leaking from the bottle) dries on the bottle.

The problem may come and go sporadically or may persist for some period of time. On rare occasions it may exhibit orientation to a small number of specific bottle cavity numbers. This could come about because of the mechanical set up of the spray device and its mode of operation.

No certain way has been found to detect the presence of cold-end coating that could be used to isolate production dates of ware that could cause the problem. Cold-end coating cannot be washed off the finish effectively. The only way it can be removed effectively is to pass the bottles through a series of burners, directed at the finish, and burn off the coating. Alternatively, the ware can be sent through a lehr with the temperature controlled to burn off the coating without reaching the softening point of the glass.

Testing Packages

"Accelerated testing" of crowned, filled bottles is a means of evaluating the effectiveness of the crown sealing performance. The choice of method, temperature and time are the factors to be considered. The USBA Closure Specifications detail one method which was discussed earlier under the section on Crown Testing.

Generally, CO_2 losses in excess of 0.2 volumes are considered unsatisfactory performance.

Other methods of accelerated testing have been used by breweries. Some use a hot water bath at a temperature of 160°F. with an exposure time of 2 hours for the packages. This is primarily a test for potential leakers, but carbonation of the test packages is still the primary measure of sealing performance.

Another approach to accelerated testing utilizes an oven heated to 110°F. where the test packages are stored for a period of one week. At the conclusion of the test period the carbonation of the beer is measured. These test conditions

have also been used as a means of accelerating the "aging" process (i.e. sim-
ulating extended shelf-life) of beer and using the packages so tested in flavor
evaluations.

Accelerated testing of finished packages certainly has merit as a means of
measuring sealing performance, but by no means does it take into consideration the shipping, warehousing and handling encountered in the trade. The
measurement of physical (mechanical) abuse the package must withstand and
its effect on sealing performance is a more difficult task.

To this end, several methods have been employed. None of these methods
are universally accepted, but they can provide useful guidance. One rather
straightforward method is that of packaging beer, including the wraps and
carton, then placing a number of cartons on a pallet, usually sufficient to
constitute one or two layers on the pallet. One or two pallets (full) of finished
packages are stacked on top of the test cartons. The test stack is left for some
period of time—a week, month, two months—after which the test packages
are removed and checked for carbonation.

Another more direct, but time-consuming method, is a shipping test. Again,
test packages are prepared, sufficient to constitute the usual shipping unit (i.e.,
one pallet or more). These are placed on a common carrier (truck or rail) and
sent to some pre-arranged destination. On arrival at the destination, the shipping units are examined for damage, appearance of the packages and finally
a selected number of packages are checked for carbonation.

There have been tests devised to obtain some measurement of the crown's
resistance to impact abuse. Impact to the crown can occur on the production
line (when filled, crowned bottles fall over) or in the trade when cartons of
filled packages are handled, stacked, unpacked or stored (individual bottles)
in coolers.

One test method involves an apparatus consisting of a three-foot long piece
of ½" I.D. copper tubing mounted in a vertical position to a stand. Just
underneath the bottom end of the copper tube is a suitable container (holder)
for the bottle; the container is designed to hold the bottle in a horizontal
position. The crown on the bottle is positioned (by moving the container on
which it was laid) so the radius of the crown (the radius joining the skirt and
the top of the crown) is directly under the end of the tube. A number of ½"
stainless steel balls are dropped down the tube one after the other. As each
ball strikes the crown, the observer notes whether or not the package exhibits
signs of leaking. If not, the next ball is dropped. This procedure is continued
until the package has (1) leaked, (2) broken or (3) thirty impacts have been
accomplished.

Another test method that has been used in evaluating impact resistance uses
an apparatus consisting of a steel tube about 18 inches long and with an I.D.
of approximately 2½ inches. The length of the tube is slotted with an opening
not quite reaching either extremity of the tube; the slot is about ½ inch wide,
and is marked off in one inch increments, measured from the base on which
the tube is mounted. The tube is mounted by supports on a base so the tube
is at an angle of 70° with the horizontal.

The test procedure begins by marking the crown on the filled bottle at
three places, 120° apart. The bottle is then inverted, guided down the tube,
and held at the one inch mark on the tube. The slot on the tube is wide

enough to insert the fingertip and hold the bottle in this position. The bottle is oriented in a manner which, when the bottle is released, will allow the bottle to fall so the crown strikes the steel base plate at one of the marks on the crown.

If no sign (or sound) of leaking occurs, the bottle is raised to the one inch mark again, rotated to the second mark on the crown, and released. This procedure is repeated at the one inch drop height until the crown has been impacted, once, at each of the three marks. If no leaking occurs, the bottle is raised to the two inch mark and the process repeated. The process continues, three times, at each successively higher incremental mark on the tube.

The data acquired from this test is designated "cumulative inch-falls". "Inch-falls" are the product of the height the bottle falls and the number of times the bottle is released from that height. Example: three falls from one inch and two falls from two inches would be: $(3 \times 1") + (2 \times 2") = 7$ inch-falls.

The acceptable limits for this test are set by each laboratory using the test. Generally, pry-off crowns will withstand more abuse of this kind than the twist-off crown.

Tests of this nature have significance only if they are related to actual production experience or distribution factors that can be demonstrated to relate to a test of this kind. Impact tests can be useful in package development work as a means of evaluating changes in crown liner design or bottle finish changes.

Two relatively new pieces of test equipment have been used to evaluate crown sealing performance. Both had been developed in conjunction with test procedures to measure the sealing effectiveness of properly applied aluminum "roll-on" closures. The Alcoa "Proper Application Tester", Figure 9-8, the Owens-Illinois "Secure Seal Tester", Figure 9-9 were both designed to test filled, capped packages from the production line. Hereafter, the Alcoa equipment will be referred to by the acronym, PAT, and the Owens-Illinois apparatus will be mentioned with the acronym, SST.

Both pieces of equipment have a means of piercing the closure; the PAT, by means of a stubby, sharpened hypodermic needle; the SST, by means of a hollow, self-threading steel needle. In both instances, the piercing needle is connected to a controllable pressure source (compressed air or CO_2). The package, now pierced and seated against the piercing device, is placed in a protective, shielding arrangement. In the case of the PAT, a thick "Lexan" shield surrounds the inverted test package. In the case of the SST apparatus, the bottle is lowered into a clear plastic cylindrical water bath so the bottle is submerged. This is done to protect against the hazards of the bottle exploding during the testing.

Pressure is introduced through the piercing needle at a predetermined rate and is increased steadily until the seal fails or the pressure reaches a predetermined maximum level. Leakage (failure) of the crown seal is detected by bubbles of gas escaping from beneath the crown skirt. When the test is completed, the pressure in the bottle is vented and the package removed from the apparatus.

Interpreting the results of PAT or SST tests must be done with an eye to all the variables that may affect the outcome. Some examples of variables are correct crown application, bottle finish variability (dimensionally), time elapsed

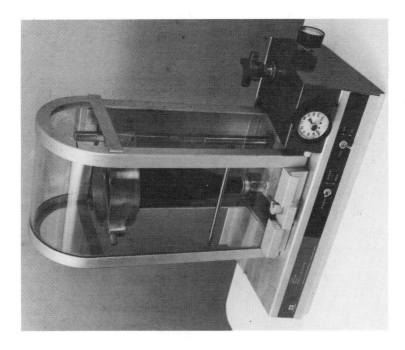

9-9. Alcoa Proper Application Tester. (PAT)

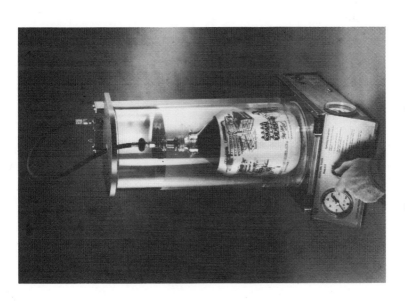

9-8. Owens-Illinois Secure Seal Tester (SST).

between closure application and testing, and package processing. As of this writing, no USBA test procedure has been adopted for this type of test equipment. Individual breweries are evaluating the equipment for use in daily bottleshop quality control procedures as well as for qualification specifications for crowns. Some have adopted their own test specifications for use with this equipment.

ANALYSIS OF PACKAGING PROBLEMS

As in any production situation, there are always problems that require analysis to determine the cause of the problem and thereby point the way to correction of the problem. To analyze crown related problems, a number of steps should be taken in order to collect evidence that can be brought to bear on the problem. If the problem is of obvious solution, i.e. a leaker caused by an obvious defect in the glass finish, or one caused by an obviously cocked crown, then the evidence is immediately at hand. However, when the solution to the problem is not so evident, the following steps will aid in the orderly collection of data.

First, mark both the crown and the bottle with a number; do the same with all samples involved in the problem. Next, with a marker, draw a line down the skirt of the crown and onto the bottle. This line will help to relocate the original position of the crown with respect to the bottle later on. Prepare a data sheet with column headings that contain (1) the number assigned each sample, (2) the cavity (mold) number of each bottle, (3) the crimp diameter of each crown, (4) in the case of twist-off crowns, removal torque of the crown (measured with a torquemeter).

Before any crowns are removed, they should be examined for unusual or repetitive marks that might provide a clue. For example, a worn plunger (presser foot) on a crowner will leave easily identifiable marks on the top of the crown. This could be an indication of bottle misalignment and consequential cocked application of the crown.

Next, the crowns should be removed carefully. When removing pry-off crowns, use an opener with some care so as not to distort the crown more than necessary. Now the sealing surface of the bottle can be examined for defects; the crown sealing ring can be examined for uniformity and completeness of impression. A note of caution: Plastic-lined crowns require exposure to heat in order to produce a permanent impression of the contact with the bottle sealing surface. Samples taken from the pasteurizer discharge will exhibit such an impression. Samples taken from the crowner discharge will exhibit the impression for only a short period of time since the "memory" of the thermoplastic PVC will cause the sealing ring to recover almost all of its original shape. To obtain a more lasting impression, the bottles should be placed in a hot water bath (about 140-160°F.) or let stand under hot tap water for five to ten minutes, then cooled. When the crowns are removed, the sealing ring impression will be visible for quite some time.

It is best to examine crown sealing ring impression with a hand lens or a low power microscope; the bottle sealing surface should also be examined in this way. Details to look for on the sealing ring impression are:
1. Completeness of the impression
2. Uniformity of the depth of impression

3. Determine if any part of the ring is cut through
4. Determine if the impression appears off-center with respect to the rest of the sealing ring. If this seems to be the case, see if the crown skirt is "pulled down" more on one side than the other. It's an indication that the crown was cocked during application.

Details to look for on the glass finishes are:

"Turn-Off" Finish (GPI series 500 finishes)
1. Fine "lines-over" the sealing surface
2. Small checks in the "E" wall of the finish
3. A "rolled-in" sealing surface, i.e. one where the sealing surface has a downward slope toward the bottle opening.
4. Dips or "saddles" in the sealing surface
5. Unfilled threads or poorly formed threads (this detail is better observed with the use of an optical comparator).

Critical dimensions of this finish, e.g. "T", "E" and "C" dimensions should be measured. These dimensions and their relevance to an acceptable finish are described in Chapter VI on glass containers.

"Pry-Off" Finish (GPI 600 series finishes)
1. Chipped sealing surface
2. Excessive glass extrusion at the parting lines on the sealing surface.
3. Locking ring contour and height (these details are best observed by using an optical comparator).

Critical dimensions of this finish, e.g. "A" dimension, locking ring height and "C" dimension and their relevance to sealing performance are described in more detail in Chapter VI on glass containers.

ALUMINUM ROLL-ON CLOSURES

The aluminum roll-on closure has been used as a closure for beer bottles since 1966, and coincided with the growth of "convenience packaging" that was in full swing. The 28mm closure is the only size used in beer packaging, although there is a 38mm size roll-on closure available. At one time or another, the 28mm closure has been used to seal 12, 16 and 32 oz. bottles. Its use in contemporary beer packaging is largely confined to the 32 oz. bottle.

The pilferproof version of the roll-on closure was first produced, commercially, in April of 1933. The American rights to produce the pilferproof closure, under a British patent, had been acquired earlier. Repeal of Prohibition in December of 1933 created a demand for the roll-on closure. The added pilferproof feature provided additional impetus for the sale of RO pilferproof closures in the wine and liquor market. The pilferproof feature minimized the possibility of tampering with product integrity. In this application, there was no need to contain pressure or withstand exposure to elevated temperatures in the packaging process.

The use of roll-on closures in beer packaging presented a different situation. A modification of existing roll-on bottle finishes was required to develop a seal that would withstand the pressure generated in packaging beer. Different lining materials were needed to maintain a pressure seal as well as withstand pasteurizing temperatures. Both these objectives were met in the development of the contemporary ROPP closure.

The contemporary roll-on, pilferproof closure is more familiarly designated the 28mm "TSPP" (Top, Seal, Pilferproof) closure. The "Top Seal" designation arises from the fact that in the course of applying the cap, the dome (top) of the cap is re-formed by a pressure block in the capping head. This serves to shape the dome of the cap and the liner immediately beneath it, into a configuration that forms a tight seal against the top and side of the bottle sealing surface.

There are two styles of pilferproof closures. The original style had a series of horizontal lances or cuts around the skirt about ⅛" up from the open end. The uncut metal between these cuts formed a series of "bridges" that held the pilferproof band to the top of the closure. When the applied closure was unscrewed, the "bridges" fractured and a ring of metal stayed on the bottle neck.

The other version of the pilferproof cap has vertical scores, plus horizontal lances and "bridges". When the applied closure is turned off, the scores crack open and the entire closure (including the pilferproof band) is removed from the bottle. (Figure 9-10)

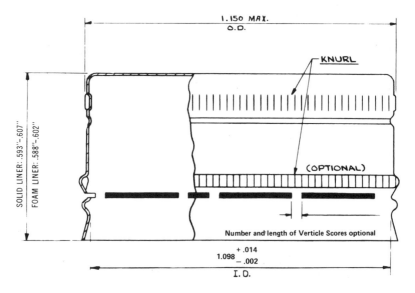

9-10. 28mm Topside Closure with or without retained locking bands. (Courtesy USBA).

When either pilferproof type closure is applied, the pilferproof band of the closure skirt is rolled (formed) under a mating bead on the glass finish. The closure cannot be removed without cracking the scores or fracturing the bridges.

Closure Manufacture

Aluminum sheet stock is the raw material for the RO shell. The aluminum is an alloy, CH14, with a hardness of H-19 and a thickness of 0.009" ± .001". For the 38mm cap, a special, high strength alloy is employed; metal thickness for this size cap is 0.0095" ± .001".

The materials and processes used to decorate the aluminum sheets are quite like those used to decorate metal used to manufacture crowns.

The decorated metal is fed, in strip form, through a single acting punch press to form cups. The punch press tooling consists of a mating punch and die which cuts a disc of metal as the punch descends and meets the die, see Figure 9-11. Inside the die is a die plug; as the punch descends, it compresses the draw ring and the aluminum disc is drawn around the die plug and pushed into the punch by the draw ring. This action forms a cup. At the bottom of the stroke, the clearances between the outside diameter of the die plug and the inside diameter of the punch are so close that it pinch trims the small ring of excess metal from the cup.

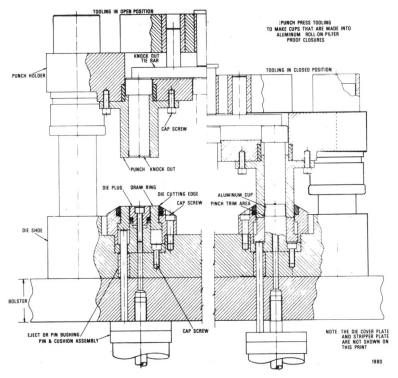

9-11. *Punch press tooling to make cups that are made with aluminum roll-on pilferproof closures. (Courtesy Zapata Industries).*

The finished cup and the pinch-trim ring are ejected from the punch press. The pinch-trim makes a cup of very uniform height; the clearances between the die plug's O.D. and I.D. of the punch are such that the diameter of the cup is quite uniform.

The cups are air conveyed to a hopper which feeds them into a beading machine that changes the outside profile to form the knurling, the roll groove, and lance the skirt of the shell to form the "bridges" that become the pilferproof band.

RO caps made with vertical scores in the pilferproof band have the vertical scores formed in the beading machine; another method of accomplishing the same end is to have the tooling in the punch press form these scores.

The shaped shells are conveyed to a lining machine, where the liner is inserted and bonded to the cap by heating the thermoplastic coating in the cap.

The liners used in RO closures are generally plasticized PVC materials, foamed or unfoamed. Other materials (e.g. EVA blends) have also been employed. The liner material is usually formulated, then extruded into tape form, from which the individual liners are punched and inserted in the shells.

After the closures are lined, they are inspected, counted and packed in Kraft paper bags. Usually, four paper bags, filled with caps, are placed in a corrugated shipping carton. The cartons are palletized, then strapped or shrink-wrapped for delivery to the customer. Palletized cartons of RO closures must be stacked properly to prevent excessive loads on the cartons of caps that would bend some caps and subsequently cause cap feeding problems on the closing machine. Caps should be stored in a clean, dry area, free from odors, insects and rodents. Partially used cartons or bags of caps must be tightly reclosed to prevent contamination.

Closure Application

Proper application of the aluminum roll-on closure is paramount in producing a finished package with a seal of assured integrity. (Figure 9-12) Proper and regular maintenance of the closing machine is imperative if uniform application is to result. Each closing machine manufacturer can supply detailed instructions to accomplish this; the instructions should be followed scrupulously.

Caps applied by the closing machine should be checked on a regular basis, noting the results of cap application, by each headset. Daily records, related to cap application, are a necessary part of any quality control scheme as well as providing useful data for maintenance.

Proper cap application can be assessed by visual examination of the caps and the basic elements of a visual examination are:

1. The top of the cap is re-formed to a uniform contour. The radius at the circumference of the re-formed dome should be well defined and of uniform depth all around the cap.
2. The threads should be fully formed for a full turn of thread. The formed thread should extend down to the thread run-out just above the pilferproof band.
3. Special attention should be given to the thread formation; two extremes of thread formation are:
   (a) Shallow, poorly formed thread and,
   (b) Thread cut-through as a result of improperly adjusted thread rollers.
4. Complete and uniform tuck of the pilferproof band. Examination of the formed band to determine that none of the bridges or scores has been prematurely broken during application.

Since proper closure application and the maintenance of the capping machine are inseparable, it is necessary to maintain regular and accurate records about each headset and its daily performance. Records of this kind will enable production personnel to anticipate problems before they get out of hand.

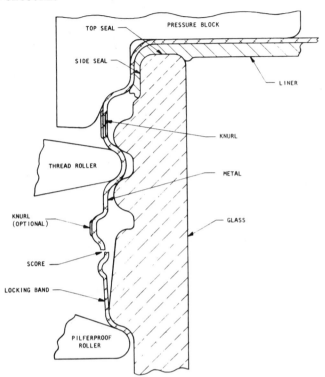

PRESSURE BLOCK

TOP SEAL

SIDE SEAL

LINER

KNURL

THREAD ROLLER

METAL

KNURL
(OPTIONAL)

GLASS

SCORE

LOCKING BAND

PILFERPROOF
ROLLER

9-12. Application of roll-on closure to G. P. I. finish 1650. (Courtesy USBA).

Besides visual inspection of the applied closure, there is another method that can be employed to ascertain the effectiveness of closure application. This involves the use of pressure testing equipment available from ALCOA or Owens-Illinois. ALCOA markets the P.A.T. (Proper Application Tester); Owens-Illinois markets the SST (Secure Seal Tester). These two pieces of equipment were described earlier in the chapter. Either piece of equipment can be used to test the pressure retention capability of a roll-on closure applied to a bottle. This is a measure of correct application of the cap. If this equipment is used as a quality control tool, sample bottles are collected from each operating headset at some predetermined interval (e.g., twice per shift). The bottles are marked with the number of the headset that produced each sample. Visual examination (as described above) of each cap then follows. Note is made of any observed departures from acceptable cap application.

The packages are tested on the P.A.T. or SST equipment following the manufacturer's instructions for correct test procedure. Typically, 28mm closures, properly applied, should exhibit pressure retention values in excess of 150 psig; 175 psig readings are quite normal. If a sample fails to retain at least 150 psig, the sample should be tagged, the headset from which it came noted, and the cause of failure should be investigated. Production that preceded discovery of a sample with unacceptable pressure retention, should be held for further sampling and investigation.

CAP REMOVAL TORQUE

Cap removal torques are another measurement of cap performance that require attention. Although removal torque of itself is not a certain measurement of proper cap application, it can under certain circumstances, provide a clue to cap application problems as well as unexpected deficiencies in the bottle finish. For example, a shallow, poorly reformed top might indicate an over maximum "F" dimension that may, in turn, cause a lower removal torque. A chipped thread, on the other hand, will cause abnormally high removal torque. Poorly formed (shallow) threads will also exhibit high removal torques; as the cap is loosened, the shallow threads tend to wedge between the bottle threads and produce that result.

There are two distinct torques evident when the cap is loosened. The first is a starting torque that breaks the seal between the liner and bottle sealing surface. The second torque occurs as the closure is further unscrewed and the vertical scores (or bridges) of the pilferproof band are broken. It is good practice to record both torques, though some laboratories record only the highest torque (i.e., the one the consumer will encounter). For the 28mm cap, a range of 5-14 in.-lbs. is usual; for the 38mm cap, 10-20 in.-lbs. is the normal range. Again, for emphasis, the cap removal torque is NOT a measure of proper cap application. A condition could exist where the removal torque of the closure is within the normal range, yet poorly applied; removal of the closure under these circumstances might result in premature release, i.e., pressure in the bottle will blow the cap off the bottle with potentially harmful results.

Certainly the bottle finish is a significant factor. Dimensional specifications for the GPI 1650 finish must, of course, be adhered to; there are other attributes which must be present (or absent) in order for the finish to function properly.

The sealing surface must be free of fissures ("lines-over"); the sealing surface should not be more than 0.020" out of parallel with the base of the bottle. These details affect the seal and cap application respectively.

Correct thread depth, profile and thread length are essential to proper application and sealing integrity.

The diameter and profile of the locking ring, as well as the "D" dimension (which controls the vertical location of the locking ring), are critical to correct application of the pilferproof band.

"F", "T", and "E" diameters must be within specification in order to provide correct diameters for proper application, especially in reforming the cap and rolling the thread. Chipped, mismatched or poorly formed thread profiles will interfere with both application and removal of the cap.

Combination finish gages are available which can be used to check these dimensional aspects of the finish. Their planned, regular use, in an incoming quality control program, can aid materially in the production of properly and safely sealed bottles.

"RIP CAP" CLOSURE

The "Rip Cap" convenience closure (T.M. American Flange & Mfg. Co. Inc.) can be used to seal bottles with the GPI 600 finish. It is an aluminum tear-off closure, produced in two sizes—26mm and 42mm size (used in conjunction with the GPI 710 finish).

A principal feature of this closure is the readily accessible gripping ring formed as an integral part of the closure; the ring is part of a scored tear strip section of the cap which allows the user to pull out and up on the ring, tear out the scored section and remove the cap.

The "Rip Cap" closure is fabricated from a light gage aluminum of special ductility which provides the cap with necessary high strength and ease of removal.

The aluminum metal used to produce the cap is coated and decorated in much the same fashion as crown metal or aluminum used for roll-on closures. The surface of the metal which becomes the interior of the finished closure is coated with a modified vinyl lacquer system to provide gasket adhesion, along with product protection. After the flat metal stock has been coated and decorated, it is fabricated by a multi-stage punch press which forms the closure blanks and ultimately the closure.

From this operation, the closures are processed through lining equipment where an annular, flowed-in gasket is accurately placed in the closure. The sealing gasket is a temperature resistant, microcellular PVC especially formulated to assure sealability and easy removal.

The closures are inspected, packed and readied for shipment.

The "Rip Cap" closure is adapted for use with existing crowning equipment that has been modified to accept special crimping heads for applying the closure as well as special cap feeding hoppers and chutes for feeding the closures in correct orientation to the crimping heads.

The cap feeding and orientation equipment is specially designed for high-speed application. The hopper can be mounted either directly on the crowner column or free standing, adjacent to it. The closures are chute fed, oriented in a ring-trailing position from the centrifugal hopper to the cap release mechanism. As the bottles pass below the release mechanism, the cap is wiped onto the bottle finish and held in place by a hold-down device that keeps the cap in position until the crimping head completes the crimping action.

The crimping heads are adaptable to Crown Cork & Seal, Meyer and many other types of crowning equipment. In most instances, a special adaptor is supplied for each of the crowner slides so that the standard crowner mechanism can be interchanged with the "Rip Cap" crimping head for maximum bottling flexibility.

This convenience closure is completely tamperproof and provides a clean, reliable seal on returnable or nonreturnable glass containers needing a hermetic seal.

ACKNOWLEDGEMENT

The author wishes to acknowledge the contributions and valuable help of the following individuals in the preparation of this chapter:

John J. Dickey, Aluminum Company of America;

Henry J. Dorn, Zapata Industries;

Frank J. Feild, Crown Cork & Seal Co.

Robert Loughery, American Flange Mfg. Co., and

James Norton, National Can Co., Closure Division.

CHAPTER X

LABELS AND LABELING

BY VICTOR SCHWARTZ

LABELING—A Brief History

The stages of development in labeling throughout the ages are fascinating. Bottle labels have changed considerably as has labeling equipment.

In medieval art, the term "label" meant the representation of a band or scroll containing an inscription. Later, and to date, the term "label" designates a slip of paper, parchment, leather, metal etc., affixed to anything, and indicating, usually by an inscription, the contents, ownership, rating, etc. Initially, a label was primarily used to mark a name on a bottle or a package. It took much manual effort to glue the printed slips to the bottles.

Changes came and so-called labeling tables were introduced which facilitated some of the manual operations. The German Imperial Register of Patents of 1895 lists a "bottle labeling appliance" which facilitated the gripping of the labels by hand. In the same year a Scotsman invented a manually operated machine which could perform some of the operations automatically. The last decade of the 19th century was characterized by the introduction of many ingenious ideas to resolve specific labeling problems. A "label attaching machine" patented in the U.S.A. in 1897 indicates a surprisingly advanced stage of technology for that time.

Illustrations of historic labels indicate that labels were used to advertise bottle contents, and even then more than one label was affixed to a bottle.

Let us look at the several stages of development from the "prehistoric age" of bottle labeling to the present sophisticated technology. We will see that labeling machines have come a long way in a short time and developed in parallel with other bottling machinery.

Initially, labeling machines could not keep up with the efficiency of technologically-advanced filling machines and multiple low speed labeling machines were required. Historic illustrations show machines with large reciprocating movements. A labeling machine in a bottling plant was considered a complicated and awkward piece of equipment.

Fortunately, this is a thing of the past. The labeling in a highly advanced bottling plant demands very specific and exacting technical requirements. And today there is, in addition, a need for versatility in bottle labeling due to the multiplicity of bottle sizes being run. Recent standards for labeling machines are oriented according to output efficiency, quality in labeling, a high degree of reliability, ease of operation and low maintenance.

The main task of the operator should be, besides providing the machine with labels and glue, the control of the machine. To facilitate his task, the machine should be equipped with foolproof control units for bottle flow control and speed regulation.

All manufacturers of labeling machines have focused their work on developing these machines which perfectly combine advanced technology and convenience in operation. The efficiency of modern high speed labeling machines is no longer second to that of fillers.

LABELS

CODE READING DEVICES

In critical applications, it is necessary to ensure that products are correctly labeled. This can be done automatically by installing "code readers" on the labelers. These are photoelectric devices which read a code printed on the labels and stop the labeler, if incorrectly coded labels are used.

In connection with code readouts, it should be mentioned that supermarkets are presently using a code on all merchandise which is scanned by a laser connected to a computer and the coded data automatically fed into the cash register as the cashier passes the item over a code reader. This coding is called Universal Product Code or UPC. The UPC identifies the product, manufacturer, package (3 pak, 6 pak) etc., and its use is discussed further in Chapter XVIII, Product Identification.

DATING DEVICES

One of the oldest methods of date coding bottles on labels was to cut the edges of the labels according to date cutting stencils. To decode the bottling date, decoding gauges were necessary. Cutting the label edges, originally done by hand, was eventually mechanised and date stamping machines were also introduced.

In some cases, the date may be printed on the back of the label if the container and product are sufficiently transparent to allow reading the printed date. Date coding on the bottle caps is still accepted as a solution in some cases.

A number of other possibilities are available. In addition to labelers with date stamping devices, machines are available which print the date on the labels before they are placed in the labeler magazines, which code the labeled or unlabeled articles, (for example, a Video-Jet or Laser), or use a perforating or embossing dating device. The latter eliminates the use of ink, since the date is punched or embossed directly into the label paper by means of dies.

In view of the variety of possibilities for dating labels, prior consultation with individual Marketing Departments is recommended.

LABEL DESIGN

The importance of a well designed and properly applied label is well recognized by every brewer, since it serves not only to clearly identify his particular brand to the consumer, but also to reflect, by implication at least, the product's quality. A pleasant, attractive label tends to predispose the consumer to expect a product that is equally pleasant in flavor and character.

This recognition of the label's importance has often led to the selection of complex label designs. While the complex labels may be very effective when hand applied, their automatic application creates difficulties, and can result in a finished package which implies carelessness of operation, i.e., a poorly labeled package.

10-1. *Drawings illustrating various label designs and applications (Courtesy Reynolds Metals Co.)*

In the design of a label, it is well to be guided by several general rules to avoid the occurrence of subsequent difficulties, without interfering with the creation of a distinctive design. These general rules may be enumerated as follows:

1. Border or peripheral margins should never be less than ⅛ inch wide, preferably ³⁄₁₆ of an inch.
2. Inside angles and small radii of any kind, except at the label corners, should be avoided. See Fig. 10-1(h).
3. Insure that the label conforms to the curvature to be covered. See Fig. 10-1(c and f).
4. Do not extend label over intersecting curvatures on the bottle surfaces. See Fig. 10-1(b) (neck label and body labels), and (g) (shoulder label-bottom tip).
5. Provide sufficient glue area. See Fig. 10-1(a and f). Do not "starve" the label, as in Fig. 10-1(d, e, g, and j) (body labels) and (i) (neck label).
6. Except for neck foil or where foiling attachments can be used (with a wiping action all around the bottle), the label should not exceed 180° around the bottle, as in Fig. 10-1(b).

7. Neither should the label fall too short of a 180° coverage as in Fig. 10-1(d) (body label), and (i) (shoulder label).
7. Observe limitations of machine design by placing label components within areas which can be wiped effectively. Thus in Fig. 10-1(d) the neck label is too low; in (g), the back side of the shoulder label, and in (h), the lower edge of the body label are also too low. The neck foil should be kept slightly below the top of crown.
8. Insure that the label box contacts the label at two points at least, and preferably three, to keep the label correctly positioned or aligned. Round body labels will turn as indicated in Fig. 10-1(e).
9. Sharp or "tailing" extremities are to be avoided. See Fig. 10-1(g) (shoulder label); and (h) (lower tip of shoulder label).
10. Label grain direction for body, neck and shoulder components should always be "around" the bottle. Incorrect grain direction will result in "flagging" labels.
11. One very common source of label protection is the use of the indented label panel on the bottle.

Observance of these precautions will help materially in circumventing some of the more common difficulties, yet need not impose serious limitations on the designer's originality.

LABEL MANUFACTURING

Marketing, Creative Service groups, and glass and label suppliers are responsible for new bottle shapes and new concepts in label design. As before, print quality and the color matching standards are monitored by a quality control group.

In recent years, a second quality control aspect has emerged. This deals with the machinability characteristics of labels. The need is made very clear when one visits a label "HOLD" area of a brewery or soft drink labeling facility. Upon close inspection of labels on "HOLD", one would probably be hard pressed to find labels with poor graphics. Chances are that the labels did not perform well on the labeling equipment. It is this area that now demands the attention of the label manufacturers.

For labels to meet performance requirements on high speed machines, it has been necessary for label manufacturers to build air-conditioned facilities to house a host of sensitive technical equipment.

LABORATORY TESTING

Laboratory tests generally performed by printers of labels for the beverage industry are as listed below. The list is by title, the purpose of the test, the equipment utilized and the references.

Graphics

1. Scuff and abrasion resistance. Ref: TT-P-141-B
Purpose: To evaluate the resistance of surfaces to rubbing abrasion.
Test equipment: Taber abraser.

2. Scuff and abrasion resistance. Ref: TAPPI RC-183
Purpose: To evaluate the resistance of surfaces to rubbing abrasion.
Test equipment: Sutherland ink rub tester.

3. Color of paper and paperboard by Hunterlab colorimetry. Ref: TAPPI 524 su-72
Purpose: To measure the color of paper and paperboard by multiple filter colorimetry from the reflectance factor signals on paper or paperboard surfaces.
Test equipment: Hunterlab Colorimeter.

4. Measuring and verifying UPC and EAN printed symbols. Ref: Photographics Sciences Instruction Manual, February, 1978.
Purpose: To measure and analyze the precision of a printed UPC or EAN symbol.
Test equipment: Photographic Sciences Corporation Auto Scan.

5. Gas chromatography. Ref: Text books, retention data, and manufacturer's periodicals.
Purpose: To separate and identify complex mixtures used in Rotogravure printing.
Test equipment: Gas Chromatographic System.

Physical Requirements

1. Water absorbency of bibulous papers. Ref: TAPPI 432-su-72
Purpose: To determine that rate at which an unsized and absorbent paper will absorb water by measuring the time required for it to absorb completely a specified quantity of water.
Test equipment: Measuring pipet and stop watch.

2. Water absorption of bottle labels. Ref: TAPPI 441-os-77
Purpose: To test for water absorption of bottle labels.
Test equipment: Cobb sizing tester.

3. Oven moisture. Ref: TAPPI 412-os-63
Purpose: To determine moisture content of paper and foil/paper laminates.
Test equipment: A. Oven
                         B. Analytical balance.
4. Spot test moisture. Ref: Hart Moisture Meter, Inc. Instruction manual
Purpose: To measure the moisture content of paper and paper/laminate materials quickly over a wide range of moisture percentages.
Test equipment: Hart moisture meter.

5. Coefficient of friction. Ref: TAPPI 503-su-67
Purpose: To determine the kinetic and static coefficient of friction on laminated and varnished products.
Test equipment: American Glass Research Friction tester.

6. Bursting strength of paper. Ref: TAPPI 403-ts-63
Purpose: To measure the bursting strength of paper and paper products; bursting strength is widely used as a measure of tensile properties of many kinds of paper.
Test equipment: Mullens bursting tester.

7. Internal tearing resistance of paper. Ref: TAPPI 414-ts-65
Purpose: To determine the average force in grams required to tear a single sheet of paper after the tear has been started.
Test equipment: Elmendorf tearing strength tester.

8. Flexural properties of paper. Ref: TAPPI T451-pm-74
Purpose: To determine the flexing resistance of paper or light weight paperboard and the handling stiffness of paper.
Test equipment: Gurley stiffness tester.

9. Weight per unit area (basis weight or substance) of paper and paper board. Ref: TAPPI T-410-os-68
Purpose: To determine the weight of a given size of paper or paperboard in pounds per ream.
Test equipment: Analytical balance.

10. Thickness (caliper) of paper and paperboard. Ref: TAPPI T-411-os-76
Purpose: To measure the thickness of a single sheet or variations in a single sheet's thickness of paper and paperboard.
Test equipment: TMI micrometer.

In addition to using the above equipment and related test procedures to produce high quality labels, the printer/converter has taken up the challenge of developing new, and improving old substrates. Equipment has been designed and built which will cut labels to tighter tolerances, in some cases to $\pm$ $\frac{1}{128}''$ (Estamat and Wadson individual label cutting dies and Chambon high speed square label cutters). Innovations will naturally continue to evolve in Package Engineering, Quality Control, label vendors, equipment manufacturers, etc.

LABEL PAPER

The selection of the paper for either paper labels or foil labels is governed by a number of factors, i.e.: smoothness, weight, strength, stiffness, cost, density, caliper, behavior in caustic soda solutions, curl characteristics, and uniformity of the product from the paper mill. Paper and foil labels should possess all of the above characteristics in varying degrees. In addition paper labels should possess the requisite wet strength and water penetration characteristics to withstand the varying conditions encountered during labeling and subsequent distribution.

Paper is usually designated by its weight in pounds per ream which consists of 480 or 500 sheets with dimensions of 24″ by 36″. The groundwood paper backing used for aluminum foil labels usually is 30 pound stock, but may be as low as 22 pound. Since stiffness increases very rapidly with a slight change in thickness (caliper) for the same paper, neither weight nor caliper alone can be used as a basis for selection. Actually, physical testing is used to insure that both stiffness and weight, as well as the other requisite properties, remain within specified limits. Paper for paper labels usually consists of 42 to 55 pound stock. The addition of an undercoating or overcoating to the paper label stock usually increases the stiffness of the label to correspond to a weight increase of 5 lbs. The application of inks and surface coating will further increase the paper weight.

ALUMINUM FOIL LABELS

The aluminum surface of foil labels consists of 99.35 percent pure aluminum reduced by repeated rolling to 0.00035″ in thickness. The extremely thin sheet of foil is laminated to paper in a special machine to provide a combination of metallic surface and paper backing of sufficient strength to withstand subsequent printing, inspection, handling, labeling and distribution operations without disfigurement.

The adhesive used to laminate the foil to the paper backing is selected for its ability to maintain the bond of foil and paper when immersed in water. The adhesive for labels on returnable bottles must also permit penetration by caustic soda cleaning solution without forming undesirable by-products in the bottle washer.

The overall caliper of laminated foil label should not exceed 0.0035″ for correct application, but may be as low as 0.00275. Acceptability will depend upon the type of paper used as well as the label component being manufactured, such as neck, shoulder or body labels. Neck foil is usually laminated to a tissue type of paper stock and usually is embossed. Embossing softens the label, reduces the effect of paper grain direction and permits a "wrap around" application.

The printing and cutting of foil labels is a specialized art involving a series of accurately controlled operations. Printing or embossing is performed while the laminated base material is still in roll form or in large sheets. The cutting operation which yields the actual labels is performed by cutting in "stacks" or "lifts" of from 100 to 1,000 sheets, each sheet containing many labels. Any labels having four straight sides are usually straight cut or guillotine cut. Labels having three, five or more sides, or having curves or inside angles, are die cut. For precision die cutting some label manufacturers use individual or single cut dies called Wadson or Estamat. These consist of a series of individual dies on one plate and cut only one sheet of labels at a time. After cutting, the labels are inspected for defects, wrapped, and cartoned for shipping. Printing techniques used for foil labels are derived from paper printing methods, but are modified to accommodate the non-absorbent metal foil surface.

PAPER LABELS

More printing methods are available for printing paper labels than foil labels. Paper requirements and weights have been discussed previously. Neck and shoulder components are not always manufactured from the same weight paper stock. While the average stock for paper labels may weigh between 42 and 55 lbs., heavier stock may also prove satisfactory, provided it is not too highly calendered or compressed, heavily varnished or inked. Thinner translucent stocks may allow the adhesive to show through and even discolor or stain the paper label. A paper of moderate but uniform absorption quality is preferred to either blottery or hard sized stock. Occasionally, spotty sizing, oily printing inks or varnish coatings will affect moisture absorption of the stock. This uneven penetration of moisture may lead to blistering and destroy the adhesive film continuity essential to successful labeling.

METALLIZED PAPER AND LABELS

Vacuum metallizing is a process in which an "ultra-thin" layer of metal is deposited on a substrate to achieve a metallic surface appearance. When the substrate is a film, the layer of metal (usually aluminum) can also impart other specific properties to the material. For films such as polyester, nylon, and oriented polypropylene, metallizing greatly enhances barrier properties, such as oxygen and water vapor transfer rates; for metallized paper, there is no noticeable barrier improvement imparted to the final structure.

So, while metallized films are most often selected for packaging applications based on their abilities to extend usable shelf lives for perishable products, metallized papers find use as decorative wraps and as label stock. The bright, glossy appearance of many metallized papers makes them ideal replacements for paper/foil laminates where gas and moisture barrier are not factors. Their costs are lower, and in many cases, metallized papers are more readily printable than their paper/foil counterparts.

The major problems with metallized papers have been in producing them at reasonable costs while maintaining high-gloss surface characteristics. Additionally, because of the vacuum metallizing process used in the past, a large portion of the original moisture content had to be removed from the paper prior to metallizing. The resulting lack of moisture in the paper created problems downstream in machinability and printability. A new process for producing metallized papers for packaging applications has been developed which has overcome many of these problems.

Metallizing directly on paper will result in a totally unacceptable material from almost any point of view. What results is a paper with a dull gray surface that does not resemble paper/foil laminates at all.

This is due to the rough texture of the surface of paper. Even the most highly finished papers have microscopically rough surfaces. Since the metal deposited in the vacuum metallizing process adheres directly to the surface of the substrate being metallized, and also since the resulting metal coating thickness is on the order of 1 to 2 millionths of an inch, it is not surprising that direct deposition of metal onto paper yields an unacceptable result.

The key to achieving a high-gloss metallized finish on paper is to place a smooth coating on the paper's surface first and then to deposit the metal onto this coating. The coating is a radiation-curable acrylic resin that is gravure-coated onto the paper at about 2 pounds per ream, and it is immediately subjected to an electron-beam curing process that yields a smooth coating.

Besides providing an extremely smooth, metallizable surface, the acrylic coating also eliminates potential problems with retained solvents used in coating the paper. Since metal deposition takes place in a high-vacuum chamber, any residual solvent retained in the paper can be pulled out in the vacuum chamber and contaminate the metallization process.

This contamination potential also holds for moisture retained in the paper. New metallizing equipment incorporates a two-stage design that reduces outgassing problems and results in finished materials retaining sufficient moisture content to be highly machinable.

The two-stage design permits unwinding and degassing of papers at high speed in a relatively high vacuum area while metallizing in a very high vacuum in a separate pressure zone. This means that the web is exposed to the greater vacuum for a short time and the finished metallized paper has higher retained moisture content.

After passing through the metallizing procedure, the web is surface treated with a print-receptive coating. This coating serves a dual purpose. First, it prevents paper-poisoning. This occurrence takes place within a 24-hour period from when a metallized paper is wound on a roll so that the metallized surface is in direct contact with a paper surface. This contact creates a contamination known as paper-poisoning. Once poisoned, the paper is no longer readily printable or able to be laminated.

The second function of the coating is to protect the aluminized surface against scuffing as it is handled and processed for packaging applications.

With the coating in place, the end result of this process is a metallized paper with a high-gloss metallic finish. The finish can be printed and the structure can be laminated to other materials for various packaging applications. Since most of the original moisture content of the paper is retained, the final product is highly machinable and can be embossed for applications such as beer and beverage labels.

VARNISHED LABELS

Varnished labels are essentially similar to plain paper labels but receive a coating of "press varnish" on the decorated surface. The varnish gives a pleasing, glossy surface to the label, making it waterproof except along the edges, but also renders the removal of labels in the soaker more difficult. Very light stock is unsuited for this type of label. Varnished labels have an increased tendency to curl and require more care and attention during application.

LABEL CURL

There are two kinds of label distortion which are often erroneously referred to as label curl. Actually, true label curl results from moisture gain or loss. The other type of label distortion is caused by the mechanical working of the label during embossing or die cutting operations. Foil labels are much more vulnerable to the effects of moisture and mechanical distortion because of the presence of the impermeable aluminum sheet.

When two materials are bonded together, one of which absorbs or loses moisture at a greater rate than the other, the more absorbent component will swell or contract at a greater rate. This swelling or contraction will follow the line of least resistance and a curving or curling effect will result. The paper used for labels usually has a definite grain or direction in which the fibres are longer and relatively unidirectional.

When the more absorbent side of the label loses or attracts moisture, the paper fibres expand or contract primarily in their cross-sectional dimension. This change in one dimension, in the absence of a corresponding change throughout the fibre, results in a curl. The direction of curl is across or at right angles to the direction of the paper grain. A laminated foil label will usually curl with less change in moisture than a paper label because the foil is impervious to moisture and any expansion will occur only in the paper backing. Paper labels, on the other hand will permit some moisture to penetrate on the printed side and, theoretically at least, should attain a more uniform moisture equilibrium throughout. While one would expect that it should be possible to straighten out a curled label by reducing its moisture content, actual experience shows that once the paper fibres have swollen, they may not always return to their original size. Also, if heat is used to remove moisture, the fibres may toughen and remain more fully expanded than if the moisture content were varied more gradually. In the case of the foil label, the metal will tend to hold the curled shape. However, the foil label can be "bent" manually to effect decurling, whereas the paper label does not lend itself well to this procedure.

Another factor which affects the degree of curling is the coarseness of the grain. A coarse or "open" grain label paper will demonstrate less tendency to curl than a fine or "closed" grain paper. On the other hand, the more open-fibred a sheet, the less desirable will be the printed surface. Sometimes a compromise is reached in paper labels by compressing and coating the paper. For foil paper backings, the paper may have to be filled and compressed. In the case of embossing, the process breaks the fibres in the paper and curling is therefore prevented.

LABEL DISTORTION

Label distortion sometimes seems to be identical to label curl but usually does not follow the direction of the grain in the paper. It is not a direct result of the effect of moisture changes, although gain or loss in moisture may aggravate the condition. Distortion due to die-cutting is the most common form. When a label is die-cut, the label edge in contact with the die edge and inside surface tends to be distorted and a small ridge is formed. The material is drawn as in any metal drawing operation. The condition can be minimized by proper die maintenance, but even then some distortion is always present with die-cut labels. The smaller the radius in the label design, the greater is the distortion that can be expected. Foil labels naturally are more susceptible to this distortion than paper labels because of the presence of metal which further reinforces and confines natural label paper fibre behavior. Sometimes, however, die-cutting a foil label, particularly a small neck label component, minimizes or offsets true label curl behavior by resisting the forces of the paper fibres as they expand or contract. Embossing sometimes produces a distortion which may be mistaken for label curl. In registered embossing, where only a selected area of the label is embossed, the non-embossed portion will curl with a change in moisture content while the embossed areas will not. The result is a distorted label.

GRAIN DIRECTION

The consensus among leading manufacturers of labeling machines, labels and adhesives is that the grain direction of paper labels should be horizontal to avoid difficulties in application. A simple method for determining the grain direction of a label stock is to moisten the entire back surface of the label with water and permit it to curl. If the resultant curl is from the top and bottom, parallel with the printing, the label is horizontally grained. Vertically grained paper will have a tendency to "flag" after it has been applied to the container. (See Fig. 10-2.)

LABEL STORAGE

The discussion on label curl and label distortion indicated that the conditions under which a label is stored will influence its condition or appearance by the time it is ready for use. Field experience has established that if long term storage conditions are too dry, the labels become hard, stiff, and perhaps brittle, rendering their subsequent usage difficult. Short term storage is protected by the individually wrapped bundles of labels. Excessively dry paper or foil labels tend to curl backward. It is evident that labels should not be stored in an absence of moist air, nor is it practical to attempt to use storage for "decurling" through dehumidification.

Paper will usually absorb moisture more quickly than it will give it up, particularly with tightly bundled stacks of labels. The objective, then, is to keep the moisture content of the paper in the label "as received", rather than to add or remove moisture from the label during storage. Since variation in the actual humidity in a storage location can directly affect the labels, the best location is not necessarily the driest, but the one where the moisture

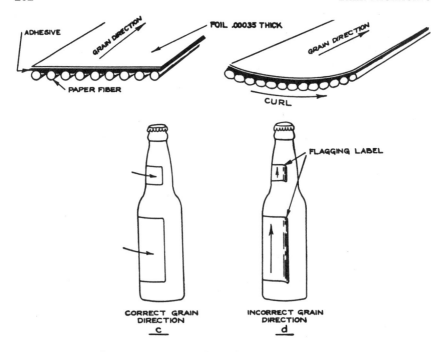

10-2. *Diagram showing correct and incorrect grain direction. (Courtesy Reynolds Metal Co.)*

content remains the most uniform. Whether this will mean different storage locations in cool and warm weather will depend upon the individual case. Ideally, label storage areas should have constant conditions of absolute humidity (moisture per unit volume of air) and a very slow movement of air at all times; in practical terms this means storage in a relatively warm location (75-85°F), and a moderately low relative humidity (40-50%). Relative humidity (% saturation at a given temperature) in potential storage areas may be determined with a sling psychrometer. Most label manufacturers wrap the bundles individually, especially foil labels, to help overcome variations in temperature and moisture.

LABEL HANDLING

In the past, a common problem in the handling of labels was their sticking together. Modern label printing and cutting techniques have been improved to a point where this phenomenon is less frequent. The problem is still prevalent with coated labels which have been stored for a long period of time in piles of great height, and with aluminum neck foil labels. Die cutting may tend to "weld" the edges together, especially on neck foil which is a light weight component. To overcome this sticking tendency, it is advisable to fan or "riffle" a bundle of labels prior to their use. The label component is quite flexible, is normally not curled and so may be forced back and forth without regard to relative foil or paper position. The use of a rubber band or bands is recommended during this procedure to maintain the general block shape of the bundle and also to make handling easier.

In the case of registered debossed foil labels, it has been recommended that heavy weight cardboard be used on the top and bottom of the individual label bundle to more tightly contain this type of label with its irregular label surface. Also, the label bundle may be reduced in size from 1,000 labels to 500 labels to decrease the bulge in the label bundle.

DE-CURLING

Curling of foil labels can be most easily and rapidly corrected by a simple manual manipulation or "working" of the labels. Bottle label components sometimes are too small to permit hammering to "break the grain", a technique sometimes employed to combat label curl in the heavy, tough, prewar foil label. Hammering foil labels is still a good technique. Two methods of curl correction are employed with small body labels, as well as with neck, shoulder and neck foil components: (1) fanning or "working" of the labels; and (2) working against the chest for larger body labels.

Too severe a treatment of paper labels may crease or otherwise disfigure them. Treatment generally is not needed on paper labels.

HANDLING OF LEFT-OVER LABELS

At the end of a day's operation, the partial bundles of labels left in the labeler box should be removed and banded tightly into stacks, with a cardboard between every 200 to 300 labels, and then stored away from the labeling area. The rubber bands on these stacks should be used on the ends of the label bundles only. These labels should be used up at the first opportunity. Label components delivered to the operator for a day's operation may also be stored away from the labeling area to avoid their exposure to the usually humid atmosphere of the bottling shop.

ADHESIVES

CASEIN AND RESIN LABELING.

Today's bottle labeling adhesives are produced in two categories: the casein types and the resin group. Because they are distinctly different in composition, we will discuss them individually.

I. CASEINS

1. Casein based ice-proof adhesive characteristics.
a. Provide maximum ice-water resistance for label retention when bottles are submerged.
b. Will adhere a wide variety of label stock under most adverse conditions.
c. Offer excellent machining characteristics during prolonged periods of operation.
d. Provide easy label removal in soakers with relatively low levels of caustic.
The casein products derive their ice-proof property from their inherent

water insolubility. Casein granules, soaked in water alone, will simply swell up and finally degrade. But with the addition of a solubilizing agent such as aqueous ammonia, they dissolve into a complete solution rather quickly. To this solution are added insolubilizers, tackifiers, preservatives and other stabilizing chemicals to provide the finished adhesive.

Chemists have a great variety of tackifiers to select from and this provides flexibility for formulations. Label adhesive manufacturers can compound a casein label glue to meet virtually any requirement on any labeler, regardless of speed or label stock. Realistically, however, adhesives have limitations. The following outline will help attain the high performance built into adhesives.

2. Adhesive operating temperature.

Best performance is attained when the adhesive is in a temperature range of 70°F to 90°F. Moderate temperature variations, perhaps 10°F in either direction will not have a pronounced effect on labeling, but glue temperatures below 60°F or higher than 100°F will generally produce problems at the labeler.

Cold adhesive will have a viscosity change inversely proportional to the temperature. A viscosity increase causes difficulty in machining at the labelers and also produces a severe tack loss within the adhesive. If the adhesive has not actually frozen, however, the conditions are reversible as the glue regains heat. Conversely, high temperatures cause rapid thinning of the glue with resultant stringing of the adhesive. Additionally, the adhesive will set extremely fast, causing torn labels and periodic double labeling.

The adhesive storage area should be in an area with ambient temperatures in the same range as the desired operating temperature of the adhesive. Remember: adhesive temperature is extremely important in attaining good labeling results.

3. Aerated adhesive.

When bottle flow to the labeler is interrupted because of problems elsewhere in the packaging department the labelers are usually allowed to idle with glue rollers continuing to run in the pots, or glue supply to vertical rollers continuing. This generally produces large amounts of entrapped air within the adhesive causing the product to take on a gray-white appearance with frothy foam present. Flagging levels will almost certainly result because of the loss of tack. It is vitally important to insure fresh adhesive at the labeler after a prolonged period of down time or labeler idling.

4. Controlled glue application.

Present day caseins are designed to provide optimum labeling when applied in thin films. Excessive glue application is as detrimental to good labeling as is lack of adhesive. Many operators, not really wanting to fault the adhesive, will increase the amount applied, compounding the problem. Excessive glue will dramatically retard the set time, and labels will "swim" and squirm off as the bottles compress on the conveyor enroute to the case packer. Additionally, this slow drying time will cause stiff or "springy" label stock to flag.

A proper glue film on the roll will measure between .003 and .005 inches. Film thickness gauges are available at any scientific supply house, but lacking a gauge, a recommended procedure is to cut the glue film down until flagging does occur and then slowly increase the glue supply until all edges of the label are snug.

Proper glue film thickness is absolutely essential to proper labeling.

5. Adhesive storage life.

Over-age label glue can be a source of problems. Most casein-based adhesives are prone to chemical change after 90 days after which the viscosity can vary sharply and usually a pronounced thinning occurs. So it is important to know your supplier's code-date system. The viscosity change is a gradual process, and some caseins are still usable after six months from date of manufacture. Proper stock rotation is the obvious answer to preclude problems of this nature.

II. RESIN BASED ICE-PROOF ADHESIVE.

The caseins, because of their great problem-solving capability, are not likely to disappear from the labeling scene, but the newer resin ice-proofs are rapidly becoming popular.

1. Resin ice-proof eliminates casein completely from the formula and uses starch or dextrine in its place. This immediate cost saving has made them attractive to the brewing industry; but there are some trade-offs. Consider these basic properties of resin ice-proofs:

a. Provide minimal ice-water resistance when bottles are submerged.

b. Slower setting speed but compensate with aggressive wet tack.

c. Give excellent machining characteristics with less glue.

d. Label removal on returnable bottles is more difficult as compared to casein and may require higher caustic strengths in the soaker at higher temperatures.

These starch based products are solubilized in water using aqueous ammonia in similar fashion as the caseins. Solution is attained more quickly, however, and the adhesives require far less cooking time. Resin tackifiers are added along with the usual stabilizers and antioxidants to complete the formula.

2. Operating temperature.

Unlike caseins, the resin ice-proofs are not highly temperature sensitive. They are usable within a temperature range of from 50°F to 110°F with almost unnoticeable changes in performance. Temperature viscosity relationship is quite flat, illustrating this relative thermal stability. While this feature minimizes the need for extra care in storage, it is recommended that all label adhesives be stored in heated areas.

3. Aerated adhesive.

Resin ice-proofs are as susceptible to aeration problems as are the caseins and perhaps they generate just a bit more incidental entrapped air. They will perform well for longer periods with higher foam content than will the caseins. Simple attention to preventing the glue from idling for prolonged periods of down time will prevent most aeration problems and avoid loss of tack.

4. Controlled glue application.

An unexpected bonus comes with the transition to resin ice-proofs. These products provide better mileage than do caseins. Glue film thickness should be very thin, on the order of .003 to .005 inch. Even slight excesses, beyond the amount required to hold the label, will substantially slow the drying time and cause label squirm and out-of-register labeling. These products do dry more slowly than casein, but they exhibit very aggressive wet tack, which locks the label in place until fiber tear develops. Lacking a film thickness gauge, use the earlier described technique for obtaining the proper amount of applied adhesive.

Remember: the more you use, the more you lose—keep it thin.

5. Adhesive storage life.

Resin ice-proofs offer a real advantage in storage stability. They are not subject to the chemical changes that occur in casein products and, therefore, the viscosity tends to remain very constant for longer periods of time. Good business practice always dictates the need for regular stock rotation on all raw materials and that remains true for the resin ice-proofs. However, it is entirely possible that a resin product six to nine months old may perform about as well as fresh stock. Many glue suppliers incorporate a seasonal change in formulation at least twice a year and some change as often as four times a year. A good practice is to use the label glue as received from the manufacturer and not attempt to use a dilutant in the bottle shop.

LABELERS

ROTARY HIGH SPEED LABELERS

Methods of Labeling

Labeling methods most commonly utilized in the beverage production industry can be described as follows:

Glued pallets with a thin film of glue applied remove the labels out of the magazine. This action includes a simultaneous gluing of the back side of the label. Best results in the picking of the labels can only be achieved by optimum contact between the glued pallet and the first label in the stack. After its removal, the label sticks on the glued area of the pallet. This procedure is illustrated in Figure 10-3. Over 90% of bottle labeling machines on the market work on this principle.

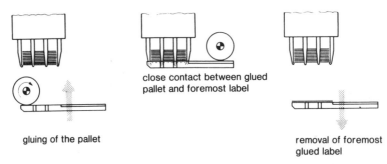

close contact between glued
pallet and foremost label

gluing of the pallet

removal of foremost
glued label

10-3. Simplified presentation of label removal in an early labeling device. (Courtesy KRONES, INC.)

Modern machines differ from earlier models in layout, design of components and in some operational motions. To meet the needs of higher operating speeds, intermittent movements were gradually replaced by a harmonic and smooth flow of operations. Figures 10-4 through 10-6 illustrate more than 25

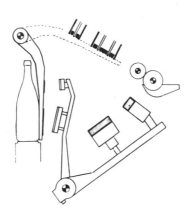

10-4. Early example of an intermittent labeling device with low output rate. (Courtesy KRONES, INC.)

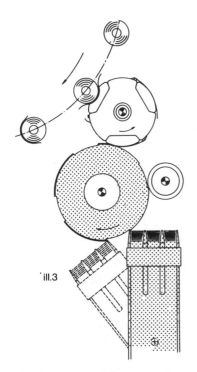

ill.3

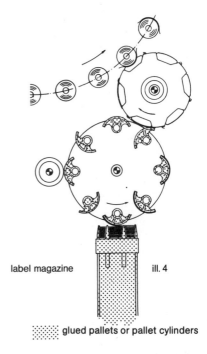

label magazine   ill. 4

▒▒▒ glued pallets or pallet cylinders

10-5. Continuous labeling with automatic oscillating device with low to medium output. (Courtesy KRONES, INC.)

10-6. Rotary high speed labeling unit. Oscillating glued pallets pick up labels from the stationary label magazines with operating speeds in excess of 1165 bpm. (Courtesy KRONES, INC.)

years of advancement and show the potential increase in operational efficiency of very old basic principles.

To obtain a higher operating speed, the centre of gravity of moving parts had to be close to the pivot point, thus eliminating large reverse movements. After these requirements and several others had been met, a labeling unit (Fig. 10-6) was realized that had a reserve capacity of 40% over design output.

Maximum operational efficiency in labeling machines is not only based on the functional principles of the labeling device but on the bottle flow speed as well. The ultimate success of any labeling machine also depends on the designer's strategy that takes maximum label length into account. In many cases, maximum label length is smaller than the bottle pitch, that is, the distance between the incoming bottles. However, the longer the distance between the incoming bottles within the labeling unit, the lower the output per unit of time at constant bottle flow speed. For the designer this means that he has to analyze the effect of the maximum possible speed of bottles at the infeed and discharge sides of the machine. In order to slow down discharge bottle speed, the distance between the bottles was kept as small as possible, i.e., the smallest possible bottle pitch.

If the interdependence between bottle pitch and maximum possible label length could not have been corrected by machine design, then a satisfactory operation could only have been achieved by using small labels; or vice versa, when using large labels, one would have to put up with low speeds. (See Figs. 10-7 and 8.) It is feasible, through a well-planned design, to coordinate bottle pitch and label length, and to obtain optimum results by using pallets that can handle a label length exceeding the bottle pitch. See Fig. 10-9.

Experience has shown that it is useful to be aware of some facts about the maximum label length that can be handled. To illustrate this point using some figures, we have body labels on bottles of which 70% are longer than (85 mm) 3.4", 75% are longer than (90 mm) 3.6", and some exceed a length of (90 mm) 3.6". Quite a few labeling systems, commonly in use, can handle extreme label lengths but have the disadvantage of large gaps between incoming bottles, which require a high bottle flow speed with potential for breakage or other difficulties. This problem can be rectified by a labeling machine that can handle a maximum label length at a minimum bottle pitch.

Gluing Devices

Good gluing of the labels is one of the most important conditions for satisfactory results and is essential for a smooth removal of the labels from the label magazine. The glue film, kept as thin as possible, has to be such that the labels have sufficient adhesive strength and do not peel off from unglued peripheral areas nor too thick in order to prevent "floating" or "swimming" of the labels. The so-called off-set effect is the decisive factor for the formation of the glue film. It consists of a glue transfer from a glued surface onto an unglued surface whereby a residual glue film still adheres to the glued surface. The thickness of the transferred glue film and that of the residual glue film mostly correspond to the relation of the two rotating surfaces. (See Fig. 10-16.)

There are several different methods and gluing devices for the transfer of the glue film onto the backs of labels. In bottle labeling the usual way is by means of glue cylinders and glue pallets.

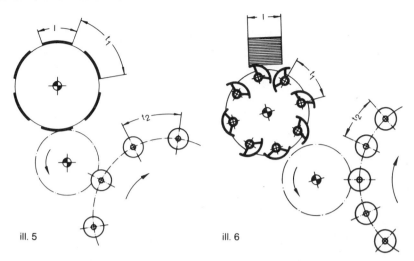

ill. 5   ill. 6

10-7. *Many labeling systems that use oscillating or stationary label magazines can handle a maximum label length that is longer than the bottle pitch, i.e. the distance between incoming bottles, but this entails a faster bottle conveyance and its associated problems. (KRONES, INC.)*

10-8. *The above system used by Krones permits using labels with the same maximum length with reduced pitch, thus permitting lower bottle speed. (Courtesy KRONES, INC.)*

10-9. *A high speed labeling station with stationary label magazine in an enclosed oil bath. (Courtesy KRONES, INC.)*

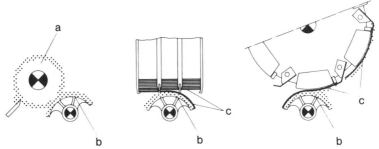

10-10. The glue roller (a) transfers a portion of the glue onto the pallet (b) which, in turn, passes the glue film partially onto the label (c). (Courtesy KRONES, INC.)

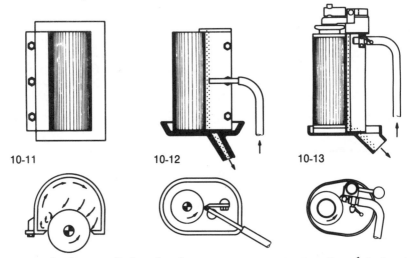

10-11.   10-12.   10-13.

10-11. Cylinder installed in the glue container: constant motion deteriorates glue quality. (Courtesy KRONES, INC.)

10-12. Glue roller separated from glue container; glue supply positioned in the middle roller height so that glue circulation in the upper region of roller is insufficient. (Courtesy KRONES, INC.)

10-13. Glue roller separated from glue container. Glue supply is in upper region of roller for better glue circulation. (Courtesy KRONES, INC.)

Figs. 10-11 and 10-14 give a summary of these variables. Research in this field was determined by the properties of the different label adhesives, especially for high speed operation. Earlier models having the glue roller rotating in a glue container soon became obsolete (Fig. 10-11). The rotating cylinder agitated the entire contents of the glue container, causing, even at low or medium speed, an undue temperature rise by internal friction. This rise of temperature and permanent circulation constantly extract moisture from the adhesive. Workability and cohesion of the glue therefore changed with resultant adhesive tack loss.

The answer to that problem was to separate glue roller and glue container. The glue roller is fed by a glue pump, and the excess glue flows back into the glue container (Figs. 10-12 and 10-13). Piston pumps, as shown in Fig. 10-15, should be given preference to geared pumps, since these ensure minimum stress and agitation on the adhesive. Infeed of the glue supply at the top of the cylinder has also proved more advantageous than an inlet in the center. This resulted in glue distribution on the entire roller surface without the formation of "dead areas" which deteriorates glue consistency, adhesive power and adhesive tack.

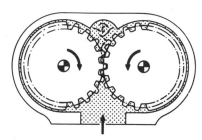

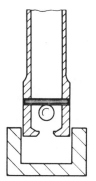

10-14 (left). Gear pump causes heavy strain on adhesive. Inadequate output compared to volume in motion. (Courtesy KRONES, INC.)

10-15 (right). Minimum "internal glue friction" with KRONES Unipump. (Courtesy KRONES, INC.)

A separate glue container has other advantages. At times it might be necessary to heat the label adhesive before use. For example: Working results from casein glue used at low temperatures are unsatisfactory, but this glue may be heated by means of the built-in, indirectly operating heating device or drum jacket warmer. A thermostat ensures maintenance of the optimum operating temperature (24°C-28°C or 75°-82°F). In addition, the large capacity glue container enables the returning excess glue to satisfactorily settle and requires longer intervals between the refilling.

The advantages of controlling glue temperatures should be noted. Raising the temperature of labeling adhesives results in a reduction in glue consumption. For example, by raising the operating temperature from 20°C to 26°C (68°F to 78°F), a saving in glue consumption of up to 30% can be obtained. Such reductions in consumption have been noted particularly during winter months when the ambient temperature in the bottling shop falls to below 20°C (68°F) and glue viscosity increases. Higher viscosity results in a thicker glue film than necessary being applied, and leads to excessive consumption. Additionally, if the glue operating temperature drops too low, serious production difficulties can result, for example, the labels may be torn when being removed from the glue pallets and the labels "swim" long after application.

In practice it is also important that the thickness of the glue film on the

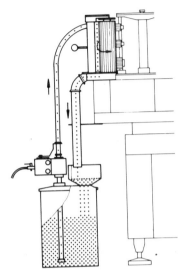

10-16. Label gluing station. Glue removal from container by means of a glue Unipump unit giving infinitely variable output control to permit maximum operational efficiency. (Courtesy KRONES, INC.)

glue roller be easily and yet precisely controlled. This is achieved with an easily removable glue scraper. Ease in removing is necessary when a label sticks to the glue roller.

For satisfactory gluing results it is essential to consider the appropriate glue pattern. Good functioning should be the first priority but economics should also be considered.

Whether it is advisable to apply the glue onto the entire label surface or any other glue pattern, depends on operational conditions and on the label paper quality used. Fully glued labels tend to "skid", when applied to wet surfaces; whereas, a striped pattern guarantees a tight fit. This can be attributed to the fact that the label paper mostly absorbs the water on the bottles. With stiff labels it is important to thoroughly apply the adhesive on both label vertical edges and to give sufficient wiping-on time and pressure. Then the adhesive strength will withstand the opposing paper strain and the labels will not "flag". If hot or warm bottles are to be labeled with foil or varnished labels, one has to watch the pallet glue pattern very closely to prevent bulges and wrinkles. The reason for this adverse effect is that the label paper contracts as long as the adhesive allows. Under normal or humid climatic conditions the paper fibres expand. As the label does not stick to the bottle on unglued areas, it expands and, therefore, shows bulges. In case of foil and varnished labels, these bulges also appear on bottles that are cold when labeled.

If the label paper used and bottle system are not compatible, damaged labels and unsatisfactory bottle labeling will be the result. In principle, one should choose to have the unglued areas small and enlarge them later as experience dictates. Fig. 10-17 shows some glue patterns which are currently in use.

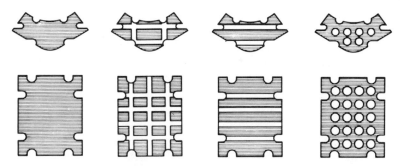

10-17. A small selection of common "glue patterns" on labels. (Courtesy KRONES, INC.)

Glue consumption per square inch of label area is an interesting point with high speed labeling. It depends on the area to be glued, thickness of the glue film and specific properties of the adhesive type being used. The yield of different glue types varies. For labels for bottles with relief surfaces, a thicker glue film is required. When setting the glue film thickness it should be noted that different glue types with the same glue scraper setting result in different film thickness at high or low operating speed. The glue film should always be as thin as possible to prevent excess glue deposit on the gripper cylinder components or the on-rolling device.

Under normal conditions, the glue thickness lies approximately between 0.003" and 0.005". In practice, however, it has been shown that different label material and glue types result in varying thicknesses of glue film.

Even if bottles and labels have optimum conditions, glue consumption can nevertheless be extremely high if the glue type chosen cannot be applied as thinly as required, or if a worn glue roller or excessive gap between glue roller and glue pallet exists. In both cases glue is wasted by being flung around. Fig. 10-19 shows excessive glue consumption due to glue type or worn glue rollers. The glue film, when separated between glue roller and glue pallet, adheres neither to the glue roller nor to the pallet, but is flung away. Glue spots on the label stack make labels stick together in the label stacks and cause severe problems. On the other hand, Fig. 10-18 shows a neat separation without any glue wasted.

Hot Melt Adhesive Application.

The glue application methods described earlier have related predominantly to the handling of cold, (usually) water-soluble labeling adhesives. However, the use of hot melt (sometimes called fusion adhesives) glues requires very different methods of glue application. Hot melt adhesives are synthetic resins which, dependent upon type and individual application, are fed to the glue application device in granules, pallets, or solid blocks. Their application temperatures range between (120°C and 170°C) 248°F and 338°F and are dependent upon the type of adhesive. The viscosity of the molton hot melt adhesive is inversely dependent upon its temperature. For example, increasing the processing temperature by 10°C (50°F) can reduce the viscosity of the molten adhesive by between 20% and 40%.

In practice, temperature differentials of between 10°C and 20°C (50°F

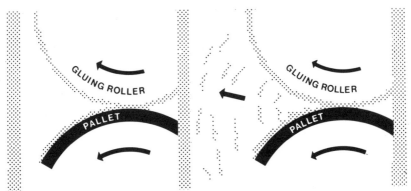

10-18. *Normal neat separation without glue wastage. (Courtesy KRONES, INC.)*

10-19. *Glue wastage due to roller wear or excessive gap between roller and pallet. (Courtesy KRONES, INC.)*

and 69°F) can often occur between the melting reservoir and the glue application roller. Therefore the glue rollers themselves must be heated in order to accurately control the hot melt adhesive temperature and viscosity to guarantee an efficient operation. Hot melt applicators require several temperature regulators and thermometers to maintain the correct temperature and viscosity of the molten adhesive.

Label Transfer Onto Containers to be Labeled.

High-speed labeling stations usually transfer the glued labels onto the containers by means of gripper cylinders. The labels adhering to the pallets are removed by the gripper fingers and are then transferred to the moving bottles. The body label transfer occurs when containers pass and are smoothly pushed into the sponge section of the gripper cylinders. (see 10-20a & 20b) For labels to be applied to the slender part of the bottle, i.e., bottle shoulder or bottle neck, the sponged gripper cylinder has to be specially designed. The sponge pads in the gripper cylinder are moved out by cams in order to make contact with the bottle. This process is in some cases augmented by an air blast from nozzles built into the gripper cylinders.

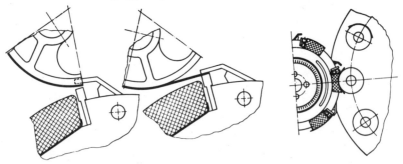

10-20a. *The process of label removal from a pallet by means of gripper fingers. 20b. Transfer of a label onto a bottle. (Courtesy KRONES, INC.)*

Coordination between gripper cylinder and the containers clamped on the bottle table is necessary for satisfactory label alignment. In order to eliminate misalignment, containers are positively clamped between the bottle plates and centering bells. Gripper cylinders and the complete labeling station are adjustable in their position relative to the bottle table.

The introduction of adjustable cross-sledges on label stations has made an improvement in label alignment. The cross-sledge allows a tangential and a radial adjustment of the labeling station relative to the bottle table. The radial adjustment enables the gripper cylinders to be precisely adjusted to any bottle size. The use of separate drives for gripper cylinders for body and shoulder labels becomes unnecessary due to the adjustable cross sledge.

Conveying of Container through the Labeling Machine.

In-line machines are used for body labeling only but rotary type machines, however, are more flexible.

With rotary type machines, the containers to be labeled are transferred from the infeed worm to the infeed star wheel. From there they reach the bottle plates of the bottle table. Then centering bells firmly position them against the bottle rotary plates. After the transfer of body and shoulder labels, the containers are rotated by 90° and pass a brushing and onrolling station with sponge rollers, brushes, etc., to ensure a positive contact between label and container.

After the labels have been firmly pressed onto the containers, they are discharged via the discharge star wheel onto the discharge conveyor. When both front and back labels are applied, the bottles turn a further 90° after the front label application so that the back of the bottle faces the back label gripper cylinder (i.e. a total rotation of 180°). After application of back labels the containers are again turned 90°. Following this, the sequence of operations is identical to that for front labels only. These machines are suitable for labeling of cylindrical, flask, rectangular and square bottles, etc.

With all high-speed labeling stations the required rotary motion of the bottle plates is controlled by a cam which runs in an enclosed oil bath. This ensures an optimum wear-resistance, a permanent, precise alignment of labels and also helps reduce the machine noise level.

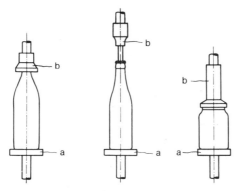

10-21. In rotary type labeling machines bottles are securely clamped between bottle plates (a) and centering bells (b). (Courtesy KRONES, INC.)

The next section of the labeler is the onrolling station whose main function is to give the best possible adhesion by smoothing out the irregularities of the glue film applied to the labels. This is achieved by brushing, rolling and thoroughly wiping the labels onto the containers. Brushes, sponges and rollers perform this duty. Additional tightening is obtained through the onrolling station. With stiffer labels and especially foil labels the onrolling process has to be of high duty.

If the onrolling facilities of the bottle table unit are not sufficient to satisfactorily wipe down the labels, some labelers can be fitted with an after-roll or brushing station, located after the discharge starwheel. This unit consists of several rotating onroll belts or brushes on one side of the unit and flexible, soft sponge pads on the opposite side. Bottles passing through this station turn approximately 2 - 4 times dependent on bottle diameter and length of the onrolling station.

Bottle Conveying before Labeling.

Bottle feed and discharge are two essential factors in the efficient operation of a labeling machine. The infeed of containers to be labeled has to be smooth and free of gaps between containers. After labeling, the bottle should be smoothly conveyed to the case packer without label damage.

Within the labeler itself, an efficient bottle flow is of vital importance. Initially, bottles accumulate on the infeed conveyor. Here, bottles may jam if there are large gaps or bottle flow to the machine may be interrupted, e.g., due to a down bottle. Dependent upon type and quality of bottles, specific limits as to impact speed are given (0.5m/sec). Poor quality bottles might create bottle breakage and the resultant conveying problems. This is especially troublesome with large back-ups at the infeed or discharge of the machine or when single bottles enter.

If we proceed from an impact speed of 0.5 m/sec. it would be possible to convey bottles—with a labeler output rate of 300 bottles per minute—in a single line. An output rate of 400 bottles per minute, however, would demand a double line infeed, and a high speed labeling machine has to have a bottle infeed of several lanes which are then combined into a single lane several feet before the labeler.

Combining is not subject to exact control. In most cases, the arrangement of the bottles into one single lane in the cone-shaped bottle guides is a random operation. To avoid jams before labeling, care should be taken in the design of bottle combiners. To prevent jams occurring in the combiners, rollers, vibrators or a combination of these devices are used. Temporary combiner jams create temporary gaps in the single line of bottles. Each time a jam clears itself, the following bottles "shoot" towards those bottles conveyed at normal speed. This means an extremely high impact shock at contact creating high internal pressure and possible breakage. The mechanical stress on bottles increases with the degree of density of flow passing through the combiner and also varies with the amount of lubrication added to the chains.

Bottle combining devices whose angled guide rails converge at an angle of 6° or less are most effective. If there is insufficient space ahead of a labeling machine for in-line combining, this can be achieved around a 90° arc. In order to avoid unacceptable increases in noise levels when combining at high

10-22. *Bottle infeed and discharge unit of a rotary high speed unit designed to reduce bottle damage and noise levels to a minimum. Infeed and discharge stars are made of flexible polyurethane to prevent bottle breakage even with extreme diameter tolerances. In full operation the noise level of the unit has been reduced to 7 dB(A). (Courtesy KRONES, INC.)*

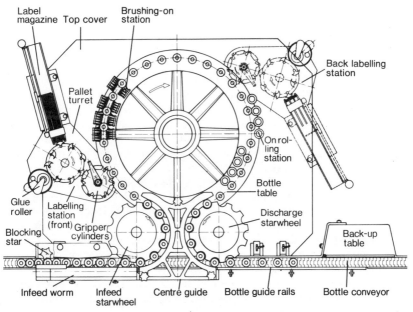

10-23. *The rotary system, from blocking star via infeed, bottle tables, discharge starwheel to bottle conveyor, is shown above. (Courtesy KRONES, INC.)*

speeds (655 BPM), it is essential to ensure a smooth, jam-free combining. This is achieved by arranging the conveyor guide rails at a very slight angle, between 2 and 3 degrees.

Experience has shown that bottle breakage before the labeler can be largely reduced but not totally eliminated. The higher the operational speed of the labeler, the more trouble that can be expected at the infeed. Jams can be caused by down bottles, bottles without necks, bottle breakage and, with labeler equipped with foilers, bottles without caps.

Conveyors within the labeler are equipped on both sides with functional devices, such as labeling station brushes, pressing on rollers etc. This makes it difficult to discharge glass fragments or bottles without necks from the system without machine damage. Even with the utmost care, the operators simply cannot detect every problem bottle.

Most high-speed labelers are equipped with a special spoked bottle table, which facilitates the discharge of broken bottles. Since this construction is not feasible for all machine types, care should be taken not to convey broken bottles from one unit to the next. Broken and fallen bottles must be removed at certain locations to reduce downtime.

High-speed labeling machines should have several additional devices. These are designed to reduce operators' duties and to contribute to a trouble-free operation of the bottling line.

An electronic gap-sensing device before the bottle infeed stops the labeler:

a. If a broken bottle bottom or similar glass breakage is conveyed between the line of bottles.
b. if the bottle infeed before the labeler is blocked or the bottle conveyor is not functioning properly.
c. if a bottle neck is broken.
d. if a bottle arrives without crown.
e. if a bottle arrives in a down position.

Besides the above mentioned problems which can be eliminated by the gap sensor, there are others. For example, over height bottles which break at the bottle infeed, or when bottles are tilted on glass fragments and, therefore, exceed the height limit for which the machine is adjusted. A height indicator installed before the gap sensor will prevent passage or knockdown of bottles which are too high or bottles riding on glass breakage. Then the electronic gap sensor will stop the machine in time.

Normally, bottle infeed is by means of the infeed worm. Its function is to ensure the correct bottle pitch. For a satisfactory infeed into the worm all gaps must be eliminated. Therefore, the bottle flow is accelerated before bottles enter the infeed worm. Single bottles entering the infeed worm at high operational speed may cause stoppages. Therefore, machines are equipped with a bottle stop star to prevent this. It is operated either manually or automatically dependent upon the operational speed. Even with all these precautions bottles may still break within the labeler. Infeed and discharge star wheels are designed so that bottles broken between the bottle conveyor and the bottle table can be discharged. Bottles which break only in the bottle table area can be removed towards the center or outwards. The labeling station itself is equipped with strong protective devices which prevent damage, particularly to the gripper cylinders. Sponge sections are frequently installed in the infeed and/or discharge stars to better control the bottle.

Individual World Tandem Labeler Unit Infeed Side.

World Tandem heads can be set up in series of one to fourteen or more depending upon production needs. Each unit operates independently of the other units.

Multi-Unit Conveyor System—Infeed Conveyor.

The multi-unit conveyor is designed to divide the bottles into a single line at each labeling unit. Bottles are fed onto the slow moving feed conveyor in a mixed pattern allowing them to utilize the full width of the 4″ and 7½″ wide chain. A spring loaded deflector equipped with an air snubbing device located ahead of the infeed to each unit crowds the conveyor filled bottles toward the inside rail keeping the infeed of each labeler full of bottles. When the infeed is full to capacity, the extra bottles bypass and are guided into the next labeling unit by another spring loaded deflector. Each labeling unit is kept full of bottles with the last unit partially full.

On the outside edge to the 4″ and 7½″ feed conveyor is another 4″ bottle return conveyor. The purpose of this conveyor is to return all excess bottles from the last labeler up to the infeed end.

The last two bottle deflectors can be equipped with an electric switch or air valve. These deflectors can be made to automatically stop the infeed conveyor feeding the multi-unit conveyor to prevent overcrowding. The adjustable spring loaded gates should be located to allow one bottle to pass freely without deflecting. A suggested opening would be the bottle diameter plus ⅛″ to 3⁄16″ clearance. Deflectors with the electrical switch or the air valve should be adjusted so they would operate the automatic controls when they are opened up to 1½ times the bottle diameter.

Some units are equipped with modulated speed controls and in addition individual heads are equipped with individual variable speed drives which slow the labelers down to slow speed when no bottles are being labeled. In some operations, the Johnson mechanical arm clutches have been replaced by Horton air clutches. This has reduced maintenance considerably and resulted in a better labeler operation.

Discharge Conveyor

The discharge conveyor is designed to collect the bottles discharged from each labeling unit and convey them to the packer. Best results are obtained if the connecting conveyor is set less than 3 bottles wide between the guide rails allowing the use of the full width of conveyor and the discharge end of the labeler conveyor. Soap lubrication for conveyor chains carrying the labeled bottles to the case packer has to be watched carefully as the lube can ride up on the labeled bottles, destroying the labels.

The conveyor guide rails should be set to contact the labeled bottle above and below the labels to prevent marring & scuffing.

Labeler Operation

Infeed Spacing Star Wheel and Infeed Turnstile Wheel.

These two wheels serve two primary purposes. First—to regulate the flow of bottles into the labeler unit, and second—to index the bottles with the turntable and labeler. The infeed starwheel also holds back bottles awaiting labeler entrance. The bottles move into the eight pockets of the starwheel and then are advanced into the infeed turnstile wheel. Through a step in the gearing, the turnstile wheel travels eight revolutions to every three revolutions of the starwheel. This increased speed is necessary to match the speed of the turntable, and allows a bottle to be seated on the turntable, secured in the bottle rest, with a minimum of movement and contact.

The infeed spacing wheel is equipped with a ball and socket clutch. If a bottle on the feed conveyor should jam on one of the eight points of the wheel, the clutch will disengage with a slight reverse motion allowing the bottle to reposition itself in either adjoining pocket.

A brake shoe in the clutch mechanism delays the forward motion of the wheel until the clutch re-engages and then bottle proceeds in normal passage through the labeler. Oversize bottles, which could seriously harm the labeling mechanism, are thus restricted from passing through the spacing wheel; they jam at the wheel and the clutch continues to slip until the bottle is removed. The infeed turnstile is directly driven and should require no adjustment. Bottle stops are needed at individual heads. Using a down bottle as a stopper wears out the clutch prematurely.

The Labeling Operation

The label station on each labeling unit consists of those parts that are concerned with label application. In the sequence of operation, they are:

a. Label control mechanism and spring guide fingers. (no bottle—no label latch)

The label control mechanism operates so as to prevent delivery of the label when there is no bottle to receive it by preventing the label pickers from entering the label holder. The spring guide fingers exert drag on the bottle and keep it seated centrally in the bottle back rest or fill-in-piece immediately before label application.

In order to reduce metal to glass contact, these parts are now recommended to be of "soft handling" plastic or plastic coated material.

b. Bottle rests and filling-in-piece.

These parts furnish support for the bottle while it travels on the turntable, also called bottle back rests.

The five bottle rests with fill-in-pieces locate and support the bottles through the labeling and wiping operation to the discharge station. The back rest is designed for specific diameter bottles. When smaller diameter bottles are labeled, a fill-in-piece is used. In all cases the bottle must be centered within two inches of the turntable's finished edge. This setting is required so the bottle will pass through the center of the label pickers.

c. Label pickers.

The pickers transfer the label from the label holder to the bottle and simultaneously apply an even film of adhesive to the label. The pickers are made of aluminum alloy. Because they are the most important labeler component, they must be perfectly flat and parallel to each other at all operating times.

The angle 5½° to which the pickers are set is the factory standard and is the starting point of adjustment. As the pickers hang down, at the low point of swing, label transfer position, the glue surface of the pickers must be 5½° ahead of the vertical. In time, the picker cam on the main shaft will wear and require angle adjustments. On some special setups, the picker angle may be set at other settings to satisfy special label sizes on bottle designs. Penetration of the label pickers into the label box prongs should be $\frac{3}{16}''$.

Picker surfaces should be wiped frequently, and cleaned thoroughly, if a stoppage of more than 15 minutes is expected.

Frequently, pickers and glue transfer roller segments begin to wear a groove in one another, particularly when label size changes employ different picker sets, and glue transfer rollers are not changed as well. This practice results in an inadequate adhesive coverage for one picker set, and may go unnoticed until "flagging" labels appear. (Generally, a $\frac{5}{8}$ inch glue pattern on the body label and a $\frac{3}{8}$ inch glue pattern on the neck label is adequate.)

d. Gripfingers.

The gripfingers transfer the label from the pickers and hold the label securely on the bottle until such time as it is wiped on the bottle, and also holds the bottle against the bottle back rest or fill-in-piece until its discharge. To accomplish this, the finger must meet the center of the bottle.

The gripfinger in its final position should be tight enough against the bottle, so that an unglued neck or body label cannot be removed without tearing. All too frequently, the pressure area of a grip finger is reduced to single point of contact. This condition may result in small tears or "cocked" labels. Gripfingers should conform to bottle surface contour just as closely as the label which they are holding.

Rubber tipped gripfingers give a more positive operation, but become fouled with adhesive and "throw" bottles and therefore should be cleaned regularly.

Convex shaped gripfinger rubber pads seem to do a better job of releasing the labeled bottle at the discharge grippers than the concave shaped gripfinger. Another problem may result from weakened or broken springs (not always apparent) which will tear or "cock" labels. An occasional check of each gripfinger as it contacts the bottle, making certain that it meets the center of the bottle, will eliminate the possibility of crooked labels.

e. Picker opening device.

Immediately after the label is secured on the bottle by the gripfingers, the pickers spread open to allow the bottle to move through without striking them. This device controls that adjustment.

f. Transfer roller.

This rubber roller transfers glue from the glue box to the face of the pickers. The transfer roller must spread a uniform film of glue over the surface of both pickers. In order to do this, it must contact the glue roller in the glue box, so as to obtain an even coating of glue. Adjustments can be made to lessen or increase the pressure of the transfer roller on the pickers. The rubber transfer roller should be milled or cut out, so that it conforms to the shape of the pickers that are being used. This is important in that it keeps the glue application on the pickers to a minimum and reduces the amount of label glue that builds up on the back of the pickers. It also reduces the amount of wear on the transfer rollers where it extends over the picker fingers.

g. Glue box assembly.

This assembly consists principally of a chain driven brass roller, a glue scraper or wiper knife and a cast bronze box. The glue box is used to store a reservoir of label adhesive glue. The glue roller revolving in the box is constantly coated with a film of label adhesive, the thickness of which is determined by the adjustment of the steel scraper. Some plants groove the brass glue roller with a groove 0.008 deep and $\frac{1}{16}$ inch apart. This imparts a smooth even film on the brass roller to be picked up by the rubber glue transfer roller. Also spiral grooves in the glue roller reduces the possibility of the label adhesive to harden and collect under the wiper knife and reduce uniform film thickness. A good glue film on the brass roller should range between 0.003 and 0.005 inch.

During the cleaning, care must be taken not to score the brass roll or steel scraper. These two parts are responsible for uniform glue thickness, and if marked or similarly damaged, will not allow the close adjustment necessary to provide good gluing. Cleaning-In-Place (CIP) has been introduced on many machines so that the glue pot, roller or wiper knife are not removed. As a precautionary measure, always grease both bushings on each glue roller immediately after washing.

For a successful operation, the scraper wiper blades should be clean, true and reground regularly. Also the brass glue roller must be resurfaced and squared at the same time as the scraper blade. At the same time the bushings of the glue roller and the glue transfer roller shaft should be inspected for looseness and replaced when worn. A total run out of 0.002 on the brass glue roller bearings or less has proved to be satisfactory. The scraper blade is generally set for 0.003" - 0.005" away from the glue roller.

h. Label holder.

A number of brass prongs, mounted on adjustable plates, make up your label holder. Its function is to hold labels and easily release them to the picker.

The two adjustments which can be made on the label holder concern the label prongs and the castings to which they are attached. The holder must be snug against the stop pins, so that the two latches will engage, thus preventing it from sliding out of position.

After placing the labels in the holder, adjust the prongs, so that the label pack is snug within the prongs, but not so snug as to prevent the stack from riding up and down in the label box with each stroke of the pickers. A label box prong of 45 degrees will operate well with a foil label and paper labels will also operate satisfactorily with this degree of prong angle.

Drop the label follower plate down on the label stack. Be certain that the follower plate is the correct shape and just slightly smaller in size. It too must ride freely.

This follower plate assembly keeps the label pack intact and also firm against the picker during picking of each label. Some plants use ¼ inch follower plates on both the neck and body follower plates and use heavy weight springs to hold the labels firm in the label box for the label pickup by the pickers.

During machine operation, keep the holder well supplied with labels at all times. Wipe excess glue from the prongs as often as possible. A film of lubricant applied to each prong tip will keep these tips free of glue. Also a little oil applied to holder parts from time to time will keep these parts free from corrosion and freezing together.

i. The wiping station.

In the vast majority of cases, label wiping on the Tandem unit is accomplished through the use of nylon brush wipers. The wiper brackets are slotted, and thus allow the brushes to be moved closer to the bottle to compensate for wear on the ends of the bristles and rubbers.

When two bottles of the same diameter are being run, such as 12-ounce export and 12-ounce throw-away, the neck label position is often different on both bottles. In such cases, the neck brushes are held in slotted holes and must be moved to either end of the slots.

Next in importance to proper application of glue to the label is the wiping action. Generally, foil labels require a stronger wiping action than paper labels. This is because the metal must be bent to conform to the contour of the bottle. A foil label will stand a far greater degree of wiping than a paper label even when wet. With a paper label, as dampness increases, the wiping action must be decreased. Label adhesives with low initial tack but fast wetting characteristics will require a more severe wiping action than an adhesive with a high initial tack. If the bottle is damp or wet, a stronger wiping action will be required to displace the water film and permit the adhesive to make contact with the glass surfaces. Bottles previously cooled to below 68°F may condense moisture on the bottle surface from humid atmosphere and for this reason require a stronger wiping action. On the other hand, if the bottles reach the labeler 29°C (85°F), they may cause the adhesive to set up too fast. 85°F may thus be the ideal labeling temperature.

The distance between the edges of these brushes which the bottle passes, will regulate the pressure applied and may have to be varied according to the kind of label, machine speed, nature of adhesive, shape of the bottle surface, and whether the label has inside notches and curves or "tailing extremities". In some cases, fibre or nylon wipers may have to be shaped to accommodate unusual bottle contours or to compensate for label weaknesses or unusual stiffness. Specific denier gauge thickness of the wiping brushes will have to be determined by actual experience. Multiple wiping stations of fibre or nylon brushes may be used. In such applications, the initial wiping contact should be strong and the subsequent contact a prolonged holding action.

The wiping action cannot readily be extended to an area beyond 180° of the circumference of the bottle. For this reason, label designs exceeding 180° coverage are usually difficult to apply. The exception, of course, is the neck foiling attachment where a special arrangement permits the complete circumference of the bottle neck to be wiped. On the other hand, a label which does not go far enough around the bottle may also present difficulties, since the wiping action may be insufficient and the glue adhesion inadequate.

Other items to be considered are as follows.

If the bottles are excessively wet prior to labeling, a centrifugal blower may be installed to remove the excess water. Water from condensation can also be controlled by regulating pasteurizer discharge temperatures. A foil label may "flag" from the bottle along the vertical edges just after labeling. This condition often corrects itself. As the bottle dries, the label edges will "hug" the surface of the bottle. Therefore, before corrective labeling procedures are sought, permit the bottle to dry, and then reinspect the offending areas.

Another very important factor to remember is the need to change-over a labeling machine to accommodate a different size and shape bottle using different size and shape labels. It is therefore extremely important that the change-over parts be numbered and color coded.

LABELER OPERATION PROBLEMS

Here are a few ideas on mechanical problems that occur within the labeler and cause improper labeling. As a reminder, consider these points for picker action types.

a. Picker arms not properly aligned.
b. Worn wiper brushes.
c. Worn glue roller with uneven glue patterns.
d. Misaligned or worn glue transfer roller.
e. Label basket prongs too tight.
f. Bottle grip fingers loose.

The new rotary type machines are highly complex by comparison and mechanical difficulties are often harder to locate. After establishing a correct glue and label supply, check these areas of potential trouble:

a. Improper glue film; too thick or too thin.
b. Inadequate glue pattern on pallets.
c. Poor timing of pallet to glue roller.
d. Pallet and/or glue roller damage.
e. Label in glue knife . . . sometimes hidden on back side.
f. Misalignment of label basket to pallets.
g. No air to gripper cylinder (if air is used on gripper cylinder).
h. Label basket too tight . . . or too loose.
i. Slightly over-sized labels.
j. Code date notches too deep or rough . . . labels hang up.
k. Badly worn rubber wipers, rollers or brushes.
l. Excess oil or grease on bottle plates . . . bottle will not turn easily.
m. Pallet dirty . . . dried glue accumulation.
n. Gripper timing off . . . torn or missed labels.
o. Gripper fingers bent.

LABEL PROBLEMS

The manufacture of labels is a complete field unto itself and diagnosis of serious problems requires an expert from that field. There are a few simple tests—when label stock is suspect.

a. Check grain direction by wetting a label with water and making sure it curls from top to bottom. If it doesn't, the edges will be difficult to glue down.

b. On foil labels, make sure the groundwood backing stock is highly absorbent. Most manufacturers use groundwood backing stock, but there have been instances where a slick stock was used, causing a slowing of set time for the glue, with resultant flagging.

c. Labels can be too heavily inked or varnished, retarding moisture transmission and again slowing the set time of the adhesive.

d. Labels can be too springy and not conform to the bottle configuration.

e. Low moisture content will cause labels to absorb adhesive too quickly causing a starved glue joint and subsequent flagging.

f. Check size against the original drawing or blank. Are present labels slightly oversized or undersized? Either condition spells trouble.

LUBRICATION

Lubricate every day all bearings provided with grease fittings. Use a pressure gun with grease resistant to water and to product being labeled. Some plants have installed complete automatic lubrication systems on all heads.

All labeling units are equipped with automatic drip oilers used to keep all cam surfaces lubricated. If your machine is not equipped with this device, all cam surfaces should be painted with a heavy fibrous grease each day, at the same time the machine is lubricated, or after the machine has been washed. Use a lubricant that is not easily washed off. On all machines equipped with automatic drip oilers, check weekly to make sure the oil level has not receded to the lower sight-glass. Your drip oiling system, when properly adjusted, should provide one to three drops of oil to each cam once every 5 minutes of operation. This device automatically stops operating when the labeling unit is not running. The amount of oil should be adjusted to suit operating conditions. There should be enough oil to lubricate the cams, but not an excess amount which would drip down on the bottles, wipers or other parts of the machine which would impair the labeling quality. In some operations it is necessary to install lube catch pans under moving parts, so that excess lube does not fall on bottles and brushes.

ACKNOWLEDGEMENTS

Thanks are due to Joe Korteum of KRONES, INC. Franklin, Wisconsin, for his help in securing permission to use some of the illustrations and text, often verbatim, in the Krones Manual of Labelling Technology by Karl Dullinger.

REFERENCES

Dullinger, K; Krones Manual of Labelling Technology, 1979, Ed. H. Kronseder.
Ruff and Becker; Bottling and Canning of Beer, 1955
Crook, R.; Findley Adhesives, Inc.
Package Engineering, July, 1980
Reynolds Aluminum Co; Foil Beverage Labels, 1979
Geo. J. Meyer, Manufacturing; World Tandem Labeler
Guldswog, D; Norway Gravure, 1980

Section III: Canning Operations

CHAPTER XI

CANS

PART I—MANUFACTURE & STANDARDS
BY CHARLES E. SCRUGGS

INTRODUCTION AND BACKGROUND

Beer in cans first appeared commercially when G. Krueger Brewing Company, Newark, New Jersey, offered their product to consumers in the test market of Richmond, Virginia, on January 24, 1935. The can was a flat top, soldered side seam tinplate style. This new package, which would compete with the traditional bottle, represented years of research and development. Cone top cans also emerged as a possible alternate, but the flat top construction proved to be the popular and successful package. No major change occurred until 1962, when the Alcoa "lift-tab" easy-open aluminum end was introduced by the Iron City Brewing Company, replacing the flat top end and its companion beer can opener. Two new side seam manufacturing techniques, cemented and welded, were introduced in 1968 to take advantage of tin-free steel, a cost saving material. Cemented aluminum three-piece cans also made a brief appearance, but the economics were not sound in view of the development of the two-piece seamless aluminum can.

Two-piece aluminum cans were first introduced by the Hawaiian Brewing Company in 1958, producing their Primo label in eleven-ounce impact extruded cans. Adolph Coors followed in early 1959 with their seven-ounce cans, also impact extruded. Gunther Brewing Company produced the first beer in seven-ounce drawn and ironed (D & I) cans in October, 1959. These cans were manufactured by the American Can Company and Kaiser Aluminum and Chemical Company under a joint arrangement. Only a limited quantity was produced, and the package was discontinued when Gunther was acquired.

The first commercial production of a twelve-ounce drawn and ironed aluminum can was in 1964 by Reynolds Metals Company. In 1972, D & I tinplate cans were introduced and were satisfactory from a performance standpoint. Recycling, deposit legislation, and other factors have proven to be more favorable to the aluminum can and hence its predominance in the market place.

The "lift-tab" aluminum end was replaced very rapidly with the ring-pull version which proved to be a reliable feature, defeating other styles of easy-open ends. However, restrictive container legislation, with anti-litter features in many States, forced the creation of nondetachable tab ends, the most popular of which is the Stay-On-Tab developed by Reynolds Metals in 1975. A similar style of end was also designed by the Dayton Reliable Tool Company. The American Can Button-Down end, a different concept, entered the marketplace and is used in Canada.

MANUFACTURING METHODS

Three-Piece Soldered Side Seam Cans

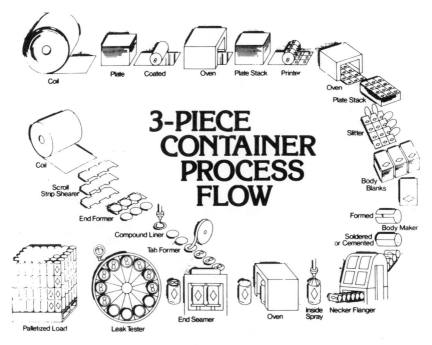

11-1. 3-piece container process flow.

Soldered beer cans are made on a series of machines collectively known as a "can line". Outside decorated and inside enameled sheets of tinplate are fed into a slitter which cuts them into body blanks. The blanks are fed into a bodymaker, where a sequence of automatic operations is performed to complete the cylindrical body of the can. (See Figure 11-2.)

The first station on the bodymaker notches the body blanks. They are next rolled around the bodymaker cylinder, hooks formed on the edges, flux applied to one hook to facilitate soldering, hooks interlocked, expanded into the correct can diameter and finally bumped to form the sideseam of the can. The formed body is preheated and then passes to the solder bath, where rolls, revolving in a direction perpendicular to the length of the can, apply solder to the outside of the can seam. The soldered body next passes over a revolving solder wipe, which removes excesss solder, after which it is moved over a cooling section to solidify the solder. The last operation in the conveyor applies a stripe of lacquer to the soldered side seam on the inside and the outside of

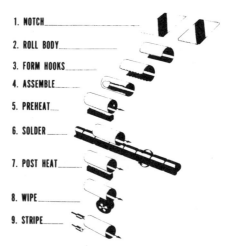

1. NOTCH

2. ROLL BODY

3. FORM HOOKS

4. ASSEMBLE

5. PREHEAT

6. SOLDER

7. POST HEAT

8. WIPE

9. STRIPE

11-2. Soldered body maker.

the can body. A later development by Continental Can Company combined the fluxing and inside stripe into one material. This "prestripe", applied in a section just prior to the soldering operation, simplified the inside stripe application system. An outside stripe was also applied at the end of the bodymaker similar to the "poststripe" previously described.

The cylindrical body then travels to the flanger where the top and bottom edges are curled outwards by special pilots to form the "flange". Modification of this operation occurred when "necking-in" of cans was introduced. Roll-necking or die-necking methods were incorporated to reduce the can body diameter on each end by one size (i.e., from 211 to 209) in combination with flanging. This process is discussed in more detail in the following section on two-piece can manufacture.

When the flanged, or necked and flanged, bodies leave the flanger after having received the top coat spray and bake, they proceed to the double seamer, where one end is applied, and then to a tester which, by means of air pressure, rejects leakers. Conveyors transfer the cans to the palletizer for shipment to the brewery.

• 1st OPERATION   • 2nd OPERATION   • ASSEMBLED

11-3. Doubleseam.

Three-Piece Welded Side Seam Cans

The commercial process developed by the Continental Can Company to weld the side seams of containers formed from tin-free steel was introduced in 1968, producing the Conoweld beer can. This process utilizes much of the equipment used in the manufacture of conventional soldered tinplate cans.

The sheets of tin-free steel are coated, printed, baked, and slit into body blanks. The blanks are fed into the bodymaker, where the margins are cleaned to remove any interfering layer where the steel is to be welded. The blank is formed into a cylinder with the edges overlapped approximately 0.040 inch at the side seam and tack welded together at four places. The cylinder is then passed between rotating wheel electrodes, which roll on each side of the seam. Control of electrical energy of approximately 4,000 amperes at 500 cycles per second and welding roll pressures by a proprietary electronic welding technique creates the bond.

Side seam coverage is achieved by pneumatically applying a powdered epoxy material to both sides of the hot side seam immediately after welding. The position of the stripe is controlled electrostatically, and the residual heat from the weld fuses and cures the stripe. Excellent coverage is achieved because of the thick film that results as compared with conventional liquid stripes.

Subsequent manufacturing steps are identical to the soldered can process described above.

• 1. CLEAN MARGINS

• 2. FORM BODY

• 3. TACK WELD

• 4. WELD SEAM

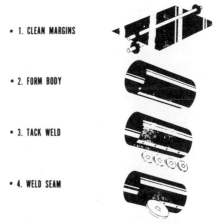

11-4. Conoweld.

Three-Piece Cemented Side Seam Cans

American Can Company developed the cemented lap seam process called MiraSeam to produce their version of a tin-free steel container. The MiraSeam can, which, like the Conoweld can, was technically and aesthetically superior to the soldered can, achieved cost savings resulting from the use of tin-free steel. As with the welded can, much of the same equipment used for soldered can manufacture is used for the MiraSeam process. However, the cemented lap seam is a sandwich of plate, organic coatings, and cement. This system, along with the thermal characteristics of the Barabond adhesive and enamels forming the "MiraSeam sandwich", makes possible the high-speed bonding required for can manufacture. Control of heat input and removal is basic to the process.

Sheets of tin-free steel body stock are coated, decoratively printed, and slit

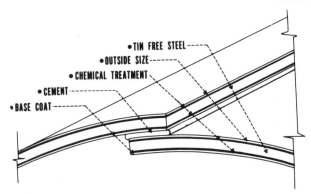

• TIN FREE STEEL
• OUTSIDE SIZE
• CHEMICAL TREATMENT
• CEMENT
• BASE COAT

11-5. Miraseam sandwich.

into body blanks. The adhesive is applied in the adhesive applicator by extruding in a continuous ribbon onto the applicator wheel, which places the material onto one edge of the preheated body blank. Following in rapid sequence are two chilling rolls and a cutter operation where the cement between the body blanks is cut and trimmed. The blanks are then transferred to the bodymaker, where they are notched, formed into a cylinder, heated again, and bumped.

The side seam bonding operation involves heating the edges of the cylinder to 475°F. by super-heat burners operating at 1,300°F. The hot thermoplastic adhesive and the heated overlapped edges of the blank are then bumped with chilled tools operating at −25°F. along the lap, creating the bond. At the operating line speed of 500 cans per minute, the cooling process and the bond is achieved in a fraction of the time of the ⅛ second total cycle, or approximately 1/50 of a second. The cans are then carried on a conveyor and a stripe of coating is applied inside and outside the cylinder to cover the exposed metal cutedges. After leaving the bodymaker, the cans are flanged (or necked and flanged, as described above), inside sprayed with an enamel top coat, baked, one end seamed on, and tested for leakage. Palletizing follows as the last operation.

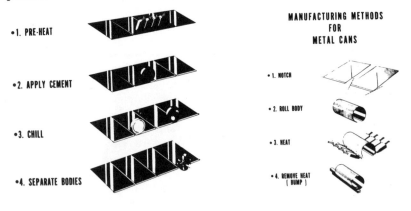

• 1. PRE-HEAT

• 2. APPLY CEMENT

• 3. CHILL

• 4. SEPARATE BODIES

MANUFACTURING METHODS
FOR
METAL CANS

• 1. NOTCH

• 2. ROLL BODY

• 3. HEAT

• 4. REMOVE HEAT
(BUMP)

11-6. A. Adhesive application.   *B. Body Maker operations.*

Two-Piece Drawn and Ironed Cans

Both aluminum and tinplate D & I cans are manufactured by essentially the same process. The major difference is that aluminum is given an extra step involving chemical pretreatment of the entire can to enhance adhesion of the outside lithography and the inside organic coating.

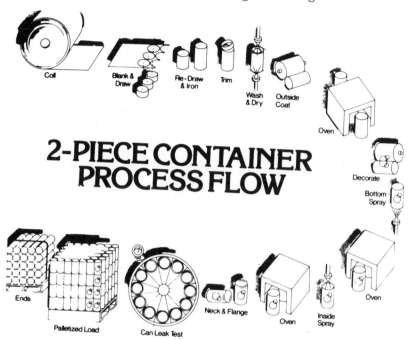

11-7. 2-piece container process flow.

Manufacturing begins with a coil of plate that is unwound, lubricated, and fed into a multiple cupping or blanking press, which forms it into shallow cups. These cups are fed into an ironing press, where successive rings or a die stack form the can side wall. More metal is left near the top and bottom to give added strength. In addition to thinning the side wall of the shell, the ironing press imparts the bottom profile. Trimming of the top end follows to produce a can of uniform height. Coolant flows through the die stack to reduce heating of the shell and, in the case of tinplate, maintains temperatures below 450°F. to prevent reflow of the tin on the side wall.

11-8. A. Drawing. B. Ironing.

During the drawing, ironing and trimming operations, the shell is covered with a film of lubricant and coolant. To remove this residue the cans are cleaned with sprays. They are conveyed upside down on a mesh belt through a series of cleaning and treating zones. After a tinplate can is cleaned, the surface is chemically passivated to prevent darkening during baking and to prevent loss of enamel adhesion. With aluminum, the surface is Alodine treated, as explained above. The final step in the washer is a deionized water rinse that eliminates any trace of the spray solutions.

Outside lithography is applied on a rotary decorator. Prior base coating on a separate unit may be required to produce the desired appearance. After printing, a clear overvarnish may be applied to protect the inks, or a combination of "no-var" inks may be used that do not require final varnish. The cans are then bottom coated (the entire bottoms of tinplate cans are covered but only the bearing rim on aluminum) and passed through a pin oven to harden the inks and varnish.

Inside coatings are applied to the can by an airless, stationary spray gun positioned outside the can. The fan spray extends from the bottom center to the top edge, and the can rotates at least two revolutions to achieve the required coverage. The cans are baked in a mesh belt oven to remove the solvent and to cure the coating.

The final stage of metal forming consists of die necking, which reduces the top of the shell, followed by flanging, testing, and palletizing.

Two of the operations described above merit additional discussion because of their importance to the performance of the can.

The first of these, necking of the container, provides several advantages beyond the obvious cost reduction of the smaller diameter end. These include a substantial space savings in shipping the empty cans (5%) and also in reduction of the carton or tray size of the filled cans. With the D & I style, empty can handling is improved because of increased rigidity of the open end, better can flow, and lack of flange contact. Double-necking to one size smaller end, which carries the cost reduction feature even farther, is a commercial success. Triple-necking is under development.

11-9. *D & I necked-in cans. From left to right: straight wall; necked-in; double necked-in; and triple necked-in (Left-stepped profile; right-smooth profile.)*

The second feature of the two-piece can is the shape of the bottom end profile. Strength requirements must meet pasteurization pressures. The rigid bottom concept employs various shapes and degrees of concavity designed for minimum thickness, maximum strength, and optimum inside coating application. Another concept, which allows the bottom end to expand under pressure, enhances these characteristics and also increases the capacity of the can.

End Manufacture

Two types of ends are required for three-piece cans: 1) the tinplate or tin-free steel bottom end, and 2) the aluminum ring-pull top end. The latter may also be a nondetachable tab style where required.

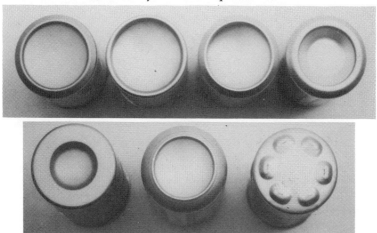

11-10. D & I can bottom profiles. Upper row, Rigid. Lower row, Expanding.

The standard tinplate or tin-free steel end is produced from flat stock which may be coated either in the sheet or coil. The roller coatings are applied to both sides of the plate, which is then baked, cut into strips, and fed into a press that stamps out the formed end with the appropriate profile. Profiles are especially designed to withstand the internal pressure developed during pasteurization. The ends then pass through a curling unit, which turns the edge inward. Compound or sealant is applied by extruding the liquid around the circumference within the end curl. After the sealant has dried, one end is double seamed on the three-piece can body for shipment to the brewery.

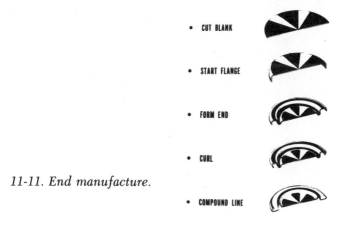

- CUT BLANK

- START FLANGE

- FORM END

- CURL

11-11. End manufacture.

- COMPOUND LINE

11-12. Examples of Ring Pull easy-open aluminum ends.

The aluminum easy-open end is manufactured in a method similar to the above to form a "basic" end. The second operation is performed in a conversion press in which the rivet and score are formed. The rings or tabs are formed concurrently from roll fed stock on the same press but with a separate set of tools. Tooling and presses are so designed that the finished ring is mated to the formed rivet on the basic end, and final assembly is effected during the staking operation. The nondetached ring or tab-type of end is produced in a similar manner. Some manufacturers prefer to manufacture the rings off-line and assemble them on the end in the conversion press.

The above style of ends is scored for openability. Another concept, wherein the opening is pierced, is the Button-Down end which is repair-sealed on the underside with a plastisol material.

11-13. Examples of non-detachable easy-open aluminum ends: Left column, DRT (Dayton Reliable Tool Co.). Center column, Sta-On Tab (Reynolds Metals Co.). Right column, Button-Down (American Can Co.).

Additional Useful information

Part II contains practical information on the shipping and storage of cans and lids as well as a discussion of some factors that may affect product quality or operational costs.

Part III contains nine tables covering terminology, specifications and standards for steel and aluminum cans as well as the alloys and coatings used in their fabrication.

BIBLIOGRAPHY

HOAG, L. E. "The Manufacture and Use of Beer Cans." *Wallerstein Communications* XIII: 40;195, 1950

SCRUGGS, C. E. "Cans For Beer and Ale." *Brewers Digest;* April, May, July, 1950

"Primo Scores a First." *Brewers Digest;* August, 1958

WILSON, R. V. "Recent Developments in Canned Beer." Technical Proceedings MBAA; 1958

"First Aluminum-Canned Beer." *Modern Packaging;* September, 1958

"New Advances in Aluminum-Canned Beer." *Modern Packaging;* February, 1959

"Aluminum Cans Make a Bold New Bid." *Modern Packaging;* October, 1959

ALTHEN, P. C. "Status of the Aluminum Can." *MBAA Technical Quarterly* 4: 2; 1965

MULLER, R. E. "New Technology in Manufacturing of Beer Cans." *MBAA Technical Quarterly* 3: 3; 1966

BURLESON, M. NEAL. "The Aluminum Beer Can—Its Manufacture and Use." *MBAA Technical Quarterly* 3: 2; 178-180; 1966

EDEN, H. A. "Evolution of Easy-Open Aluminum Ends for Beer Cans." *MBAA Technical Quarterly* 4: 2; 1967

KIDDER, D. R.; KAMM, G. G.; and KOPETZ, A. A. "Tin-Free Steel Beer Cans." Am. Soc. Brewing Chemists; 138; Proc. 1967

LEMELIN, D. R. "The Seamless Necked Aluminum Can." Society of Soft Drink Technologists Proceedings of the 16th Annual Meeting; 1969

"A History of Packaged Beer and Its Market in the United States." American Can Company Publication; 1969

HAFELI, J. M. "Coating for Metal Containers." *MBAA Technical Quarterly* 7: 1; 1970

ELLIS, R. F. "New Can Constructions—Bonded Lap Seams." *Modern Packaging;* March, 1970

CHIAPPE, W. T. "New Can Constructions—Forge-Welded Seams." Modern Packaging; March, 1970

GLASER, M. A. "Beer Can Linings." *MBAA Technical Quarterly* 8: 3; 1971

SCRUGGS, C. E.; KRICKL, J. L., and LINDE, N. J. "Metals Used for Beer Cans." *MBAA Technical Quarterly* 8: 1; 63-71; 1971

KAERCHER, R. W. "Drawn-and-Ironed Steel Cans". *Modern Packaging;* October, 1972

LUDWIGSEN, R. J. "Coating for Metal Containers." *Radiation Curing;* February, 1975

LANDAUER, L., and SCRUGGS, C. E. "New Can Coatings to Meet Air Quality Standards—Status Report." Society of Soft Drink Technologists Proceedings of the 22nd Annual Meeting; 1975.

MAEDER, E. G. "The Drawn-and-Ironed Beer Can". *MBAA Technical Quarterly* 12: 1; 1975

STRAND, R. C. "Waterborne Coatings in Metal Packaging." Chem Coatings Conference, Nat'l Paint & Coatings Assn., Inc.; April 23, 1976

MOORMAN, R. W. "Cans Today—Cans Tomorrow." *MBAA Technical Quarterly* 13: 1; 1976

"Steel in Packaging." Committee of Tin Mill Products Producers. AISI; 1978

"Aluminum Standards and Data." 2nd Ed. The Aluminum Association, New York, 1978

"Steel Products Manual." Tin Mill Products. Am. Iron and Steel Institute; Washington, D.C. 1979

QUINN, R. "Slipsheets: A Modern Approach to Unitization." *MBAA Technical Quarterly* 16: 4; 1979

"Steel for Cans: Where It Stands, Where It's Going." *Brewers Digest;* December, 1980. Steel Product News Bureau, AISI

"Brewery Packaging: Examining the Container." *Modern Brewery Age;* October 20, 1980

SULLIVAN, COLEMAN. "Containers—Cans, Metal." 1981 Packaging Encyclopedia; 157-160

O'BRIEN, ROBERT J. "Alcoa's New Designs Change Can Construction." *Beverage Industry;* December, 1981

PAWLOSKI, C. H. "Stretchwrapping of Palletized Packaged Beer." *MBAA Technical Quarterly* 17: 2; 1981

PART II: EMPTY CAN SHIPPING AND STORAGE
BY JAMES HAMMERSMITH

UNITIZING AND SHIPPING EMPTY CANS

Procedures for transferring empty cans from the point of manufacture to the user have progressed through a number of different systems. Some of the earlier systems, which are still used for low volume operations, are reviewed here briefly to give the reader further insight into the development of can handling in the beverage industry.

Reshipper Cartons

Cans are packed open end down into corrugated cartons which are then conveyed into freight cars or trucks, and manually stacked. Upon receipt, the cartons are conveyed to the production filling line. Just prior to filling, operators open the carton flaps, turn the carton upside-down onto a mesh belt conveyor and lift the cartons away from the empty upright cans. The cans then travel to a rotary disk which orients them into single file for conveying to the filler. The empty carton is placed onto another conveyor and travels to the can packers to be refilled with full product. Obviously this system is labor intensive and slow.

Automatic Unscrambling for Three Piece Cans

In an effort to speed up production and decrease costs associated with the previous system, several machines have been developed to automate the process. All of the machines perform the same basic function. Cans are delivered in corrugated cartons and conveyed to the automatic unscrambler. The machine automatically opens all four carton flaps and turns the carton upside-down so that the cans fall into an accumulating bin. Cans from the bin are then oriented bottoms down. As cans roll along a raceway with a ridge down the center, the heavier bottom end drops and thereby orients the can. Figure 11-14 explains this principle further.

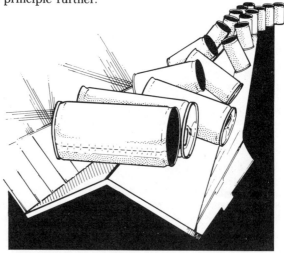

11-14. Device to upright empty jumbled cans.

Compartmentized Trucks (Cell Bin)

A truck trailer is compartmentized to permit loading by rolling cans on their side into a series of compartments one can wide. At the point of unloading, the truck unit is tilted so the cans may roll from each compartment onto conveyors leading to filling machines. This system is discussed in more detail in the next chapter and shown in figures 12-3, 4 and 5.

Other Systems

Other systems have been adapted to fit given conditions, including conveying cans directly from an adjacent can-making facility as one example. The use of a fork to move bulk cans in and out of cars as shown in figure 11-15 is another.

11-15. Sketch showing use of "fork" for loading or unloading bulk cans.

The most common procedure used today for transferring cans from the manufacturer to the user unitizes 7,000-8,000 cans onto a pallet. The number of cans stacked onto the pallet will vary by can dimensions and user facilities. In order to permit using unitized material interchangeably between can manufacturers and users, specifications have been developed standardizing dimensions and other characteristics for pallets, top frames, and paperboard slip sheets. A typical unit is prepared by first placing a paperboard slip sheet on a wood pallet. A quantity of empty cans is placed on this base, patterned to cover the area with the greatest count, without overhang. Additional layers of cans are stacked, with a paperboard slip sheet between each layer, until reaching the prescribed number of layers. After placing a paperboard slip sheet on the top layer, a wood top frame is placed on the unit, and the unit is secured with steel or plastic straps in both directions. Figure 11-16 illustrates

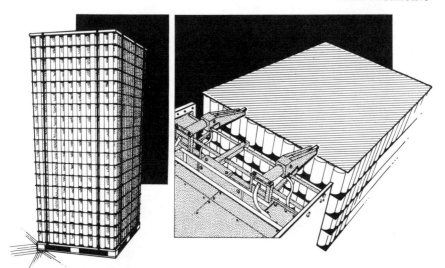

11-16. Unitized pallet
load of empty cans.

11-17. Sketch showing depalletizer grip fingers
holding slipsheet. Note can pattern that avoids
grip finger contact with cans.

a completed unit. In order to add further protection during shipping and storage the user may elect to have each pallet unit wrapped in plastic film or a corrugated sleeve.

Delivery is made by loading a number of units into standard or roller-bed trucks or rail cars. Upon receipt and unloading at user location, units of cans are fed by fork lift or pallet conveyor connecting to the roller-bed truck system into automatic depalletizers which sweep cans off the unit, one layer at a time, and automatically remove the slip sheets. Pallets, slip sheets, and top frames are returned to the can maker for reuse.

Successful use of this system of can handling requires a number of precautions to prevent damage, contamination, can loss, and operating efficiency loss. Since these are important, we will discuss each in some detail.

Unit Layer Pattern

The goal is to get as many cans per layer as possible on the pallet to maximize the number of cans handled per pallet movement to assure the greatest number of cans per square foot of storage space, to minimize the number of trucks required for transferring cans to their destination. While it is a temptation to add an extra row of cans to the layer pattern and exceed the dimension of the pallet and slip sheets, this may increase rather than cut costs. If the can pattern exceeds the dimension of the layer of slip sheets, and if cans are unitized with the open end up, they are subject to contamination during warehousing and shipping. Insects, warehouse debris, road dust, and airborne materials may enter the exposed cans on the pallet perimeter.

Can Pattern Interface With Depalletizer Equipment

Some can depalletizers include metal grip fingers which hold slip sheets in place while the cans are swept off the slip sheets. The stacking pattern and grip fingers need to be matched so that the slip sheet is gripped at a point void of cans. If the pattern allows the depalletizer grip fingers to contact the cans, those cans will be damaged, resulting in significant can loss, a potential source of conveyor jams and related lost time. Figure 11-17 illustrates the relationship between the pattern and the gripper fingers. Sometimes a pattern is different on one end of the pallet load than on the other end. When this condition exists, proper pallet orientation on the depalletizer in-feed is required.

Can Damage and Losses

Cans overhanging pallet slip sheets and top frames are more subject to damage from contact with adjacent pallets, truck and car bulkheads, dunnage, fork trucks, warehouse walls and posts, etc. The loss incurred is not only the value of the damaged cans, but the increased production stops and operational costs resulting from conveyor and equipment jams. Overhanging and inadequately supported cans will fall from the unit and be lost. When this occurs during shipping, these cans may become lodged between units or bulkheads and damage other cans.

Identifying Manufacturing Lots

Each pallet load of cans should be identified by some system that will reveal information necessary for quality control. Usually this is accomplished by affixing a tag to each pallet load with such information as the manufacturing date, date shipped, manufacturing line, and pallet sequence number. The more complete the information on this tag, the fewer the number of pallet loads of cans that need to be isolated when problems arise. If pallet load orientation is required for the depalletizer gripper fingers, the pallet identification tag is useful for this purpose.

Inside Can Contamination

Regardless of whether the unit pattern permits exposed can openings or not, it is prudent to monitor the insides of cans for debris to assure that adequate measures are being taken to protect against contamination during can manufacturing and handling. One way of monitoring is to invert cans just prior to the rinsing operation. Install collection trays under this section of the conveyor and examine the debris collected. The types of debris collected will give some insight into what corrective action may be required. For example, insects may indicate need for added pest control during warehousing. Wood splinters point to improved handling of pallets and top frames, or to cull out more split and damaged material. Generally, fibers from paper board slip sheets will point to the need for improved handling and/or culling of slip sheets. Slip sheet contamination during collection at the user's plant, during handling and return to can manufacturers, and during storage at the various points may lead to all kinds of contamination including glass, oils, insects, floor sweepings, etc.

Should glass particles be found, check nearby bottle handling equipment and conveyors. Truck or car cleaning prior to unloading is another important preventive measure against contamination. Can contamination need not be a major continuing problem if steps are taken to monitor and correct deficiencies.

TRUCK AND CAR PREPARATION

In addition to the previously mentioned areas of contamination, the condition of the vehicle itself is a major factor. It is important to assure adequate inspection and cleaning of the vehicle prior to loading and reject all deficient vehicles. Criteria must be established defining what constitutes unusable vehicles and procedures established to reject them.

Some conditions to watch for include the following:

1. Holes in the roof, floors, or walls which would permit water, snow, or other contaminants including vehicle exhaust to enter the unit.
2. Previous loads of a material which cannot be completely removed or which may have sifted between the bulkheads.
3. Odors remaining from prior loads.
4. Holes or broken inside surfaces, or protruding fixtures and nails which can damage cans.
5. Damaged or unsuitable undercarriages which can create unusually rough transit conditions.

It is equally important that the drivers be trained in handling their equipment and in taking the best routes to protect the load.

Exercising reasonable care in preparing equipment, developing procedures and training personnel to minimize contamination and damage results in an improved operation and lower costs for the can manufacturer, the shipper and user as well.

OUTSIDE WAREHOUSING OF EMPTY CANS

In order to balance can manufacturing capacity against the user's seasonal requirements, it is often necessary to store cans at some location other than the can manufacturer's or packer's plant. When this condition exists, precautions should be taken to protect the inventory from damage or contamination. Since such storage requires at least two additional handlings of each pallet, the warehouse should have the proper equipment and trained fork truck operators.

Even if the dock is protected, operators should be instructed to move pallets directly from the truck to their final storage spot in one movement rather than pre-staging the load on the dock. Staging may permit unloading and releasing the truck faster, but it also generates at least one additional handling, longer exposure to weather conditions, and potential for damage from other traffic in the area.

Rodent, insect, and bird controls are required to prevent contamination from these sources. Such controls are covered in Chapter XXVII.

Ceiling and wall conditions should be observed for dirt, loose panels, flaking paint, and other debris. As an added precaution, it helps to cover the top of the inventory or individual pallets with plastic sheeting. It is necessary to protect not only against contamination falling inside cans, but to prevent accumulation of debris, etc., on the top of the load and the edges of the slip sheets, since this debris may be swept into cans during depalletizing.

Water damage may be experienced from leaking roofs, windows, walls, vents, etc. Look for evidence of such conditions. Equally important is trace moisture resulting from condensation through floors and walls. To guard against this condition, provide for adequate ventilation, minimize temperature changes, and check for other possible sources of moisture. This precaution is especially important for steel cans to prevent their rusting.

Determine what else may be stored in the facility and what other activity may be in the neighborhood which could result in odors or other conditions unfavorable to can storage.

When it is necessary to store empty cans in out-of-plant locations, it is suggested that the can manufacturer and user jointly develop specifications for the facility and handling procedures well in advance. The premises should be carefully inspected prior to contracting for their use and periodically while the facility is in use.

Earlier in this chapter, in the discussion of transit damage, it was suggested the can manufacturer and packer monitor test loads in order to isolate causes of damage, and it is advisable to include this step in the checklist.

TEST LOAD SHIPMENTS

When it is likely that a quantity of cans will be stored for a period of time prior to use, the manufacturer and packer should develop a system for regularly screening can production to assure against storing large quantities of cans with undetected defects. In order to minimize this risk, a procedure should be designed to accumulate identified test loads (for example, every tenth pallet manufactured until a truck load is accumulated) from lots being warehoused, which lots are then sent to the packer for immediate inspection and use. This precaution not only protects against the likelihood of accumulating large numbers of defective cans but also assures that usable cans will be available when they are required by the packer.

UNITIZING AND SHIPPING LIDS

Systems for unitizing and shipping can lids are much more simple than the requirements for empty cans. Lids are more compact, less subject to damage and fewer changes have been made over the years in the way lids are used by the canner.

With minor variations and exceptions by individual users, stacks of lids are packed in paper sleeves three or four feet long. Sleeves of lids are packed in cartons or on wood skids for shipment to the user. Figure 11-18 illustrates a typical bulk skid of lids secured to the skid by interlocking sleeves with strips of paper or plastic material. Little change has been made over the years in the procedure for moving lids to the closing machine, and removing them from sleeves and placing them in the closing machine lid feed rack. Some companies have developed systems of highly mechanizing lid handling; however, these are usually designed to meet special conditions and will not be discussed here.

Many of the manufacturing, shipping, storage and handling precautions previously noted for cans also apply to lids. Without repeating all of the details and rationale, these procedures are summarized below:

1. Transportation vehicles need to be cleaned and free from conditions which could damage or contaminate the lids.
2. Skids should be identified to aid in isolating suspected defective lots.
3. Warehousing and storage conditions should be monitored and controlled for operator training to prevent any handling damage.
4. Due to requirements of special markets, a number of different designs or identifications must be printed or stamped on lids. Additionally, the

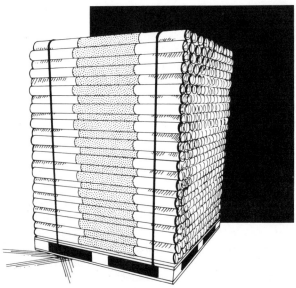

11-18. Unitized pallet load of can lids. Note stabilizing of sleeves of lids by means of interleaving of paper strips and strapping.

plant inventory may include lids with different styles of easy-open systems. Precautions must be taken to prevent using the wrong lids on the wrong cans. If a large number of different types of lids are used, it is helpful to develop a special system for identifying types of lids by printing colors or designs on the paper sleeves.

FACTORS AFFECTING PACKER PRODUCT QUALITY OR OPERATIONAL COSTS

Detailed lists of can and lid specifications, defects, and test procedures may be found in various publications, including those published by the United States Brewers Association Can Specifications Subcommittee. This chapter will therefore discuss general conditions which may negatively affect product quality or operations and are routinely checked by the Quality Assurance Department (see chapter XXII.)

Printing Quality and Colors

The first impression a product makes on potential customers is dependent in a great measure upon the quality of printing (ink coverage, register, scratches, etc.) and the consistency of colors.

Inside Coatings

Flavor, shelf life, and chemical tests tailored to the product are used to monitor the inside coating system.

Exterior Coatings

Decorating inks and exterior coatings affect many factors in production and shipping cycles. The amount of coating, evenness of distribution, and lubricants in the material are all factors which must be controlled, and in many cases, specifically tailored to the individual operation. A coating material or system which may perform quite satisfactorily in a relatively slow speed operation, or one with one type of conveying system, may not perform at all in another operation which uses high speed or different types of conveyors, or inclines or declines.

Exterior coatings must also be suitable to survive the shipping environment. Cans which are severely scuffed, rusted, or covered with aluminum oxide soil add nothing to the visual qualities of the package. Under severe conditions, scuffing may become sufficient to wear completely through the metal. When this occurs, it not only makes that can unsalable, but also the product leakage contaminates other surrounding packages. Additionally, moisture on aluminum cans significantly increases the abrasive characteristic between can surfaces and creates more severe scuffing and aluminum oxide damage. Shipping tests to evaluate scuff resistance of coatings are becoming much more sophisticated and effective, and worth consideration for long distance shipping conditions.

Bottom Bearing Surface Coatings

Requirements for coatings on the bottom bearing surface seem to vary greatly, again depending upon types and lengths of conveyors, elevation changers, conveyor lubricity, twists, etc. The equipment used for applying bottom coating material is generally a roller with varying degrees of control over the amount and evenness of coverage. Additionally, much of the coating is worn off during conveying in the can manufacturer's and packer's operations. Even though the coat application is usually inconsistent and much is worn off in the process, the remaining bottom coating may provide the difference between good can mobility or poor. If a can conveyor mobility problem arises, one of the first things to check is the bottom coating—how well and consistently it is applied, and how much is worn off before the cans reach the trouble spot in the operation.

Can Denting

This is not only an appearance problem, but also affects efficiency in conveying and vertical load resistance at the filler, the seamer and during shipping. All conveying and can handling systems must be engineered to prevent can-to-can and can-to-equipment impact, or pressure which may dent, score, crush, or cause any physical damage which may weaken the vertical load crush resistance. Should there be an increase in stops at the filling and seaming operation, or abnormal damage in finished product, it is advisable to check conveyors and handling equipment all the way through the can manufacturing and packing operation for problems that might cause denting.

CAN SEAMING

This subject is discussed in depth in Chapter XIII. It is mentioned here to point out that material specifications for cans and lids must provide for maximum consistency between different suppliers as well as between shipments from the same supplier. Levels of specification tolerances which may have been considered "interchangeable" in the past, are no longer adequate to guarantee maximum efficiency at today's speeds. Lid and can plan configurations, thickness and other dimensions, require clear specifications with tight tolerances and careful monitoring in order to provide the seaming operation with material which can be uniformly machined into secure double seams.

PART III: APPENDIX

TABLE I
TYPICAL METAL SPECIFICATIONS FOR BEER CANS IN THE UNITED STATES

BODIES		
Cemented or Welded	53#, 55# DR-8 or DR-9	TFS-CT
Soldered	53#, 55# DR-8 or DR-9	#25 Electrolytic
2-Piece Drawn and Ironed	85#-112# T-1 or T-4	#20/30 or
		#25 Electrolytic
		Tinplate
	3004 H19	Aluminum

TABLE II
TYPICAL METAL SPECIFICATIONS FOR BEER CANS IN THE UNITED STATES

		ENDS							
	PASTEURIZED					NON-PASTEURIZED			
DIA.	STEEL*		EASY OPEN ALUMINUM			STEEL*		EASY OPEN ALUMINUM	
211	95#	DR-9	.0135″	5182	H19	80#	DR-9	.0115″	5082	H19
	90#	DR-10				85#	DR-9			
209	90#	DR-9	.0130″	5182	H19	80#	DR-9	.0115″	5082	H19
	95#	DR-9								
	90#	DR-10								
207.5	85#	DR-9	.0125″	5182	H19	80#	DR-9	.0115″	5082	H19
	90#	DR-9								
206	—		.0125″	5182	H19	—		.0115″	5082	H19
202	—		.0125″	5182	H19	—		.0115″	5082	H19

*TFS-CT or #25 Electrolytic

TABLE III
TYPICAL BEER CAN LOAD STRENGTH (PSI)
12 OZ. 211 DIAMETER

	VERTICAL CRUSH		10° OFFSET CRUSH	
	Ideal	Minimum	Ideal	Minimum
EMPTY CANS				
3 Pc. Straight Wall	1700	1200	265	165
3 Pc. Necked-In	800	650	140	110
2 Pc. Aluminum	390	300	80	60
2 Pc. ETP Steel	550	400	130	100
FILLED CANS				
3 Pc. Straight Wall	2000	1500	300	200
3 Pc. Necked-In	925	825	165	135
2 Pc. Aluminum	570	480	110	90
2 Pc. ETP Steel	750	600	165	135

TABLE IV
INTERIOR COATINGS USED FOR BEER CANS

THREE-PIECE CANS	TYPES
Body Base Coats	Mod. epoxys, polybutadiene
Top Coats	Vinyls, Mod. Vinyls
Stripes	Vinyls, epoxys
TWO-PIECE CANS	
	Mod. epoxys, Mod. vinyls, acrylics

ENDS	
ETP & TFS-CT	
Base Coats	Mod. epoxys, polybutadiene
Top Coats	Vinyls, Vinyl organosols
Aluminum	Mod. epoxys, epoxy-acrylics, organosols

TABLE V
CAN TERMINOLOGY FOR BEER CAN SIZES

CAN SIZE DESIGNATION*		THREE-PIECE NOMINAL CAPACITY
Straight Wall	**Single Necked-In**	
211x306	209/211x307	8 fl. oz. (US)
211x307	209/211x307	8 fl. oz. (US)
211x410.5		341 ml Canada
207.5x413		10 fl. oz. (US)
207.5x413	206/207.5x413	295 ml Venezuela
211x413	209/211x413	12 fl. oz. (US)
211x413		355 ml Mexico (340 ml domestic)
207.5/209x504		12 fl. oz. (US)
207.5/209x504		355 ml Mexico (340 ml domestic)
211x413		14 fl. oz. (US)
209x607	15 fl. oz. (US)	15 fl. oz. (US)
211x604	209/211x604	16 fl. oz. (US)
207.5/209x612		16 fl. oz. (US)
300x709		25 fl. oz. (US)

CAN SIZE DESIGNATION*		TWO-PIECE NOMINAL CAPACITY
Single Necked-In	**Double Necked-In**	
202/204x401		7 fl. oz. (US)
206/207.5x400	202/207.5x400	8 fl. oz. (US)
206/207.5x413		10 fl. oz. (US)
206/207.5x413		295 ml Venezuela
207.5/209x504		12 fl. oz. (US)
209/211x413	207.5/211x413	12 fl. oz. (US)
209/211x413		355 ml Mexico (340 ml domestic)
209/211x509		14 fl. oz. (US)
209/211x603 or 604	209/211x603 or 604	16 fl. oz. (US)

*First numbers = Nominal diameter of end and/or body (inches)
 Second numbers = Nominal can height (inches)

TABLE V (Con't)

Example No. 1	211 = 2-11/16″ diameter of top end and body
"211x413"	413 = 4-13/16″ height of can
Example No. 2	209 = 2-9/6″ diameter of top end
"209/211x413"	211 = 2-11/16″ diameter of body
	413 = 4-13/16″ height of can

TABLE VI
CAN TERMINOLOGY FOR TIN OR TIN-FREE STEEL PLATE

BASE BOX	—Standard unit of measurement for steel shipped to can makers which refers to area, rather than weight. One Base Box = 31,360 square inches
BASIS WEIGHT	—The weight of one Base Box 53 lbs. to 135 lbs. (aim)
GAUGE	—Plate Thickness in inches Gauge (inches) = Basis Weight (lbs.) x .00011
TEMPER	—Hardness aim expressed on Rockwell Scale (30T) Single reduced plate refers to sheet steel that is rolled in five-strand reduction mills while cold, then annealed and temper rolled to produce thin gauges for cans. 49 to 70 HR 30T Temper Designation T1 - T6 Double reduced plate is can making stock which is given a partial cold reduction to gauge, then annealed and given another major cold reduction to final gauge. 73 to 80 HR 30T Temper Designation DR8 - DR10
TIN COATING WEIGHT	—The weight of tin in lbs. applied to one Base Box of plate (both sides) 0.25 to 1.25 lbs. also No. 25 to No. 125 ETP
TIN-FREE STEEL	—Can making stock without a tin coating. Usually a much thinner coating of chrome—1/50th the weight of tin coatings—is applied to improve performance. TFS-CT (or TFS-CCO) - Chromium type TFS-210 - Chromium phosphate type TFS-CMQ (or QAR) - Black Plate
CHEMICAL COMPOSITION	—Type L, MR, MC (all suitable for beer cans)

TABLE VII
CAN TERMINOLOGY FOR TIN MILL PRODUCTS
NOMINAL BASIS WEIGHTS AND IDEAL THICKNESSES

Basis Weight (lb. per base box)	Thickness (inch)	Basis Weight (lb. per base box)	Thickness (inch)
45	0.0050	90	0.0099
50	0.0055	95	0.0105
55	0.0061	100	0.0110
60	0.0066	103	0.0113
65	0.0072	107	0.0118
70	0.0077	112	0.0123
75	0.0083	118	0.0130
80	0.0088	128	0.0141
85	0.0094	135	0.0149

TABLE VIII
TEMPER AND MECHANICAL DESIGNATION FOR TIN MILL PRODUCTS

Temper or Mechanical Designations	Aim Rockwell Hardness Value* R30T	Typical Tensile Strength (psi.)	Characteristics and Examples of Use
T-1	49 ± 3	47,000	Soft for deep drawing, e.g., nozzles, closures.
T-2	53 ± 3	50,000	Moderate drawing, e.g., closures, special can parts.
T-3	57 ± 3	55,000	General purpose, e.g., large diameter closures, bottle caps.
T-4 or T-4 CA	61 ± 3	59,000	General purpose, increased strength, e.g., can ends and bodies, crown caps.
T-5 or T-5 CA (TU)	65 ± 3	64,000	Strength and stiffness, e.g., can ends and bodies.
T-6 or T-6 CA	70 ± 3	75,000	Rephosphorized steel for greater stiffness.
DR-8†	73	80,000	Harder, stiffer, less ductility than single reduced plate, e.g., can bodies and ends, 211 dia. or smaller.
DR-9†	76	90,000	Harder, stiffer, less ductility than DR-8, e.g., can bodies and ends, 211 dia. or larger.
DR-10†	80	100,000 (min.)	Nitrogenized steel for greater hardness and stiffness, e.g., beer and carbonated beverage ends.

*Values based on use of diamond anvil.
†Double reduced.

TABLE IX
CAN TERMINOLOGY FOR ALUMINUM PLATE

GAUGE	—Thickness in Inches
ALLOY	—Designated by a four-digit system (eight series) 1000 to 8000
TEMPER	—The designation H plus two digits denotes not only general strength level, but also includes a reference as to how much the product has been strain hardened and what its thermal history has been.
	H = Temper attained by strain hardening a nonheatable alloy
	1st Digit = Basic operation performed
	2nd Digit = Final degree of strain hardening

ALLOY AND TEMPER DESIGNATION OF COMMONLY USED WROUGHT ALUMINUM CAN STOCK WITH
TYPICAL COMPOSITIONS, TENSILE STRENGTH AND USES

			TENSILE STRENGTH		
ALLOY	TEMPER	MAJOR ALLOY COMPOSITION	AS REC'D. (psi.)	SHEET AFTER BAKE (psi.)	USE
1100	0	—	13,000	—	Impact extruded 2-piece aerosol
3004	H19	1.2% Mn 1.0% Mg	43,000	—	Drawn and ironed 2-piece beer can
5052	H34	2.5% Mg 0.25% Cr	38,000	36,000	Drawn 2-piece can for meat
5052	H19	2.5% Mg 0.25% Cr	47,000	40,000	Full panel and spiral easy-open ends. Drawn sardine can. 3-piece cemented side seam can for cocktails and luncheon meat.
5082	H19	4.5% Mg	57,000	48,000	Beer and beverage ends, tab stock, full-panel, and spiral easy-open ends.
5182	H19	5.0% Mg 0.45% Mn	61,000	54,000	Beer and beverage ends
5352	H19	2.5% Mg	44,000	37,000	Drawn 2-piece for meat, F.P.E.O. ends
5042	H19	3.5% Mg 35% Mn	52,000	47,000	Tab stock; F.P.E.O. ends

ACKNOWLEDGEMENT

The tables used in this section were provided by American Can Company.

CHAPTER XII

CAN FILLING

BY HENRY HEINS and
JAMES F. HEUER

INTRODUCTION

Can filling is essentially the heart of a can packaging line; it encompasses several processes. Basically, the filling process itself involves depositing beer in an aluminum or steel container with a high speed machine in a controlled environment. Seaming a lid on the filled container immediately after filling completes the "can", and this companion process is described in detail in the following chapter. Can filling, its related processes, and the man/machine interface, especially the latest automation, will be explored in this chapter through four avenues:

1. Evolution of can filling and acquaintance with specific equipment associated with this process in the brewing industry,
2. Step by step explanation of the can filling operation,
3. Specific examples of control techniques presently utilized to monitor beer can filling, and
4. Insights into service required to properly maintain a productive beer can filling operation.

HISTORY

The beginnings of our modern beer canning process is traced back to work done by Louis Pasteur (1876) with German breweries. Shortly thereafter, breweries worldwide started packaging beer in glass bottles, enabling consumers for the first time to take their favorite brew home or transport it beyond the brewery locale. Max Ams' "sanitary can" in 1905 (i.e. three piece metal fully open top flat can) and the introduction soon thereafter of corresponding semi-automatic can filling/seaming equipment launched the modern "can" process. Early can fillers operated at fairly slow speeds of 100 CPM (cans per minute) compared to modern day standards. During the next 40 years, filler speeds increased to only about 250 CPM. However, in the last two decades, the increased demand for convenience packaging, especially in North America, has encouraged the packaging industry to develop more convenient beverage containers. To keep up with this growing demand, manufacturers produced fillers capable of 1000-1250 CPM, as seen in Figure 12-1. With seamers as pacesetters, Cozens (1969), can line economics in the 1970's dictated further increases to high speed fillers capable of over 1500 CPM, Figure 12-2. Further, the desire to minimize packaging costs has now led to the introduction of ultra-high speed fillers which are capable of 2000 CPM from a single machine. Despite the aura associated with the recently introduced ultra-high speed

12-1. Photo of CEMCO 72 spout can filler. (A. Coors Company)

12-2. Photo of H&K 120 spout can filler. (A. Coors Company)

fillers, only a few are operational because the size and cost of these fillers limit their use to large capacity packaging shops. The majority of carbonated beverage operations presently utilize the medium speed fillers (1000 CPM), but machine improvements, and especially increased output per operator, are incentives for conversion to the higher speed equipment.

EQUIPMENT

In addition to the filler, there are two other major areas of the modern can line associated with filling—bulk can handling and fill quality control—that will also be evaluated in this chapter.

Packaging equipment development has historically been led by higher speed progression of fillers/closers, the key producing units; high productive efficiencies of these two units dictate that support equipment also have substantially higher output.

BULK CAN HANDLING

The condition and supply of cans to a filler is a key factor in the success of any filler operation. With the increased speed, empty can handling has become more critical. Can delivery systems utilize either the cell bin trailer concept or the more popular palletized bulk can method.

Cell bin systems are usually associated with nearby, satellite, can manufacturing facilities and are designed to minimize can handling and exposure, especially for aluminum cans.

A typical cell bin trailer is designed as follows: it is an over the road tandem trailer approximately forty-eight feet long with the body consisting of ninety-six lateral can cells holding approximately 130,000 cans. The cells are open on the top for individual cell loading with side discharge doors. To prevent weather and debris from entering the cells the trailer is covered with a tight fitting roll-on tarp. Figure 12-3 shows a typical cell bin trailer.

12-3. Photo of cell bin trailer (A. Coors Company)

12-4. Photo of cell bin can unloading system. (A. Coors Company)

12-5. Photo cans being unloaded from a cell bin.

The operation of a cell bin system works as follows: the cans are loaded on their sides in the cell bins with a loading snorkel at the can manufacturing plant; the trailers are then transported to the brewery's bulk can handling facility; trailers are brought into the BCH (bulk can handling) building and tipped sideways approximately 10°, an operator hooks the auto-unloader (often called a "boot") to the trailer; cans feed by gravity into the unloader as it moves along the trailer a cell at a time; cans are turned 90° in the unloader and deposited on conveyors to the filler. There are two drawbacks to this system; first, it's dependent on a single supply source; and second, the speed of the gravity fed unloader is restricted to approximately 1500 CPM, requiring multiple systems to feed newer high speed fillers. Figure 12-4 shows a cell bin trailer with two auto-unloaders operating. Figure 12-5 is a close-up of cans feeding from trailer cell to unloader.

The most common method for delivering incoming cans to packaging facilities uses palletized cans and a depalletizer system. Several supply sources for cans may be used along with seasonal-surplus warehousing. The physical size of the pallet and tier "height" will vary to accommodate the user's facility "trailers, doorways, depalletizer, etc." There is a wide selection of depalletizers to choose from and they are available with electric or hydraulic drives and manual or semiautomatic controls. Existing empty container depalletizers have speed capabilities in excess of 2000 CPM, therefore are singularly able to feed high speed fillers. The negative side of this system is the exposure and multiple handling of empty containers easily susceptible to damage. A depalletizer system is shown on Figure 12-6.

High speed line economics dictate an uninterrupted container flow to the filler; therefore, regardless of which empty container handling system is chosen, an inventory accumulation control facility is required between supply and filler. This facility may utilize a long single line transport, or large capacity, low speed accumulation tables, sized to provide precise control over expected can supply lapses or surges.

These inventory accumulation systems have changed considerably in the last decade in order to handle the aluminum can and high speeds, as noted by Draebel (1971). Plastic material variations such as Delrin, nylon, Bernco (nylon 6-6), polyethylene, and LF (low friction) chain have replaced most metals for accumulation conveyor table top chain and wearstrips. In addition, most single line conveyors have changed from table top chain to plastic coated cable and can twists now have replaceable plastic guide rails.

RINSER

Empty cans pass through a rinsilizer before entering the filler, as illustrated in Figure 12-7. The rinser guarantees removal of dust and any foreign particles which the containers may have collected in storage or during handling. The system functions by spraying hot, cold, or treated water into the inverted can as it gravity feeds through the rinser. Airjets may be used prior to the water sprays to remove dust, and after the water sprays to help remove water. Cans are twisted back top-up after the rinser prior to filler infeed. To prevent any effect on filling, adequate distance must be provided between rinser and filler for cans to have sufficient time to drain and cool. Many rinsers now have

12-6. Photo of can depalletizer. (A. Coors Company)

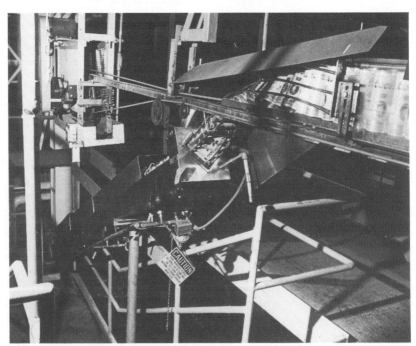

12-7. Photo of empty can rinser. (A. Coors Company)

water conservation systems with a filter, holding tank, and fresh water make-up.

FILLER

A typical beer can filler is a rotary machine with a cylindrical or torrodial tank containing beer and CO_2 counterpressure. It carries the container through pre-indexed stations from infeed to discharge, and during the cycle it feeds the beer through a multi-stage valve system into the container. See Figure 12-8. There are as many variations in details between these filler components as there are filler manufacturers. Several of these differences will be discussed more in depth under the operation section of this chapter.

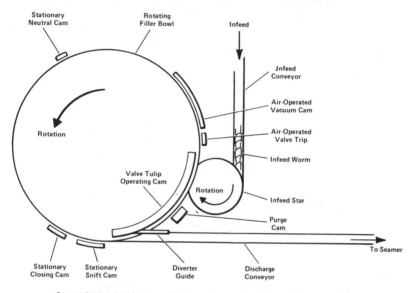

Cans are fed into the infeed star, which places them onto the filler bowl platforms . . . one can beneath each filling valve. After the can is placed on the platform, the valve tulip operating-cam lowers the tulip onto the can top to hold the can in position and to seal the filling valve onto the can. As the bowl rotates, successive cams remove air from the can, charge the can with gas, fill the can with beverage, close the valve and remove residual gas. At the discharge, the valve tulip operating cam again raises the tulip to allow the can to be removed from the filler. After this, the filling valve is purged in preparation for receiving the next empty can.

12-8. Schematic of can filler operation. (Holstein & Kappert Co.)

Can fillers are driven from their adjacent can seamer and, in turn, drive the filler infeed screw or star. The filler/seamer drive is close coupled with variable speed, clutch and brake for precise indexing, finite control, soft starts, and safety.

As previously mentioned, can fillers have had substantial development in the past two decades both in output and product quality control parameters. The most noticeable improvements have been in speed as the 2000 CPM (12 oz.) can filler shown in Figure 12-9. Since most carbonated beverage fillers operate with a basic gravity-counterpressure fill system (although with many different techniques to accomplish same), the size of the empty container opening and overall capacity have direct relation to its speed of filling. Most

12-9. Photo of CEMCO 130 spout filler. (Crown Cork & Seal Co.)

filler manufacturers offer the same fill and control techniques in their machines; their variations are then for output based on the filler's number of fill stations and overall size. Crown Cork and Seal Co. (CEMCO) for instance, presently markets four can fillers of 40, 72, 100, and 130 fill stations; all are able to fill the same size cans, from 2⅛" to 3" diameter and 3⅜" to 7½" in height. The CEMCO fillers vary in overall dimensions from 6'6" diameter for the 40 station to 20'1.5" for the 130 station while their output for 12 oz. cans varies respectively from 600 CPM to 2000 CPM. The Holstein and Kappert Co. (H&K) offers a similar cross section of available can fillers from 50 stations (665 CPM, 12 oz.) to the largest can filler built to date with 165 stations (2000 CPM, 12 oz.) as seen in Figure 12-10.

While machine output is similar between these company's fillers, their techniques to accomplish the fill differs. CEMCO, after infeed, uses an air-lift system to raise the can to a cam operated three tube valve which counterpressures, fills to a ball check, and vents gases back to a vent ring tank separate from the bowl. H&K, after infeed, uses a release cam which lowers a spring-operated valve down onto the can, pre-evacuates, counterpressures, fills to a vent tube gas shut off, and snifts (the release of counterpressure prior to the lowering of the can.) Several other filler suppliers use similar or combinations of these two techniques.

CAN FILLING PROCESS

While it would seem that the filling process could be scientifically set-up to operate each filler with identical settings and get the same results, experience shows that each filler has slightly different specific capabilities.

There are many variables in the filling operation which determine the control of container fill volume and O_2 content. Some of these variables are carbonation, temperature, bubble breaker—foamer, undercover gasser, counterpressure, lift or cam pressure, micromat valve vent settings, and filler speed. The success of the filling process is a combination of filler specialist's knowledge

12-10. Photo of H&K 165 spout filler. (A. Coors Company)

in analyzing these variables, proper filler equipment, and maintenance set-up adjustments.

Starting with cans entering the filler infeed, it is critical that each can is spaced and fed smoothly into the filling station. This requires precise timing of the infeed worm to the infeed star with filler rotation speed. It is essential that the can is completely stabilized on the fill station prior to contact with the filling adapter to prevent can damage and to permit proper filling. There are two basic concepts for can to tube contact prior to can purge. One filler concept uses an air manifold to raise cans on lifts to meet and seal the can to stationary adapters mounted on the filler as it rotates. The other concept is just reversed; as the filler rotates, the valve tulip operating cam lowers the tulip onto the can top, holding the can in position to seal the filling valve onto the can.

The next step in the filling process, after the can and tube are in the sealed position, is the elimination of oxygen from the can by purging with CO_2. One filler method is to counterpressure the can at the opening trip until the bowl and can pressures are equal. At the fill trip, the resultant CO_2-air mixture is released as the container starts filling with liquid. The released CO_2 returns to either the filler bowl or a vent control system. Another method purges the can with CO_2 and then as the filler rotates, a vacuum button on the filling valve contacts a vacuum cam which allows the mixture of air and gas to flow into the vacuum ring on the bowl. After the valve leaves the vacuum cam, gas continues to flow into the can until the pressure inside the can is equal to the gas pressure inside the bowl.

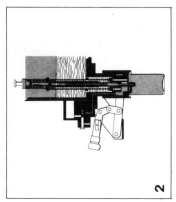

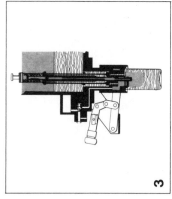

1. **Pre-evacuation**

2. **Counterpressurizing (CO2)**

3. **Filling**

4. **Snifting**

5. **Lowering can-filling element**

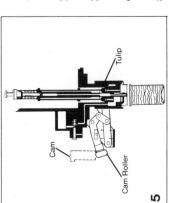

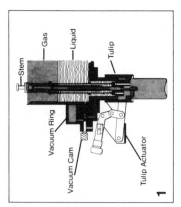

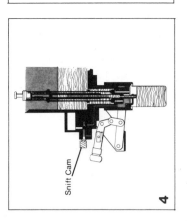

12-11. Schematic of can filling valve. (Holstein & Kappert Co.)

When the bowl and can pressure are equalized using either method mentioned above, the liquid automatically flows into the can by gravity. Counterpressure adjustments will have a direct effect on controlling the rate of fill; if counterpressure settings are raised or lowered, lift pressure settings also may need to be changed to compensate. Additionally, incoming beer supply temperatures are very critical to good filling capabilities—maintaining temperatures near 0°C allows for better fill control. Beer carbonation also plays a major role in the filling process. Carbonation, either too low or extremely high, will have adverse effects on filling.

The filling process stops automatically when the fill level in the can reaches the vent tube opening or check ball shut-off, which blocks the return of CO_2 to the bowl or vent ring. Vent tube fillers control fill using the length of the vent tube for the desired height of fill in the can; check ball fillers use spacer washers and check ball seating rubbers to determine height desired. Some fillers are designed with a Micromat valve to restrict or control the discharge of CO_2 from the container as the can is filling. This valve is very beneficial in increasing or decreasing the rate of flow in containers.

After the can has the desired fill, the valve rotates to a closing cam or trip (depending on type of filler) which closes the filler valve. Then the valve makes contact with either a snift cam or valve trip (here again, depending on filler type) to allow controlled release of any remaining gas from the can prior to the can discharge from the tube or valve. Cemco fillers use the pressure in the can to break the seal. Figure 12-11 shows schematic operation of spring-valve-vent tube type filling.

The liquid level in the bowl of the fillers is maintained through a flow control system. Since liquid continually flows in and out of the bowl, the flow must be balanced precisely. Control set points are used on all fillers to maintain the desired bowl levels. These set point devices transmit signals to either a valve or a variable speed pump in the filler supply line, which reacts to control the flow so as to maintain the desired level in the bowl. The better the level control, the more uniform will be the can fills; bowl levels variations should not exceed ½″. A typical filler level control system is shown in Figure 12-12.

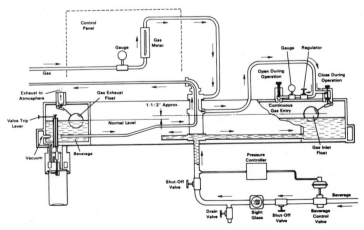

12-12. *Schematic of can filler beer level control. (Holstein & Kappert Co.)*

The can being discharged from the filler lifts follows the same functional concept as the can entering the filler. On fillers using the air manifold, the air shuts off allowing the pull-down cam to lower the lift to the height of the transfer between the filler and seamer. In the Cemco manifold, a shifting spool valve is used to take the lift station to low pressure prior to transfer to reduce spillage. On other filler designs, the valve tulip operating cam raises the tulip and allows the transition of the can to transfer. It is very critical that as the cans leave the discharge of the filler lifts or platforms and enter the transfer bed to the seamer, the can entry contact to the transfer be precise, smooth, and level. Cans stumbling at this point can cause fill losses, O_2 pickup and jams. Also, the distance between the filler discharge and seamer is very critical, as this is also a controllable area for fill and O_2 content.

Located between the filler and seamer, above the transfer bed, is a bubble breaker and/or foamer. A bubble breaker is used to break large bubbles (fish eyes) which contain trapped air. A foamer is used to agitate the beer to induce foaming (mostly CO_2), eliminating head space in the can when the end unit is attached at the seamer. CO_2, water, or steam are used in these units, since they are or can be made sterile. Breweries which elect to use what is termed a "black fill", i.e., no foaming action, would probably not use these units. However, it should be realized that in order to maintain excellent container O_2, elimination of excess O_2 in the container head space is imperative, but a small beer loss must be accepted. Another area of O_2 control is in the undercover gasser area of the seamer, discussed in detail in the SEAMING chapter.

There is a well supported theory that speed has a direct correlation on fill and O_2 content of containers. Speed has to be regulated to compensate for variations in beer temperature and carbonation. It is also felt that each filler has its own specific capabilities, and good operating parameters vary from filler to filler, even the same models from the same manufacturer.

BEER QUALITY PARAMETERS

The container filling and seaming operations have an effect on numerous beer quality parameters. The two characteristics that are probably most directly affected are the container fill level (volume) and air or O_2 level. The first of these two characteristics, the fill volume, is important because of legal ramifications and manufacturing practices. The second characteristic, O_2, has a direct effect on the shelf life and the flavor of the product. These two characteristics will be discussed separately.

FILL LEVEL

As stated previously, the fill is important from both a legal and good manufacturing practice standpoint. The United States Government monitors fill levels, and over- or underfills, outside of certain control limits, may result in federal penalties or fines. Additionally, many states also request that the average container fill volume be within certain control limits as stated on the label. In some states (California) individual containers must be at least infinitesimally above the declaration of content on the container. Breweries throughout the country use various sampling and measuring methods to meet these standards.

At Coors, an automatic fill volume check weighing system is used to monitor fill levels. This system automatically takes cans off an accumulator table, places them onto a scale, weighs the individual can, inputs the actual can weight into a computer and then, using standard statistical quality control methods, calculates the fills and automatically reports the weight data back to the filler operator. In detail, this system sidetracks one can off a line approximately every 40 seconds, weighs the can and inputs gross weight into the computer. The computer then subtracts the predetermined tare weight (the empty weight of the can and end unit) of the container and stores the net weight of the contained beer. After the net weight of ten individual containers has been taken, the computer calculates the statistical average and range of these ten containers. This ten-container average is then immediately transferred to the filler operator on a display unit in the filler room. The supervisor also has a display unit showing all of the data for each filler including the last seven average sub-groups of ten containers and the sub-group range. See Figure 12-13. If the average or range of a sample of ten containers exceeds a predetermined specification a light automatically comes on to reflect an out of control condition. Also, any time seven consecutive averages of ten containers is on one side of the predetermined value, the light will come on to signal a shift in the filling process.

12-13. *Photo of fill check weight machine. (A. Coors Company)*

As noted, with this system a ten can average and range is recorded every seven minutes. To do this without an automatic system would require sampling by one person per shift for every three can lines. Most breweries without an automatic system take one sample of five containers about every two hours. It can be seen that the automatic check weighing system gives better fill volume data with a much faster feedback response to the filler operator. If an out of control condition occurs the operator can take corrective action within minutes and adjust his filler.

The fill volume target limits (± limits from a known or desired average) used in this system are designed to control the "outgoing" container fill volume. There are two schools of thought on outgoing fill volume: one is "to contain" and the other is "to deliver". The container "to contain" fill volume is the amount of actual beer in a container while the "to deliver" is the amount of beer a consumer will get out of the container. The control limits that are established must be realistic so that the filler operator, who is the controlling force using the equipment and beer he has available, has a realistic chance of meeting these limits. Limits commonly used are ± 3 grams from a specified target average. The target average can be a declaration of content (D/C) or an overfill condition of 0.10%, 0.20%, or whatever is desired. This target average value does not have any effect on the ± 3 gram limit. The ± 3 gram limit is determined by the capability of the filling equipment, product, people, etc. The capabilities of the filler equipment is determined by taking a three revolution sample of the filler to determine the "within" station and "between" station variance of the filler.

Daily reports, generated by use of the computer, show the number of containers that were sampled on that packaging line, the deviation from the target average for the date (the daily average deviation from average goal is ± 0.5 grams), the average daily range, and each filler's capability. See Figure 12-14.

```
            CAN LINE OPERATION 12/ 1/81      16:16:28

CAN LINE  FILLER  LINE    LINE   DEVIATION OF LAST 7 SAMPLES FROM TARGET VALUE
NUMBER    DISPLAY STATUS  RANGE  SAMPLE   S-1    S-2    S-3    S-4    S-5    S-6

   1       1.4          0   6.7    1.4   -0.9   -0.6    0.3    0.0    1.2   -0.4
   2       1.0          0   3.2    1.0    2.3    1.7    1.3    1.6    1.6    0.0
   3       1.7          0  14.2    1.7   -1.1   -0.1   -0.1   -2.0    1.0    0.5
   4      -0.9          0   7.0   -0.9   -0.8   -0.6    0.2    0.1   -0.1    0.1
   5       0.0   CALIB. 0   0.0    0.0    0.0    0.0    0.0    0.0    0.0    0.0
   6       0.0   CALIB. 0   0.0    0.0    0.0    0.0    0.0    0.0    0.0    0.0
  7-1      1.0          0   9.7    1.0    0.5   -0.9   -1.1   -0.4    1.0    0.7
  7-2      4.0   ALARM  2   6.0    4.0    0.1    1.1    1.7    1.7   -0.9    1.9
  8-1      0.6          0   2.8    0.6   -0.3   -0.2    0.3    0.2   -0.6   -0.4
  8-2     -1.0          0   6.2   -1.0    0.0   -0.1   -0.5    0.1   -0.3   -1.0
  9-1      1.0   ACK.   0   4.7    1.0    0.4    1.4    0.3    0.0    0.6    1.0
  9-2      0.0          0   0.0    0.0    0.0    0.0    0.0    0.0    0.0    0.0
 10-1      0.0          0   0.0    0.0    0.0    0.0    0.0    0.0    0.0    0.0
 10-2     -0.6   ACK.   0   3.8   -0.6   -0.3    0.7    0.7    0.7   -0.9    1.2

BJR TGV
>

            DAILY REPORT 11/29/81

LINE      NUMBER OF    AVERAGE DEVIATION      AVERAGE       CAPABILITY
NUMBER    CANS SAMPLED FROM TARGET VALUE      RANGE

   1         20          0.4 GMS.          16.9 GMS.       32.9 GMS.
   2       1250          0.3 GMS.           9.1 GMS.       17.7 GMS.
   3          0          0.0 GMS.           0.0 GMS.        0.0 GMS.
   4       1630         -0.2 GMS.           7.9 GMS.       15.3 GMS.
   5          0          0.0 GMS.           0.0 GMS.        0.0 GMS.
   6          0          0.0 GMS.           0.0 GMS.        0.0 GMS.
  7-1         0          0.0 GMS.           0.0 GMS.        0.0 GMS.
  7-2         0          0.0 GMS.           0.0 GMS.        0.0 GMS.
  8-1       2030        -0.0 GMS.           6.8 GMS.       13.3 GMS.
  8-2       1890        -0.3 GMS.           7.2 GMS.       14.1 GMS.
  9-1       1920         0.1 GMS.           9.2 GMS.       17.9 GMS.
  9-2         0          0.0 GMS.           0.0 GMS.        0.0 GMS.
 10-1         0          0.0 GMS.           0.0 GMS.        0.0 GMS.
 10-2       1990         0.3 GMS.           8.2 GMS.       16.0 GMS.
```

12-14. Printout of can check weights. (A. Coors Company)

On a typical CEMCO filling machine of 72 stations, it was determined during tests that there was a large "within station" variance. A method to control the flow of beer through each station was devised, thus resulting in a decrease in the "within" station variance. The "between station" variance was then investigated and reduced by an improved maintenance system. This capability study resulted in a 50% reduction in the capability target limits, and as a result the filler operator has more latitude in operating his equipment. This overall capability is monitored by the check weighing system. Using statistical methods, the legal requirements were also considered in arriving at this value. As stated in the filling section, the temperature of the beer and the CO_2 content have an effect on the fill volume, and therefore they are also considered in these values.

Another part of the outgoing fill volume control system is "Filtec" and/or "Accuray" machines as seen in Figures 12-15 and 12-16. Both filtecs and accurays are often used in a dual system since studies have shown this increases the reliability of the outgoing product. The filtec and/or accuray are "go no go" type of inspection devices that inspect the container and say it is either a good container or a low filled container. This system is not a total control system since it does not give the actual weights. It is a reject procedure and should not be confused with the automatic check weighing system. These devices reject gross underfilled containers, meaning the container must be underfilled about 5% from its D/C in order to be considered a gross underfilled container.

AIR CONTROL

The lower the O_2 content of the packaged beer, the better the flavor stability and the shelf life will be. Once O_2 dissolves in beer there is no practical way to remove it. A number of studies have been conducted attempting to correlate the fill volume with O_2 level of the filled product; however, the data produced have not shown good correlation as of this writing. In order to reduce the O_2 level in a container, the foam over the beer must be dense and level with the top of the container. This can and does result in a large beer loss if not controlled. As previously stated, the dense foam is obtained by the use of steam, CO_2, or air in a foamer. This system creates dense foam in the beer at the top of the container head space when the end unit comes into contact with the container prior to the seaming operation.

There are three methods of measurement of O_2 in use; they use 1) Gasometric air test meter, 2) Dissolved oxygen meter, and 3) Coors package beer analyzer.

GASOMETRIC

This method has been used for a number of years and is still the method used by most breweries. Its use is covered in Chapter XXII, Quality Assurance.

DISSOLVED OXYGEN METER

An example of the second method is the Hays meter. This system is not as popular for packaged beer as the gasometric because such meters appear to

12-15. Photo of filtec beer level control. (A. Coors Company)

12-16. Photo of accuray beer level control. (A. Coors Company)

have less repeatability and reliability under plant conditions. The meters have a tendency to drift and readability is also a major concern.

COORS PACKAGE BEER ANALYZER

The current method of measuring O_2 at Coors utilizes the Coors Package Beer Analyzer, as seen in Figure 12-17. This system uses an ultrasonic conditioning bath, a temperature stabilization bath, and the package beer analyzer. A random sample of two containers every hour from each can filler is sampled and analyzed. Each can is placed in a temperature stabilization bath as a

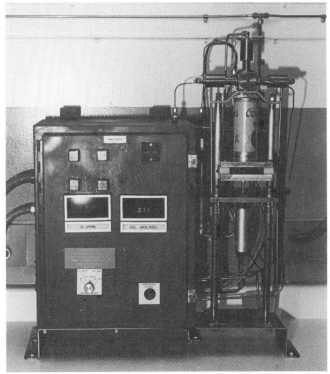

12-17. Photo of air analyzer. (A. Coors Company)

constant temperature is a vital requirement. Once the temperature has been stabilized, the O_2 content of the container is taken automatically by the package beer analyzer and the O_2 value obtained is displayed on a digital display. As in the program with fill control, the O_2 readings of the cans are immediately made available to the filler operator. If possible, corrective adjustments on the filler are taken immediately to reduce the O_2 level in beer. Figure 12-18 shows an O_2 analyzer print-out for a typical can line at Coors.

The O_2 measurement values used for container air control in most breweries are given in parts per million (PPM). As stated before, the goal of any brewery is to maintain the flavor and shelf life of its product, therefore zero O_2 content in every container of beer would be the ideal situation. However, this is not possible and O_2 limits have been established. Since there are several measurement methods, O_2 value parameters will vary among breweries so specific numbers will not be discussed.

FILLING OPERATION SUPPORT

Two very key elements in every filling operation are biological control and a structured cleaning program. Since quality has a top priority in the industry, these functions of the filling operation are of vital importance. Regardless of the filling process, "sterile" or "pasteurized", microbiological control and

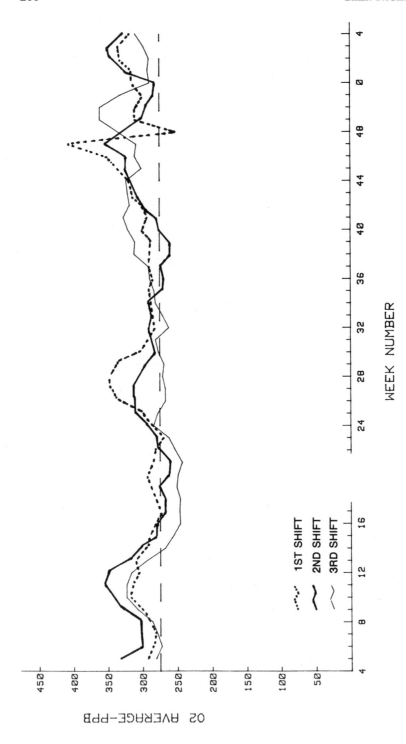

12-18. *Graph of O₂ levels. (Author)*

cleanliness play a major role in assuring that a quality product is being packaged. The success of bio control and proper cleaning is the responsibility of all personnel assigned to the filling area. Excellent training and written procedures which cover proper cleaning techniques and chemical usages are essential.

The filler design and the overall environment surrounding the filler are critical. The design should provide areas as open and accessible as possible to provide thorough cleaning. Equipment must be able to withstand extreme conditions involving heat, moisture, and chemicals. The use of parts and equipment made of chromium-nickel steel or stainless steel is very practical and is becoming very common because these materials eliminate the need of painting and prevent the problem of rust. Floors and walls made from stainless steel for special "sterile" filler rooms are excellent as they require minimum maintenance and can be easily cleaned. These materials are also excellent in coping with problems involving heat, moisture, and chemicals.

MICROBIOLOGICAL CONTROL

To ensure consistent control, measurable parameters should be set for each critical point of the filling process. After the critical points are identified, samples are taken for control data. The number of samples taken may vary from point to point of sampling and frequencies are established according to process flow and sample confidence levels. Targets are set for average data and also upper control limits. It is very important that upper action targets be defined as this is the time to react to problems causing an upper control condition. Sample processing procedures are based on standard laboratory methods or those developed by company or industry research.

As was stated earlier, the number and frequency of samples taken will vary, as will sample types, sizes, and media used. Laboratory results should be reported daily to production personnel and supervision so that they can react immediately with corrective measures to eliminate problems. Results can also be reported on a weekly or period basis, which is useful to show rising or lowering trends and for historical purposes.

Filler operators play a major role in microbiological control, especially if the product is being filled within a "sterile fill" atmosphere. Filling personnel in a "sterile fill" area are required to wear clean white uniforms and hair coverings. It should be emphasized that personnel in either regular or "sterile fill" areas must follow strict sanitary rules; they are handling a food product. The net result of good microbiological control should be a better product with longer shelf life.

CLEANING—INTERIOR/EXTERIOR

Chapter XXVII, Cleaning and Sanitation, covers the subject in more detail but since the cleaning and sanitation of the filler is so necessary to a successful packaging operation, it is important to present here the principles involved in cleaning and sanitizing a can filler.

The key to thorough cleaning is proper technique. If you combine technique, trained personnel, the right chemicals, heat sanitization, and sufficient downtime scheduled for cleaning, the net result should be a good cleaning program.

Having quality control personnel monitoring the cleaning process along with line personnel can be very beneficial.

Each filler and piece of support equipment for the filler system has a cleaning frequency recommended by equipment manufacturers and established by research and bio testing during operation. The amount of running time before a filler requires external cleaning depends on each company's requirement for "sterility", and data information from the bio tests. Typically, it is essential, after any extended run, that the filler be cleaned externally and internally with a caustic cleaning solution. Filler support equipment is cleaned each time the filler is cleaned, and fillers are always heat sanitized before the start of each production run, if "sterile" filling is required.

One of the first things to remember when cleaning is clean from top to bottom. The two processes normally used in external filler and equipment cleaning are direct or high pressure, and immersion with low pressure wash down. The high pressure process tends to be more effective as it has a more cutting effect in the removal of grease, residue, and debris. This system is most often used in cleaning the majority of the filler, the transfer chain from filler to closer, infeed and discharge conveyors, and also the closer. The immersion process can achieve similar results but is not as time effective. The low pressure system works well to wash off the filler after shutdown and washing accessible areas such as walls and floors.

External cleaning with a high pressure system uses a mild alkaline soap and can also include foam cleaning with a strong liquid caustic solution. Acid solutions are used externally to clean equipment when mineral or stain removal is necessary. There may be times when fillers are cleaned internally with a caustic solution if removal of beer stone is necessary. Filler systems using CO_2 may sanitize the system with live steam.

Most fillers today are equipped with cleaning-in-place (CIP) cups for internal cleaning and can be sanitized by using a temperature of 80°C (175°F) for at least 30 minutes. Either steam or hot water can be used but hot water is probably more satisfactory as it offers a scrubbing action when circulating and its temperature is easier to control than steam. A CIP system consists of water holding tank, pump for circulation, a heat exchanger, and a cooler. The flow of the water is in a direction which is the reverse of normal beer flow. The same water used for sanitizing can be used for cooling down the filler by shutting off the steam to the heat exchanger and turning on the chilled water to the cooler. An additional sanitizing element can be achieved by adding 25 PPM iodophor or chlorine to the cooled down water and circulating it.

MAINTENANCE

As in the case with any precision high-production machine, it is important to periodically check a filler for wear, alignment, or out-of-tolerance conditions. This procedure, known as PM (Preventive Maintenance) is designed to prevent costly work stoppages because of breakdowns, and is as important as the actual operation of a filler.

All filler manufacturers supply an instruction manual with their machines detailing proper inspection procedures. Following is a typical (suggested) can filler PM table listing minimum frequency, item, and procedures[*]:

Frequency	Item	Procedure
As Needed	No Can/No Fill Sensors (if equipped)	Check setting to cans, flag and gear.
Twice Daily	Lube Pump System	Check reservoirs for level.
Daily	Valves	Check for tightness and leaks.
Daily	Platforms and Lifts (if equipped)	Observe as filler is running for level and free up and down movement (if has lifts).
	Entire Filler	Check for dents, cracks, discarded cans and remove.
Weekly (or at 100-150 hours)	Screws on Lift Cylinders (if equipped) and all star wheels	Check for tightness and check timing.
	Worm and Star Infeed	Check timing and setting of control switch, points for wear.
	Air Manifold Filter and Regulator (if equipped)	Drain any accumulated oil from these units.
Monthly (or at 400-600 hours)	Screws on Platforms and Cams	Check for tightness.
	Cams	Check for wear and re-adjust.
	Check Balls or Vent Tubes, Sealing Rubbers and Springs	Check for buoyancy or plugging and sealing ability.
	All Fastenings	Check for tightness.
	Pull Down Cam (if equipped) and Striker Cams	Check for adequate lube and wear. Remove deposits, repolish, and adjust for proper position.
	All Star Wheels	Check for excessive play and correct can fit.
	All Gear Reducers	Check for proper oil level.
Bi-Monthly	Can Seals	Check for wear, replace if needed.
Six Months	Packing Gland and all Bearings	Check for good seal and wear.
	Ring Gear and Drive	Check backlash between gears.
	Pinion, Couplings	Must not exceed .007″. Check for lubrication.
	Entire Filler	Check level.

[*]Provided by Crown Cork and Seal Co.

LUBRICATION

Lubrication is a vital part of a PM program. Most filler manufacturers list three (four, if lift equipped) critical areas of concern for lubrication to maintain good filler operation:

1. Grease Fittings: Usually located on a central block, lines lead to internal or main bearings. Grease once each shift.
2. Gearboxes: Usually #90 oil. Change oil every 2500 hours (or when contaminated, if operating a "sterile fill" process).
3. Infeed Star and Main Bowl Gear: Brush with grease every 120 hours.
4. Lifts: Usually equipped with auto-oilers. Check levels each shift.

Minimum lubrication frequencies are recommended by the filler manufacturers and are designed to give maximum safety for the filler's operation. The type of lube, i.e. regular, bio-degradable, or FDA approved, will also vary with the individual packaging shop's type of fill.

TROUBLESHOOTING

Most filler instruction manuals include a troubleshooting guide which provides a ready reference for some of the more common and serious operating problems. The following guide is supplied with Holstein & Kappert (non-lift type) can fillers and applies only to that type. It is used here only to illustrate the detail that should be readily available for each type of filler in use.

Symptom	Cause	Solution
A. Overfill	1. Damaged sealing rubber.	a. Replace rubber.
	2. Product snift leaks.	a. Installation should be tight.
		b. Damaged gasket.
	3. Vacuum snift leaks.	a. Installation should be tight.
		b. O-ring may be damaged on poppit.
	4. Can damaged.	a. Check filler infeed alignment.
	5. Screen damaged.	a. Replace screen.
		b. Check for proper vent-tube installation.
	6. Valve block leaks.	a. Valve O-ring could be installed incorrectly.
	7. Vent-tube not seated.	a. Vent tube installation must be snug.
B. Underfill	1. Screen damaged or dirty.	a. Replace screen, check vent-tube installation.
	2. Bowl level low.	a. Set bowl level correctly with float.
		b. Check pressure valve.
	3. Valve lever too low.	a. Loose clampscrew adjust lever.
	4. Neutral cam too high.	a. Lower neutral cam.
	5. Sealing rubber worn or cut.	a. Replace sealing rubber.
	6. Vacuum system not working.	a. Check cam position.
		b. Check for plugged vacuum hole.
C. No Fill	1. Can damaged.	a. Check infeed.
	2. Contact rubber damaged.	a. Replace rubber.
	3. Vacuum valve stuck open.	a. Vacuum valve must be clean.
	4. Snift valve stuck open.	a. Snift valve must be clean.
	5. Filling valve sticking.	a. Remove bent top works. This indicates installation problem.
	6. Filling valve spring broken.	a. Replace spring.
	7. Tulip seal worn.	a. Replace seal.
	8. Neutral cam too high.	a. Adjust cam.
D. Heavy Foaming While Can Leaves Filler	1. Vacuum pump not working.	a. Vacuum pump must be operating correctly.
	2. Three-way valve positioned incorrectly.	a. Valve must be returned to operating position after cleaning.
	3. Vacuum too low.	a. Look for vacuum system leaks.

Symptom	Cause	Solution
	4. Product too warm.	a. After prolonged stoppage product pressure in filler may need to be increased.
	5. Filler pressure low.	a. Check pressure controller and pressure valve.
	6. Cans not clean.	a. Foreign substance can react with product.
	7. Bowl level too high.	a. Check float orifice for damage.
	8. Vacuum valves not operating.	a. Check vacuum cam for correct location.
	9. Dirty screen.	a. Clean screen.
	10. Damaged can.	a. Check infeed.
E. High Air in Can	1. High air may be in product entering filler.	a. Check air in product entering filler.
	2. Vacuum too low.	a. Vacuum system must operate correctly.
	3. Can underfilled.	a. Too little liquid allows larger % of air reading.
F. High Bowl Level	1. Damaged orifice on float.	a. Replace orifice insert.
	2. Gas pressure too low.	a. Adjust regulator to provide sufficient gas supply.
	3. Exhaust float does not close orifice.	a. Float may be stuck in down position.
		b. Float may be leaking.
	4. Excessive product pressure.	a. Check pressure valve and controller.
	5. Gas not entering bowl.	a. Broken gas hose.
		b. Plugged center column.
	6. Float not adjusted.	a. Remove float and readjust correctly.
	7. Gasket and butterflies leaking.	a. Replace gaskets.
G. Low Bowl Level	1. Float not adjusted correctly.	a. Remove float and readjust correctly.
	2. Product valve not operating.	a. Check air supply to instruments, controller must operate correctly.
	3. Over pressure on bowl.	a. Float cap must be opened for venting during start-up.
H. Erratic Bowl Level	1. Pressure controller not adjusted.	a. Pressure system should be properly tuned with position of adjustments recorded.
I. Damage at Stop Gate	1. Stop gate positioned incorrectly.	a. Adjust stop gate.
	2. Rail positioned incorrectly.	a. Check rail distance from can stop.
	3. Can stop pressure incorrect.	a. Adjust pressure regulator.
J. Damage at Infeed Worm	1. Infeed worm not properly timed.	a. Time worm with infeed star.
	2. Infeed worm rail loose.	a. Broken spring on rail.
		b. Rail too tight on swivel shafts.
	3. Can not fed smoothly into infeed worm.	a. Wear strips may be worn.
	4. Infeed worm damaged.	a. Replace worm.
	5. Wrong infeed worm.	a. Replace worm.

Symptom	Cause	Solution
K. Damage at Infeed Star	1. Star not timed with infeed worm.	a. Time worm with infeed star.
	2. Wear plates not proper height.	a. Plates should be replaced periodically. b. Watch for bent plate.
	3. Screw head protruding.	a. Screw heads need to be flush with wear plates.
	4. Star pocket vs. guide clearance insufficient.	a. Guide casting loose and shifted.
	5. Star not timed with platforms.	a. Star gear needs to be adjusted.

Since the filler is the heart of a packaging line, the goal of troubleshooting is operational safety, protection of product quality and productivity. Troubleshooting should follow three basic rules.

1. *Analyze Carefully:* Carefully analyze each problem to determine its most likely and logical cause before making any adjustments or repairs. Do not solve symptoms; solve problems.
2. *Follow a Logical Sequence:* Proceed with corrective measures and adjustments in a logical sequence from the most likely to the least likely causes. Make sure any debris (cans—often the cause of problems) is cleaned out of the filler before proceeding with adjustments or repairs.
3. *Do One Step at a Time:* Make only one correction or adjustment at a time and observe results before proceeding to another adjustment. If the adjustment does not correct the situation, restore the original setting before making a different adjustment.

SUMMARY

Safety of the Operation

In a successful packaging operation, safety must have top priority. Safety training on filler operation and filler area environment should be included in every production and maintenance job description. Safety conscious personnel are operationally responsible.

Continued emphasis must be placed on good housekeeping practices because a clean area creates a safe and quality working environment. It is the responsibility of management to provide a filling area with equipment designed and installed with safety in mind. Labeling of the filler to indicate danger areas is a must. Proper safety gear such as footwear, clothing, face shields, and gloves are essential for the clean-up personnel. The usage and understanding of chemical ingredients is very important and should be included with the filler operator procedures. Most important, "equipment tag out" procedures are a must for operators and maintenance personnel and must be adhered to at all times.

Importance of Quality Control of Program

Quality control is a very vital function in the packaging of any product. It is the check and balance needed to maintain a quality filling operation. Production personnel operating fillers need hourly, daily, and weekly data covering bio control, O_2, and fill content. The need for monitoring alcohol, ballings, and carbonation is also performed by Quality Control and are checks needed prior and during the filling operation.

Quality is the key factor in consumer acceptance so it is important that Quality Control and Production personnel work together in the filling operation.

Productivity Associated with Filling and Packaging

Productivity is one of the keys to the financial success of any business. Stable or increasing productivity normally indicate a successful business.

Knowledgeable personnel, plus well designed and carefully maintained equipment is a formula for excellent productivity. Each filler has its own capabilities in speed and overall performance. Operational trends in filler performance ultimately determine the overall line productivity.

References for further reading:

Cozens, G.R. "Canning Line of the Future", *Brewers Digest,* May, 1969.

Draebel, Jorgen "New Concepts and Materials in Bottle and Can Handling" *Brewers Digest,* October, 1971.

Nekola, William "Back to Basics in the Bottleshop", *MBAA Technical Quarterly,* Vol. 3, No. 1, 1966.

Nigrelli, B.J. "High Speed Packaging" *MBAA Technical Quarterly,* Vol. 3, No. 3, 1966.

Pasteur, Louis "Studies on Fermentation (Trans. Etudes Sur La Biere)" Krause Reprint, 1969.

CHAPTER XIII

CAN SEAMING

BY J.F. HEUER

INTRODUCTION

The preservation of beer quality is premier, and in cans it is dependent on proper mating of lid to can, an operation commonly referred to as "seaming" or "closing". The modern double seam is the result of interlocking five thicknesses of can and lid with a sealing compound in two operations, assuring a hermetic seal, i.e., air-, liquid-, and bacteria-tight, thus preventing leakage and spoilage. Beer production and processing are of little value unless the completed closed can is durable enough to withstand internal pressures, high speed packing, storage, and, finally, distribution to consumer.

This chapter first addresses the evolution of seaming, including equipment and lids, with specifications on types of equipment presently used and latest state-of-the-art. The chapter's main emphasis is to describe the man/machine relation necessary to insure good seams in a beer packaging operation and is twofold:

1. to provide basic seaming operation data, including closing machine function, cleaning, lubrication techniques and programmed maintenance;

2. to acquaint operating personnel with proper seam testing, identifying common specific problems and their causes together with corrective procedures for continuing control.

HISTORY

In the late 1700's most of Europe was at war with France whose armies extended over great distances. Their armies subsisted mostly on salted meats and bread, suffering the ravages of nutritional diseases such as scurvy. The French Government, gravely concerned with the problem, offered a prize to any citizen who could devise a method of preserving food for transport. After 14 years of diligent work, Nicolas Appert won the prize. His theory of sufficiently heating food and excluding air in cork-sealed glass containers, thereby keeping food unspoiled, is the principle of modern canning.

Necessity was the impetus that developed better containers, equipment and timesaving methods from Appert's crude beginning. A patent was granted in 1810, by England's King George III, to Peter Durand for the use of tin-coated steel containers. Two fellow Englishmen, John Hall and Bryan Donkin, further developed Durand's idea to tin-coated iron cans, at the rate of ten per day. The hole-and-cap tin canister was then utilized for many decades; its body had a soldered side seam and ends with a hole for filling before the final cap was soldered on by hand.

In 1900 a German immigrant to the U.S., Max Ams, had the inventive genius to develop the technique for the open top sanitary can. The "Ams

Can" enabled food and beverages to be filled rapidly in a fully open tin can topped with a gasket-sealed crimp-on lid by an automatic machine. This can, similar to containers in use today, in two decades replaced the majority of former types of commercial food containers. The crimp-on lid was soon improved to the now universally used double seam, enabling canning at higher internal pressures such food and liquids as pasteurized carbonated beverages and beer.

Improvements in canning since 1900 have been principally associated with progression in the speed of the fillers and closers after Ams' initial technique was mastered. The original Ams can equipment operated at about 50-60 cans per hour. 1910 era equipment ran at 40 CPM (cans per minute) and by the late 1930's had reached speeds of 150-200 CPM. In another decade, closer speeds again doubled to over 500 CPM. The 1960's craze of consumers for take home beverages gave the impetus for manufacturers to develop high-speed closers of 1200-1600 CPM operating in breweries today. Demand for even higher speed and efficiency has seen the advent in 1980 of ultra-fast closers capable of 2000 CPM.

EQUIPMENT

Double Seamer

The double seamer or closing machine as used by most breweries "rolls" the top or lid component onto the can body, forming a hermetic seal between the two parts. Double seamers are so named because two distinct operations are performed by the machine: first the seam is "interlocked" or formed; second, the seam is "tightened" or sealed. There are a variety of double seamers presently being utilized, but all fall into three basic categories; *differential, stationary, and rotating.*

Differential

The differential double seamer, or DDS, uses profiled rails or rings in place of the roll mechanism on the other two types of seamers. Cans with lids rotate between the rails causing the seam to form. Although in detail the operation is different, the same basic five layer double seam is the end result. The DDS, or sometimes called "Rail Seamer" has special application in the food industry, but its speeds have not been developed sufficiently for needs of high speed beer filling/closing.

Stationary

In a stationary or can-stand-still seamer, the can body and end component are held stationary on a chuck by a lift while seaming rolls revolve around both can parts. Most seamers of this type have two diametrically opposed first and second operation seaming rolls equally spaced in a seaming head (however, there are a few stationary machines with multiple seaming heads, each with four opposed seaming rolls). Cans are transferred from the first seaming head to the second head by a turret. Twin-head seamers of this type are normally run at speeds to 85 CPM, but there are some four-head versions running 180 CPM.

Rotating

The can-rotating seamer in the last several decades has had the most development due to its adaptability to higher speeds. In a rotating seamer the can and end components are held between a driven rotating chuck and base plate lift. First and second seaming rolls respectively, driven by their own inertia, are brought in contact with the can/lid to form the seam. Some rotating type machines have free revolving or non-driven lifters and are more susceptible to can skid problems, therefore limited in speed. The vast majority of seamers utilized by breweries are of the rotating type with driven chuck and lift. Machines of 6 to 12 seaming heads and single lid feeds are the most common and operate at speeds from 400-1600 CPM. (Figure 13-1) Several manufacturers have recently further developed this type seamer with dual lid feeds into 12, 16, and 18 seaming head machines capable of 1800-2000 CPM. (Figure 13-2)

In addition to the three types of seaming machines, seamers also have available four categories of closing condition to exclude or minimize pickup O_2 in canning: atmospheric, steam flow, cold vacuum, and most common to breweries, under-cover gassing (CO_2). In practice, this operation, if utilized, takes place in the seamer over the top of the can immediately prior to mating the can with lid. By definition, the closing condition determines the type of apparatus attached to, or made part of, the seamer for either gas, steam, and vacuum operation. No mechanism is required for atmospheric operation. Many manufacturers offer seamers with or without the under-cover options.

Although the largest can usage per capita is in the U.S., the use of the recyclable aluminum can is causing can consumption ratios to increase outside North America. Therefore, the list of seamer manufacturers is extensive and world wide, although centered primarily in North America. The majority of brewers utilize the multi-head rotating type seamer with under-cover gassing because of its speed and air/fill control capabilities. The following is a brief discussion of the principle components of this type of seamer.

Seamer Components
1. Drive.

Whichever brand and size of seaming machine chosen, it will have several drive alternatives. Since the seamer usually drives the can filler, manufacturers of seamers work closely with filler suppliers to mate their respective machines properly. Both suppliers will have the necessary engineering data for this marriage and can suggest several specific filler/closer combinations based on their own machine's operational parameters.

The match-up is accomplished by coupling the filler to the drive mechanism of the seamer and includes an in-motion timing device to synchronize the two machines. To compensate for operational jams and to provide safety, the drive shaft incorporates a clutch and brake, especially in large high speed units. The seamer's own propulsion unit is one of three variable speed systems: commonly an electric D.C. motor; an Eddy Current motor; and, thirdly, a hydraulic drive. Size of the drive motor, including some two-speed, will vary from 7½ to 30 HP on the majority of seamers in use running up to speeds of 1600 CPM. The 1980 ultra-high speed closers of 1800-2000 CPM use 40 to 60 HP electric motors, with two-speed combinations. The use of variable speed drives provides operation flexibility for changing conditions of products or containers and offers low spill start-ups. The drive systems themselves are controlled with solid state electronics. The latest equipment offers PLC (Programmable Logic Control) and micro-process control.
2. Infeed.

The infeed section, as the name implies, is where cans and lids are fed into

13-2. *Ultra-fast seamer, the FMC 952 (Adolph Coors Co.)*

13-1. *Commonly used seamer, the Angelus 120L. (Adolph Coors Co.)*

the seamer. The can portion, referred to as the transfer, is a conveyor from filler to seamer. This transfer conveyor is actually a track with guides and a stainless horizontal or vertical chain (or combination of both) with lugs to push cans at proper spacing. On the transfer conveyor near the seamer is located the mechanism to synchronize lid feed to can feed, called NC/NC or NC/NL (no can/no cover or no lid). Slow to moderate speed closers use a trip lever to actuate cover feed while high speed machines now use a proximity switch, (two for dual lid feeds). At the termination of the transfer conveyor inside the closer is the can feed turret incorporating under-cover gassing.

Lids are manually fed from their protective bags into a vertical magazine, which gravity feeds on demand triggered by a proximity switch, into a cover feed turret inside the closer. High speed systems are now being utilized with automatic remotely located lid feeds. One operator continuously places lid bags on several carousel type machines which in turn feed several seamers. Sensors are located on lid feed and under-cover-gasser, stopping the closer if either supply is interrupted.

3. *Center Column.*

Actual seaming of lid to can takes place in the center section of a closer in the seaming turret or sometimes referred to as mould turret. The turret has pockets corresponding in number (6 to 18) to attached powered seaming chuck and lift assemblies. The seaming chucks or spindle assemblies each consist of several parts mounted on sturdy bearings. The chuck itself, made from hardened material, is profiled to correspond with the particular lid being run. Through its center is a cam actuated knock-out rod (or make-up pad) which puts slight pressure on lid during can to lid make-up, to control the lid as it is being placed on the can. It contacts the lid again at the discharge to prevent the can and lid from sticking on the chuck. Mounted on the spindle adjacent to the chuck are the first and second operation seaming rolls, usually finitely adjustable for seam countersink and seam thickness.

4. *Discharge.*

A discharge turret completes the final operational sequence of the closer. Synchronized with the previous operating turrets, it guides the seamed can off the lifts and guides it onto a discharge conveyor. In case of jams, safety stops actuating the electric brake are located on the upper discharge rail.

Closers now incorporate automatic lubrication systems that operate while the machine is in full production. Both grease and oil, including FDA grades, are pumped to the many precision bearings of the machine through injectors, flooding or immersion.

As aforementioned, closing machine options are extensive and offer the beer packaging operator a wide range of choices depending on his needs. Largeness and ultra-high speed is not always good for everyone, so a prospective canner should be happy to know that the manufacturers offer the latest seaming machine technology on a wide range of machines.

The primary machines presently marketed in North America for breweries range from 6 to 18 spindle heads with output of 400 to 2000 CPM. This equipment includes the latest electronics (NC/NL, jam sensors, solid state, PLC), auto lubrication, variable speed, cover and code markers, improved safety and automatic shut offs, less noise, under-cover-gassing or steam, and improved bio control and cleaning with extensive use of stainless steel. In general, efficient seaming machines.

Seamer Capabilities

A chart showing the capabilities of some popular seamers, including the latest high speed models of three manufactors, follows. The list is provided to give a brief cross section of representative available seaming equipment and is not intended to be complete.

Angelus Sanitary Can Machine Company

Model	61H UCG
Spindles	6
Min/Max Can Diameter	2.00″-4.25″ (51mm-108mm)
Min Max Can Height	1.625″-8.00″ (41mm-203mm)
Horsepower Required	15
Speed	Up to 600 CPM

Model	120L UCG
Spindles	12
Min/Max Can Diameter	2.00″-3.00″ (51mm-76mm)
Min/Max Can Height	1.625″-8.00″ (41mm-203mm)
Horsepower Required	25
Speed	Up to 1600 CPM

Model	180S
Spindles	18
Min/Max Can Diameter	2.00″-2.687″ (51mm-68mm)
Min/Max Can Height	2.375″-7.00″ (60mm-178mm)
Horsepower Required	60
Speed	Over 2000 CPM

Continental Can Company

Model	490-HCM
Spindles	6
Min/Max Can Diameter	2.125″-4.25″ (54mm-108mm)
Min/Max Can Height	2.00″-7.5″ (51mm-190mm)
Horsepower Required	15
Speed	Up to 600 CPM

Model	751-HCM-3
Spindles	12
Min/Max Can Diameter	2.375″-2.6875″ (60mm-68mm)
Min/Max Can Height	2.00″-8.00″ (51mm-203mm)
Horsepower Required	50/25 or 50/33
Speed	Up to 1800 CPM

Model	2200-HCM-1
Spindles	12
Min/Max Can Diameter	2.375″-2.6875″ (60mm-68mm)
Min/Max Can Height	2.00″-8.00″ (51mm-203mm)
Horsepower Required	50/33
Speed	Up to 2000 CPM

FMC Food Processing Machinery Division

Model	659
Spindles	6
Min/Max Can Diameter	2.125″-4.25″ (54mm-108mm)
Min/Max Can Height	2.0625″-8.00″ (53mm-203mm)
Horsepower Required	15
Speed	Up to 600 CPM

Model	952
Spindles	16
Min/Max Can Diameter	2.125″-2.6875″ (54mm-68mm)
Min/Max Can Height	2.375″-8.00″ (60mm-203mm)
Horsepower Required	40
Speed	Up to 2000 CPM

LIDS

The development of the can lid corresponds with the can and seaming in general. The lids used on the first Ams type sanitary cans in the early 1900's were simple by today's standards. The lids were round flat-top tin coated panels with a natural rubber sealing compound in an outer curled seaming ring. Except for differently shaped non-round cans, lids remained little changed until World War II and the development of synthetic rubber materials. Previously, compounds aged and deteriorated rapidly. In the next two decades, thinner tin plate and improved compounds were the only changes for lids. In 1959, Adolph Coors Company started marketing beer in the first all aluminum container (7 oz.). This can was produced by impact extrusion from a continuous cast slug blank forming a single open top 1 piece unit eliminating the previous double seamed bottom and side seam. A rolled annealed aluminum flat panel lid was double seamed on top. Flush panel aluminum lids were utilized for many years on tin-plate cans, giving way in the mid 1960's to the easy open ring pull covers (Reynolds, 1963). Also in 1963, Adolph Coors Company started marketing their beer in the now common draw and iron process aluminum can and lid (11 oz.). Ecology pressures and legislation have given impetus in the late 1970's for lid suppliers to develop new easy-open lids with self contained tabs. A canner presently has approximately 30 variations of lids from which to choose. Several examples including self-contained, are shown in Figure 13-3. Although there are still tin-plate lids used on many products, the beer and soft drink industry have almost universally converted to aluminum easy-open lids. A cross section description of a typical lid is shown in Figure 13-4.

Since the first aluminum production lids in the late 1950's, considerable economic improvements have been implemented. The metal thickness of the first aluminum lids was about .016″ to .019″, and stabilized in the mid 1960's at .012″ to .014″. In 1971 Coors Container Company reduced the aluminum can height by .050″, flange diameter by .005″, and lid thickness to .0115″. With improved technology in 1979, Coors again reduced metal in their C79 cans; wall thickness to .0068″; .0005″ thinner in dome area; flange shortened .005″, and lid thickness at .0105″. Continental Can Company's patented "mini-seam" with less can/lid interlock than a normal double seam, also has savings in can/lid metal.

The last decade has also seen improvement in end compound. After World War II, synthetic compounds essentially replaced most natural rubber sealing compounds because of improved quality and economics. Canning compounds presently consist of rubber, rubber synthetics, water base (latex) and the solvent base material utilized most for beer and beverage seaming. Solvent based compounds initially applied to aluminum lids for steel, tin-free steel and aluminum can seaming weighed 70-80mg (milligram). In 1972 Coors reduced compound weights to 35-40mg with their improved can/lid.

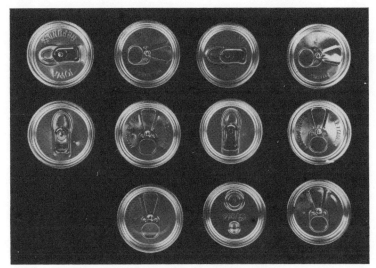

13-3. *Various can/lids. (Coors Container Co.)*

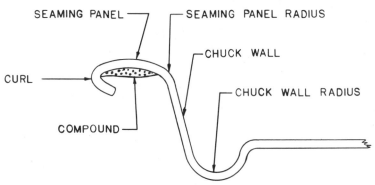

13-4. *Typical end cross section. (Author)*

OPERATION

To discuss the principal operation of double seaming, it is necessary to have an understanding of component parts involved. Note a cross section of a typical completed double seam in Figure 13-5. The same terminology will be used in seam examination procedures later in the chapter.

Following is a glossary of general seaming terminology.

Seam Terms and Definitions

Base Plate Pressure	The force of the base plate holding the can body and end against the chuck during the seaming operation.
Body	Principal part of a container—the sides with bottom. May be round or cylindrical or other shape.
Bottom Seam	Also known as factory end seam. The double seam of the can end put on by the can manufacturer.

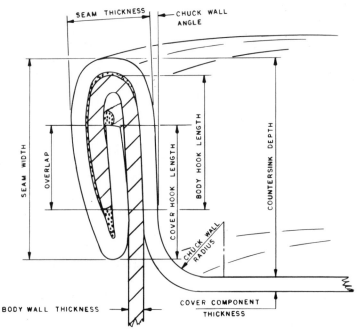

13-5. Cross section diagram showing typical good seam. (Author)

Can, Sanitary	Full open top can. Single one-piece or with side seam and doubled seamed bottom. Cover double seamed on by packer. Ends are gasket or compound lined. Used for products which are process packed. Also known as a "Packer's Can".
Chuck	Part of a closing machine which fits inside countersink and in chuck ring of can lid or end during seaming operation.
Closing Machine	Also known as double seamer. Machine which double seams can end onto can body.
Cocked Base Plate	A base plate on a double seamer which is not parallel to seaming chuck. This results in a top double seam having a body hook uneven in length.
Compound	A sealing material consisting of a water or solvent emulsion or solution of rubber, either latex or synthetic, placed in the curl end of the can end. During seaming operation, the compound fills spaces in the double seam, sealing them against leakage thus effecting a hermetic seal.
Countersink Depth	The measurement from the top edge of the double seam to the end panel adjacent to the chuck wall.
Cover	Can end placed on can by packer. Also known as top, lid, packer's end, canner's end.
Cross Section	Referring to a double seam, a section through the double seam.
Curl	The extreme edge of cover which is bent inward after end is formed. In double seaming, the curl forms the cover hook of the double seam. To alter the shape of an edge by rolls or dies so that the metal is turned on a radius, providing a rounded edge.
Cut-over	Sharp bend or break in the metal at the top of the countersink. The cut-over occurs during seaming due to excess metal being forced over top of seaming chuck. May be due to improper adjustment of the double seaming equipment.

Dead Head	Term used to describe a seam which is incomplete due to chuck spinning in the countersink during seaming operation on a can revolve seamer.
Double Seam	To attach an end to a can body by a method in which 5 thicknesses of metal are interlocked or folded and pressed firmly toether. A joint formed by interlocking the edges of both the end and body of a can. It is commonly produced in 2 operations. The first roll operation forms the metal to produce the 5 thicknesses, or folds, and the second operation roll flattens these to produce the tight seam.
Double Seamed End	Part of a can which is attached to the body of a double seamed can to form the top or bottom.
Droop	A condition which permits a smooth portion of the seam to extend below normal seam line. Generally, where the double seam crosses over a side seam.
Factory End	Bottom or can manufacturer's end.
False Seam	A small seam breakdown where the cover hook and body hook are not overlapped, i.e. no hooking of body and cover hooks.
First Operation	The first operation in double seaming. In this operation, the curl of the ends is tucked under the flange of the can body which is bent down to form cover hook and body hook, respectively.
Flange	To flare out the top of a can body to prepare it for double seaming to an end. The flaring projection about the end of a can body. The outermost projection of an end, cover, or cap.
Hook, Body	That portion of the flange of a can body which is turned back for the formation of an end double seam.
Hook, Cover	That portion of the curl of an end which is turned back between the body and the body hook for the formation of an end seam.
Hook, Uneven	A body or cover hook which is not uniform in length.
Knockdown Flange	A seam defect in which the flange is bent against the body of the can. Thus, the cover hook is not tucked inside the body hook, but lies outside of the body hook. False seams, knockdown flanges, and "soft crabs" are degrees of the same defect. In order to distinguish the degree of the defect, the following terminology is suggested: *False Steam:* The cover hook and body hook are not tucked for a distance of less than an inch. Thus it may not be possible to detect a false seam until the can is torn down. *Knockdown Flange:* As above, but more than an inch in length. Body hook and cover hook in contact, but not hooked.
Lid	Can end applied to open end of can in a cannery. Also known as top, cap, or packer's end.
Lip	Irregularity or defect in double seam occurring at the lap. Due to insufficient tucking of cover hook resulting in a short cover hook and characterized by a blowing or sharp "V" projection at the bottom of the double seam. Also known as a "droop", although lip is the preferred term. The "V" notch in the cover hook is caused by an excessive wrinkling in the seaming operation.
Open Top Can	Another term for sanitary can.
Overlap (Double Seam)	The distance the cover hook laps over the body hook.
Pressure Ridge	The pressure ridge is formed on the inside of the can body directly opposite the double seam and is the result of the pressure applied by the seaming rolls during seam formation.
Seam, Thickness	The maximum dimension measured across or perpendicular to the layers of the seam.
Seam, Width	The maximum dimensions of a seam measured parallel to folds of the seam. Also referred to as seam length or height.
Seamer	Machine for double seaming can ends to the body of a can.
Second Operation	The finishing operation in double seaming. The hooks formed in the first operation are rolled tight against each other in the second operation.
Side Seam	The seam joining the 2 edges of a blank to form a can body.

Slipper or Skidder   A can having an incompletely finished double seam due to the can slipping on the base plate. In this defect, part of the seam will be incompletely rolled out. Term has same meaning as dead head when referring to seamers which revolve the can.

Wrinkle—Cover Hook   A degree of waviness occurring in the cover hook, acting as an indication of the tightness of the seam. It is graded from 0 to 10, depending on the depth of the wrinkle from the edge; 0 indicating no waviness and 5 indicating a waviness more than ½ the distance from the edge.

Seamer Machine Operations

The following is a brief description of the seamer machine operations to create a double seam, sequenced in Figure 13-6.

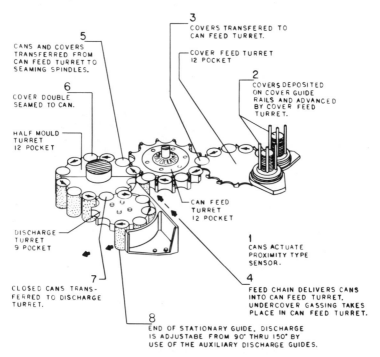

3
COVERS TRANSFERED TO CAN FEED TURRET.

5
CANS AND COVERS TRANSFERRED FROM CAN FEED TURRET TO SEAMING SPINDLES.

COVER FEED TURRET 12 POCKET

2
COVERS DEPOSITED ON COVER GUIDE RAILS AND ADVANCED BY COVER FEED TURRET.

6
COVER DOUBLE SEAMED TO CAN.

HALF MOULD TURRET 12 POCKET

DISCHARGE TURRET 9 POCKET

CAN FEED TURRET 12 POCKET

1
CANS ACTUATE PROXIMITY TYPE SENSOR.

7
CLOSED CANS TRANSFERRED TO DISCHARGE TURRET.

4
FEED CHAIN DELIVERS CANS INTO CAN FEED TURRET. UNDERCOVER GASSING TAKES PLACE IN CAN FEED TURRET.

8
END OF STATIONARY GUIDE. DISCHARGE IS ADJUSTABE FROM 90° THRU 150° BY USE OF THE AUXILIARY DISCHARGE GUIDES.

13-6.   Schematic of 12 head seamer operation.
(Continental Can Co. schematic of 751 HCM-3)

Cans are transferred from the filler with a minimum of acceleration to the closer on the transfer conveyor by chain. In passing, cans trip 1 or 2 proximity sensors that actuate lid feed(s) to the lid feed turret. As the can enters the can feed turret, CO_2 or steam from the under-cover gasser is used to purge the head space of the can of residual air. At the center of the revolution of the can feed turret, can and lid are brought together for transferring to seaming turret. Actual bringing together of can and lid occurs as can is elevated by lifter and lid gets slight pressure from make-up pad or knock-out rod by cam action. Pressure continues until the seaming flange is positioned against the seaming chuck and first operation occurs. First operation roll mechanically interlocks can flange with lid seaming panel and curl partially tightening,

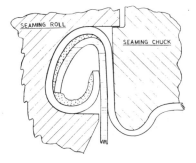 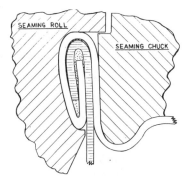

13-7. *Cross section diagram show-* 13-8. *Cross section diagram show-*
ing typical first operation. (Author) *ing typical second operation. (Author)*

Figure 13-7. Second operation then irons formed seam into a tight hermetic seal, Figure 13-8. At the end of the second operation the lifter descends, knock-out rod applies gentle pressure, and can is removed from seaming chuck. Completed can transfers to a discharge turret for conveying to packaging.

To return briefly to the undercover gasser, it is, as previously noted, a closing machine option and is used in some form in the majority of beer can seamers. The undercover gassing is part of the can feed turret operation, as shown in the operation sequence, step 4 in Figure 13-6. Its purpose is to prevent deterioration of the quality of beer which is adversely affected by the air (oxygen) remaining in the headspace of the can after closure. Any increase in headspace air hastens deterioration and shortens the commercial shelf life of beer. Conversely, any reduction of headspace air lengthens its shelf life and, secondly, lowers the internal can pressure developed during pasteurization, storage and handling. It is therefore very advantageous to remove as much air as possible from the can/lid headspace during the seaming operation.

The function of the under-cover gassing unit is to purge the headspace by injecting an inert gas into the headspace to displace air just prior to can/lid sealing. It should be noted that the under-cover gasser can only purge the air from the can/lid headspace; it is unable to remove air previously dissolved in the beer itself.

For the under-cover gassing unit to operate efficiently, the product must be relatively free of excess foam or "boiling". Conversely, modern high speed filler/closers utilize a foam-inducing or bubble-breaking unit. The bubble-breaker is a spray mechanism mounted on the transfer in close proximity to the seamer. The spray or stream is precisely directed across the top of the filled can to induce a small amount of foaming while at the same time ridding the beer of large air bubbles just prior to entering the seamer. The bubble-breaker spray can be water, steam or CO_2.

The majority of brewing seaming operations use CO_2 as the undercover gas because it is available as surplus from the brewing process. In recent years, the fluctuations in CO_2 availability caused by the differences between seasonal schedulings of brewing and packaging has given rise to the use of steam (50 psi at 80°C?) as a more economic under-cover gas. Steam flow is regulated and vented from the undercover gasser in the same manner as CO_2.

While the whole seaming operation is dependent on smooth, coordinated effort of noted functions, the quality of the seam itself is most related to consistency of first and second operations. Although formed in two operations, it is imperative to form the first operation seam correctly or it is relatively impossible to complete a good finished seam. The length of body and cover hook, countersink depth, degree of wrinkle, and, to a certain extent, the width of finished second operation seam, are mainly controlled by the first operation. The seaming turret (seaming chucks, rolls, and lower lift assemblies), the heart of the seaming machine operation, performs both first and second operation very rapidly and therefore requires extremely accurate settings as well as proper care and attention for sustained production runs. The working parts of a seamer, especially the seaming turret section, can get out of correct adjustment as a result of such factors such as jams, wear, changes in can or lid, and lack of cleaning or lubrication. Whether setting up initial seamer machine, installing replacement chucks and rolls, or re-adjusting for jams or malformed seams, the general rule to follow is: back off or hold settings of second operation rolls, achieve near perfect settings of first operation rolls, check first operation seams for correctness, and then adjust and check second operation for good completed seam.

From initial start-up to ongoing seam quality, it is important that the operator follow proper procedures well defined by instruction or manuals, and establish a continuously monitored program. Machine manufacturers supply detailed step-by-step, well illustrated manuals covering the various operation functions of their seaming machines. In addition, they offer instructions at the user's facility or at their own for more in-depth hands-on training. The manuals and instruction will be explicit concerning seamer operation, safety precautions, maintenance and adjustments, cleaning, lubrication, and seam evaluation, discussed later in this chapter under Testing.

MAINTENANCE

The seaming machine is probably the single most important piece of equipment in a beer can packaging operation, requiring good no-compromise maintenance. A closing machine requires proper precise set-up, good PM (Preventative Maintenance) and continuing close attention, or seam/beer quality or line efficiency may suffer. Working hand in hand with Quality Control monitoring seams, maintenance personnel should adjust the seamer to correct any problem as needed. But maintenance should also operate a program to prevent problems, especially those associated with high wear. This PM program may consist of manually monitoring input and work by a small well trained staff on a single seamer, or it may be a computer assisted, seven days per week, multi-shift maintenance organization covering many seamers.

Regardless of operation size, a seamer PM program should follow well established guidelines. A good PM starts with proper machine set-up. Secondly, adjustments, retiming, and replacement of loose or worn parts are planned and performed as needed based on machine history and, especially, periodic inspection.

In reality, a good PM program is a *planned* maintenance system. Some problems lie outside of maintenance control, such as jams or differences in can or lid, but normal and extraordinary wear and tear should be closely monitored and recorded. This information then enables a maintenance force to form a history and *plan* corrective action during regular or pre-scheduled downtimes, minimizing breakdowns associated with the seamer.

The degree of effort put into a seamer PM program cannot be stressed enough. A direct correlation can be drawn between the emphasis put on seamer maintenance and the seaming operation overall efficiency. A "poor-boy" or breakdown maintenance program, or an untrained, even though overstaffed maintenance force, will often yield poor seams with 2 to 3 SC's (Seam Corrections) on a seamer per day as well as low efficiency runs of 70% to 84% (actual time and rate run vs. time and rate planned), while a good seamer PM program will return results of only 2 to 3 SC's per week and the seamer will run at 85% to 94%. The even further sophisticated *Planned Maintenance* program will yield extremely good seams with as few or less than 1 SC per week and the machine will consistently operate over 95%.

Although maintenance is covered in depth in a later chapter, proper maintenance is so crucial to the efficient operation of a seamer, that it is in order to explain briefly the two major differences between a normal PM program and Planned Maintenance. The first and most important difference is increased commitment by packaging management for more operations intergroup teamwork than already expended for PM. This commitment includes: flexibility with line schedules and personnel to enable timely maintenance; slightly increased maintenance costs in personnel and parts stores for self-sufficiency and as needed readiness; and training of team attitude in all area operational employees including operator check-list involvment for near total cooperation. Secondly, seasonal or yearly line overhauls are dropped and replaced with a continual mini-overhaul program based on hours run; each piece or section of large equipment gets its needed major and minor work as often as, or slightly before, needed. Hours for work are predetermined by past history and verified by periodic inspection. The maintenance planner then coordinates work with other area units. Actual equipment hours can be monitored manually or be fully automated with the assistance of meters input to computer. The system may be even further sophisticated to provide computer assistance for large portions of maintenance administration and planning, ("Computerized Maintenance"). A seamer lends itself well to this system: hours and wear measurements, especially in seaming turret, are input; trends are forecasted; parts automatically ordered; regular and overhaul type work pre-planned and issued; costs captured and history available on short notice.

Whichever maintenance system is pursued, periodic checks and inspections of a closing machine are very necessary. Manufacturers have detailed instructions for measuring wear in sections of their machines, particularly the seaming turret. They also have an extensive list of specific parts and functions, recommending timely checking and follow-up actions on a daily, weekly, or longer time basis. The daily checks are performed prior to any production start-up but include inspections to be done during early operation (seam checks). Obviously, discrepancies noticed during these checks should receive immediate attention. The weekly, monthly, or longer (in "planned" programs, 100, 500, 1500 hours, etc.) inspections are obviously carried out while the closer is out of production or scheduled down, and they involve more timely in-depth work. It is also advisable to increase the sequence and effort whenever trends dictate or actual problems are noted to prevent inadvertent loss of quality seams or shutdown. "Think Safety" should be stressed to the seamer service personnel and the machine should always be stopped before any adjustments are made.

The following is a brief general outline of checks to be made for good PM on a typical beer can seamer:

Daily Maintenance Check (or at any start-up):

1. Action and adjustment of all automatic safety controls.
2. Can transfer and discharge.
3. Lower lift assemblies.
4. Seaming rolls.
    a. Make sure rolls are not contacting chuck flange.
    b. First operation at high point of cam.
    c. Second operation at high point of cam.
5. Seaming chucks for cracks or scuffing.
6. Gear cases for oil level.
7. Grease lines.
8. Rotary marker (if equipped).
9. Under cover gassing (if equipped).
10. Inspect complete set of seamed cans.

Weekly Maintenance Check (or at 100-150 hours).

1. Knock-out mechanism.
2. Oil and lubrication force feed mechanism.
3. Manually lubricate per manufacturer's instructions.
4. Clean auto-lubricator per recommendations.
5. Timing of can and lid turrets.
6. Alignment of can infeed and discharge rails.
7. Lower lift assembly for looseness and height.
8. Seaming lever assembly (measurements).

Monthly Maintenance Check (or at 400-600 hours).

1. Filler drive, brake, and clutch.
2. Auto-lube system operation.
3. Wear of transfer and chain (measurements).
4. Rotary marker (if equipped).
5. Cover feed assembly.
6. Settings of lower lift assemblies.
7. Vari-speed brake.
8. Clean feed turret and under-cover gassing.
9. Gear lube levels.
10. Seaming spindles (measurements).
11. Seaming levers and shafts (measurements).

Lubrication

Proper lubrication of a seaming machine follows closely with maintenance. If not properly and continuously lubricated, the machine will soon break down. In principle, lubrication takes place before, during, and after a seamer is run. This is to insure that the gears and precision high-speed bearings of the machine continue to function without failure caused by heat, rust, and the beer itself. In addition, a seamer is always manually or auto-cycle lubed after maintenance work and especially after cleaning. This purges foreign material or lube stripping cleaning agents from the bearings preventing contaminants lingering long enough to damage or corrode the system.

For economic reasons, in small seaming operations maintenance mechanics also perform seamer lubrication. Multi-seaming plants generally have a semi-skilled lubrication crew specially trained to perform this function. In practice, it matters not who performs the manual lubrication as long as the personnel are knowledgeable and timely with the work.

As previously noted in the maintenance check lists, a good share of lubrication and its system checking is performed during normal maintenance. In addition, seamer manufacturers have small adendum lubrication check lists. These lists generally spell out minutes and hours for manual or auto-lubing cycles (if equipped) for specified hours of operation, especially lubing of the seaming rolls.

The seamer requires three weights of lubricants; gear lube, grease and oil. These lubes are dispersed or applied manually or semi-automatically as in older or smaller seamers, or automatically in the latest 2000 CPM seamers with Manzel, Lincoln, or similar types of lubricators. Gear lube is used in a semi-sealed or sealed system such as gearboxes, requiring periodic checks. Grease is applied manually or pumped through injectors and requires periodic clean-up, especially on seaming rolls, to prevent excess lube getting into cans. Oil is continuously pumped to the seamer, generally splashed and cascaded down through the various bearing systems and allowed to exit near the bottom of the machine.

A wide choice of brands and classifications of lube are available and each seamer manufacturer will recommend several for the three types used, including those with FDA (Food and Drug Administration) approval. Breweries reclaiming beer spilled around their fillers and closers also have the choice of using emulsifying or non-emulsifying classification oils. If emulsifying oils are used, lube cycles are increased as this type oil loses lubrication qualities if overly diluted by mixing with water or beer.

Cleaning

In conjunction with maintenance and lubrication, cleaning also plays an important part in efficient seamer operation. "Normal" cleanliness, as defined for a seamer in the majority of breweries, means the machine is free of visual accumulation of waste beer, grease, oil, cleaning chemicals, stains, and debris from cans or lids. "Sterile" cleanliness requires an additional, more complex step in the cleaning process; this step is often utilized by breweries not pasteurizing their beer and will be discussed later. Whichever process is used, it should be stressed that the cleaning be done correctly and often, since leftover residue and debris is harmful to seamer operation.

Good cleaning starts with proper training of the personnel involved and in following correct procedures. The seamer manual has a chapter specifically on cleaning with suggestions for sequence, durations, process solutions and temperatures, and instructions on technique and precautions. Two types of processes are used: immersion with low pressure wash down of the machine; or high pressure directed type cleaning, sometimes called pop gun cleaning. Either system requires a from-top-to-bottom technique, getting most foreign material out of the closer during initial clean-up. The high pressure pop gun system is generally accepted as being the most rapid and visually effective.

The closing machine builder's list of parts or areas requiring cleaning will essentially duplicate many items previously noted for maintenance and lubrication. The list includes several areas requiring special and frequent cleaning, particularly the under-cover gasser, seaming chucks and rolls. Can/lid debris caused by jams is also immediately cleaned out of the seaming turret and discharge areas to guarantee continued seaming operation.

Whichever cleaning system is used, personal safety must be adhered to by the operator, as the seamer is usually revolving at slow speed during much of the cleaning. The slow turning prevents hot spots from developing which may cause parts to bind or pockets of excess condensation. Obviously, the seamer is stopped to clean out by hand any large accumulations of foreign material and lodged-in pieces of cans and lids.

Since most cleaning systems use hot solutions and some even steam, the final rinse or wash-down to remove cleaning agents must also be hot water. The hot water rinse and subsequent slow cooling down of the seamer will prevent undue build-up of condensation inside the machine. The closer manufacturer also provides a list of "Do Not Clean" areas to prevent failure of these items from corrosion by cleaning solutions.

If utilizing the pop gun system to clean a seamer, several procedures should be followed. Besides protective suits and foot wear, personnel should always wear face shields to guard against flying pieces of cans or lids kicked up by the high pressure. Best cleaning results are obtained when the wand tip is held at 12 inches or less from the surface cleaned. At the same time, the operator must use caution not to point the cleaning gun directly at seals around bearings or at electronic components, or the high pressure will unknowingly destroy the seal's usefulness or the electronics.

The sterile cleaning process, as previously noted, is a secondary step to the normal process and requires more application time and technology, including restrictive monitoring. The actual technique will vary with a company's requirements for "sterility", but the following is a brief, rather strict, interpretation of "sterilizing" a seamer.

During normal cleaning and immediately after, but prior to the rinse, the seamer is subjected to lengthened use of steam, typically 50 pounds of steam at approximately 80°C. The duration may vary slightly, but normally steaming time is 20 to 30 minutes after each production run. Occasionally the seamer steaming time may be extended to 45 minutes if a microbiological problem is noted, after overhaul or maintenance work, or if the machine has sat idle for several months. Most seamer manufacturers normally recommend running steam through the under-cover gasser during regular cleaning cycles to insure keeping the orifices open. The additional steaming of the closer with shrouds in place for "sterile" clean essentially raises the overall temperature of the machine, ridding it of micro-organisms. Quality Control personnel monitor the cleaning effectiveness regularly, including use of culture samples. After the sterilization process is completed with final rinse, the seamer is lubed to purge out any lingering cleaning solutions and then allowed to cool.

TESTING

Testing for completed seam integrity is as important as the seaming operation itself. The seams produced must be adequate to retain the product within the can. With beer or other carbonated beverages, internal pressures impose the additional requirement on the seam of not allowing any loss of gas. The completed seam must also prevent the entry into the can of air, bacteria or any substance which might adversely effect the product. The seaming shop must therefore have a continuing program of routine sampling, inspection, recording, and evaluation to assure that they are producing good tight seams within tolerances and without defects.

The majority of can, lid, and seamer machine manufacturers supply manuals dealing specifically with seam evaluation. These manuals are of great assistance to start a seam testing program and are a helpful reference for ongoing operations. Included in the manual are: a list of the testing equipment needed; recommended sequences; inspection technique; sample record forms; tolerances; and problem/cause/correction explanation sections.

The personnel in most seaming operations performing the tests are referred to as "seam inspectors" and are generally attached to the Quality Control Department. In small operations without specific Q.C. units, the inspections are often an additional function of the seamer maintenance mechanics. Regardless of the operation's size, the "seam inspector" is a responsible, semi-skilled position requiring knowledge, training, and technique to properly judge seam quality. Required inspector traits include: an understanding of close tolerances and attention to detail; keeping of accurate records; familiarity with the parts of a double seam and their terminology; competence using specific tools and gauges; and ability to recognize defects.

Actual evaluations of completed seams is made by the inspector from two methods of examination: non-destructive and destructive.

Non-destructive or Visual Examination requires close visual inspection and feel of the completed seam for general formation and possible defects. This visual and feel inspection will immediately determine if any defects are present such as dead heads, cut-overs, false seams, knockdown flanges, or bad droop, as seen in Figure 13-9. A visual inspection will also include external measurement of the seam for width, thickness, and countersink depth with seam micrometer and countersink gauge. (Figure 13-10)

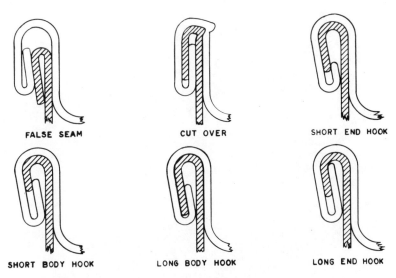

FALSE SEAM   CUT OVER   SHORT END HOOK

SHORT BODY HOOK   LONG BODY HOOK   LONG END HOOK

13-9.   *Cross section diagram of several seam defects.(Author)*

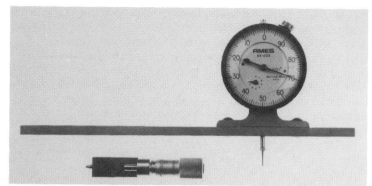

13-10.   Can seam micrometer and countersink gauge. (Adolph Coors Co.)

13-11. Seam lathe. (Adolph Coors Co.)

13-12. Seam inspection projector operation. (Adolph Coors Co.)

Most seam evaluation manuals recommend visual inspection of randomly selected seamed cans by the seamer operator or, preferably, the inspector at every start-up and at 15- to not more than 30-minute intervals. General practice is for the inspector to take and record the external measurements every 2 hours. In addition, a visual examination should be made immediately after a can or cover jam in the closing machine or following prolonged shutdown.

Destructive or Cutting and Tear Down Examination utilizes special tools, such as a seam saw, to cut out a segment or cross section of the completed seam for inspection and measurement of details in a seam scope or projector. (Figures 13-11 and 13-12) The cut seam is then further stripped or torn down for micrometer measurement. Destructive examination provides check of first operation seaming, precise measurement of seam height, overlap, body, and cover hook, and determination of wrinkle and final seam tightness.

The minimum frequency recommended for making destructive examinations is usually one can inspected per seamer station every four hours. The tear down inspection is also performed as soon as possible following start-up or extended shutdown after the machine has had two to three minutes warm up. Generally, cans used for visual and external measurement are also used for destructive examination. Whenever one or more measurements do not fall within the operating control limits, a re-sampling should be made for confirmation before adjustments are made.

Both non- and destructive examinations require accurate recording of the gathered data. This information provides feedback to maintain quality seaming, details on specific can and lid lots, and prove the evaluations and corrections to problems were made. The data also indicates trends of forthcoming problems of wear requiring action. In some localities these records are also documentation to meet regulatory requirements. Although details will vary with different operations, generally two forms are used to maintain a seam inspection program: the first, SIR (Seam Inspection Record, Figure 13-13), to record examination information; and the second, SCR (Seam Correction Report, Figure 13-14) to request corrections.

Computers are now being used in conjunction with seam projectors in multi-seaming operations. The shadow graph is connected to a console enabling the seam inspector to rapidly record or call up examination data. This data input on tape eliminates the manual input SIR but for exceptions, and provides operations with a readily available history.

Along with various PM and SIR/SCR type forms, most seaming operations will also utilize a seaming troubleshooting guide. This form will be used by seam inspectors to request action and maintenance personnel for consistent repairs of noted defects. Following is a brief general troubleshooting guide.

Trouble	Cause	Correction
Long Body Hook	1. Excessive base plate pressure.	a. Reduce base plate pressure by 5# for each .001" to be lowered.
	2. Improper seaming chuck height (pin height).	a. Raise chuck in relation to base plate. Refer to set-up procedure.
	3. Faulty can (tall, long or overflanged can).	a. Inspect and reject if unable to adjust.

SEAM INSPECTION DATA SHEET

CI-538-A

LINE _9-1_   SHIFT _Graveyard_   MFG CANS _Coors_
DATE _12-19-80_   TIME _1:00 Am_   MFG ENDS _Coors Ring Pull_

H E A D	THICKNESS		HEIGHT		CSK DEPTH		BODY HOOK		OVERLAP		COVER HOOK		% TIGHT	CORRECTIVE ACTION
	MIN	MAX	MIN	MAX	MIN	MAX	MIN	MAX	MIN	MAX	MIN	MAX		
1	53	54	126	126	217	218	82	87	47	49	75	80	100%	
2	52	53	125	126	216	218	87	89	49	53	79	82	100	
3	51	53	124	125	218	219	81	88	50	55	80	83	100	
4	52	54	125	126	215	217	80	89	60	61	79	81	100	
5	51	52	126	127	219	219	76	85	58	60	80	84	100	
6	52	53	125	126	217	217	80	86	49	53	77	80	95	
7	53	54	126	127	216	218	85	90	52	55	79	82	100	
8	51	53	124	125	216	217	77	84	57	59	80	84	100	
9	52	53	125	126	217	218	86	91	53	55	82	86	95	
10	52	53	126	127	218	219	87	90	59	61	81	84	100	
11	51	54	126	127	219	219	79	85	60	61	79	83	100	
12	52	53	125	126	216	217	82	88	57	60	80	82	100	

MECHANIC _Leon_   LEADMAN _Joe_

13-13. Typical seam inspection report. (Adolph Coors Co.)

SEAM CORRECTION REQUEST

CI-873-A   107619

ORIGINATOR _LoRA_
CLOSER NUMBER _#4_

DATE _12-20-80_
CHARGE CODE _EEXA2B_

PRIORITY
(A) EMERGENCY
B WITHIN 24 HOURS

CORRECTION REQUESTED (Circle out of spec condition)

		AVERAGE
BODY HOOK		.082
(COUNTER SINK)	#3 STATION HIGH	.226
(OVERLAP)	#3 STATION LOW	.041
COVER HOOK		.073

INSTRUCTIONS   SET 1st AND 2nd OPERATOR ROLL HEIGHT TO SPEC. SET 1st OPERATOR TIGHTNESS TO SPEC.

WORK PERFORMED   Set 1st operator height to .001. Set 2nd operator height to .005. Set 1st operator tightness to .096.

RECHECKS (To be completed before order is finished)

BODY HOOK	.082	COUNTER SINK	.218
OVERLAP	.054	COVER HOOK	.081
1st OPERATOR	OK - .096	2nd OPERATOR	OK - .052
TIGHTNESS	100%	CHUCK COND.	OK

	DESCRIPTION	COMPLETION	
		SCH	ACT
1.		2.0 HRS.	1.5 hrs.
2.			

LOG WORK ON BACK OF SEAM CHARTS

MECHANIC _Kearns_   LEADMAN _____   DATE _12-20-80_

DISTRIBUTION - GREEN -   BLUE -   WHITE -

13-14. Typical seam correction report. (Adolph Coors Co.)

Trouble	Cause	Correction
Short Body Hook	1. Insufficient base plate pressure.	a. Increase base plate pressure by 5# for each .001" to be raised.
	2. Improper seaming height (pin height).	a. Lower chuck in relation to base plate. Refer to set-up procedure.
	3. Faulty can (short can).	a. Inspect and reject if unable to adjust.
Excessive C'Sink	1. Improperly set roll height.	a. Lower 1st and 2nd operators .001" for each .001" to be lowered.
	2. Seaming chuck lip height excessive.	a. Check specifications.
Insufficient C'Sink	1. Improperly set roll height.	a. Raise 1st and 2nd operators .001" for each .001" to be raised.
	2. Worn seaming chuck.	a. Replace chuck and reset 1st and 2nd operator rolls.
Short Cover Hook	1. Excessive c'sink. A. Improperly set roll height.	a. Lower 1st and 2nd operator .001" for each .001" to be lowered.
	2. First operator loose.	a. Tighten.
	3. Long body hook. A. Excessive base plate pressure.	a. Reduce base plate pressure by 5# for each .001" to be lowered.
	4. Faulty cover.	a. Inspect and reject if unable to adjust.
Long Cover Hook	1. Insufficient c'sink. A. Improperly set roll height.	a. Raise 1st and 2nd operators .001" for each .001" to be raised.
	B. Worn seaming chuck.	a. Replace chuck and reset 1st & 2nd operator rolls.
	2. First operator tight.	a. Loosen.
	3. Faulty cover.	a. Inspect and reject if unable to adjust.
Excessive Seam Height	1. First operator loose.	a. Tighten.
	2. Second operator tight.	a. Loosen.
	3. Worn second operator.	a. Raise 2nd operator. b. Replace.
Insufficient Seam Height	1. First operator tight.	a. Loosen.
	2. Second operator loose.	b. Tighten.
Excessive Overlap	1. Long body hook. A. Excessive base plate pressure.	a. Reduce base plate pressure by 5# for each .001" to be lowered.
	B. Improper seaming chuck height (pin height).	a. Lower chuck in relation to base plate. Refer to set-up procedure.
	C. Faulty can (tall or long cans).	a. Inspect and reject if unable to adjust.
	2. Long cover hook. A. Insufficient countersink. 1. Improperly set roll height.	a. Raise 1st and 2nd operators .001" for each .001" to be raised.

Trouble	Cause	Correction
	2. Worn seaming chuck.	a. Replace chuck and reset 1st & 2nd operator rolls.
Insufficient Overlap	1. Short body hook.	
	A. Insufficient base plate pressure.	a. Increase base plate pressure by 5# for each .001″ to be raised.
	B. First operator tight.	a. Loosen.
	C. Second operator loose.	a. Tighten.
	D. Improper seaming chuck height (pin height).	a. Lower chuck in relation to base plate. Refer to set-up procedure.
	2. Short cover hook.	
	A. Excessive countersink.	a. Lower 1st and 2nd operators .001″ for each .001″ to be lowered.
Excessive Thickness	1. Second operator loose.	a. Tighten.
Insufficient Thickness	1. Second operator tight.	a. Loosen.
Excessive Tightness	1. Second operator tight.	a. Loosen.
Insufficient Tightness	1. Second operator loose.	a. Tighten.
Miscellaneous Cut Over	1. Excessive tightness.	
	A. Second operator tight.	a. Loosen.
	2. Worn seaming chuck.	a. Replace chuck and reset 1st & 2nd operator rolls.
	3. Second operator too high from chuck.	a. Lower operator.
	4. Worn operators (1st and/or 2nd).	a. Replace roll.
	5. First operator tight.	a. Loosen.
False Seam	1. Damaged can prior to seaming (bent flange or mushroomed flange).	a. Check for a bad, sticky lift on filler.
	2. Misplaced ends.	a. Check infeed guides.
Can Buckling	1. Lower base plate not turning freely.	a. Clean or replace bearing.
Pressure Ridge	1. Excess pressure from 2nd operator.	a. Relieve pressure (loosen).
	2. No pressure ridge.	a. Loose seam. Tighten second operator.
Wrinkles	1. Loose first operator.	a. Tighten.
	2. Loose second operator.	a. Tighten.
	3. Excess or misplaced lining compound.	a. Reject lid lot.
	4. Improper curl of cover.	a. Reject lid lot.
Whiskers	1. Worn first operator.	a. Tighten or replace roll and/ or adjust cover feed.

Close coordination between seam inspection and maintenance personnel is needed for seam corrections. As soon as defects are noted they are recorded, prioritized, and scheduled for correction. Obviously, some seam problems call for immediate correction, while other normal wear problems can be conveniently scheduled. Whenever any corrections are made to a seamer, it is important that follow-up seam checks be made to insure continuing quality seams.

SUMMARY

High quality and efficient seaming will result if close partnership is maintained among seamer operator, inspector, and maintenance personnel. Five important guidelines for good seaming are:

1. Set-up equipment as recommended for specifications of can and lid.
2. Provide effective PM on seamer machine.
3. Clean and lube per appropriate specifications.
4. Confirm seam quality with systematic inspection.
5. Record and graph seam operation. Control seamer history.

REFERENCES FOR ADDITIONAL READING:

Angelus Sanitary Can Machine Co., "Preventative Maintenance and Troubleshooting Guide", volume 2, 1975.

Continental Can Company, "Top Double Seaming Manual", volume 3, 1966.

Container Products, Dewey and Almy Chemical Co., W.R. Grace and Co., "Can Seaming Efficiency Manual", and "Can Dimension Dictionary", volume 7, 1973.

Metal Box Co., Ltd., U.K., "Double Seam Manual", volume 4, 1975.

National Canners Assoc. Research Foundation, (grant from Angelus Sanitary Can Machine Co.), "Evaluation of Can Double Seam", Parts 1 and 2, slides with text.

Can Division, Reynolds Metal Company, "Double Seaming Aluminum Can Manual", volume 8, 1972.

Section IV

CHAPTER XIV

DRAFT OPERATIONS

BY CARL F. HOLMER and
ARNOLD N. McLEAN

COOPERAGE

Materials of Construction

The containers for the movement of draft beer from the brewer to the consumer have changed radically since beer was first brewed. The transition from open ollas or skin bags to oak casks, and finally to the first metal kegs or barrels, covered many centuries. The last twenty-five years have witnessed the greatest change, with metal containers and processing modifications making the packaging of draft beer more sanitary and more efficient.

This change has been from traditional oak or carbon steel barrels, which had to be pitched on a regular basis, to barrels of aluminum or stainless steel with their inherent advantages. Stainless steel, because of its resistance to abrasion, acid and alkali cleaning solutions, has achieved greater acceptance. Both materials have made it possible to achieve significant weight reductions, and have provided containers that can be sanitized more effectively. The most recently introduced parallel-sided stainless steel barrels are particularly well suited for automatic cleaning and filling operations. In this chapter the terms barrels and kegs will be used interchangeably and do not indicate a particular size container.

The improved container sterility, elimination of air, plus increased sanitation in plant, in retail handling, and in dispensing, has lengthened shelf life and improved draft beer quality.

Some typical examples of today's cooperage are illustrated in Figures 14-1, 14-2, and 14-3.

In the purchase of kegs it is important to establish uniform procurement and operational specifications. These specifications should cover such items as:

1. Basic material formulation
2. Internal volume
3. Welding specifications and finished weld appearance
4. Bursting strength of keg
5. Quality assurance sampling programs
6. Workmanship

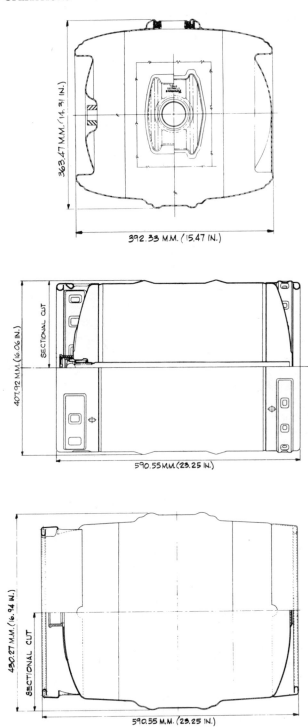

363.47 M.M. (14.31 IN.)

392.33 M.M. (15.47 IN.)

SECTIONAL CUT

407.92 M.M. (16.06 IN.)

590.55 M.M. (23.25 IN.)

440.27 M.M. (16.94 IN.)

SECTIONAL CUT

590.55 M.M. (23.25 IN.)

14-3. *Firestone stainless steel quarter-barrel*

14-2. *Hoover Universal straight sided stainless steel half-barrel*

14-1. *Coors stainless steel half-barrel*

7. Dimensions
8. Color Coding
9. Any embossed or debossed information
10. Cleanliness
11. Bung and tap hole dimensions
12. Shipping instructions.

Tapping Systems

Dramatic changes in tapping equipment have also occurred in recent years, progressing from the Peerless tap valve (sealed with a cork and tapped with a conventional tap rod) to the Golden Gate, Hoff Stevens, Perlick and Sankey systems. These tapping systems differ from the Peerless in that the barrel can be removed from the serving unit and remain sealed and under pressure. These innovations have led to more simplified tapping dispensing and servicing. See Figure 14-4 (a) (b) (c) and (d).

14-4. Tapping systems. a. Peerless b. Golden Gate c. Hoff Stevens, regular draw d. Sankey

CONVENTIONAL RACKING OPERATIONS

Keg Preparation

Pitching of oak barrels was an essential step in the preparation of barrels in earlier days, but this practice is now obsolete.

When aluminum barrels are used, these barrels are generally wax lined, using a microcrystalline wax that is clear to white. This wax should be odorless and tasteless, and should not flake or separate from the keg surface.

The waxing procedure is as follows:

Preheat kegs by rinsing with water at 87.8°C (190°F) at 1.2 hectoliters per minute (32.5 gallons) to melt and remove old wax lining. The mixture of wax and water runs into a wax separation tank where the wax is removed from the water and sent to a collection tank. The water separated is directed to a second baffled tank for further separation of remaining wax which floats to the top and is removed and discarded. No water drains to waste. The kegs are moved forward through an exterior chemical scrub with mild alkaline solution followed by exterior ring and internal flush. The barrels are next moved into the interior wash and tapper rinse section. Next, the barrels move to interior water rinse at 93°C (200°F) and forward to a hot air drying area where air at 248.9°C (480°F) is blown into them. This heats and sterilizes prior to waxing. Approximately 102.1 grams (3.6 ounces) of wax is sprayed into each aluminum barrel. This wax is supplied from a tank system below the process machine. This system consists of three tanks—two for melting and holding tanks, and the third for recirculating and supply to the waxing sprays. Wax is held at 112.8°C (235°F). Waxed barrels are cooled by cold water sprays. Barrels are inspected visually through the bung hole to assure that complete and thorough waxing has been achieved.

Conventional System for Keg Washing and Filling

The so-called conventional system can either be entirely manual or include varying degrees of automation, including automatic depalletizing, debunging, washing, inspection semi-automatic racking arms, bunging and automatic palletizing. See 14-5, 14-6 and 14-7.

A typical system includes the following stages:

1. Empty kegs palletized 3 high are depalletized automatically. Prior to debunging Golden Gate style valves are keyed to be sure both valves are locked.
2. Kegs are next debunged manually or automatically prior to transfer to washer infeeds.
3. Washer operation includes
   (1) Infeed to washer—Exterior rinse with cold water
   (2) First Station (prefill)—Partial fill with warm water 60°C (140°F) —Exterior warm water rinse
   (3) Second Station (brush cleaning or outside sprays)—As the barrel rotates, the interior is rinsed while the exterior is brushed or jetted
   (4) Third Station (drain)—Rinsed barrel is allowed to drain.
   (5) Fourth Station (caustic rinse)—Interior hot caustic wash with 2.5–3.0% solution at 77°C. (180°F.)
   (6) Fifth Station (hot water)—Interior of barrel is pressure rinsed with 48.9–60°C (120 – 140°F) water. Tapping valve is opened automatically either by high pressure water or mechanically. Both the valve and the tube inside the keg are cleaned with hot water at 82.2 – 93.3°C (180 – 200°F)
   (7) Sixth Station (cold water)—Interior and exterior of barrel is rinsed with cold water.
   (8) Seventh Station (drain)—Barrel is allowed to drain.

After approval of a tank meeting company specifications on oxygen content, carbonation, temperature, clarity and tasting approval, the beer is pumped to the racker through a meter. The beer pumping rate is matched with the

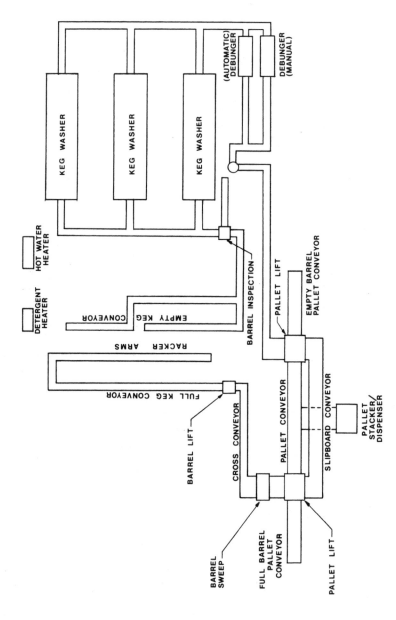

14-5. Plan view of conventional system for washing and filling

14-6. Enzinger Duriron six arm racker (Courtesy of Enzinger Duriron)

racking rate. Metered volumes are compared with calculated volume derived from units produced to determine beer loss.

Points to Check for Successful Racker Operation

A racker arm properly installed and operated should fill a ½ bbl. in not more than 45 seconds after counter pressure is established. The capacity of a four arm racker will average 160 to 200 bbls. per hour.

1. Counter pressure on the racker tank should be slightly greater than on the beer supply tank.
2. Beer temperature in the racker tank should preferably be below 1.1°C (34°F).
3. Counter pressure should be established on the keg with the filling tube well down into the keg, but never far enough to permit the filling valve to open.
4. The counter pressure position of the filling tube stops the seal cock plug rotation so that both the front and rear pressure pipe ports are partly open, permitting beer trapped in the front back pressure pipe (the one with the sightglass) during the previous fill to drain back. This eliminates restriction of the vent line and equalizes pressure throughout the system.
5. The hose between the racker tank and the arm should be in good condition, the elbows should swing freely and the hose should be free of kinks when the racker is in the filling position. The hoses on the back pressure pipe lines (on some rackers these are 1.6 cm [0.625″] on others they are 1.9 cm [0.75″]should be examined to make sure that there are no breaks in the inner lining, and also that the couplings have properly fitted gaskets with a full size hole, so that the air flow is not restricted.
6. The 3-way washout and back pressure pipe cocks on the top of the racker tank, should be checked to see that they are in full open position for normal operation. This position opens one port to the front counter

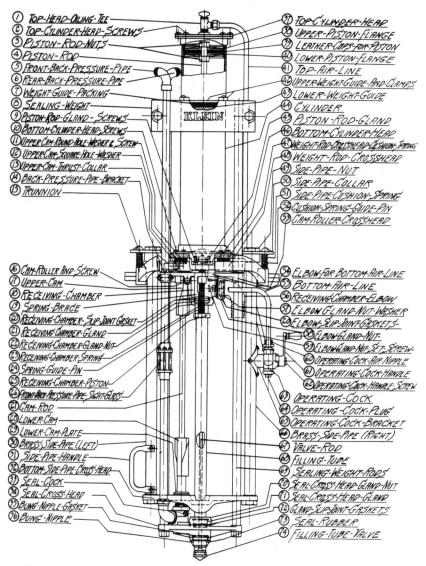

① TOP-HEAD-OILING-TEE
② TOP-CYLINDER-HEAD-SCREWS
③ PISTON-ROD-NUTS
④ PISTON-ROD
⑤ FRONT-BACK-PRESSURE-PIPE
⑥ REAR-BACK-PRESSURE-PIPE
⑦ WEIGHT-GUIDE-PACKING
⑧ SEALING-WEIGHT
⑨ PISTON-ROD-GLAND-SCREWS
⑩ BOTTOM-CYLINDER-HEAD-SCREWS
⑪ UPPER-CAM-ROUND-HOLE-WASHER & SCREW
⑫ UPPER-CAM-SQUARE-HOLE-WASHER
⑬ UPPER-CAM-THRUST-COLLAR
⑭ BACK-PRESSURE-PIPE-BRACKET
⑮ TRUNNION

㉗ TOP-CYLINDER-HEAD
㉚ UPPER-PISTON-FLANGE
㉙ LEATHER-CUPS-FOR-PISTON
④⓪ LOWER-PISTON-FLANGE
④① TOP-AIR-LINE
④② UPPER-WEIGHT-GUIDE-AND-CLAMPS
④③ LOWER-WEIGHT-GUIDE
④④ CYLINDER
④⑤ PISTON-ROD-GLAND
④⑥ BOTTOM-CYLINDER-HEAD
④⑦ WEIGHT-ROD-CROSSHEAD-CUSHION-SPRING
④⑧ WEIGHT-ROD-CROSSHEAD
④⑨ SIDE-PIPE-NUT
⑤⓪ SIDE-PIPE-COLLAR
⑤① SIDE-PIPE-CUSHION-SPRING
⑤② CUSHION-SPRING-GUIDE-PIN
⑤③ CAM-ROLLER-CROSSHEAD

⑯ CAM-ROLLER-AND-SCREW
⑰ UPPER-CAM
⑱ RECEIVING-CHAMBER
⑲ SPRING-BRACE
⑳ RECEIVING-CHAMBER-SLIP-JOINT-GASKET
㉑ RECEIVING-CHAMBER-GLAND
㉒ RECEIVING-CHAMBER-GLAND-NUT
㉓ RECEIVING-CHAMBER-SPRING
㉔ SPRING-GUIDE-PIN
㉕ RECEIVING-CHAMBER-PISTON
㉖ FRONT-BACK-PRESSURE-PIPE-SIGHT-GLASS
㉗ CAM-ROD
㉘ LOWER-CAM
㉙ LOWER-CAM-PLATE
㉚ BRASS-SIDE-PIPE (LEFT)
㉛ SIDE-PIPE-HANDLE
㉜ BOTTOM-SIDE-PIPE-CROSS-HEAD
㉝ SEAL-COCK
㉞ SEAL-CROSS-HEAD
㉟ BUNG-NIPPLE-GASKET
㊱ BUNG-NIPPLE

⑤④ ELBOW-FOR-BOTTOM-AIR-LINE
⑤⑤ BOTTOM-AIR-LINE
⑤⑥ RECEIVING-CHAMBER-ELBOW
⑤⑦ ELBOW-GLAND-NUT-WASHER
⑤⑧ ELBOW-SLIP-JOINT-GASKETS
⑤⑨ ELBOW-GLAND-NUT
⑤⑨ ELBOW-GLAND-NUT-SET-SCREW
⑥⓪ OPERATING-COCK-AIR-NIPPLE
⑥① OPERATING-COCK-HANDLE
⑥② OPERATING-COCK-HANDLE-SCREW
⑥③ OPERATING-COCK
⑥④ OPERATING-COCK-PLUG
⑥⑤ OPERATING-COCK-BRACKET
⑥⑥ BRASS-SIDE-PIPE (RIGHT)
⑥⑦ VALVE-ROD
⑥⑧ FILLING-TUBE
⑥⑨ SEALING-WEIGHT-RODS
⑦⓪ SEAL-CROSS-HEAD-GLAND-NUT
⑦① SEAL-CROSS-HEAD-GLAND
⑦② GLAND-SLIP-JOINT-GASKETS
⑦③ SEAL-RUBBER
⑦④ FILLING-TUBE-VALVE

14-7. *Conventional racker arm (Courtesy of Enzinger Duriron)*

pressure pipe and one port to the rear counter pressure pipe and the other port connects to the tank. Generally this places the handle on the 3-way cock over the tank opening; however, this should be checked.

7. Lower the filling tube to the filling position "all the way down", with the beer shut off and without a keg on the machine. Check the opening of the beer filling valve. There should be approximately 2.5 cm (1″) clearance between the valve and the end of the filling tube.

8. The filling tube valve should have approximately 2.5 cm (1″) clearance

from the bottom of the keg. Excess clearance will result in foaming. With the racker in the full down position, measure from the trunnion pin to the bottom of the filling tube valve. Retract the arm, place a keg on the keg rest. Measure from the trunnion pin through the bung hole to the inside bottom of the keg. The dimensions between these two dimensions, should be approximately 2.5 cm (1″) to insure proper clearance.

9. To check the proper setting of the seal cock plug, place a keg rest and lower the arm into its open position without beer or counter-pressure on the racker tank. Remove the washout plug on the seal cock tee (this is connected to the line with the sightglass). With a light, observe the opening of the seal cock plug, which should be in the fully open position. This plug rotation can be adjusted on a Heavy Duty Klein Arm by rotating the seal cock coupling. On other types of arms this porting is fixed by the position of the cams on the cam rod and should not require any adjustment. In time, the cams and cam rollers will become worn and should be replaced. New parts will properly re-establish the position of the seal cock plug.

10. Snifting or release of the counter-pressure in the keg is extremely important to prevent excessive foaming when the arm is retracted from the keg. Snifting must occur just prior to lifting of the racker bung from the keg bung seat. Usually failure to snift can be traced to faulty cams or seal cock rotation.

11. The elevation of the racker tank affects the rate of flow of beer into the keg. The distance from the floor to the center of the Schlangen Racker tank is approximately 175.3 cm. (69 inches); on the later model Klein and Enzinger, the distance is 198.1 cm. (78 inches), and on some special rackers, this distance has been increased considerably to provide a faster flow to the keg. Flow is by gravity.

AUTOMATED SYSTEMS FOR KEG WASHING AND FILLING

The automated systems currently in use in North America consist of three main types:
(1) Sankey and Burnett and Rolfe modular automatic systems,
(2) The custom-designed Adolph Coors Company automated system.
(3) The custom designed Thermovac System—JSBC. (Not discussed here)
Sankey and Burnett and Rolfe modular style systems
The Sankey and Burnett and Rolfe systems are similar in the way barrels are depalletized, inverted, cleaned externally, marshalled into modular lanes, cleaned, filled, check-weighed, labeled and palletized. (Figure 14-8.)
1. The depalletizer
The keg depalletizer is a machine designed to unload four ½-barrel size beer kegs from a wooden pallet automatically (Figure 14-9). When the pallet board is destacked and conveyed by the pallet chain conveyor, it will pass a series of limit switches that set up the following operation:
—The pallet board will enter the keg unloader system at which point the kegs are removed from the board and placed onto the keg chain conveyor.
—The pallet board is then conveyed by the chain conveyor into the correct

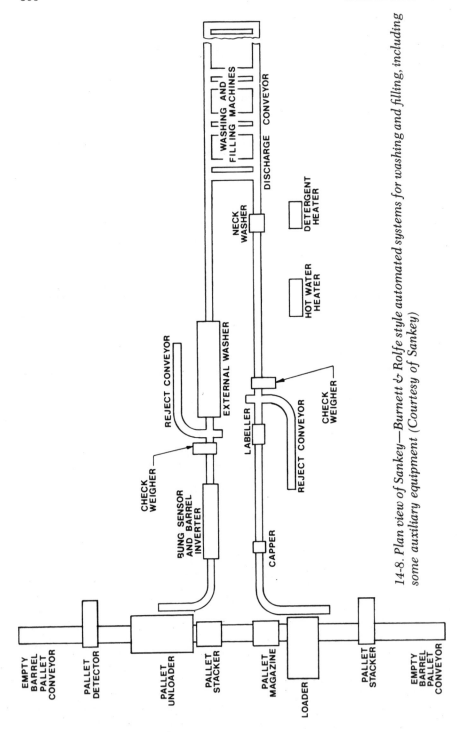

14-8. Plan view of Sankey—Burnett & Rolfe style automated systems for washing and filling, including some auxiliary equipment (Courtesy of Sankey)

14-9. Destacker and depalletizer (Courtesy of W.C. Pantin Ltd.)

position. The keg fingers are then energized to raise through the pallet board. The kegs will not be lifted from the pallet board by the keg fingers when the keg fingers are in the fully raised position.
—Next the keg pusher sweeps forward pushing the first two kegs onto the keg chain conveyor where they will be carried into the system.
—The keg fingers are next lowered to their ambushed position below the pallet board.
—The pallet chain conveyor then will start again and the pallet board, together with the last two kegs, will once again move into position for unloading, which is a repeat of the first operation.

2. External Barrel Washing

Currently high pressure in-line units are being tested for external barrel washing to assist in label removal. One of the latest units being tested is the *Automatic Lambrecht External Keg Washer High Pressure Jetting Type.* In this unit upright kegs are conveyed through the tunnel, carried by two 1400 D Pantal Chains, running at different speeds, in order to cause a slow turning of the kegs. Pumps are used for re-circulating detergent at 70°C (158°F) and for feeding the nozzles which are accurately positioned to clean the entire surface of the keg, especially the label position and the neck of the keg.

In order to remove all detergent from the kegs before they leave the machine, a header with 14 nozzles, giving a fan-shaped spray at 48.9°C (120°F) is mounted to spray the complete surface of each keg. The spent and diluted detergent falls into the rinse tanks, overflows to waste or, when the by-pass

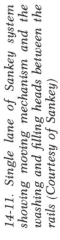

14-11. Single lane of Sankey system showing moving mechanism and the washing and filling heads between the rails (Courtesy of Sankey)

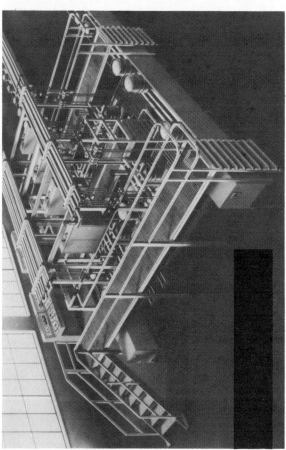

14-10. Sankey automatic washing/filling system with four lanes (Courtesy of Sankey)

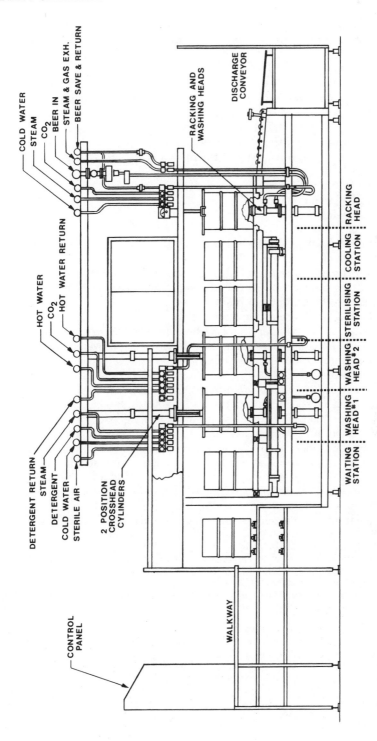

14-12. Sideview of Sankey automated washing and filling system. (Courtesy of Sankey)

is open, returns to the detergent tank. The total water consumption of these rinse jets is 9.1 hectoliters per hour at 1.4 Kg./sq. cm (200 GPH at 20 PSI), approximately equivalent to the water carried out of the machine by the kegs and evaporation.

3. Combined, Inverted Fill, Keg Washing and Filling Machine

The machine is designed to automatically wash, sterilize and fill both ¼ and ½ U.S. barrel size, straight sided, containers all fitted with a concentric, two valve, 'well' type fitting (Figure 14-10 and 11).

The basic machine is made up of the following stations arranged in series.

1. Keg Waiting Station
2. 1st Washing Station
3. 2nd Washing Station
4. Sterilizing Station
5. Cooling Station
6. Inverted Filling Station (Figure 14-12).

The transfer of kegs through the machine takes place on a fixed slide, using hydraulic cylinders to transfer kegs from one station to the next station. At the end of the transfer movement, the kegs have been pushed to the next station ready to be clamped in position.

The washing heads are manufactured from stainless steel. Designed as part of the head is a lift cylinder and a probe cylinder. The probe cylinder has an electrical sensing device to ensure that the probe has moved correctly. The complete assembly is designed for quick removal and replacement for maintenance purposes.

The filling head is manufactured from stainless steel and is mounted in the frame of the machine similarly to the washing heads, the kegs being filled in the inverted position. The complete assembly is designed for quick removal and replacement for maintenance purposes. Also fitted to the filling head are a probe sensing device and a dual supply shuttle valve to minimize beer loss.

The operator platform is at one level throughout the machine, above keg height. The platform is positioned across the front of the machines above the infeed conveyor, it extends around the sides and through the gaps between each twin lane module in a line of machines. Access to the platform is by steps at the front of the machines, and ladders at the rear of the end walkways.

Features of Combined Machine

A temperature controller regulates the washing and sterilizing cycle and can be isolated from the main process controller. Then the machine is operable without temperature checking for operation on a timed program only.

The control panel is fitted with a reset button which, when required, resets washing cycles 1 and 2 from any position within those cycles, and resets the racking cycle from the steam sterilize operation.

Pressure sensors are fitted between the beer supply stop valve and the changeover shuttle valve at the racking head, to detect any beer valve leakage. This detection of leakage protects the sterility of the beer as supplied to the racking head.

Fitted to the probe cylinders of the washing and filling heads is an electrical sensing device which magnetically senses the movement of the cylinder piston. The electrical sequence will not continue unless the switch contact has been made.

During the cold water, detergent and hot water cycles, sterile air is injected into the keg. This has the effect of improving the washing pattern and pressurizing the keg so that liquid drains out immediately, thus allowing the complete surface of the keg to be continuously washed.

An air test is carried out at each process head to determine the efficiency of the seal between the head and the keg neck. If pressure is not sensed in a set time, the keg is rejected. If pressure is achieved, then the cycle will proceed.

The unwashed keg arriving at the first washing head is clamped in position and before the wash cycle commences, any remaining beer left in the keg is removed by opening the keg and pressurizing it with sterile air to force out the remaining liquid through a separate drain valve to a collection tank.

To check that no carryover of liquid is left in the container after the second washing cycle, a conductivity probe is fitted in the CO_2 exhaust line on the second washing head. The amplifier and controller of this check are sited with the temperature controller in the electrical panel. If residual liquid is sensed, the keg is rejected.

The meter is a semi-rotary piston meter, with 'in-line' connections. Its design enables the rotation of the piston within the measuring chamber to be registered by the action of two magnetically operated reed switches. The metering system can be isolated electrically by means of an isolating switch. The meter chamber and body parts are manufactured in stainless steel, and the piston in bronze. The accuracy of the meter is $\pm 2.0\%$ with a repeatability of $\pm \frac{1}{2}\%$.

An alternative method of beer filling is by pressure switch control, which system can also be fitted with an isolating switch.

Size changeover is achieved simply by means of operating one pneumatic switch per bank of machines to alter the movement of the crosshead cylinders, and one electrical switch per lane to change the cycle time basis, meter count, etc.

Each installation is externally fenced for safety. Individual lanes are shielded from each other, and from the walkways and access gaps, by plastic type splash screens to protect operator and engineers when working on individual lanes.

Machine is provided with a switch to enable the kegs to be washed only. The machine sequencing is as previously described with the exception that the keg enters the racking station and is not clamped to the racking head.

If the keg fails on test at the washing station, or if the reject button is operated, the washing cycle is arrested and the head lowered. A pneumatic signal is memorized so that when the rejected keg arrives at the racking station, it is not lifted by the head, thus eliminating the cycle.

The machine sequence is as follows:

Incoming kegs are marshalled onto the infeed conveyor and positioned against stops in front of each machine. When the conveyor is full, the last keg signals the conveyor to stop. If the washing and racking heads are ready to receive a keg, the machine signals the keg to be lifted clear of the infeed conveyor, by means of a lift platform, and the conveyor pusher to operate. Kegs are then transferred to the machine waiting station. The following sequence then occurs simultaneously:

(1) Keg is transferred to the 1st washing station
(2) Keg is transferred to the 2nd washing station
(3) Keg is transferred from washing station to the sterilizing station
(4) Keg is transferred from the sterilizing station to the cooling station
(5) Keg is transferred from the cooling station to the racking station
(6) Keg is transferred from racking station to discharge station
(7) Keg automatically transfers itself from discharge section to slat conveyor

At the end of this sequence of events, the pusher mechanism returns to its starting position. This then signals the machine to carry out the following operations:

The keg is lifted by the washing head, clamped by the crosshead, and the washing cycle commences automatically.

At the same time the keg at the racking station is raised by the racking head and clamped by the crosshead and the racking cycle started automatically.

The washing cycle for 1st washing head is as follows:

(1) Keg is located and clamped on washing head
(2) Pressure test of seal between keg and washing head. If the pressure is not achieved in a pre-set time, a reject mode is selected and a test fail light flashes in the operator panel. The keg is then rejected by the operator. If pressure is achieved, the cycle continues.
(3) Open combination unit by means of washing probe.
(4) Beer Drain
   Beer remaining in the keg is removed by sterile air pressure during a set time, by means of a separate drain to a collection tank.

(5) Cold Water Rinse[1]
This operation is time controlled.
(6) Steam Ejection
This operation is time sequenced. During this operation a heat sensing thermocouple in the exhaust checks the temperature at pre-set times. If at start of steam ejection the temperature is too high, this indicates that the fitting has not opened and steam is going directly to exhaust and a reject mode is selected. Temperature too low at the end of steam ejection indicates that the fitting is not properly opened and that the flow of liquid is being impaired and again, a reject mode is selected. If the temperature is in the correct temperature band (approx. 50°C (122°F), the cycle continues. The selection of a reject mode by the machine will cause a temperature fail light to flash in the operator panel. The operative must then press the reject button to reject the keg.
(7) Detergent Wash[1]
This operation is time controlled. It is known at this stage that the fitting has opened correctly. The detergent is delivered in the machine at a known rate and thus the quantity of detergent passed through the keg can be determined. (Loss of detergent pressure is sensed by a pressure switch which arrests the cycle).
(8) Steam Ejection
This operation is time sequenced. The removal of all liquid from the keg is checked by a heat sensing thermocouple in the exhaust. In the event of the pre-set temperature not being achieved in a set time, a reject mode is selected and the cycle stopped.
(9) The head retracts leaving the keg.
The Washing Cycle for the 2nd Washing Head is as follows:
(1) Keg is located and clamped on washing head.
(2) Pressure test of seal between keg and washing head. If the pressure is not achieved in a pre-set time, a reject mode is selected and a test fail light flashes in the operator panel. The keg is then returned by the operator. If pressure is achieved, the cycle continues.
(3) Open combination unit by means of washing probe.
(4) Hot Water Rinse[2]
This operation is time controlled.
(5) Steam Ejection
The complete liquid removal check is carried out as for detergent. On reaching a pre-set temperature 100°C (212°F) exhaust valve closes and steaming continues for a pre-set time.
(6) Purge Steam Condensate and CO_2 Pressurize Keg
Operation is time controlled with pressure switch override. Machine does not operate unless pressure has been achieved. The pressure of CO_2 in the container is controlled by a pressure relief valve fitted to the CO_2 exhaust valve.
(7) Probe retracts leaving the keg pressurized with CO_2.
(8) The head lowers the keg to the slides.
In the Sterilizing Cycle the keg moves from the second washing head to the sterilizing station where it remains for a full cycle of the machine.
In Cooling Cycle the keg moves from the sterilizing station to the cooling station where the keg is sprayed externally with water to remove the heat from the keg prior to filling.
The Racking Cycle is as follows:
1. Keg located and clamped onto racking head.
2. Pressure test seal between keg and racking head. If the pressure is not achieved in a pre-set time a reject mode is selected, and a test fail light flashes in the operator panel. The keg is then rejected by the operator. If pressure is achieved, the cycle continues.
3. Steam
The filling head and combination unit are steamed for a set time.
4. Opening combination unit by means of a racking probe.

[1]During the cold water and detergent cycles, sterile air is injected into the keg. This has the effect of improving the washing pattern and pressurizing the keg so that the liquid drains out immediately, thus allowing the complete surface of the keg to be continuously washed.

[2]During the hot water cycle, sterile air is injected into the keg. This has the effect of improving the washing pattern and pressurizing the keg so that the liquid drains out immediately, thus allowing the complete surface of the keg to be continuously washed.

5. Beer Fill[3]
Beer filling is by Neptune beer meter and the volume to be filled is set on a counter. On completion of the counts, the beer valves are closed.
6. Beer Save
Beer remaining in the filling head is removed and saved by CO_2 pressure.

Proposed time cycles are shown in TABLE I.

In an industrial environment, the function of relays or solid-state electronics is to provide the logic for decision making in control applications. A Programmable Controller (PC) is a solid-state device which has been designed as a direct replacement for relays or 'hard-wired' electronics and whose logic can be altered without wiring changes. Features of a PC compared to other industrial control devices include the following:

—Solid-state for maximum reliability and fast response.

—Designed to operate in hostile industrial environments such as electrical interference, poor supply regulation, heat and vibration—without fans, air-conditioning, or external filtering.

—Programmed with simple relay ladder diagram language.

—Easily reprogrammed if modifications required.

—Controller is re-usable if plant becomes obsolete.

The system is designed to replace systems requiring 25-400 relays.

—Wide range of functions—includes logic, timing, counting, calculate, sequencing, skip, data transfer, analogue inputs/outputs and with choice of memory sizes. Expandable input/output with four point modules, on-line programming, comprehensive range of peripheral devices.

The Processor (the brain of the 484) is a completely solid-state device designed to replace relays and timers/counters. The main function of the Processor is to continuously monitor the status of all inputs and direct the status of all outputs. Operations can be expanded to include other abilities such as calculate analogue I/O. The 484 Processor is programmed in relay ladder symbols utilizing up to ten relay contacts per rung. Once the relay ladder program is entered into the Processor, it remains resident until deliberately changed by the user with one of the programming devices. The program is unaltered through power failure or power off conditions.

The complexity of monitoring the performance of multi-laned automatic keg washing and racking machines has led to this application of micro processors to both control and monitor production. A single lane requires about 30 output signals to drive automatic valves, to route in place cleaning, steam, beer, etc. and to operate pneumatic cylinders to locate and clamp kegs at each stage. Less than 20 input signals are required to detect events such as presence or correct location of kegs and whether or not temperatures have been reached, and the control system operates on the principle of checking events before proceeding to the next stage and rejecting the keg if the event does not occur within a predetermined time. Failures occurring in the washing cycle are remembered as rejects and not presented to the filling head. The problem becomes more complex when many lanes are grouped together to form a multi-lane racker. Identification of the lane causing rejects is no longer obvious.

[3]If, for any reason, the beer meter fails, then a pressure switch fitted in the beer return line operates to close the beer in valve. The operation of this switch activates an indicator light in the operator panel.

TABLE 1
PROPOSED TIME CYCLES

No. 1 Washing Head Cycles   Times given in seconds.

	¼ Barrel	½ Barrel
Air Test	2	2
Beer Drain	4	4
Cold Water	7	7
Steam	11	11
Detergent	14	14
Steam	11	11
Movement	12	12
TOTAL	61	61

No. 2 Washing Head Cycles   Times given in seconds.

	¼ Barrel	½ Barrel
Air Test	2	2
Hot Water	13	13
Steam	12	12
Steam to Stop	15	15
CO_2	7	7
Movement	12	12
TOTAL	61	61

Sterilizing Cycle

	¼ Barrel	½ Barrel
Sterilize (including movement time)	61	61

Cooling Cycle

	¼ Barrel	½ Barrel
Spray Cool	49	49
Movement	12	12
TOTAL	61	61

Racking Head Cycles   Times given in seconds

	¼ Barrel	½ Barrel
CO_2 Test	3	3
Steam	5	5
Fill	19	37
Save	4	4
Movement	12	12
TOTAL	43	61

Based on a filling rate of 100 liters (22 imperial gallons) per minute using a differential pressure of 4.7 Kg./square cm (60 p.s.i.).

100% Efficiency Machine Output Per Lane

Container Size	¼ Barrel	½ Barrel
Output/Containers/Hours	59	59

With suitable software and hardware coupled together, a printer can produce a wide variety of useful analytical information pertinent to the operation, e.g.;

Total kegs filled for each lane

Total kegs rejected for each lane

Reason for each rejection such as:

(1) Overall time—total washing cycle exceeds pre-set time

(2) Probe guard—temperature in scavenge line exceeds pre-set temperature indicating insufficient cleaning fluid present

(3) Temperature failure—temperature in scavenge line too low

(4) Reject button can be used to reject for a reason such as steam leak.

(5) Head switch failure—keg not properly centered for washing head

(6) Spear switch failure—The broaching device has not correctly opened or closed the valve on the keg.

(7) Steam temperature failure—after the sterilizing hold, the keg is steamed through and if the temperature set point is not achieved immediately, the keg is rejected.

(8) Three rejects in succession can be programmed to shut the operation down until the problem is resolved.

5. Checkweigher, Pusher and Escapement (Full Kegs)

The unit has the capability of checkweighing kegs to determine adequate filling of each keg at 630 kegs per hour and has a zone edge tolerance of plus or minus 56.7 grams (2 oz.). Equipment comprises a mechanical platform checkweigher of the steel-yard type and an associated control cabinet.

The checkweigher is set to weigh a particular size of keg by adjusting the internal steelyard to the required weight. The weigher indicates zero when a keg of the correct weight is on the platform. Kegs which are under-weight or over-weight are shown by the dial head pointer moving away from the center zero position, towards the light or heavy segment of the dial respectively.

The weighing platform is designed to fit within a chain conveyor and therefore the weighing platform lifting members are adjustable for pitch. When not weighing, the members lie just below the level of the conveyor allowing unrestricted flow of kegs. When weighing, a pneumatic cylinder is pressurized and by a crank arrangement, lifts the members and the keg above the conveyor to prevent interference with the weighing. This raising and lowering of the weighing area is initiated by a keg interrupting a light beam to a photocell mounted on the outside of the weigher.

In the dial head, a disc is attached to the pointer assembly. The disc interrupts the light beam to another photocell. The disc has a segment cut away so that if the pointer moves into the zero or overweight section, the light operates the photocell, which in turn disconnects the reject circuit.

Conversely, if the pointer registers underweight, the photocell is not operated and the reject circuit is not disabled. When the platform lowers and the keg continues on the conveyor, it trips a limit switch which operates the reject mechanism and the keg is propelled by a pneumatic ram down the reject path.

6. In-Line Keg Capping Unit

The Unit is basically a free standing press, which manufactures and applies the cap directly onto the neck of the moving keg, and a sealing head which seals the cap onto the neck of the keg at a sealing station.

7. Press and Cap Applier

All Machines are filled with a pre-aligned, interchangeable tool set, where the caps are actually cut and formed. A change from one to another takes approximately five minutes.

All machines are fitted with stepless adjustment on the foil feed so that the gap between caps can be regulated. Press tools take foil thickness from 0.050mm to 0.070mm (0.0020 inches to 0.0028 inches). Tools to special order can be made for paper or plastic laminated foil and thicker foils up to 0.3mm (0.0118 inches) depending on cap size. Embossing dies can be supplied with any design. Inserts for the days of the week or coding are also available. The cap applier allows the neck of the keg to collect the cap as it passes by.

The sealing head is a machined plastic block which floats on a central shaft. When the keg is stopped by the escapement, the keg is lifted off the conveyor by a lift platform assembly and the sealing head is moved down to the keg neck by means of an air cylinder.

8. Keg Tap Cap Machine

The machine is a free standing unit mounted over the conveyor which will automatically apply caps to kegs as they pass through the machines. It is capable of capping up to 750 kegs per hour of either ¼ or ½ barrel size. The machine guides an applicator head needing to be reset on different size kegs.

9a. Keg Palletizer For Palletizing Barrels Horizontally

This Keg Palletizer is a machine designed to load four ½ barrel or six ¼ barrel size beer kegs horizontally onto a wooden pallet automatically. (Other palletizers are available for loading barrels vertically).

The Operation Sequence (½ U.S. Barrel Size) is:

(1.) This section deals solely with the loading of the pallet board with four kegs.

(2.) With the pallet board in position for loading, the keg carrying fingers lower the first two kegs onto the pallet board below.

(3.) With the pallet board in position, the kegs are conveyed to the loading position by the keg chain conveyor which runs at right angles to the loader and carries the kegs when they have been filled and weighed.

(4.) The second keg is brought into position by the keg chain conveyor and comes to rest alongside the first keg.

(5.) Both kegs are now in position and lifted clear from the keg chain conveyor.

(6.) Provided the keg fingers are in the Up position, the keg steady would now be in the Down position.

(7.) The switch that locates the keg steady in the lower position is closed. This in turn causes the keg pusher to sweep forward, pushing both kegs from the infeed chain conveyor onto the keg fingers.

(8.) When the keg pusher is fully forward, the two additional kegs are swept into the keg fingers.

(9.) The keg fingers next lower the kegs onto the pallet board below.

(10.) The entire operation is repeated for the second pair of kegs. When the second pair of kegs have been loaded as before, the pallet board is moved by the pallet chain conveyor.

9b. Keg Palletizer for Vertical Palletizing

(1.) Pallets leave the depalletizing operation and are moved into the empty pallet stacker. When stacked, the empty pallets move into the

14-13. *Keg palletizer for vertical palletizing, with empty pallet dispenser in foreground and full pallet stacker in background (Courtesy of W.C. Pantin Ltd.)*

pallet magazine to await being used to handle full kegs.

(2.) Two full barrels enter the loader where they are pushed onto a pallet.

(3.) The pallet moves into the stacker where pallets of full barrels are stacked.

(4.) Finished pallets of barrels are conveyed on a pallet conveyor for pick up by a fork lift truck and transfered to a truck or cold room storage.

(5.) Vertical stacking requires the use of a pallet between each layer of barrels. When stacking pallets of barrels, three loads high or nine barrels high, the overall height will be close to 6.1 meters (20 feet) (where cask shaped barrels are stacked horizontally using pallets and slipboards a similar number of barrels will result in a stack 4.6 meters [15 feet] high.) (See Figure 14-13)

Automated System for Barrel Washing, Waxing and Filling at the Adolph Coors Company

This keg system consists of a process area where the returned kegs are debunged, decorked, washed inside and out, sterilized, waxed, cooled, inspected, corked, and then sent to the racking area. The racking area consists of twelve enzinger racker arms where the kegs are filled, racked, and conveyed on to the grouper. Each keg is washed with 99.5 liters (26.3 gallons) of water. However, the recycling aspects of the process machine water flow is set up so that the actual water used is 17.0 liters (4.5 gallons) per keg.

The main process machinery and associated conveyors are operated by three hydraulic systems—one 70.3 kilograms per square centimeter (1000 p.s.i.) and two 38.7 kilograms per square centimeter (550 p.s.i.). All controls for the process are electronic except for the rack arms which use a pneumatic timing device for controlling the purging, counter pressuring and filling cycles. The corking and decorking machines are pneumatic.

Two sizes of aluminum kegs are used at Coors: ½ barrel—58.7 liters (15.5 gallons) and ¼ barrel—29.3 liters (7.75 gallons). The system is designed to rack kegs at a rate of 640 half barrel kegs per hour. The actual production average of this system is 638 kegs per hour. The quarter barrel kegs average 575 per hour. The crew, including relief, consists of one supervisor and nine operators per shift.

The Process Machine

The kegs are unloaded from the rail cars and from trucks using a fork truck equipped with special forks capable of handling 36 kegs at a time. Each tier consists of nine kegs. The kegs are placed on a depalletizer which depalletizes the kegs and places them on a conveyor which carries them over to an elevator from which they are transported up to the fourth floor of the building where the Keg Department is located. The operation of the keg depalletizer and associated conveyors and elevator is completely automatic and controlled electronically through the use of photo-eyes located throughout the system. As the kegs reach the keg processing area on the fourth floor, pusher bars eject the kegs from the elevator onto a gravity conveyor which feeds them into the process machine. (See Figure 14-14.)

The process area consists of 72 stations which start with the end straightening and end with the cold rinse. The kegs move through the area in pairs so each keg sees 36 processing stages. These stages take place in this order:

a)	keg end straightener	1 stage
b)	orientation	1 stage
c)	debung	1 stage
d)	reorientation	1 stage
e)	decork	1 stage
f)	hand decork	1 stage
g)	preheat	1 stage
h)	exterior chemical scrub	3 stages
i)	exterior rinse and interior flush	3 stages
j)	interior wash and tapper rinse	2 stages
k)	interior rinse	5 stages
l)	hot air drying	7 stages
m)	waxing	1 stage
n)	wax drain and tapper clearing	4 stages
o)	keg cooling	4 stages

The first action that takes place with the kegs as they enter the process area is to pass through an end straightening device operated hydraulically which compresses the kegs from both ends and straightens out dents which may occur during handling. The kegs then go over a locating device which senses the bung area and turns the keg so that it is in the proper position for debunging. From this point on through the process, the kegs are moved by a device called a "walking beam."

When the kegs reach the debunging area, hydraulic rams extend down to the top of the keg and hold them in position while the bungs are being removed. Hydraulically operated augers turn into the bungs and then pull down removing them from the keg. These bungs are then stripped from the screw and returned to be washed, ground up and re-processed into new bungs.

The next stage is decorking. Here an air controlled guide rod is driven into the tap plug, fingers grip the edge of the plug, then a reverse action takes place where the rod and fingers are removed pulling the tap plug and stripping it in the same action.

After being decorked, the kegs enter the process machine, where they are washed inside and out, and the wax is removed. The kegs are sterilized, waxed with fresh wax in a single spraying

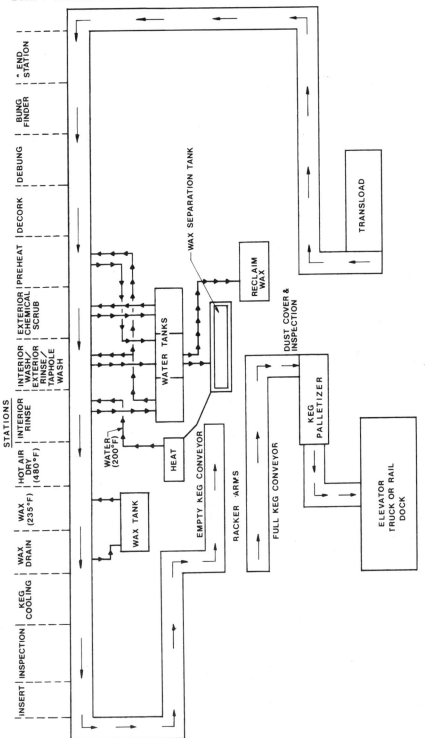

14-14. *Adolph Coors automated system for washing, waxing and filling barrels (Courtesy of Adolph Coors Company)*

operation, cooled and inspected manually at the discharge end. As the kegs enter the process machine, they are first preheated by being rinsed inside and out with water at 87.8°C (190°F). During the washing phases, the hot water melts and removes the old wax from the keg with the wax and water running into a wax separation tank. This wax is then removed and discarded.

After leaving the preheat area, the kegs run through an exterior chemical scrub. A mild caustic solution is added to tank #1 which serves as a reservoir for the chemical cleaning. The solution from this tank is pumped through sprays in the chemical scrub area at a pressure of 7 kilograms per square centimeter (100 p.s.i.).

After leaving the exterior chemical scrub area, the kegs then move into the exterior rinse and interior flush section. Next, the kegs move into the interior wash and tapper rinse section. In this area sprays are located even with the tap holes so that the direct rinse of hot water can be injected into the tap well of each keg.

After leaving the interior wash and tapper rinse area, the kegs move to an interior rinse which is the final preheated fresh water rinse the kegs receive prior to being waxed. They then move to a hot air drying area of the process machine where air at a temperature of 248.9°C (480°F) is blown into the kegs to sterilize them just prior to waxing. One application, approximately 102.1 grams (3.6 ounces), of wax is sprayed into each keg.

The wax system consists of three tanks, two of which are melting and holding tanks and the third consists of the recirculating tank and supply tank from which the wax is pumped to the waxing sprays. The wax temperature is held at 112.8°C (235°F). After being waxed, the kegs are then cooled by being passed through external cold water sprays.

Upon leaving the process machine each keg is manually inspected. The kegs stop momentarily in front of high intensity lamps. The inspector looks through the bung hole to check for complete and thorough waxing of each keg and also for cleanliness internally and externally.

After being inspected the kegs go through a tap corking machine which operates in a manner similar to the decorking machine. New rubber tap corks are inserted into each tap well automatically.

At this point, the kegs are ready for filling and are conveyed to the keg racking area.

Racking

The racking area consists of twelve Enzinger racking arms supported by a dual header system. One header for beer supply and a second header for the venting system. Three racker operators fill kegs at an average rate of 638 kegs per hour. Each racker operator handles four racking stations. The bungs that are used are new, dated, plastic bungs which have been sterilized by being washed in a sanitizing solution.

The beer is supplied to the keg beer header from tanks located in the basement of the Packaging and Warehouse buildings. The beer enters the center section of the beer supply header and flows from the center to both ends and into a second header system which returns the beer to the supply area in the basement. An automatic valve located in this return line restricts the flow in order to maintain the beer level in the header at approximately 50% full. Beer from the racker beer supply header is furnished to each rack arm through hoses connected at the bottom of the header. Each rack arm is also supplied with a CO_2 source, with a CO_2 venting line and with an air supply. The rack arm mechanical action is controlled by an air cylinder and by a pneumatic timing mechanism.

The operator places the keg in the saddle. He then pulls the control lever forward and guides the rack arm for proper fit over the bung box. (See racker Illustration).

By pulling the control handle, the complete filling operations is set in motion. An air valve is opened to allow compressed air to flow into the top of the cylinders and vent from the bottom. As the cylinder fills with air, the fill tube is pushed into the keg. At the same time friction allows the fill tube to pull the ring valve open allowing fresh CO_2 gas to enter the keg and pressurize it to 1.3 Kg/sq.cm (18 PSI). Also, when the control handle is pulled forward, the time mechanism starts. After 7 seconds, the keg is pressurized and the timer opens an air valve which allows air at 2.5 kilograms per square centimeter (35 PSI) to flow into a cavity located above the diaphragm. This pushes the diaphragm down and opens the foot valve located at the bottom of the fill tube.

When the foot valve opens the keg begins to fill with beer. As the beer level rises in the keg, the CO_2 is compressed, causing the ball check valve in the CO_2 line to close. This condition also slows the initial filling speed so less foam is produced. As the pressure increases, it overcomes the weight of the beer left in the vent line from the previous fill. The ball check on this line opens and allows the CO_2 to vent, pushing the beer and foam into the vent header. From here the beer flows to the purge beer system and the gases are vented to the atmosphere.

During the filling operation, the operator observes the sight glass located in the vent valve. When filling starts, the glass shows white foam; when the keg is full, the glass shows clear beer.

Beer flows from the full keg through the vent line only to a level equal to the level of the beer in the beer header.

From the vent line the beer flows to the purge beer system and the gases are vented to the atmosphere.

When the sight glass is clear, the operator removes the fill tube by pushing the control handle to the rear position.

Once the keg is racked, the cycle is complete and the next keg can be filled. See Figure 14-14.

After racking, the operators push the kegs onto a chain conveyor which takes them to a cold water external rinse. Located just prior to the rinse is check weighing station where the kegs can be pulled off and weighed to determine the accuracy of the fill.

After the external rinse, the kegs pass through a metering station where they are counted and then to a final inspection area where the kegs are inspected for leakers and for cleanliness. At this point, a plastic dust cover is placed over the tap plug. The dust covers are color coded to indicate the type of beer in the keg. (Any kegs the inspector finds that are not up to standards are rejected by pushing them off the conveyor onto a rollerdeck.) The filled kegs then enter the grouping machine where they are grouped in sets of nine. After being removed from the grouper, a forktruck transports the kegs for loading into rail cars and trucks.

CLOSURES

The traditional style barrel is sealed after filling by using a wooden bung or plastic bung which is driven manually or automatically into the bung box opening.

Compressed Wooden Bung Specifications

Type of Wood

Yellow tulip poplar required; heartwood is preferred. The wood shall be untreated or uncoated in any way other than the identifying color on the top driving face. The lumber shall be seasoned adequately and care shall be taken to properly control the moisture content of the wood before fabrication. Obvious defects shall be eliminated. Any lot of bungs containing more than 1% of wood defects or fabrication defects, such as worm holes, knots, splits and cracks, can be cause for rejection.

Taper

The taper shall be obtained by compression. Cut bungs are not acceptable. The bungs shall not be serrated on the sides. (Some brewers prefer bungs with serrated sides). The taper shall not exceed 5° ± 1° on any one bung.

Plastic Bung Specifications

Material: Polyethylene material approved by F.D.A. under federal regulation #121.2501, 121.2508, 121.2510. No odors or flavors are allowed, material must be tested by taste panel. Material must be clean and free from foreign matter.

Color: As specified for brand

Finish: Smooth with no voids or occlusion

Dimensions: Must be held to specified tolerances

Bung Marking: Each bung must have mold cavity number stamped and must be clearly dated prior to use.

Coding: Coding can identify racking production according to brand shift, day, month, year racked. Branding of wooden bungs or printing or notching of labels can provide effective coding. Bung color can also be varied to correspond to a given brand identification.

BIOLOGICAL CONTROL—RACKING AND OTHER SAMPLING

Microbiological Sampling Racking Tank to Racker Arm
Purpose

To monitor the biological effectiveness of the racker sterilization procedure. Samples are collected at the beginning of racking following sterilization.

Procedure

Swab samples from sterile racking arms are collected immediately prior to racker startup. Collect beer sample at the racking tank aseptically in a sterile brown bottle. Samples from transfer line and following meter are collected in sterile needle sampling bottles. (Figure 14-15.)

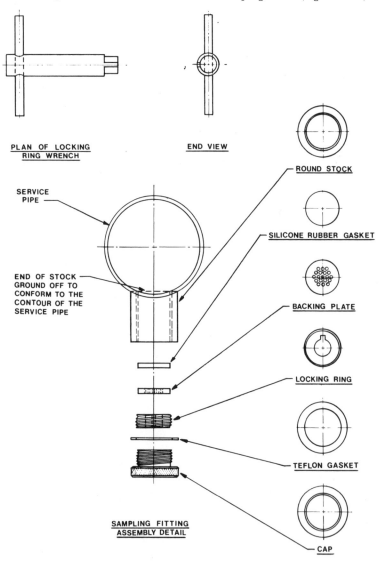

14-15. Fitting for sampling with sterile needle.

First and 5 minute beer samples from the racking arm are collected in sterile wide mouth plastic bottles.

Beer samples are millipore filtered (100 mL) on beer and Nutrient Agars. Beer from racking tank is millipore filtered on Beer, Nutrient and Universal Beer (anaerobic) Agars.

Transfer swabs to sterile 100 mL dilution blanks and plate 1.0 mL on Beer and Nutrient Agars.

Record date, racker no., maximum temperature and time above 87.8°C (190°F) as well as the lapse between sterilization and startup.

Millipore plates are incubated 48 hours at 32°C (89.6°F) Universal Beer Agar plate and poured plates, 7 days at 27°C (80.6°F) Universal Beer Agar plate incubated anaerobically.

Microbiological Sampling for Stability

Purpose

To evaluate the Microbiological Stability of Draft Beer in Half Barrels at 7.2°C (45°F) over a two month period.

Procedure

This sample is collected in conjunction with the Racker startup samples.

Sampling of Half Barrel:

Remove filled half barrel from Conveyor Line. Sterilize the tapping fitting with dilute microclene (iodine solution). Rinse well with city water to remove all trace of iodine. Engage sterile tap, and collect approximately 200 ml beer. Remove tap, rinse away any residual beer with city water and replace plastic cover.

Repeat sampling after 30 and 60 days.

Initial Sample: Millipore 100 ml of beer, incubate membrane on Beer Agar.

Thirty and Sixty Day Samples: Plate 1.0 ml of beer on Beer Agar.

Purpose:

To evaluate the microbiological stability of unpasteurized draft beer at 27°C. (80.6°F).

Apparatus: Sterile 16 oz Beer Bottles
Sterile Sampling Needle
Sterile Half Barrel Tap

Procedure: Samples are collected as part of the racker startup sampling procedure, after the racker has been running 15-20 minutes.

Collect a 16 oz. beer sample from the sampling diaphragm after the meter using the sampling needle and rubber tubing.

Collect a further 16 oz sample from a full half barrel using the sterile tap. Following incubation, plate 1.0 ml from each bottle on Beer Agar. Taste beer for any microbiological off flavor.

Microbiological Sampling Washed Barrels

Purpose:

To monitor the microbiological effectiveness of the keg washing operation by sampling clean half barrels.

Apparatus: Five Sterile Rubber Sampling Stoppers
Sterile Brown Bottles

Procedure: After the half barrel has received the final city water rinse and before half barrel drains, turn barrel on rack to prevent draining from bung hole. Insert sterile rubber stopper fitted with copper tubing. Turn barrel to drain and collect water in sterile brown bottle.

Sample five cleaned barrels. Collect a city water sample as a reference from the final external water set.

Plate 1.0 ml samples of water on Beer and Nutrient Agars.

Other Sampling For Racking Operation

(1) Draft beer in government cellar is sampled and tested to determine Alcohol, Oxygen, Original gravity, Haze, and Taste.

(2) Rinse water drained from a cleaned barrel is checked to confirm effective rinsing of caustic cleaner by measuring pH using a Phenolphthalein indicator.

(3) Barrel washer caustic strength is measured through titration with acid to maintain concentration at 2.0 - 2.5%.

(4) Barrels are check weighed to confirm proper fill.

(5) New cooperage is examined to evaluate quality.

SAFETY

Protection From Excessive Noise Exposure

Prolonged exposure to excessive noise over a number of years may cause deafness. The subject in treated in more detail in Chapter XXI, Safety.

PROBLEMS

Rejects

Returns from the trade can represent a wide variety of potential problems:

Barrel Rejects
  Bung box leakers
  Pin hole leakers
  Weld leakers
  Dented or bulged
Valve Rejects
  Valve leaker
  Loose tap
  Bad tap thread
  Difficulty in tapping
Bungs
  Bung leakers

Beer
  Error in shipment
  Off taste
  Flat
  Wild
  Old code
  Sour
  Foreign matter
  Cloudy
  Frozen

Specific arrangements are necessary to provide for proper identification of rejects and evaluation of claims. Policy regarding returns must be developed so that claims are treated uniformly. Records should be detailed and summaries published to compare reject levels by category monthly and year to date versus previous year. This comparison will highlight trends or new problems.

Control of Beer Loss in Racking

Beer loss in racking can be controlled by:
1. Accurate barrel counters counting in series independently.
2. Accurate daily barrel inventories taken by two different supervisors.
3. Accurate beer metering with regular meter calibration. (Immediate calibration of meters is necessary whenever unusual losses are observed.)
4. Daily reconciliation of inventories, production totals, shipments and in house draft beer consumption.
5. Regular weighing of barrels racked against specifications for ranges and averages.
   (The new Sankey and Burnett and Rolfe automatic racking systems can be designed to monitor all full barrel weights. Results from each line can be segregated.)
6. Reducing beer changeovers will reduce losses.
7. Lower new barrel volume specifications can influence losses.
8. Repair of damaged barrels may influence losses.

Barrel Repairs

Barrel repairs may be required for a variety of reasons, including such problems as:

1. pin hole leakage
2. denting or bulging of barrel
3. leaking bung box
4. weld leakage
5. valve leakage
6. damaged bushings
7. loose tap valves
8. bad tap thread
9. difficulty in tapping

The repaired barrel should be guaranteed for one year with dimensions and capacity guaranteed as unchanged and pressure tested at 6.3 Kg/cm² (90 PSI).

Additionally, where barrels are being returned to a shop for repair, arrangements can be made to leave the valves in the barrels. During normal repair of these barrels, the valves are removed, cleaned and tested at 6.0–6.3 Kg/sq.cm. (85–90 PSI) prior to reinstalling in repaired barrels. Valves which fail this pressure test can then be returned for a complete overhaul by valve supplier. This procedure is usually less costly than in plant valve repair. Damaged bushings should also be replaced with machined bushings if required.

RACKING EFFICIENCY

Racking efficiency should be monitored. Downtime causes need to be recorded with corresponding times assigned to mechanical, electrical or other factors. Downtime for each main stage in the overall racking line should be indicated separately on a shift downtime report. This practice will assist in directing mechanical and electrical efforts to those problems which are most critical. Similarly, weekly summaries of downtime charged to individual equipment identified as mechanical versus electrical and to other areas can provide useful information to assist in improving efficiency. Graphing of recorded downtime experienced at each stage of the line also presents a useful visual expression of trends in actual downtime. Weekly review meetings with all personnel who have direct supervisory responsibility for performance in racking is essential if downtime is to be controlled.

Racking efficiency can be measured in several ways based on total volume racked or based on units racked with and without downtime included in the calculation. Efficiencies can be compared by shift both daily and cumulatively.

High efficiencies in racking depend on such factors as:
1. Equipment
   (a) Convenient layout with adequate surge capacity before and after the racker.
   (b) Barrel debunging and washing capacity to provide at least 10% over maximum racking capacity.
   (c) Palletizing capacity at least 20% over maximum racking capacity.
   (d) Pallets in good condition.
2. Maintenance and Electrical Servicing
   (a) Well trained supervisors, machinists and electricians.
   (b) Precise well organized reference manuals and prints.
   (c) Adequate spare parts.
3. Scheduling
   (a) Minimum planned package and brand changeovers.
   (b) Accurate forecasting to prevent over or under production.
4. Materials
   (a) Adequate inventory of all required materials.
   (b) Adequate supply of empty barrels at all times.
5. Effective Recording and Communication of
   (a) Causes of downtime
   (b) Efficiencies by shift
   (c) Barrel shortages

  (d) Requests for maintenance or electrical assistance
  (e) All downtime analytical information such as downtime graphs, efficiency
      graphs, downtime summaries.
6. Training
  (a) Formal training program for supervisors and operators
  (b) Documented procedures for all operations
  (c) Documented references for all equipment.
  (d) Specific instruction for operators concerning automatic steps to be taken
      whenever the racking operation is affected in order to reduce downtime.
8. Effective Supervision
   Knowledgeable supervisors who have the respect of their operators and
   peers are essential to the achievement of high racking efficiency. Supervisors
   need to lead their shift by co-ordinating effectively with the previous shift,
   by being aware of the progress throughout their shift through meter and
   counter readings and by communicating regularly with all operators to
   respond to potential problems. Each supervisor must assign his overall staff
   to positions on the line which will draw on the strengths of each operator
   for most effective overall operation.
9. Adequate empty barrel and full barrel storage to provide for empty barrel
   supply surges and to respond to fluctuations in shipping plans.

ACKNOWLEDGEMENTS:

The authors wish to express appreciation to the many colleagues and associates
who assisted so much in providing photographs, drawings, and pertinent in-
formation. Particular mention should be made of:
R.A. Clarke, The Duriron Company
H.F. Cowles, GKN Sankey Ltd.
Greg Muro, Hoover Universal
Dave Schroeder, Labatt Breweries Ltd.
E.R. Sulier, Sav-A-Barrel Corp.
Darrell Templeton, Adolph Coors Company
R.F. Wenz, Burnett & Rolfe Ltd.
R.G. Wyant, Adolph Coors Company
K.F.C. Avey, W. & C. Pantin Limited

References:

1. BABCOOK, D.R. and HOLMER, C.F. Packaging/Draft Operations. *The Practical Brewer*, p.
   271-287 (1977).
2. COX, G.T. Health and Safety in the Brewing Industry, Part III, Noise, *The Brewer*, p. 8-10
   (January 1981).
3. KESSON, J. Microprocessor Control of Keg Washing Racking Machines, *Brewers Guardian*, p.
   13-17 (August, 1980).
4. OLDMAN, K. The Approach to Noise Problems in the Brewing Industry, *MBAA Technical
   Quarterly*, Vol. 17, No. 3, p. 107-119 (1980).

Section IV: Operations Common to Bottling, Canning and Draft.

CHAPTER XV

BEER HANDLING

BY MICHAEL LLOYD
and WOLFGANG BAYERLEIN

INTRODUCTION

This chapter deals with the handling of beer for packaging. The subject is covered both from the point of view of the product and from the point of view of the systems necessary to handle the product properly up to the filling machines.

The following topics are covered:
—Packaging beer process description
—Packaging beer quality control procedures
—Description of tankage in the packaging cellar
—Description of systems used to move beer from packaging tanks to fillers
—Description of filler bowl level control techniques
—Comments on handling packaged beer beyond the filler
—Some thoughts on future trends in packaging beer handling

The chapter is written with a slight bias towards large breweries. As of this writing, almost all beer in the United States is produced from breweries having a capacity larger than 1,000,000 barrels (1,170,000 hl) per year. More than 70% of this beer originates from plants having capacities greater than 4,000,000 barrels (4,680,000 hl) per year. In many other parts of the world, the trend towards similar concentration of production facilities is evident.

Individual operations in large breweries are usually quite similar to those found in smaller plants. However, in large breweries the problem of moving multiple brands of beer in large quantities to multiple filling lines requires that the individual operations be conducted within a very formal organizational and planning structure. Consequently, some of the operating methods and equipment which are described in this chapter may be useful only in the bigger breweries.

The overall objective of any beer packaging system is to move an adequate quantity of beer at an acceptable rate from the bulk beer production facilities via packaging equipment into finished packages. This must be done routinely,

economically and the quality of beer must be maintained and assured throughout.

PACKAGING CELLARS—GENERAL

General

The section of the bulk beer production facility which is discussed in this
chapter is variously referred to as the Packaging Cellar, the Packaging Release
Cellar or the Government Cellar. The name "Government Cellar" refers to
the historic fact that in earlier days the U.S. Government collected its beer
tax on the basis of the quantity of beer transferred from a locked cellar to
the filling machines. By 1980, most of the mechanical and operating regulations
which had been established to simplify physical monitoring of beer flow to
fillers had been withdrawn in favor of paper reporting schemes. Today, the
U.S. brewer has considerable latitude in designing the method of transferring
beer and in selecting the process monitoring procedures which he wishes to
employ.

In typical American practice, brewers employ a 2-stage filtration for beer
clarification. The second of these filtration stages is known variously as the
Secondary Filter, Final Filter, Polish Filter or some similar name. This process
step is the source of beer for the packaging cellar.

In general, the polish filtration station consists of one or more filters running
in parallel. Some brewers favor pad/pulp filters for this service, while others
use diatomite filtration followed by trap filters to catch stray diatomite particles.
Normally the polish filtration station provides assured removal of all particles
to 5 microns.

It is desirable that the polish filtration should take place at the coldest
temperature that the beer will normally encounter. Thus it is usual practice
to locate a cooler upstream of the polish filter so as to operate the filtration
at 28°F to 31°F (approx. -1°C to -2°C). This provides for removal of
filterable chill haze components.

As part of the final filtration operation, a carbonator injects CO_2 into the
beer stream to adjust its CO_2 content. The amount of CO_2 required to be
injected at this station depends upon the cellaring methods employed by the
brewer upstream of this station. Brewers using Kraeusening or related cellaring
techniques with good control of operations will frequently require only touch-
up carbonation at this point.

The carbonation level at the discharge of this station must be 0.10 to 0.20
volumes higher than that specified for the destination package. This anticipates
the carbonation losses which will occur in beer handling and filling.

Product marketing considerations generally set the in-package carbonation
specification. A wide range of values is possible, ranging from just above 2.00
volumes to about 3.00 volumes. Products low in that range are perceived by
the drinker as very lightly carbonated, while levels high in that range are
perceived as very effervescent. Beers having carbonation levels between 2.45
and 2.85 volumes will generally be perceived as being "normally" carbonated.

Some typical carbonation levels, volume per volume of product, are:

Package	Package Carbonation	Bulk Beer Carbonation
Bottles	2.60 − 2.70	+0.15
Cans	2.60 − 2.70	+0.18
Kegs	2.50 − 2.60	+0.10

Beer from the polish filter is generally pumped to the packaging tanks. These tanks are generally administered as a batch operation, with the sequence being to fill a tank (or group of tanks) with the required quality control approval on the beer prior to releasing the tanks for packaging.

Some continuous-flow packaging cellars have been put into operation. In these systems the packaging tanks serve as a surge or buffer between the polish filtration station and the filling machines. Such facilities require tighter operating control and more frequent quality monitoring than conventional batch-type installations in order to minimize the risk of packaging unacceptable product.

No matter what configuration of packaging cellar is used, the beer must be handled correctly. Some of the conditions which must be satisfied are as follows:

A) Air pickup must be avoided. This is accomplished by providing a CO_2 atmosphere in the tanks and by providing for gentle handling of product flow into packaging tanks. It is common practice to use the same packaging tanks for several batches between cleanings and to maintain some beer in tanks between batches in order to reduce air pickup caused by the turbulence of beer flowing into an empty, newly cleaned, air filled tank. (Interest is emerging in acidic cleaning materials for use in packaging tank CIP systems. These materials permit tanks to be cleaned without requiring the CO_2 to be replaced by air prior to cleaning, as is necessitated when caustic cleaning materials are employed.)

A variety of tank inlet devices, including "mushroom" deflectors and directional pipe nozzles, are available to reduce turbulent contact between inflowing beer and the tank atmosphere at low tank levels.

B) The brilliant appearance of polish filtered beer cannot be allowed to deteriorate. In this regard, several hazards are present:

i) Non Biological Turbidity: Broadly speaking, such turbidity can be divided into 2 classes: - turbidity due to solids and turbidity from chemical sources.

a.) Dried foam flakes constitute the most important solid turbidity risk. The flake material is created when beer is mishandled so as to create foam on the surface of the beer in packaging tanks. If this foam clings to tank walls and solidifies, it can later collapse into the beer. It does not redissolve but appears as flecks of material suspended in the beer at near neutral buoyancy. This condition is avoided through the same gentle methods of handling the beer as those needed for air control.

Packaging tank cleaning frequency is usually selected so that dried foam is eliminated before it becomes a problem. This is the most significant cleaning requirement for packaging tanks. A typical cleaning requirement for packaging tanks might be stated as "every fourth filling, but in any case not less than once every 10 days".

Other solid materials which enter packaging tanks generally result from accidents in the process. It is not possible to anticipate every accident which might occur. However, vigilance at this process stage is essential, since this is the last line of defense against the packaging of defective product.

The outlet of a packaging tank is usually equipped with a stand pipe so that any solids which have settled to the bottom of the tank cannot be carried forward to fillers.

b.) The sources of chemical turbidity are usually associated with malfunctions of additive systems or with metal contamination.

ii) Biological: Severe biological problems in packaging tanks are unusual. However, under extreme conditions, biological growth can induce turbidity. This problem is addressed through three mechanisms. First, the temperature of the beer should continue to be maintained below 32°F (0°C) in the packaging cellar—a temperature which inhibits most biological growth. Second, beer should be scheduled into the packaging tanks near to the time that it will be packaged, so that it is not left in packaging tanks for more than 3 or 4 days.

Third, it is necessary to provide adequate cleaning and sanitation for the tanks and their surrounding piping systems. Experience shows that the tank cleaning which must be done to eliminate dried foam is generally sufficient for maintaining biological control. Line cleaning requirements depend upon the intensity of use of the pipeline as well as the ambient temperature surrounding the pipeline. Pipeline cleaning frequency falls between daily and weekly, with the shortest cleaning intervals being used for pipelines which are used intermittently and which pass through warm areas.

C) Carbonation levels must not be allowed to vary outside the specified range. Since carbonation is an equilibrium phenomenon, it is important to hold the packaging tank counterpressure at a value consistent with the expected carbonation level and temperature of the product in the tank. Packaging tanks are held at 10–12 PSI (0.68 to 0.82 bar) for typical beers. However, Table I can be used to establish correct conditions for any particular product.

The amount of CO_2 in solution in a full tank is great in comparison to the rate of CO_2 interchange between the beer and its head space. Thus many hours of minor variations in counterpressure or large variations over short periods of time have little practical effect on the CO_2 content of the beer. An exception is that a very low counterpressure can sometimes cause rapid CO_2 release—particularly if the beer is somehow agitated while the pressure is low.

Normally, counterpressure for packaging tanks is supplied from a "Balanced" system. That is, the gas displaced from a filling tank is permitted to flow into tanks which are emptying. Only in cases where the filling and emptying rates are different is gas made up to or vented from the whole system. By necessity, such a system must operate at a compromise pressure if several carbonation levels are required for beer in the system. Another compromise is caused by the fact that balanced systems generally have a dead band of 2 to 4 PSI (approx. 0.1 to 0.3 bar) between the make up point and the vent point in order to conserve CO_2.

D) Unwanted dilution of product in packaging tanks must be avoided. This problem is usually addressed by making sure that product push-outs with water are closely controlled. Positive isolation techniques must be used to isolate product piping from push-out water connections. It

Table I: CO₂ Temperature-Pressure Equilibrium in Beer

MINIMUM SATURATION PRESSURE

F°	C°	1 Vol.	1 %	2 Vol.	2 %	3 Vol.	3 %	4 Vol.	4 %	5 Vol.	5 %	6 Vol.	6 %	7 Vol.	7 %	8 Vol.	8 %	9 Vol.	9 %	10 Vol.	10 %	11 Vol.	11 %	12 Vol.	12 %	13 Vol.	13 %	14 Vol.	14 %	15 Vol.	15 %
30.	-1.1	1.82	.354	1.92	.373	2.03	.395	2.14	.416	2.23	.433	2.36	.459	2.48	.482	2.60	.505	2.70	.525	2.82	.548	2.93	.570	3.02	.587	3.13	.608	3.27	.636	3.35	.651
31.	-0.6	1.78	.346	1.88	.365	2.00	.389	2.10	.408	2.20	.428	2.31	.449	2.42	.470	2.54	.494	2.65	.515	2.76	.536	2.86	.556	2.96	.575	3.07	.597	3.19	.620	3.30	.642
32.	.00	1.75	.340	1.85	.359	1.95	.379	2.05	.399	2.16	.420	2.27	.441	2.38	.463	2.48	.482	2.59	.503	2.70	.525	2.80	.544	2.90	.564	3.01	.585	3.10	.603	3.20	.622
33.	.06	1.71	.332	1.81	.352	1.91	.371	2.01	.391	2.12	.412	2.23	.433	2.33	.453	2.43	.472	2.53	.492	2.63	.511	2.74	.533	2.84	.552	2.96	.575	3.05	.593	3.15	.612
34.	1.1	1.67	.324	1.78	.346	1.86	.361	1.97	.383	2.07	.402	2.18	.424	2.28	.443	2.38	.463	2.48	.482	2.58	.501	2.68	.521	2.79	.542	2.89	.562	3.00	.583	3.10	.603
35.	1.7	1.62	.315	1.73	.336	1.83	.356	1.93	.375	2.03	.395	2.14	.416	2.24	.435	2.34	.455	2.43	.472	2.52	.490	2.62	.509	2.73	.531	2.83	.550	2.93	.570	3.02	.587
36.	2.2	1.56	.307	1.68	.326	1.79	.348	1.88	.365	1.99	.387	2.09	.406	2.20	.428	2.29	.445	2.39	.465	2.47	.480	2.57	.500	2.67	.519	2.77	.538	2.86	.556	2.96	.575
37.	2.8	1.54	.299	1.64	.319	1.74	.338	1.84	.358	1.94	.377	2.04	.396	2.15	.418	2.24	.435	2.34	.455	2.42	.470	2.52	.490	2.62	.509	2.72	.529	2.80	.544	2.90	.564
38.	3.3	1.50	.291	1.60	.311	1.70	.330	1.80	.350	1.90	.369	2.00	.389	2.10	.408	2.20	.428	2.29	.445	2.38	.463	2.47	.480	2.57	.500	2.67	.519	2.75	.535	2.85	.554
39.	3.9	1.47	.285	1.56	.303	1.66	.323	1.76	.342	1.86	.361	1.96	.381	2.05	.399	2.15	.418	2.25	.437	2.34	.455	2.43	.472	2.52	.490	2.61	.507	2.70	.525	2.80	.544
40.	4.4	1.43	.278	1.52	.295	1.62	.315	1.72	.334	1.82	.354	1.92	.373	2.01	.391	2.10	.408	2.20	.428	2.30	.447	2.39	.465	2.47	.480	2.56	.498	2.65	.515	2.75	.535
41.	5.0	1.40	.272	1.50	.291	1.58	.307	1.69	.328	1.78	.346	1.87	.363	1.97	.383	2.06	.400	2.16	.420	2.25	.437	2.35	.457	2.43	.472	2.52	.490	2.60	.505	2.70	.525
42.	5.5	1.36	.264	1.46	.284	1.55	.301	1.66	.323	1.74	.338	1.83	.356	1.93	.375	2.02	.393	2.12	.412	2.21	.430	2.30	.447	2.39	.465	2.47	.480	2.56	.498	2.65	.515
43.	6.1	1.33	.258	1.43	.278	1.52	.295	1.62	.315	1.71	.332	1.80	.350	1.90	.369	1.99	.387	2.08	.404	2.17	.422	2.25	.437	2.34	.455	2.43	.472	2.52	.490	2.60	.505
44.	6.7	1.32	.256	1.42	.276	1.50	.291	1.58	.307	1.67	.324	1.76	.342	1.86	.361	1.95	.379	2.04	.396	2.13	.414	2.21	.430	2.30	.447	2.38	.463	2.47	.480	2.56	.498
45.	7.2	1.30	.252	1.38	.268	1.47	.286	1.55	.301	1.64	.319	1.73	.336	1.82	.354	1.91	.371	2.00	.389	2.08	.404	2.17	.422	2.26	.439	2.34	.455	2.42	.470	2.51	.488
46.	7.8	1.28	.249	1.36	.264	1.44	.280	1.52	.295	1.61	.313	1.70	.330	1.78	.346	1.88	.365	1.96	.381	2.04	.396	2.13	.414	2.22	.431	2.30	.447	2.38	.463	2.47	.480
47.	8.3	1.25	.243	1.33	.258	1.43	.278	1.50	.291	1.58	.307	1.67	.324	1.74	.338	1.84	.358	1.92	.373	2.00	.389	2.09	.406	2.18	.424	2.25	.437	2.34	.455	2.42	.470

Courtesy Wittemann Hasselberg, Inc.

should be noted that most brewers who practice high gravity brewing do their dilution far upstream of the polish filtration station. This is at least partly due to their concern with avoiding the risk of improper beer concentration in packaging tanks.

A related concern is the avoidance of unwanted interbrand mixing of beer. Most brewers have a spectrum of products and they establish tight rules regarding whether mixing of one brand into another is permissible. If such mixing is allowed, restrictions are set as to circumstances (usually sequence and degree of mixing) in order to protect the integrity of brand characteristics.

Quality Control of Beer for Filling

Modern cellars/packaging/warehousing/shipping facilities represent an extremely large capital investment which must be operated very intensively if they are to yield a reasonable rate of return on the money which has been invested in them.

The plant operating characteristic which has come to dominate packaging beer quality control considerations is the fact that large modern breweries use extremely short in-process times after the polish filtration stage of the brewing process. In the cellars, the industry's ratio of packaging tank volume to daily packaging volume appears to be in continual decline. This, in turn requires that the Quality Control department must provide very fast turn arounds for approval of beer to be released for packaging.

In the extreme, some brewers are operating packaging tanks only as a surge capacity, simultaneously accepting output from the polish filtration facility and providing a supply of beer to the fillers. Safe administration of such a system requires almost continuous attention by QC personnel.

In the packaging and warehousing departments, the operating objective is to move filled beer containers from the fillers to trucks or rail cars as directly as possible—bypassing any warehousing operations whenever it is practical to do so.

Under these near-critical operating conditions, it is imperative that production practices must be sound enough to routinely produce product of acceptable quality. The penalties associated with production halts or necessary reprocessing of product (particularly in the peak production season) often can go far beyond the direct labor and materials cost of the product.

The actual QC procedures which must be applied to the process can be broadly divided into three classifications:

—Certifying product as suitable to proceed downstream
—Identifying trends in product parameters
—Gathering historical data.

The classification which is under the most pressure because of the intensity of operations is the first listed above. This is the only aspect of QC with which this chapter deals.

Prudent operation requires that analysis and other checks be performed on a tank-by-tank basis prior to the release of any beer from the packaging cellar to the filling lines. Where flow-through tanks are used to supply fillers, a sufficient frequency to limit the brewery's losses in the event that product attributes are found to be unsatisfactory. The list which follows provides the minimum complement of necessary tests.

1. CO_2: Carbonation must be within the range specified as acceptable by the brewery, taking into account the expected CO_2 losses in filling. Typically, this value will be in the range 2.70 to 2.85 volumes.
2. Dissolved Oxygen: The acceptable range for D.O. varies widely among breweries. Typically, current practice requires a value less than .25 ppm. A continuing downward trend for acceptable levels has been noted for all brewers.
3. Clarity: Typical clarity requirements involve both an instrumental value and a visual check. Typical requirements from the instrumentation are: Clarity equal to or better than 16 Nephlos (Coleman #9 Nephelometer). Visually, the product must be bright and free of "floaters".
4. Taste: Beer should be tasted—preferably by the plant taste panel, but at minimum by a taste-qualified person—before release for packaging. In order to be approved for release, the product should be within the limits of its required taste profile.
5. Legal Requirements: Many units of government regulate the alcohol content of beer, either on an Alcohol by Weight or an Alcohol by Volume basis. In some jurisdictions, original gravity requirements exist. Usually, government regulation of these matters results from taxation strategies or from an attempt to deal with the abuse of alcohol. In either case, government can be expected to be zealous in monitoring and enforcing its regulations. The brewer must perform whatever analytical work is needed to assure that he satisfies the applicable regulations. In many places, the brewer risks fines or limitations on his right to sell beer if he ships product which does not satisfy the legal requirements.
6. Label Requirements: Some products have particular requirements which result from label claims. One such requirement which is encountered in most breweries is the need to assure that calorie claims for light beers are satisfied in the packaged product. Similarly, label claims concerning carbohydrates may require analytical certification.
7. Advertising/Marketing Requirements: The minds of personnel in the brewery's marketing and advertising function are very fertile with regard to making claims about production procedures and product characteristics. To the extent that these claims result in a company commitment to some particular course of action with the product, it is important to assure that the product embodies the claimed characteristics.
8. Special Product Requirements: The brewer may have particular standards for parameters such as color. It may be necessary to check such parameters prior to product release.
9. Temperature: Typically beer temperature should be at or below 32°F (0°C) to be suitable for release to filling.

In-line analyzers for some beer parameters have become widely accepted. Equipment for in-line monitoring of clarity, dissolved oxygen and carbonation is available. In spite of the fact that these devices are quite reliable, most brewers use them as production control devices rather than relying on their accuracy to perform the QC function of releasing product to downstream production stages. When such devices are installed on the brewing process, they are most likely to be found between the polish filter and the packaging tanks.

In the packaging plant itself, routine monitoring of packaging line operations by QC personnel generally includes a sub set of the overall packaging beer release tests. These tests are performed on samples taken at the sample valve on the beer line at the base of each filler. The testing at this point must confirm that the major analytical attributes of the beer flowing into the filler are unchanged from those found in the bulk beer. One of the purposes of these tests is to assure that the beer which has been scheduled to run at the filler is indeed the beer which is present.

The analytical testing of in-package beer is dealt with elsewhere in this text.

PACKAGING TANKAGE

The number, size and arrangement of tanks which are assigned for service in supplying beer to packaging reflects the circumstances of the particular brewery in which they are installed. However, there are some general characteristics which appear widely.

In multi-million barrel-per-year breweries, the size of most packaging tanks is usually between 1000 and 2000 barrels (approx. 1170 to 2340 hl). However, even in such large plants there are usually a few small tanks for handling minor brands. In smaller breweries, the size of individual packaging tanks tends to be quite large relative to overall plant capacity. This is because the percentage of variation in the instantaneous rate for individual fillers is less than the percentage variation in overall size between the smallest and the largest breweries. Of course, the major factor in selecting packaging tank size is the desire to reduce the number of tank change-overs during any particular filler run.

Horizontal cylindrical tanks are generally used in packaging cellars. Packaging tanks are constructed of stainless steel or lined carbon steel. They are generally built to withstand at least 15 PSI (1 bar) internal pressure, with 25 PSI (1.7 bar) tanks the most common.

Required tank accessories generally consist of separate filling and emptying connections, a counterpressure connection, a pressure/vacuum relief assembly, a manhole for tank entry, one or more sampling points, a thermometer, provision for determining the beer quantity contained in the tank and provision for tagging the tank to indicate its contents. Frequently, packaging tanks are equipped for CIP. Occasionally, packaging tanks are equipped with carbonating stones or similar devices to allow touch-up carbonation of beer. The practice of carbonating beer in packaging tanks appears to be in decline due to improvements in the consistency of product delivered to the packaging cellar. Generally, packaging tanks are unjacketed and the surrounding area is maintained at 33°F (approx. 1°C) or lower.

It is quite common for tanks to be filled and emptied in groups, particularly where major brands are concerned. Sometimes one tank or group of tanks feeds more than one filler at the same time. The highest rate filling equipment currently on the market has an average capacity of almost 350 barrels per hour (approx. 400 hl per hour). Ganging several fillers of such high rate onto a single set of packaging tanks requires close attention to flow rate and pressure drop considerations.

The overall beer capacity of packaging cellars ranges from about one shift's throughput to several days' throughput. The decision as to how much capacity is assigned to packaging service is distinctive for each brewing company and each plant. This capacity represents a complex trade-off among the circumstances and operating philosophy of each brewing company. It has been observed, however, that brewing personnel find it difficult to administer packaging cellars which are sized substantially smaller than one day's throughput with a normal mix of brands. Brand proliferation increases the difficulty associated with administering a small packaging cellar.

FILLER BEER SUPPLY CONFIGURATIONS

Single-Ended Supply Lines

Most packaging beer supply systems consist of a single separate pipeline to each filler from the packaging cellar. Historically, low rate beer fillers ran at low pressure, so it was often possible to use the packaging tank counter pressure to press the beer into a filler. Current high rate filling machinery generally operates with the beer under higher pressure than the counter pressure used on packaging beer tanks. Thus, in current installations some method has to be provided to boost the beer pressure high enough to cause it to flow into the filling machinery. This is done in two ways. The first technique places the packaging tanks at an elevation in the brewery high enough relative to the fillers so that gravity will allow beer flow. This configuration is referred to as a *Gravity Single-Ended Supply Line*.

In many breweries the plant layout does not permit beer to be supplied to fillers by gravity. Thus, a more common configuration is one which provides one or more pumps in the line. This arrangement is known as a *Pumped Single-Ended Supply Line*. Generally, the pumps which are used are sanitary rotary positive displacement pumps such as those manufactured by Ladish Tri-Clover (Kenosha, WI) or by Waukesha Pump Company (Waukesha, WI). These are generally referred to by plant personnel as "Bump Pumps". Some filler manufacturers recommend the use of centrifugal rather than positive displacement pumps. A sketch of a pumped single ended beer supply system is provided in Figure 15-1.

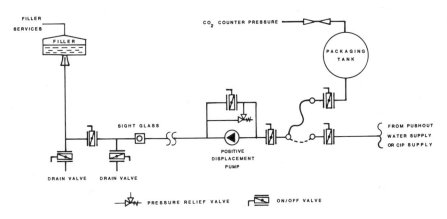

15-1. Pumped ended beer supply system.

Whether gravity or pumped, the majority of such systems are operated manually except for the automatic filler bowl level control system.

In the packaging cellar, various brewers have installed a wide range of piping configurations to deliver beer from the packaging tanks to the filler supply line inlets. The simplest such configuration is a single tank connected to a single filler line by a hose as shown in Figure 15-1.

Another common arrangement relies on the use of *Brand Headers*. These are pipelines which are routed in the packaging cellar so as to allow any or all of several tanks to supply beer to the headers and then to allow the headers to supply beer to any or all of several filler supply lines. Header systems are almost universally applied in manually operated packaging cellars in big breweries.

There are several problems inherent in simple single ended beer supply systems:

1. The beer pipeline generally runs through warm areas on its way from the packaging tanks to the filling machines. Whenever beer flow stops, heat gain through the pipeline's insulation allows the beer to warm up. The result of allowing warm beer to enter the filler is that short-filled packages will be produced at the filler until the system is again handling the normal cold product.

   This problem requires that special procedures be established to push beer back from the filler and its associated pipe line during filler down time and to otherwise assure that the contents of the pipeline are cold after any prolonged filler stop.

   The extreme condition of concern in handling a single ended beer supply system is the packaging line shut down and startup which bracket one or more shifts when the filler is not operating. Biological hazard to the warm beer becomes an additional factor requiring the brewer to recover all of the beer from the filler pipelines prior to a non-operating period. At the end of the down time it is common to CIP the line and then to run chilled water at about 35°F (approx. 2°C) through the lines and fillers to prechill the equipment prior to restarting beer flow.

   In addition to scheduled shut downs, periods of poor packaging line efficiency pose a particular problem. This is because frequent filler stops cause the filler to receive beer at erratically warmer temperatures.

2. With single line manual filler supply systems, all pipeline operations involving filler startups, filler shutdowns, brand changes and line cleaning require close team work between personnel in the packaging cellar and those at the fillers. In large breweries, this is often the working interface between the Brewing Department and the Packaging Department. The physical and departmental separation of the packaging cellar from the fillers is often the source of communication problems between operators in the two areas.

3. In large plants having multiple fillers and multiple brands, the operating complexity of manual single line supply systems becomes quite great. Under such conditions, overtime is often built into operating strategies in order to accommodate actions needed prior to start up of fillers and following packaging line shut down.

In spite of the above list of disadvantages, single-ended systems are very simple and inexpensive. Thus they remain in widespread use for supplying beer to fillers.

Many brewers have attempted to design systems which overcome the problems of single-ended systems. In general, their work can be divided into two distinct areas. First is automation of the valving between the various packaging tanks and fillers. Second is the installation of recirculating beer supply pipelines generally known as "Packaging Loops" or "Filler Loops".

Automated Supply Systems

Many schemes have been used to automate all of the flows associated with single ended filler supply systems. Typically these schemes provide for:

—Clean in Place (CIP) of all of pipelines,

—Precooling pipelines with chilled water,

—Displacement of water with beer,

—Final recovery of beer at filler shut down.

Some brewers have gone beyond automating the functions of the filler supply line itself by providing valving which permits packaging tanks to be selected automatically. Such equipment provides additional automation capabilities as follows:

—Automatic brand changeover,

—Automatic switchover when supply tanks empty.

The equipment used for achieving the latter level of automation is generally referred to as an *Automated Packaging Release System*. Systems such as this can be used as part of an overall filler supply system based upon either single line or packaging loop concepts.

The state of the art in equipment for this service is the prefabricated valve manifold assembly based upon mixproof valves and matrix piping techniques. Figure 15-2 shows a small manifold of the type that might be used to automate the packaging release function of 4 packaging tanks to 2 single ended filling lines.

15-2. Example of a small automated packaging release system.

When very large breweries adopt matrix piping concepts in their packaging release systems, the size of the packaging release manifold can become quite large. For example, a system which provides beer from 10 separate sources of beer to 10 filler lines will require a matrix of 100 valves for product, as

well as the additional valves needed to provide for services such as push-out
water and cleaning connections.

Packaging Loops

This design provides one or more flowing beer pipelines which can be
accessed by each filler. Appropriate valving and piping is provided to allow
some of the packaging loop beer stream to flow into any of the fillers which
are to be serviced by the loop. A *Pumped Packaging Loop* is the most common
configuration. Pumped Loops are able to obtain all of the benefits associated
with Packaging Loops under a wide range of overall brewery layouts. An
example of a pumped loop is shown in Figure 15-3.

In this diagram the beer is supplied by a centrifugal pump which is equipped
with a variable-speed drive. Speed of this drive varies as necessary to satisfy
a pressure control system. The sensor upon which this control system is based
is a beer pressure transmitter mounted in the beer loop near the fillers.

The same loop may be used to simultaneously serve several fillers which
are filling a common product. The recirculating line with its cooler assures
that the beer in the loop is always moving. Thus the beer cannot become too
warm for filling, even if no filler is taking beer from the loop.

The advantages of Pumped Loops are as follows:
—The administration of such a system is often simpler than single ended
systems. Only one loop needs to be active per beer brand which is currently
being filled. In plants which have many fillers but only a few predominant
brands, this can lead to significant labor savings.
—Since cold beer is always available at the base of each filler, problems of
dealing with a long line full of warm beer after a filler shut down are
minimized.
—This beer supply pipeline configuration tends to provide for clearer responsibilities for the personnel at fillers and in the packaging cellar. Filler
personnel are able to start and stop beer flow from the loop to the filler
almost at will, with little regard for what is happening at the cellar end
of the system. Also, since the entire pipeline which brings beer from the
loop to the filler can be within sight and under the control of the filler
operator, communication difficulties are eliminated in the cleaning, cooling
and filling of this pipeline. Cellar personnel need only assure that the
proper brand of beer is flowing in the pipeline and that there is sufficient
beer available at all times to avoid starving the loop. This simplification
implies the possibility of further labor saving in cellars operations.
—Users of Pumped Loop systems report extremely long intervals between
scheduled cleaning operations. Cleaning frequencies of once or twice per
year appear to provide satisfactory performance. It has been observed
that the content of a loop reflects the condition of the beer being fed
into the loop, except for the diluting effect of the continuous recirculation.
Of course, these loops are generally left circulating during non-operating
periods such as weekends. This results in extremely quick and easy start-
ups following down times.

In normal operation, beer flows simultaneously out of one or more packaging
tanks into the loop suction pipe. The variable speed pump runs with its speed
controlled by the associated pressure control system. This delivers beer at
constant pressure to the header which runs past the several fillers served by
the loop.

Each filler operates independently with regard to startup, shut down and bowl level control. Each of these operations is seen by the loop as a change in pressure which requires a compensating speed change by the variable speed pump to bring the pressure back to its set point. For example, if a filling operation is suddenly interupted—perhaps because the filler runs out of containers to fill—the filler bowl level starts to rise. This increase in level causes the filler's own level control system to close its supply valve. When this occurs, loop pressure rises above its set point because the loop is no longer delivering as much beer. This, in turn results in the loop's pressure control system calling for a reduction of pump RPM and thus a reduction in pump output. This causes pressure to return to the loop set pressure.

In all known installations the filler supply pipelines have been sized quite generously. In addition, pumps are generally selected to have curves which are quite flat. The effect of all of this is to reduce systematic pressure variations and to make the job of the pressure control system somewhat less critical.

In actual loop installations it is common to provide redundant pumping capability by installing a backup pump in parallel with the single pump shown in Figure 15-3. Also, it is usual to provide a parallel jockey pump having only enough capacity to provide for recirculation during periods when no filler is scheduled to run. This is an energy-saving measure.

A variation of Packaging Loop design is a configuration known as a *Gravity Packaging Loop*. This design is shown in Figure 15-4.

It may be seen that the Gravity Loop is somewhat simpler than the pumped loop. However, this configuration is analogous to the Gravity Single-Ended Line in that it requires packaging tanks which are of sufficient elevation relative to the fillers. Because of this inherent design limitation it is unusual to find a Gravity Loop which achieves all of the advantages which are available with a Pumped Loop.

In either type of loop the recirculation rate is selected on the basis of holding loop temperature within certain design limits. The typical temperatures of concern in this regard are as follows:

Beer Freezing Temperature: 28°F (-2.2°C) or less
Ideal Packaging Beer Temperature: 29°F (-1.7°C)
Highest allowable packaging Tank Temperature: 32°F (0°C)
Highest allowable Beer Temperature in Loop: 34°F (1.1°C)

In this group of numbers the most significant ones for loop design are the temperatures 32°F and 34°F. A rational design based upon these figures requires that the recirculating line operate at a rate which will always have beer at the last filler by the time that it warms up to 34°. For Pumped Loops it has been found that a recirculation rate equal to 10% of the full loop flow provides a good compromise between controllability and pumping energy cost. It is not recommended to select Pumped Loop recirculation rates any lower than this. However, it may be necessary to provide higher recirculating rates under some conditions in order to meet the 2F° (1.1°C) maximum rise requirement for the beer.

The heat which is added to the beer during operations originates from two sources. The first of these is heat gain from pump energy, and the second is heat gain through the pipeline insulation.

For beer, the values for specific gravity, specific heat and viscosity are all close to the equivalent values for water. Thus the basic data needed to estimate

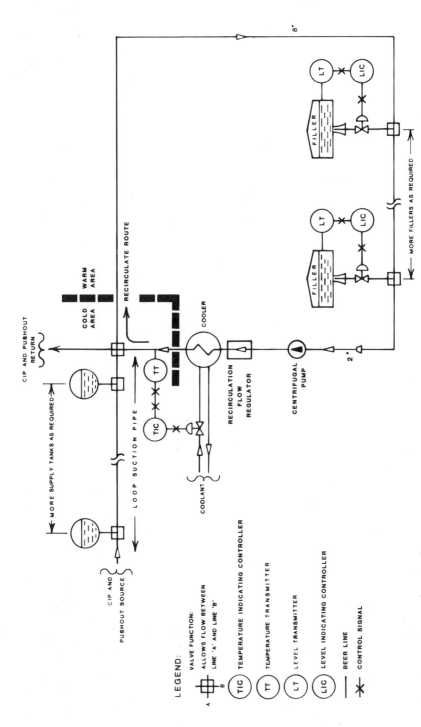

15-4. Gravity packaging loop.

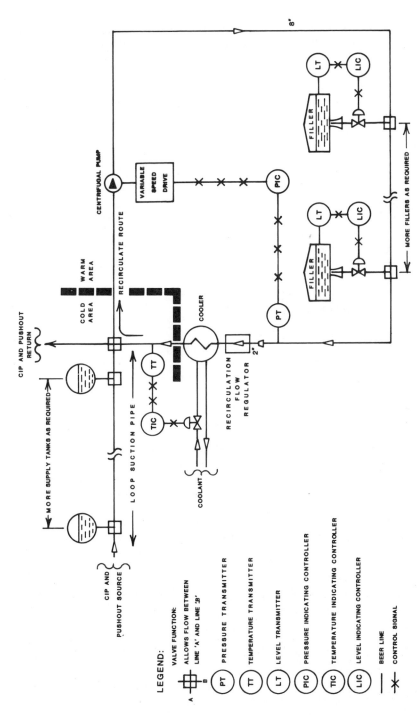

15-3. *Pumped beer loop system.*

heat gain due to the mechanical energy input by the pump is readily available from the standard pump curves provided for water by the manufacturer of the pump. Similarly, the heat gain through the pipeline insulation can be calculated using data for water.

The cooler that is shown on the flow sheet is required to remove the heat from the recirculating stream so that the beer returns to the suction side of the pump at the specified temperature. All parts of the pipeline system must either be in the recirculating path or else they must be in an area which is kept cold. Frequently, the line from the packaging tanks to the pump suction is not included in this recirculating loop. This exclusion results from a desire to keep the flow rate as low as possible in the loop suction line and thus to reduce its pressure drop due to friction. This is significant because of the fact that satisfactory flow conditions in the loop suction line often represent the most critical challenge in designing a packaging loop.

The cooler is generally selected as a cocurrent glycol plate cooler, using glycol at a temperature above the beer freezing temperature. A very small cooler is enough to do the job for a large packaging loop. This fact can permit several loop coolers to be mounted within a single plate cooler frame where several packaging loops are installed in a brewery.

BEER FLOW INTO FILLERS

Can and bottle filler types currently in wide use are equipped with bowls between their supply line and the containers which are being filled. The manufacturers of fillers have devised a variety of methods for sensing liquid level in their bowls. These sensed signals are used as inputs to the controls of the beer supply system.

There are two possible strategies in controlling the flow of beer into a filler. The first of these strategies involves single point level sensing on a filler bowl. The on/off signal is used to stop or start the inlet flow to the filler. This type of control is generally employed where bump pumps are used to supply beer to the filler. In its simplest form, this technique simply turns the pump on whenever level falls below the control point and turns the pump off when the level goes above the control point. A manual mechanical speed adjustment such as a Reeves Drive is used to adjust pump output to a rate slightly higher than maximum filling rate. Dead band in the level switch system is used to assure that the pump runs for fairly long periods once started. A typical cycle for such a system is 15 seconds on, 5 seconds off. Such systems work quite well where filling machines are tolerant of varying bowl level and where filling rates are reasonably constant.

In some cases, single point sensing systems are interfaced via on/off valves to beer supplies from gravity systems or from systems which use a centrifugal pump. However, in these cases it is more normal to use the second type of bowl level control—namely, analog control using a signal from a proportional level sensor. This system generally interfaces to a proportional control valve on the inlet to the filler via a level controller. This system is generally more adaptable to varying filling conditions than is a straight on/off control scheme.

Another area where bowl level sensing strategies vary is in the question of the location of the level sensor. In some designs the sensor is mounted on or in the rotating filler bowl. This arrangement requires that the signal be passed

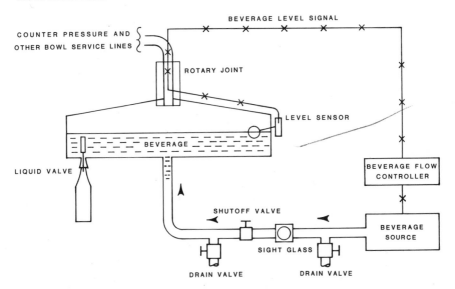

15-5. Filler bowl level control system with bowl mounted sensor.

from the bowl via the rotary gland at the filler's axis of rotation. An example of this technique is sketched as Figure 15-5.

Recently designed filler level control systems have relied on indirect sensing of level. Typically, these systems have a level-operated counterpressure system which causes bowl pressure to increase or decrease as beer level in the filler bowl changes. The variations in bowl pressure are then sensed by a pressure sensor mounted just upstream of the filler on the fixed beer piping. Systems of this type are very adaptable and are quite simple to interface with any of the several beer supply systems which are presently in use. An example of such a system is shown in Figure 15-6.

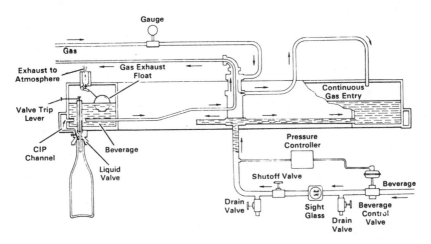

15-6. Filler bowl level control system with indirect sensor.

The filler supply piping must be configured to permit flushing and cleaning of the filler internals as well as the beer piping itself. Also, the beer line valving must permit the filler bowl to be shut off from the beer supply and drained. Provision is generally made to permit beer to be recovered from the filler bowl. Such recovered beer is generally reprocessed before going to another filler. Sight glasses are provided in the beer line to provide visual confirmation of the presence of beer at the filler inlet. These sight glasses are also used as an easy means for operators and supervisors to monitor beer clarity. Other specialty devices found on the filler inlet piping usually include a sample valve or trycock to permit lab samples to be taken immediately upstream of the filler. A line thermometer may be present as well as a meter.

BEER RECOVERY

As well as assuring that beer is handled systematically to the filler, some brewers are faced with recovering beer spillage at the filler and elsewhere on the packaging lines. The seamers on high speed can filling lines often receive special treatment in this regard, since they represent intensive sources of spillage. The usual motive for recovering this beer is to permit the waste stream to be preprocessed before sewering to reduce the cost of waste treatment. In some cases, alcohol is recovered from such waste streams, but more generally, the beer is simply processed through a biological reactor to reduce its BOD before releasing it to the sewer. In some countries, brewers recover waste beer, such as from underfilled containers, for reprocessing into the product stream.

BEER IN PACKAGING, WAREHOUSING AND DISTRIBUTION

There is an old adage in breweries that once beer leaves the cellars, little can be done to improve it, while a lot can be done to damage it.

The first place that the beer can be harmed is at the filler. In order to reduce the chance of such harm, the filler must be administered in such a way that external contamination cannot be incorporated into the beer. Some of the risks in this regard are:
—unclean containers or closures
—improper rinsing of cleaning agents from containers
—incomplete rinse water drainage from empty containers
—casual wash-down water, with or without cleaning chemicals
—glass fragments from breakage at bottle fillers
—lube soap from conveyors
—other lubricants used on fillers, crowners or seamers
—litho dust from can, lid or crown decorations
—airborne dust from construction or similar activity
—insects and other pests
The brewer should maintain an absolute requirement that beer containers must never be used for any purpose other than being filled with beer.

In addition to the above items, proper operation of the filler, particularly at start-up and during brand changes is required to avoid product deterioration due to conditions internal to the filling machinery.

In this regard, it is almost universal practice to pre-chill fillers prior to bringing beer into them. Chilled water at 35°F (approx. 2°C) is the normal cooling medium. Usually, this water is permitted to flow into the filler bowl via its beer fill line until the desired bowl temperature is reached. This water performs the secondary function of assuring a complete rinse of any cleaning agents which might remain in the filler following CIP operations. This water must be completely removed from the filler bowl and the filler valves prior to filling containers which are to be sold. Generally, this involves blowing all water out of the bowl and the valves prior to allowing any beer into the filler.

CO_2 counterpressure may be used on filling equipment in order to minimize air pick-up into the beer while it is being processed through the machine. The gas pressure should be higher than the CO_2 equilibrium pressure in order to minimize carbonation losses.

The filler should be operated to minimize the number of short filled containers that are produced. In addition to the obvious legal and consumer risks associated with short filling, beer in short filled containers is more likely to suffer from oxidation due to high air content than is beer in packages which are properly filled.

Most filling and closing machinery has been designed to provide features which protect the beer from known risks. It is essential that this machinery be operated and maintained to exploit its product protection features.

Beyond the filler, the major risks to beer in the packaging plant are from temperature inadequacies at the pasteurizer. This device must operate within a narrow range in its time-temperature relationship. If the pasteurizer does not provide sufficient heat to the container, a package may be subject to biological spoilage. On the other hand, if a container is exposed to too much heat, this can cause an unpleasant "cooked" taste to be present in the beer.

The beer container's exit temperature from the pasteurizer and its temperature during storage and shipment must be maintained as low as possible, to minimize flavor deterioration of the beer. Most brewers seek to minimize the exposure of the product to temperatures above 85°F (approx. 30°C) beyond the pasteurizer. Some brewers have established even more rigorous temperature standards which require beer to be refrigerated at all times after leaving the packaging line.

Packaged beer must also be protected against freezing. In addition to the obvious risk of container bursting due to freezing, the product's stability can be upset if beer temperatures become low enough for ice crystals to form.

Other risks to the product which occur in the packaging, warehousing and distribution system are as follows:

— *Vibration:* Excessive vibration can cause beer to become destabilized. Long shipping distances over poor roads or poor railroad tracks are of some concern in this regard.

— *Light:* Exposure to daylight or flourescent lighting can cause beer to become "light struck". This characteristic presents itself as a "skunky" or "ribes" aroma and flavor which is usually regarded as unpleasant. Beer in glass containers is subject to this problem. Clear bottles present the highest risk, while green bottles offer some protection and brown bottles offer considerable protection.

Some brewers have devised special formulations for their products to improve their resistance to light. In general, their techniques involve modifying certain hop constituents which are activated by light. In cases where special formulations are not used, it is necessary to protect the beer from intense or prolonged exposure to light all the way from the filler to the consumer. Obvious protective measures include the avoidance of skylights and intense fluorescent lighting in packaging plants, plus the use of 6-packs and other secondary packaging materials which are designed to exclude light.

—*Time:* All packaged beer deteriorates with time. Thus, good operating practice requires that the distribution network must deliver beer from the filler to the consumer as quickly as possible. The major tools used in this regard are known as "stock indexes" which regulate the maximum length of time that beer can be held at any point in the distribution network, and "stock rotation", which is a method of assuring that all beer stocks at every storage point in the distribution network are administered on a first-in, first-out basis.

It is well known that beers that are inherently unstable or that have excessive levels of dissolved oxygen deteriorate more rapidly than normal beers.

THE FUTURE

As this chapter is being written, several trends are apparent that are expected to affect the future handling of beer for packaging. With few exceptions, today's beer handling practices in the Americas are based upon filling containers with chilled beer. Further, in-package pasteurization using tunnel pasteurizers for cans and bottles is the norm for most brewers. Both of these practices are energy intensive. Thus, alternate beer handling methods are expected to become more attractive in the future, in response to rising energy costs.

Tunnel pasteurizers are intensive users of steam, water and electricity. They must be operated within narrow limits if they are to do their job properly without causing beer flavor to deteriorate. Interest in aseptic filling as practiced by Adolph Coors Company in the USA and many brewers elsewhere, is expected to grow.

Some new fillers on the market are designed for warm filling. This energy-efficient method is being practiced in a few places in the world. This method may become more widespread in the future.

These techniques will bring new requirements to the handling of beer. In particular, aseptic handling methods can be expected to intensify the need for biological control of operations.

In spite of the disadvantages of in-package pasteurization using tunnel pasteurizers this process remains the easiest and most reliable method for eliminating most problems with biological instability. It is the safest way to guarantee the sterility of filled cans and bottles over a wide range of biological conditions in the bulk beer.

Any move away from tunnel pasteurization will eliminate process tolerance and will force a more rigorous approach to the systems and methods used in handling bulk beer.

APPENDIX
USEFUL CONVERSION FACTORS

CARBON DIOXIDE

	Multiply By:
Cubic feet of carbon dioxide to pounds of carbon dioxide	0.1227
Cubic feet of carbon dioxide to ounces of carbon dioxide	957.5
Grams of carbon dioxide to milliliters of carbon dioxide	506.0
Liters of carbon dioxide to grams of carbon dioxide	1.976
Liters of carbon dioxide to cubic feet of carbon dioxide	0.0352
Milliliters of carbon dioxide to grams of carbon dioxide	0.00198
Ounces of carbon dioxide to grams of carbon dioxide	0.0584
Pounds of carbon dioxide to cubic feet of carbon dioxide	8.1499
Pounds of carbon dioxide to fluid ounces (U.S.) of carbon dioxide	7803.85
Per cent carbon dioxide by volume to per cent carbon dioxide by weight	0.1943
Per cent carbon dioxide by weight to per cent carbon dioxide by volume	5.1470

CONTAINERS PER BARREL

Size of Container	7 oz.	8 oz.	11 oz.	12 oz.	16 oz.	32 oz.
Bottles or cans	566.9	496.0	360.7	330.7	248.0	124.0
Six-Packs	—	82.7	60.1	55.1	41.4	20.7
Twelve-Pack	—	41.3	30.0	27.6	20.6	10.3
Cases of 24	23.6	20.7	15.0	13.78	10.35	—

BEER VOLUME

	Multiply By:
Beer barrels (U.S.) to cubic feet	4.114
Beer barrels (U.S.) to gallons (U.S.)	31.0
Beer barrels (U.S.) to hectoliters	1.1734
Beer barrels (U.S.) to barrels (Imp.)	0.728
Beer barrels (Imp.) to barrels (U.S.)	1.373
Beer barrels (Imp.) to gallons (Imp.)	36.0
Beer barrels (U.S.) to gallons (Imp.)	26.23
Beer barrels (Imp.) to gallons (U.S.)	43.23
Beer barrels Canadian to U.S. gallons	30.024
Beer barrels Canadian to Imperial gallons	25.0
Beer barrels Canadian to hectoliters	1.1365
Beer barrels Canadian to cubic feet	4.012

PIPING SYSTEMS

Materials
The material of choice for pipelines and pipeline accessories that contact beer is a grade of stainless steel containing 18% Chromium and 8% Nickel. The specification for this material is AISI Type 304, commonly called "304 stainless" or "18-8 stainless". This material is virtually corrosion-free in normal beer applications.

However, a few brewers use a low-Carbon variation of 304 stainless, AISI Type 304L, for the actual piping because they believe that its improved welding characteristics justify the extra cost.

The preferred method of joining lengths of stainless steel piping is by welding under an inert gas atmosphere, without filler.

Product-contacting metallic parts of pumps, valves and other elements of the piping system ideally should also be made from stainless steel. Frequently, some of these parts (e.g. valve internals) may be available only in AISI Type 316 stainless. This alloy is more corrosion-resistant than 304 stainless, but is more expensive. Its extra corrosion resistance is not necessary for product applications in the brewery.

For beer pumps, bronze is sometimes selected instead of stainless steel in order to save money. This material causes no known problems in this application.

Copper piping systems are often found in older breweries. Turbidity in filtered beer has sometimes been traced to pickup of copper from such piping systems. Because of this, copper has fallen into disfavor as a material for contact with beer. Where copper is still in use, it is common to find that piping specialties such as valves and hose fittings are made of bronze.

Elastomer materials in the form of hoses, gaskets, O-rings, seals and other miscellaneous parts come in contact with product in beer piping systems. A wide variety of possible formulations exist for such elastomers. It is imperative that the brewer satisfy himself that these materials will be acceptable to regulatory agencies and that they will not impart foreign taste or aroma to the product. (See chapter XXIII.)

Counter pressure piping near beer tanks is usually fabricated from the same materials as beer. However, there are a few installations where PVC plastic or fiberglas gas piping has been installed with no reported problems.

Systems of Pipe Sizes

Once the piping material is selected, the next step in specifying brewery piping is to select the piping standard to be used. There are 3 separate standards in the world for stainless steel piping suitable for product applications in breweries. Each of these standards deals with pipe diameter and wall thickness. The three standards are described below:

I.P.S.

The initials I.P.S. stand for "Iron Pipe Size". This standard covers inch sizes of piping used in general industrial applications. Piping can be obtained under this standard in a series of wall thicknesses for each nominal pipe diameter. The various wall thicknesses are specified through the use of schedule numbers. In any particular pipe size, a low schedule number (e.g. Schedule 5) is a thin-wall pipe, while a high number (e.g. Schedule 120) is a thick-wall pipe. Schedule 40 is considered to be the "standard" wall thickness for pipe made from iron or steel and for use in low-pressure plant utility services. The nominal diameter of I.P.S. pipe represents the approximate inside diameter of Schedule 40 pipe.

For most product piping in U.S. breweries, I.P.S. Schedule 5 Type 304 Stainless Steel pipe has become the standard for new product piping installations. Although this is thin-wall pipe, it is capable of withstanding all normal pressures encountered in brewery product piping systems. This thin-wall pipe provides the maximum practical length of pipe per unit weight of metal and, since this pipe and the fittings which are used with it are widely stocked by piping distributors, it can be purchased at competitive prices.

Another attribute of Schedule 5 pipe is that its large inside diameter provides greater flow capacity than is available with thicker wall pipe of the same nominal diameter.

A few brewers in the U.S.A. have opted to use Schedule 10 type 304 stainless pipe because its extra thickness provides greater resistance to mechanical damage.

It is the authors' opinion that this practice is not cost justified.

O.D.:

The initials O.D. stand for "Outside Diameter". This standard covers inch sizes of tubing used in many parts of the dairy, food and related industries. Dairies were among the earliest industrial users of stainless steel tubing. Their use of this material evolved without regard to the I.P.S. standards.

This tubing is made so that the nominal size is exactly the same as the outside diameter of the tube. The wall thickness corresponds to the thickness of standard stainless steel sheet. For example, 3-inch O.D. tube has a wall thickness of .065 inches which is the same thickness as 16 gauge sheet. Only one wall thickness is available for any particular tube diameter under the O.D. system.

O.D. tubing has not generally been used for beer in the United States. However, in Canada, this system of tubing sizes is the standard for new brewery installations. In both the USA and Canada, O.D. tubing is widely distributed and can be obtained at competitive prices.

Metric (DIN 11850)

Metric (DIN 11850) is the European standard for thin-wall stainless steel piping systems such as are used in the brewing industry. Of course, all sizes in this system are metric, with diameters being stated in milimeters.

Where copper piping systems are used in breweries in the U.S.A. and Canada, copper tubing sizes have generally been selected. Copper tubing is available in a range of wall thicknesses for each pipe diameter. The wall thickness is designated by a letter as follows:

Type K—heaviest wall
Type L—medium wall
Type M—thin wall

Copper tubing diameters and wall thicknesses for each nominal diameter are different from any of those used in the previously listed standards. Within the authors' experience, Type K is the normally-used wall thickness for brewery product piping systems when copper tubing is used.

Silver soldering is the preferred joining method for copper piping systems used for product. This is because soft solder joints are subject to attack by some pipeline cleaning solutions.

Tables at the end of this chapter provides data on common brewery pipe sizes for each of the standards that have been mentioned.

Calculations

A detailed discussion of pipe sizing calculations is beyond the scope of this chapter. For readers who need to perform flow rate and pressure drop calculations, the authors recommend the following publications for further information:

1. *Flow of Fluids Through Valves, Fittings, and Pipe,* Technical Paper No. 410, Crane Company, Chicago, IL
2. *Cameron Hydraulic Data:* Ingersoll-Rand, Woodcliff Lake, NJ 07675

In general industrial situations, piping is sized based on overall system economics. The same considerations generally hold in breweries. However, there are several additional factors which must be considered in beer piping:

1. Some brewers have established maximum allowable flow velocities for beer. 6 feet per second (approximately 2 meters per second) is a typical limit. The limit reflects concern about product problems which may occur because of excessive turbulence during transfers. The authors have seen little evidence to support this concern in normal beer transfer situations. However, it is generally agreed that low velocities at the inlets to beer tanks and filling machines is desirable to minimize foaming and air pickup at these points.

2. Pipeline C.I.P. flow velocities are generally selected to be between 2.5 and 5.0 feet per second (approximately .75 to 1.5 meters per second). The lowest of these velocities should be used only for well designed piping systems which are cleaned frequently.
3. It is generally accepted that beer flowing in pipelines should not be exposed to pressures below the carbonation equilibrium pressure.

NOTE: All dimensions are in inches unless stated otherwise.

STAINLESS STEEL
I.P.S. SCHEDULE 5 PIPE

NOMINAL I.P.S. SIZE	OUTSIDE DIAMETER	WALL THK	INSIDE DIAMETER
1½	1.900	.065	1.77
2	2.375	.065	2.245
2½	2.875	.083	2.709
3	3.500	.083	3.334
4	4.500	.109	4.334
5	5.563	.109	5.345
6	6.625	.109	6.407
8	8.625	.109	8.407

STAINLESS STEEL
I.P.S. SCHEDULE 10 PIPE

NOMINAL I.P.S. SIZE	OUTSIDE DIAMETER	WALL THK	INSIDE DIAMETER
1½	1.900	.109	1.682
2	2.375	.109	2.157
2½	2.875	.120	2.635
3	3.500	.120	3.260
4	4.500	.120	4.260
5	5.563	.134	5.295
6	6.625	.134	6.357
8	8.625	.148	8.329

STAINLESS STEEL
I.P.S. SCHEDULE 40 PIPE

NOMINAL I.P.S. SIZE	OUTSIDE DIAMETER	WALL THK	INSIDE DIAMETER
1½	1.900	.145	1.61
2	2.375	.154	2.067
2½	2.875	.203	2.469
3	3.500	.216	3.068
4	4.500	.237	4.026
5	5.563	.258	5.047
6	6.625	.280	6.065
8	8.625	.322	7.981

STAINLESS STEEL
O.D. TUBING SIZE

TUBE O.D. SIZE	OUTSIDE DIAMETER O.D.	WALL THK T	GAUGE	INSIDE DIAMETER I.D.
1½	1.500	.065	16	1.370
2	2.000	.065	16	1.870
2½	2.500	.065	16	2.370
3	3.000	.065	16	2.870
4	4.000	.083	14	3.834
6	6.000	.109	12	5.782
8	8.000	.109	12	7.782

STAINLESS STEEL
METRIC TUBING DIN 11850

NOMINAL SIZE DN	OUTSIDE DIAMETER O.D. mm	WALL THK mm	INSIDE DIAMETER I.D. mm	inches
32	34	1.5	31	1.221
40	40	1.5	37	1.457
50	52	1.5	49	1.929
65	70	2	66	2.598
80	85	2	81	3.189
100	104	2	100	3.937
125	129	2	125	4.921
150	154	2	150	5.906
200	204	2	200	7.874
250	254	2	250	9.843

COPPER TUBING

SIZE	INSIDE DIAMETER	WALL THICKNESS
2″ Type K	1.959	.083
Type L	1.985	.070
Type M	2.009	.058
3″ Type K	2.907	.109
Type L	2.945	.090
Type M	2.981	.072
4″ Type K	3.857	.134
Type L	3.905	.110
Type M	3.935	.095

CHAPTER XVI

MICROBIOLOGICAL STABILIZATION

BY J.R. WILSON

INTRODUCTION

The art of brewing has been a part of man's heritage for thousands of years. For most of that time, beer was brewed and consumed without the benefit of the microbiological stabilization processes practiced today. As late as the end of the 19th century, brewing was predominantly a local enterprise and, since the beer was not shipped long distances or stored for any appreciable period of time, lack of stability was not a problem. It is only in the last 100 years that the technology and need have been present for the brewer to produce a packaged beer which remains stable even after extended storage at room temperature.

The beginning of our modern microbiological stabilization processes can be traced to work done by Louis Pasteur of France. He began his work on fermentation in 1857 when requested by a distillery to study yeasts. His early studies in fermentation led him to investigate beer and brewing in the 1870's.

Pasteur's experiments, based on the German brewing practice of cleaning equipment with boiling water, demonstrated that heating the finished product to sufficiently high temperatures would destroy undesirable microorganisms and prevent subsequent quality impairment. His findings were published in 1876 in his *Etudes sur La Bière* (Studies on Beer).

Several other discoveries and developments were taking place about this same time which fostered the development and demand for a microbiologically stable product. Most notable was the finding of a solution to the non-micro-biological haze problem which plagued the brewer who endeavored to store or ship his bottled product. Also important were the increasing consumer acceptance of bottled beer, the introduction of the modern crown top in 1892, and the growth of transcontinental railroads which opened new remote markets.

The objective of any of the modern microbiological stabilization processes is to prevent microbial impairment of the beer quality while minimizing any adverse effect on the other characteristics, and thereby achieve extended shelf life.

Fortunately for the brewer, the task is made easier by the fact that beer is not a good microbial growth medium and supports slow growth of only a relatively small group of microorganisms, namely certain yeasts and a few bacteria. (Rainbow, C., *Process Biochem., 1971.*) Of equal importance to the brewer is the fact that even though beer will support the growth of a few organisms which impair quality, it does not support the growth of pathogens. (Bunker, H.J., *E.B.C. Proc., 1955*). Therefore, the objective of the micro-biological stabilization process for the brewer remains strictly a matter of product protection (quality) and not consumer protection. This selectivity of beer to the growth of so few organisms can be attributed to its low levels of nutrients, low oxygen levels, low pH, and the presence of alcohols, esters and hop bitters.

This chapter will discuss the different commercial processes developed over the last 100 years for achieving microbiological stabilization. Each section will cover theory and principles, equipment, operating parameters, advantages and disadvantages, and operational pitfalls.

The sterile filling process will also be covered because of its close relationship with two of the stabilization processes. The chapter will conclude with a brief look at the future and what it might hold for the microbiological stabilization process.

PASTEURIZATION IN THE PACKAGE

Theory and Principles

Since its inception in the late 19th century, the practice of pasteurizing of beer in the package has continued to gain acceptance and widespread application. Today in both North and South America, it is by far the most widely preferred and practiced method of achieving microbiological stabilization of beer. Well over 90 percent of the package beer sold in this hemisphere is pasteurized in the package. Europe, on the other hand, has been slower to accept this method, and its application there is not nearly as widespread. The situation is changing, however, as more of the European brewers develop "export" beers. The present trend is to go to pasteurization in the package with its greater assurance of effective microbiological stabilization for these beers.

The basic principle underlying pasteurization of beer is the use of heat to destroy undesirable organisms. The aim, however, is not complete sterility. Those yeasts and bacteria capable of impairing beer quality are completely destroyed. Certain harmless spore-forming molds and bacteria may survive, but they present no problem to the brewer since they cannot propagate in beer.

Prior to the 1950's, the degree of pasteurization given the beer was arrived at empirically which led to a wide variation of treatment. Early pasteurization treatment utilized 60°C (140°F) temperatures and a holding times of 20-30 minutes as a rule of thumb. In 1950, it was shown that the same mathematical reasoning applied to thermal processing of canned foods could be used in the pasteurization of beer. (Baselt, F.C., *Comm. Mstr. Brew, 1949*). For the first time, it was possible for the brewer to define his treatment requirements and his pasteurization process more precisely.

To evaluate any pasteurization cycle, two components are required: a lethal rate curve (also referred to as a thermal death time curve) of organisms which can gain entrance to and grow in a particular beer, and a time-temperature curve of the beer as it is pasteurized.

Lethal rate curves (see Figure 16-1) disclose the time required for the destruction of a known concentration of specific organisms at a given temperature. Lethal rate data are plotted on semi-log paper; time, in minutes, is on the logarithmic scale (ordinate), and temperature, °F, on the linear scale (abscissa). The curves are practically straight lines and can be defined by a

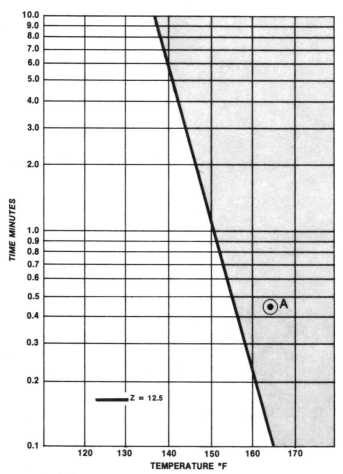

16-1. *Lethal rate curve.*

point and a slope. The point is the intercept at a reference temperature. The slope is commonly called the "Z" value.

Reference temperature furnishes a standard of comparison. In the canned food industry, for low acid foods, 121°C (250°F) is a reference temperature and one minute at 121°C is a unit of lethality. For acid foods, 82°C (180°F) is a reference temperature and one minute at 82°C is a unit of lethality.

For beer, the suggested reference temperature is 60°C (140°F). One minute at this temperature is termed one Pasteurization Unit (P.U.), (Benjamin, H.A., *Amer. Can Lab Report, 1936*).

Lethal rate data were determined for a group of organisms commonly found in beer, including abnormal yeast cells, acetic acid bacteria, lactic acid bacteria and thermo bacteria. (Del Vecchio, H.W., *ASBC Proc., 1951*). The thermal death time for this suspension was determined at various temperatures and results plotted on semi-log paper to obtain a lethal rate curve. The point at which the curve crosses the 60°C (140°F) line gives the thermal resistance of the particular suspension of organisms at the reference temperature. For Del Vecchio, the intercept point turned out to be 5.6 minutes or 5.6 P.U.'s with a slope or "Z" value of 12.5. This means that to insure effective pasteurization, it is necessary for the holding time at a pasteurization temperature of 60°C (140°F) to exceed 5.6 minutes. Other time-temperature combinations can be used as long as they fall directly on or to the right of the lethal rate curve as does point "A" in Figure 16-1.

The effectiveness of any tunnel pasteurization process may be evaluated from information derived from the lethal rate curve for organisms in the particular beer in question and the time-temperature curve of the coolest part of the package during the pasteurization process. These two components can be applied to a mathematical formula to calculate the lethal rate at any given temperature. Lethal effect (P.U.) is simply the lethal rate multiplied by duration (time at a given temperature). Since the lethal effect at the various temperatures in a process are additive, the sum of the lethal effect is the quantity of sterilization achieved. If the sum exceeds the resistance of the organisms, microbiological stabilization has been accomplished.

Lethal effect $= PU = Lt$

Where $L =$ Lethal Rate $= \dfrac{1}{Log^{-1}\left(\dfrac{140-T}{Z}\right)}$

$t =$ time held at temperature T

$T =$ temperature °F

$Z =$ slope of lethal rate curve

Early work to quantify pasteurization treatment led to the adoption of 12.5 as the Z value to be used in these calculations. Additional work shows that this value is not as easily nor as well defined as might be expected and that it can vary depending on the particular organism and the conditions under which it is tested. (King, L.M., ASBC, 1978).

The amount of heat treatment (PU's) necessary for microbiological stabilization of the product depends on a number of variables. The final number of PU's decided upon by the individual brewer represents a compromise between a minimal theoretical figure and a higher empirical figure incorporating a safety factor to cover beer and process variables. Under ideal conditions, beer with low microbial populations could be treated effectively with as few as 5 PU's and still be stable. However, most brewers feel uncomfortable at that level and use 5-15 PU's. Treatment levels higher than these are generally avoided in order to avoid undesirable effects on the character of the beer.

Some of the variables considered when deciding on the level of treatment are: physical condition of the beer (pH, carbon dioxide tension, levels of nutrients, hop resins, oxygen, alcohol, etc.) and the type and number of organisms present, including the possibility of sporadic high count conditions. Also important is the presence of suspended matter, including colloids, which might shield or otherwise protect the organisms from the treatment.

Equipment

The equipment for pasteurization of beer in the package has changed dramatically over the last eight decades. Early methods involved submerging the packages in a tank of water which was raised to the desired temperature and held there for a period of time before cooling. This practice resulted in a batch type of operation and one which was very slow and labor intensive.

The early methods quickly gave way to a number of varied approaches aimed at making it a continuous and labor-saving operation. One technique was the basket-type machine which still required hand loading and unloading of bottles. The baskets were carried by a chain drive through a series of tanks or hot water sprays. The bottles were gradually heated, held at pasteurizing temperature, and then cooled. The treatment was varied by adjusting temperatures and times in each portion of the process.

Attempts were made to use a pocket approach similar to that used in bottle cleaners. Machines of this type were built which carried the bottles up and down through various tanks. The agitation and mixing of the beer with headspace air were felt to be detrimental to the beer quality and the design never gained wide acceptance.

These earlier designs led to the development of our present day horizontal spray type machine. This approach conveys the packages, in an upright position, on a horizontal conveyor through a long tunnel—hence the name "tunnel pasteurizer". (See Figure 16-2.) Overhead water sprays heat, then cool the packages as they pass through the machine. Water running off the packages is collected in reservoirs under the conveyor and pumped back to the overhead sprays.

The packages pass through several zones and are showered with sprays of increasing and decreasing temperatures. In the case of glass packages, zone temperatures are carefully graduated to avoid thermal shock and subsequent breakage. Zone temperature gradients are easily controlled in newer machines with multiple preheat zones. During heating, gradients in excess of 22°C (40°F) are common practice on both bottles and cans. However, since glass is more sensitive during cooling, the upper gradient limit of 22°C (40°F) is usually adhered to between cooling zones.

Cans may be pasteurized using greater temperature gradients during both heating and cooling, thereby requiring shorter process times: 30 minutes for cans compared to 45 minutes for bottles. The process time for cans may be further reduced by using "superheat" temperatures in the heating zone.

A package headspace of approximately 4-7% has to be provided to permit the beer to expand without breaking, rupturing or otherwise damaging the package. Doubling the headspace will result in approximately one half the usual pressure buildup. Excessive headspace should be avoided because it will yield higher package air values and greater container material costs.

Packages are conveyed through the machine by means of "walking beams." This method gives the best results since the conveyor only steps forward a matter of inches on each stroke and each section remains at the same temperature as the zone in which it operates. The conveyor bed is made up of stainless steel strips, standing on edge, which run longitudinally through the machine. The strips are alternately supported and attached to two separate transverse grate beams. One or both of the grate beams are free to move and

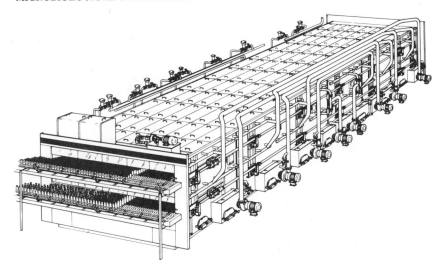

16-2. Double deck tunnel pasteurizer (Courtesy Barry-Wehmiller).

can be lifted under the packages, moved forward a few inches, and lowered again, depositing the packages on the other grate. The grate beam then returns to its initial position ready for another stroke.

Today's tunnel pasteurizers are capable of handling line speeds of up to 150,000 bottles or cans per hour. In order to double capacity and/or reduce space requirements, tunnel pasteurizers are offered in double deck as well as single deck configurations.

There are two styles of double deck pasteurizers. In one style, the pasteurizer is furnished with a single drive which operates both decks simultaneously. In the second style, each deck is operated by separate drives so that two different packages can be run concurrently on the same machine. It is possible to run small packages on one deck with a short process time and large packages on the other deck with a longer time.

The power units for the machines are hydraulic with electric drive motors. Cycle times and speeds are controlled by flow control valves and/or digital electronic controls.

A typical tunnel pasteurizer system is depicted in Figure 16-3. It includes the usual preheat, heating, holding, precooling and cooling zones and shows the regeneration circuit concept in slightly heavier print. All four preheat and precool zones shown in the figure are regenerative, however, only one is shown in heavy print for greater clarity.

The larger modern machines are being built with regenerative circuits in order to minimize water use, maximize energy recovery and cut costs of operation. Recovery rates of 100% on water and 71% on steam are possible in these machines during balanced running conditions. In addition to regeneration, they also utilize recirculatory circuits. These two types of water flows can be combined in various combinations and arrangements for maximum savings in both water and energy. In a regeneration circuit, water is chilled

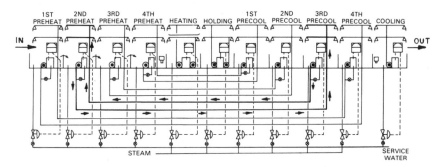

16-3. Schematic of tunnel pasteurizer system (Courtesy Barry-Wehmiller)

in the preheat compartments as it flows over the cold packages entering the pasteurizer. This chilled water is pumped to the precool zones where it is utilized to cool the packages leaving the holding zone. Water flowing over the hot packages in the precool zone is heated and pumped back to the preheat zone where the cycle is repeated. The process shown has four preheat and four precool zones all coupled together in regeneration circuits to yield the highest level of energy conservation.

The heating and holding zones are recirculatory (closed loop) circuits and are self-contained. Water from the reservoir tanks below the respective zone is pumped to the spray headers. From there it cascades over the packages and returns to the reservoir for recirculation. Steam coils, injectors, or heat exchangers make up any lost heat.

The very latest pasteurizer designs incorporate an additional energy and water saving feature which comes into play during gaps in package flow. As a gap enters a pasteurizer without this feature, automatic controls sense the temperature rise in preheat zones 1, 2, 3 and 4 and admit cold water to preserve thermal balance. The addition of cold water normally causes an overflow of warm water to the sewer or tower. As the gap proceeds through the heat and holding zones and enters the precool area, controls sense a drop in temperature in zones 7, 8, 9 and 10, steam is added to those tanks for thermal balance.

In the "energy storage" design, instead of discarding excess preheat zone water to the sewer, it is caught in an additional reservoir capable of holding approximately 1,000 gallons. Now, as the gap reaches the precool zones, the warm water from the extra tank is added as needed to zones 7, 8, 9 and 10 and excess cool water from these tanks is sent to the sewer, yielding a net energy savings. This small change reflects a savings of approximately 74% in steam usage in these zones.

The excess cool water from zones 7, 8, 9 and 10 can be held in a second holding tank and put back into the preheat zones when the next gap occurs. This saves approximately one-half the water normally used in these zones as well.

Operating Parameters

Operating parameters of a pasteurizer depend upon the brewery's process requirements. The design specifications of a pasteurizer are based on the following criteria:

1. Type and size of packages to be run
2. Desired capacity or rate of production
3. Degree of treatment—number of PU's
4. Maximum spray temperature to which beer can be subjected
5. Temperature of packages in and out of pasteurizer
6. Summer and winter water service temperature

From these specifications, a computer program will determine the operating parameters for a particular package, namely:

1. Process time (minutes)
2. Spray temperatures for each zone
3. Gallons per minute of service water
4. Steam requirement

Figure 16-4 is a chart showing temperatures and times for a tunnel pasteurizer process utilizing a modern machine with four preheat zones, four precool zones, and a cooling zone. This particular process was designed for 12-oz. N/R bottles at a speed of 1800 bpm (bottles per minute) and produced 7.5 P.U.'s of effective treatment.

Zone	Spray Temp °F	Spray Temp °C	Spray Time	Process Time	Infeed	Beer Temp* 1°C	Beer Temp* 34°F
					In		
1st Preheat	72	22	3.30 Min.	3.30 Min.	Out	2°C	35°F
					In		
2nd Preheat	80	27	3.30	6.60	Out	13°C	56°F
					In		
3rd Preheat	97	36	3.30	9.90	Out	25°C	77°F
					In		
4th Preheat	115	46	3.30	13.02	Out	36°C	97°F
					In		
Heat	154	68	5.15	18.35	Out	60°C	140°F
					In		
Hold	140	60	5.15	23.05	Out	60°C	140°F
					In		
1st Precool	113	45	3.30	26.80	Out	51°C	123°F
					In		
2nd Precool	94	34	3.30	30.10	Out	41°C	106°F
					In		
3rd Precool	76	24	3.30	33.40	Out	32°C	89°F
					In		
4th Precool	70	21	3.30	36.07	Out	26°C	78°F
					In		
Cooling	66	19	2.57	39.27	Out	23°C	73°F
					Disch		

*Coldspot Temperature on Central Axis, ¾" up from inside bottom of Container.

16-4. Chart of tunnel pasteurizer operating parameters for 12 Oz. NR bottles at 1800 BPM and 7.5 P.U.'s.

Advantages and Disadvantages

The pasteurization of beer in the package has a number of advantages. Of all the methods we have today for achieving microbiological stability, it offers the greatest assurance of a totally stable product. It has proven to be a reliable and effective method throughout the world under an almost infinite variety of brewery conditions. Because it takes place after the filling and closing operation, it is effective against organisms introduced during these operations as well as those occurring in the beer itself; thus only normal sanitation and cleanup efforts in the filling and closing operation are required. A further advantage is the fact that it is a variable process and the degree of treatment can be optimized depending on a particular brewery's needs, thus avoiding any adverse effects of over-treatment.

Pasteurization in the package has some disadvantages which should be given consideration. Perhaps the most important is the adverse effect of heating on the flavor of the beer. Heating of beer to pasteurizing temperatures, particularly in the presence of oxygen, accelerates the formation of unwanted off-flavors. This problem has been minimized in recent years by holding pasteurization times and temperatures as low as possible and by reducing the amount of oxygen added during filling. It can never be totally eliminated, however, since heating is basic to the process.

A second major disadvantage is the requirement for heavier, stronger packages in order to withstand the higher internal package pressures occurring during pasteurization. With the price of packaging materials steadily increasing, this requirement becomes an increasingly important factor and one which can add significantly to the cost of the product. Optimization of the pasteurization process and container design is taking place to minimize the weight and cost differential. Additional costs are also incurred when shipping these heavier containers to remote markets.

Operating costs are high for tunnel pasteurizers and are increasing primarily due to increased costs of energy. Even when equipped with heat regeneration provisions, tunnel pasteurizers have the highest energy requirements of any of the methods. The package materials as well as the beer itself are heated and cooled. Water usage is also higher and can be a significant cost factor, particularly in those areas where water is scarce. It is necessary to provide for extensive treatment of the process water in order to protect against biological fouling, corrosion and scale formation.

Initial costs are higher for tunnel pasteurizing because of the size and complexity of the equipment. The tunnel pasteurizer is many times larger than a filter or flash pasteurizer of equal capacity and much more complex because of its conveyors, drives, pumps and controls. Initial costs can be further increased because of greater floor space requirements.

Operational Pitfalls

As with most automated processes, there are certain operational and equipment difficulties which warrant attention. Few problems are likely to occur in the process during steady run conditions where the packages are being constantly fed into and removed from the pasteurizer. The main concerns under steady run conditions are plugged spray nozzles, improper cycle times, improper zone temperatures, loosely packed or down bottles, and bottle breakage. The first of these, if uncorrected, can cause over or under pasteurization of the beer. Bottle breakage can reach unreasonable levels if not given proper attention. However, it can be reduced to practically zero if the following conditions are avoided:

1. Poor glass and/or rough handling
2. Overfilling
3. Abrupt temperature changes and/or overheating
4. Jams and fallen bottles

With the exception of poor glass, all of these factors are directly controlled by the brewer himself and should be given constant surveillance. (Lieberman, C.E., B.A.A. Bulletin 2045, 1979).

As discussed earlier, additional process problems occur during intermittent feeding of packages and result in process temperature imbalance in the various zones.

Production stops downstream of the pasteurizer are a common occurrence in all bottle shops. Those of short duration (1 or 2 minutes) can be ignored, but longer stops will adversely affect the pasteurization process and should be compensated for. A commonly used method is to stop the pasteurizer and shut off the heating and pasteurizing water pumps. A more preferred method is to install a line accumulator conveyor of sufficient size to allow the pasteurizer to continue to run until the product can be cleared out of the heating and pasteurizing zones. The latter is a more costly approach and requires additional space in the packaging operation.

Proper temperature control in each of the zones is also critical to the process, especially during intermittent or imbalanced running. Improvements have been made in this area by utilizing properly sized reservoirs and faster responding control systems. The temperature controls and associated diaphragm valves are designed for a particular pressure and quality of steam. If the pressure or quality of steam are variable, zone temperatures will not be within the process specification and under or over pasteurization will occur.

The pasteurizer process performance must be monitored on a regular schedule to determine whether the process conforms to design specifications. "Pasteurizer clocks" are available specifically for accomplishing this task. These instruments are run through the pasteurizer under normal conditions, and record such vital information as time, temperature within the test package, and spray temperatures. In the past, the information was recorded as a curve which then had to be analyzed for its P.U. value. Now there is an electronic P.U. computer which not only measures the process parameters, but also automatically computes the related P.U. value.

Operational performance must be monitored as well, and on a much more frequent basis. This monitoring is carried out by floor personnel with the aid of proper checklists and record sheets. Part of the monitoring involves simply being observant and catching such problems as jams, fallen bottles, broken glass, and pressure damaged containers.

Another important part of monitoring is the observation and recording of pertinent data such as zone temperatures and process time, reviewing control charts and checking for plugged sprays. A detailed checklist is particularly important if more than one package is run and the parameters are reset between runs. *Each* pasteurizer should have a checklist based on the manufacturer's data sheet (or on plant experience) for *each* package to be run so that the variables can be set to provide the desired P.U. value. Operation manuals or procedures with run details for each package are also useful and are strongy recommended.

Equipment problems associated with a tunnel pasteurizer are most likely to occur in three areas: the conveying mechanism, the temperature controls and automatic valves, and process water treatment.

Those problems relating to the conveying mechanism are typical for equipment of this type and include leaking hydraulic seals and fittings, malfunctioning valves, and binding or jamming of conveyor parts. These would result in slowing or stopping the conveyor and a resultant change in the process time/ temperature relationship. Problems of this sort are best handled by an effective preventive maintenance program involving scheduled, routine inspection of the hydraulic drive components, the conveying mechanism, and timing and observation of the conveying cycle.

Problems can occur at any time in the temperature controls and valves. It is extremely important that the air supply to the temperature controllers be clean, dry and at a constant pressure. Dirty, wet compressed air will adversely affect the controller operation and will result in pasteurizer shutdown and improperly pasteurized beer. Regular monitoring of the temperature controls during pasteurizer operation is a must. In addition to regular monitoring, it is also important to have an effective preventive maintenance program for both the controllers and valves in order to keep them functioning properly. High and/or low temperature safeguards, especially in the superheat and pasteurizer zones, can be added to the control system to give warning and stop the process if out of control conditions exist. The temperatures in these two zones should be recorded continuously on a 24-hour chart. As a further safeguard pressurestats or flow sensitive devices can be installed on the discharge lines of water pumps to trigger alarms and/or shut down the pasteurizer in the event of a pump failure.

Certainly the most critical of the equipment problems is proper process water treatment. Failure to adequately treat the water will lead very quickly to problems with biological fouling, scale buildup and corrosion. These result in additional problems of plugged sprays, inadequate heat transfer and equipment metal attack.

Consequently, tunnel pasteurizers cannot be operated without proper water treatment. Constant monitoring is required to maintain the system under control and the attention of a specialist in the field of water treatment is required.

Unfortunately, tunnel pasteurizers are subjected to all the factors which promote biological fouling, scale buildup and corrosion. Biological fouling occurs because of such favorable factors as low pH, nutrients from package breakage or washdown, oxygen, favorable growth temperatures, and air borne organisms from the bottle shop.

Scale buildup is determined primarily by the quality of the water. Some waters have scaling or noncorrosive tendencies, others have corrosive tendencies. Proper water treatment can alter these tendencies and make the water suitable for use in the pasteurizer.

Corrosion occurs as a result of water quality, low pH, oxygen, turbulence, dissimilar metals, and elevated temperatures. Corrosion is best controlled by proper initial design and effective water treatment.

With the current trend toward reduction of water usage, many brewers are turning to the use of softened water. This has advantages in scale control and corrosion, and also aids in delivering clean, film-free packages from the pasteurizer.

Controlling pH within the normal levels of 7.5 to 9 is important. Caustic soda is usually available in a brewery for other uses and can be used in the pasteurizer to maintain proper pH. Biocides, algaecides and slimicides may also be necessary, so the treatment can be very complex, since all materials must be compatible and must have government approval.

The final element of control is competent, interested supervision and operating personnel. These people must realize the importance of their part of the operation and must receive the support of top management.

PASTEURIZATION—BULK/FLASH

Theory and Practice

There is a second method of heat pasteurization in use in the brewing industry which involves pasteurization of the beer prior to filling the containers. In this process the beer is handled in bulk and subjected to higher temperatures, normally 71°C (160°F), for shorter periods of time—approximately 20 seconds. Because of these characteristics it is commonly referred to as bulk or flash pasteurization. When used in combination with an effective sterile filling operation, a flash pasteurization system will do an economical, effective job of microbial stabilization.

Flash pasteurization is not widely used in either North or South America for purposes of achieving microbial stability of packaged beer. It is estimated that at this time (1981) there are less than ten units in use in the Americas for this purpose and that the amount of beer flash pasteurized is only a very small percentage of the total sold each year. Europe, on the other hand, uses this process extensively and there are several hundred such systems in existence, some of which are used for kegs as well as cans and bottles.

Flash pasteurization is similar to pasteurization in the container in one major aspect: both utilize a heating process to destroy the organisms, thereby achieving microbial stability of the product. Because of this similarity, many of the same principles and much of the same technical information apply to both processes. However, there are some major differences which are worthy of mention.

First of all, since flash pasteurization is done in bulk prior to filling, it cannot possibly have any effect on organisms introduced during filling. Therefore, in order to achieve a stable final product, flash pasteurization must be followed by a well controlled, sterile filling operation to prevent reintroduction of organisms.

Secondly, even though both processes utilize heating of the beer, this is accomplished in quite different ways. Flash pasteurization uses a plate type heat exchanger with hot water as the heat exchange media. (See Figure 16-5.) This allows the use of controlled flow and thin film heat transfer which assures that the beer is evenly heated. Overheating is minimized by using hot water temperatures only 2-3°C (3-5°F) higher than the desired pasteurization temperature. This thin film design also allows the use of higher temperatures for a shorter time and very rapid cooling of the beer, which further limits the time that the beer is exposed to elevated temperatures.

16-5. Flash pasteurizer installation (Courtesy APV).

In comparison, pasteurization in the package involves a volume of beer which must be heated from the outside. Thin film principles do not apply and temperature gradients occur within the beer giving variation in treatment.

Equipment

A schematic of a typical flash pasteurization system for installation in a beer packaging operation is shown in Figure 16-6. The system consists of a series of standard components integrated into a total process design which guarantees pasteurization of the carbonated beer despite internal or external process variations that might occur during operation. Total systems, including all auxiliary hardware, can be ordered in a variety of sizes to handle flow requirements up to 490 hl/h (216 gpm).

Major flash pasteurization system components include: a high head centrifugal beer pump; a plate type heat exchanger consisting of a regenerator, a heating section and a cooler section; an external holding tube; a recirculating hot water set including a pump; and a panel-mounted control system incorporating all the necessary instruments and controls for automatic or semi-automatic operation.

In addition to the major components, a complete system requires a CIP (Clean In Place) tank with a means for heating water, such as direct steam injection or in line heat exchanger. Also, a method is needed for providing a cooling solution such as glycol or alcohol/water to be circulated through the cooler section for final cooling to desired filling temperatures. The cooling section should be under automatic control to allow variation of the outlet temperature as desired and also to prevent freeze-up to the final cooler section in the event of a beer shut-down.

Operating Parameters

Normally, final filtered beer at 0-1°C (32-34°F) is pushed from the cellar tank by counter pressure or a boost pump to the system high-head beer pump. From the pump, it enters the heat exchanger where it is heated quickly to pasteurizing temperature, 71°C (160°F), by hot water. The beer leaves the

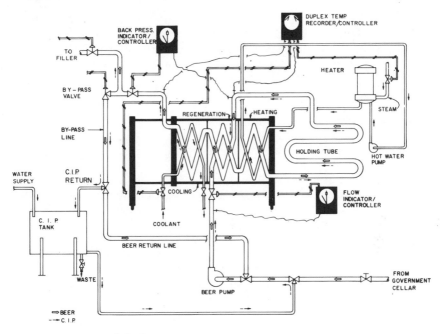

16-6. Schematic of flash pasteurizer system.

exchanger and enters a holding tube where it is held at pasteurizing temperature for a predetermined time interval. The pasteurizing temperature
and time (normally in the range of 71°C and 20 seconds) are dependent upon
individual beers and are agreed upon between the brewer and vendor prior
to designing and building the system.

After being pasteurized, the beer leaves the holding tube and returns to
the heat exchanger for cooling, first passing through the regeneration section
where the temperature is lowered to 7°C (45°F), and finally through the
cooler section where it is cooled by a secondary refrigerant to the required
filling temperature, usually 1-2°C (32-34°F). It then leaves the heat exchanger
and passes to the filling machine or sterile tank as desired. Most systems
connect directly to the filler providing it has sufficient bowl capacity for
absorbing slight control flow surges. Where this is not possible, a buffer or
surge tank is incorporated in the line between system outlet and the filler.

Automatic valves control whether the pasteurized beer goes to the filler or
is diverted back to the pump suction as the filler slows down or stops. During
stops on the filler, the beer is bypassed and recirculated back through the
entire pasteurization system until such time as the filler starts again. The claim
is made that this recirculation has no harmful effect on beer flavor because
of the low oxygen level present in cellar beer as opposed to packaged beer.
If recirculation is felt by the brewer to be a problem, provision can be made
to lower the heat section temperature to 63°C (145°F) automatically after
a predetermined period of time and to hold it there until the filler starts again.
A safety is built into the controls which will not let the filler start again until

the system has come back to desired pasteurization temperature. A less common approach is to automatically divert this recirculation beer to a purge holding tank after a predetermined amount of time in recirculation.

Three of the key aspects of the system design involve:

1. Controlling pasteurization temperature.
2. Maintaining pressure so the beer remains carbonated and degassing does not occur.
3. Handling the situation during filler stoppages.

As one might expect, these requirements demand an elaborate system of controls in order to successfully integrate the pasteurizing system with the filler.

The major controls are as follows:

1. Temperature control—It is desirable to control automatically both the pasteurization temperature of the beer in the holding tube and the temperature of the beer leaving the cooler section. This is done by utilizing a duplex temperature recorder/controller unit. The pasteurization temperature is sensed by the unit at the discharge of the holding tube. It is controlled by an automatic valve in the steam line to the hot water set heater. The same unit also controls the temperature of the beer leaving the cooler section. It senses the beer temperature at the exit of the cooler and controls it through an automatic valve in the coolant line.

2. Back Pressure Control—It is very critical to the operation that an adequate back pressure be maintained on the beer to keep the carbon dioxide in solution. A back pressure valve is incorporated in the design to ensure that system pressures at the holding tube discharge are constantly maintained at least 10% above the carbon dioxide equilibrium pressure at pasteurizing temperature. For our example of 71°C (160°F) and 4.7 g/l (2.5 volumes), this will require pressures above 8 kg/cm² (114 psig). Pasteurizer inlet pressures will be higher still, depending on pressure losses inherent in the regeneration and heating sections. Proper back pressures are maintained by use of an indicating pressure controller and an automatic valve. Since part of the back pressure is expended in the regenerator section, only a portion of it is actually taken across the back pressure valve itself. The pressure is sensed at the discharge of the holding tube and the control valve is located at the outlet of the cooling section.

   Failure to hold the carbon dioxide in solution creates several process problems. The most critical problem is creation of a gas pocket in the holding tube which reduces the holding tube volume and subsequently the holding time as well. Release of carbon dioxide also creates general foaming conditions. A haze problem will develop when the beer is cooled even though the carbon dioxide goes back into solution.

3. Flow Control—For optimum system performance, automatic flow control should be provided. This will require a sensing unit, an indicating controller, and an automatic valve at the beer pump discharge. The setting should be such that the filler requirements are met plus 5% additional to assure a constant forward flow through the bypass line.

4. Fill Level Control—Once it is started, the system operates continuously at a constant flow rate. An automatic valve in the line to the filler opens

and closes to control the level of the beer in the filler bowl. When the level rises due to slowdowns or filler stoppages, this valve closes. A second valve in the pasteurizer bypass line opens to maintain flow through the system.

In addition to the major controls listed, a complete array of switches, sensors, interlocks and safeties are required. These control auxiliary equipment, give visual readouts of temperature and pressure, assure unpasteurized beer doesn't reach the filler at start up, and protect against low pasteurizing temperatures.

Proper cleaning (removal of residues and deposits) and proper sanitization (destruction of organisms) are as important to the success of a flash pasteurization system as is proper operation. Because there is no treatment of the beer following the pasteurizer, the system itself and the piping to the filler must be kept clean and free of organisms. In order to accomplish this, a CIP tank is incorporated in the system to permit hot water flushing after a run and high temperature water sanitization prior to a run. It also allows chemical cleaning (usually with a 2-5% caustic solution) prior to initial system start up and at infrequent intervals (1 week to 3 months depending on use cycle) during its lifetime.

Hot water flushing following a run is accomplished by first purging beer from the system with carbon dioxide or water. Fresh water is added to the CIP tank and heated to 85°C (185°F). The hot water set pump is started and the temperature control is also set to 85°C (185°F). Flow is established by starting the beer pump and letting the water either flow forward to the filler or recirculate to waste at the holding tank. After a 10-15 minute flushing to remove beer residues, the system is secured. The hot water is usually left in the system rather than draining it and leaving the system empty.

Sanitization prior to a run is accomplished in a similar fashion except that circulation at 85°C (185°F) is established and continued for 30 minutes to 1 hour to sanitize the system and lines. After this period of time, the steam to the CIP tank is shut off and cold water added to the tank. The hot water set temperature is lowered to pasteurizing temperatures and the cooling section is activated.

After the system stabilizes at normal operating conditions, the water is replaced with beer and is ready for the run. The use of hot water to flush and sanitize is preferred over chemical sanitizers since heat can penetrate into the small crevices where chemicals sometimes cannot.

Advantages and Disadvantages

Flash pasteurization has a number of advantages. It is a simple, relatively easily controlled process, which, because of its thin film concept, can be counted on to give repeatable, uniform treatment to beer passing through it. Because of the normally low oxygen levels associated with cellar beer and the short duration at pasteurization temperatures, flash pasteurization minimizes off flavors usually associated with heating of beer. In addition, it can claim lower capital and operating costs, space savings, mechanical simplicity, lower maintenance costs, permanent records for check back purposes and low energy consumption. The low energy consumption results from being able to recover 90% or more of the energy in the regeneration section. A final advantage is that lighter weight containers can be used because they don't have to withstand the pressures induced by pasteurization in the package. Since container costs represent a major part of the brewer's expense, considerable savings can result from container weight reduction.

Disadvantages are few. The major one is the requirement for a sterile filling operation following flash pasteurization. This opens up possibilities for reintroduction of organisms and lowers the brewer's assurance of a stable package. Other disadvantages are the problems of labelling cold wet bottles and condensation on cold packages in the warehouse. Labelling problems have been partially overcome by improvements in labelling and adhesives. Condensation is eliminated by the installation of can and bottle warmers after filling, but prior to labelling or warehousing. Package warmers are abbreviated and simplified tunnel pasteurizers which bring the package temperatures up to near ambient conditions. Obviously they represent additional equipment, floor space, capital outlay and energy usage, but they are smaller and cheaper to buy and operate than tunnel pasteurizers. By comparison, a bottle warmer would require approximately 80 percent of the energy of a modern well designed pasteurizer incorporating all the latest energy conservation ideas. The bottle warmer energy consumption compares more favorably when measured against more conventional pasteurizer designs. Another approach to solving the labelling and condensation problems is to use fillers capable of filling at warmer temperatures—25°C (77°F), which eliminates the need for the warmers.

Operational problems in a flash pasteurization system are minimal because of the simplicity of the process. Once pasteurization requirements are established for the particular beer involved, operating parameters can be easily set and adhered to on a continuing basis. The process problems which do exist center on start up conditions and slow downs and stops of the filler. The difficulty arises in designing and operating the control system in such a way that it does not upset the balance of flows, times and temperature within the unit during these disturbances. A properly designed system can do the job and give visual or graphical evidence that proper control is taking place within prescribed limits of the process specifications.

Equipment problems are limited to proper maintenance of the heat exchanger, pumps, valves and controls. Periodic chemical cleaning of the unit to prevent buildup and loss of heat transfer plus an occasional gasket replacement are all the maintenance needed for the exchanger itself. A preventive maintenance and calibration program is recommended for controls and instrumentation, particularly for the control of key parameters such as temperature, back pressure and flow.

Even though the process is stable and reliable, it is still recommended that occasional microbiological checks be made of the beer entering and exiting the pasteurizer. This will give the brewer an indication of change in numbers and types of organisms involved and the effect of the pasteurization level chosen on the organism population. It will also point up any drift in the process as well before problems with loss of stability result.

STERILE FILTRATION

A third method for achieving microbiological stability is sterile filtration. Whereas the first two methods involved pasteurization to destroy the organisms, sterile filtration works on a totally different principle which is physical removal of the organisms from the beer.

Sterile filtration in combination with sterile filling offers an effective means of producing a stable product while totally eliminating all the problems commonly associated with heating of the beer. Brewers in Europe have been using sterile filtration successfully for many years and it remains the most common method in practice there for producing a microbiologically stable bottled beer. It is only in the last few years that European brewers have begun to switch from sterile filtration to heat pasteurization for a small segment of their business designated as "export" beers. On the other hand, in North and South America, the practice of sterile filtration is extremely limited.

Like pasteurization, sterile filtration is a relative newcomer to the art of brewing, and its origin can also be traced to work done by Louis Pasteur. It is believed that the first filters for removal of organisms from a solution were constructed by Pasteur and Chamberlain in 1884. (Block, S.S., Disinfection, Sterilization, Preservation, 1977). These were made in the shape of small, hollow, unglazed candles by heating a mixture of sand and kaolin to a temperature just below the sintering point. Later on, fibrous asbestos pad filters, developed in Germany and known as Seitz filters came into use. Finally in 1922, Zsigmonly and Buchmann introduced membrane filters composed of cellulose esters.

The Hoffman Brewery of Newark, New Jersey is believed to be one of the first in this country to utilize sterile filtration. This brewery employed sterile filtration in 1933 shortly after the repeal of Prohibition. Sterile filtration was rediscovered in the 1960's as breweries in the U.S. took advantage of the fact they could put the term "Draft Beer" on the label by eliminating the use of heat pasteurization. The trend to sterile filtration did not last long due to low throughput problems, and most brewers returned to pasteurization in the package. (Lieberman, C.E., B.A.A. Bulletin 2045, 1979).

In the brewing industry, sterile filtration has come about largely as an outgrowth of filtration technology developed over the last 100 years in response to the needs for improved nonmicrobiological stability in packaged beers. Some of the same filtration techniques used for nonmicrobiological stability such as powdered kieselguhr, perlite (diatomaceous earth), pulp, and sheet filters have been claimed to be effective for sterile filtration as well. At least two of these, pulp and sheet filters, have been used commercially to produce a microbiologically stable beer. A picture of a sheet type sterile filter installation is shown in Figure 16-7. These two, along with a more recent development, membrane filtration, constitute the list of commercially proven methods for sterile filtration of beer.

While the basic principle, physical removal of organisms, is the same for all three sterile filtration techniques, it is accomplished in a variety of ways and merits further explanation. The pulp and sheet techniques fall into the broad category of depth filtration while the membrane filter is classified as surface or screen filtration.

The two depth filters used for sterile beer filtration are made up primarily of fibrous material (cellulose), pressed or otherwise formed into a pad or sheet containing millions of tortuous flow channels. Microorganisms in the beer that passes through these irregular channels are retained by a combination of effects and mechanisms. The most readily recognizable is the absorption action or mechanical entrapment that occurs throughout the depth of the filter. Small

16-7. Sterile sheet filter installation (Courtesy Adolph Coors).

particles, and some of the larger organisms, are literally trapped and retained by the filter matrix. In addition, small particles and organisms are retained by an adsorption effect resulting from intermolecular forces. The negatively charged organisms are attracted and held to the positively charged surfaces of the filter matrix. It is this second adsorptive effect which deserves most of the credit for achieving removal of the organisms and for making these two techniques effective for microbiological stabilization of beer.

Over the years it has been found that the addition of various filter aids to the basic cellulose matrix can improve overall filter performance and allow tailoring of the filter to the job to be done. Traditionally, the most popular and effective filter aid has been chrysotile asbestos. It has been used effectively in both pulp and sheet filters and has been felt necessary in order to achieve the level of organism removal required for microbial stabilization. It has been ideal because of its adsorptive properties and its excellent fiber properties which allow processing in different ways to optimize filter performance. Unfortunately, inhalation of asbestos fibers especially by smokers has recently been implicated in the development of lung cancer in humans. Despite the fact that ingestion of asbestos has not been proven to be a problem, asbestos is losing acceptance with the consumer as well as the government agencies. Substitutes are being found for asbestos, particularly in the area of adsorption or intermolecular attraction properties. These substitutes, primarily surface charge modified fibers, are yielding organism removal levels equal to asbestos and should be acceptable replacements for asbestos.

Another major additive, particularly in sheet filters, is kieselguhr (diatomaceous earth) which is added to the filter primarily to extend life. Filter tightness and removal rates can be adjusted by varying the amount and grade of kieselguhr used.

The membrane filter technique mentioned earlier and classified as surface filtration relies primarily on a sieving principle for removal of organisms. The filter membrane is of a uniform, continuous structure with regularly spaced, uniformly sized pores. When beer passes through the filter, all particles and organisms larger than the pore size are trapped and retained on its surface. Varying the size of the pores controls what passes through the filter. In the case of brewery organisms, a pore size of 0.45 micrometers is considered small enough to achieve organism retention. The screening principle of the membrane filter turns out to be both its strongest and weakest point when filtering beer. Membrane filtration is the only method, of the three types mentioned, which will give absolute and total removal of undesirable organisms. On the other hand, because of their surface retention mechanism, membrane filters have a low dirt loading capacity and tend to plug up and blind off, preventing fluid flow. Membrane filters were used extensively in sterile beer filtration in the 1960's and were successful in producing microbiologically stable beer. However, variable throughput and unpredictable shut downs due to blockage curtailed their use and led to their eventual discontinuance in the brewing industry.

The point should be made that sterile filtration is more than just an additional filtration step between finish filtering and the packaging operation. In those companies where it has been successful, the sterile filter itself is but a small piece of a much larger corporate commitment to achieving overall biological control. In order for sterile filtration to work on a consistent basis, excellent biological control must be established and maintained as far back in the process as brewing. Control must then be demonstrated through the fermenting, lagering and finishing processes right up to the inlet of the sterile filters. Those breweries attempting to utilize sterile filtration without first recognizing or committing to the rest of the job are destined for failure.

Two conditions must be met before sterile filtration can be done successfully:
1. The population of organisms must be closely controlled throughout the operation.
2. Finishing filtration must be especially good, leaving the beer essentially free of particles which will plug or blind off the tighter, final, sterilization filters. Finishing filtration would typically include a diatomaceous filter followed by a single pass sheet or pulp filter.

Figure 16-8 shows a schematic of a typical sterile filtration system utilizing a sheet type filter. Sheet filtration was chosen for this example because of its widespread use and popularity. The system is made up of standard components incorporated in such a way to give a steady, continuous flow of beer through the filter and to prevent pressure shocks to the system.

Equipment

Major system components include the sheet filter itself, centrifugal beer pump, chiller, surge tank, controls and instruments. A complete system also incorporates a CIP system for providing hot and cold water for sanitization and back flushing of the filter.

Filter frames can be purchased from a number of manufacturers. Different throughput rates can be achieved by utilizing different size sheets, from 40 centimeters square up to 1 meter square, and by adding more filter leaves. For sterile filtration, flow rates of 2.0 to 2.85 $hl/m^2/hr$. are recommended. Flow rates will be beer dependent and will be especially sensitive to the amount of material left in the beer by prior filtration steps.

Operating Parameters

Under normal operation, a freshly sanitized and cooled filter is charged with beer by supplying beer from the cellar tank to the inlet of the system beer pump and allowing water previously introduced to the system during

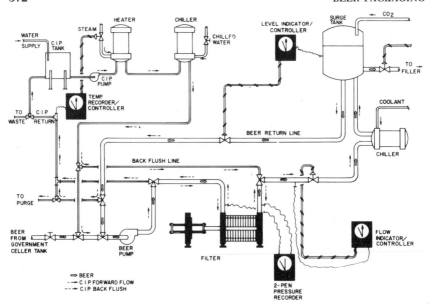

16-8. Sterile filter system schematic.

sanitization to be displaced to waste. The beer flows through the filter and the flow is controlled automatically at the desired rate by the throttling valve and flow indicator/controller. It continues through a low capacity ammonia chiller which removes the small amount of heat picked up in the filtration loop and flows into the surge tank. From the surge tank, beer goes either to the filler or back through the return line and valve to the pump inlet. Normal flow rates meet the filler needs plus 5% so that there is always some beer recirculating through the surge tank and return line.

The two key aspects of the system design are to maintain a constant flow at all times through the filter and to minimize pressure shocks despite the fact that the filler starts and stops.

The major controls are:

1. Flow control—Flow is controlled automatically with a throttling valve at the discharge of the filter and a flow indicator/controller.
2. Pressure Shock Control—Pressure shock control is achieved through utilization of a surge tank. Filler starts and stops are handled without causing pressure shocks to the system by sensing the level of the beer in the surge tank and relaying that information through a control system to the automatic return valve. The same counter pressure is carried on the surge tank as on the cellar tanks.

As with flash pasteurization, it is absolutely necessary to maintain a sanitary system that is free of organisms. An adequate CIP system is as important to success as the filter itself. Cleaning, sanitization and back flushing of the system are accomplished with the CIP system utilizing hot and cold de-aerated water flowing through the filter in a forward or backward direction depending on the operation. After packing, and during the initial sanitization, water from the CIP tank is pumped by the CIP pump through the heat exchanger where the temperature is raised to 80°C (176°F) and then through the entire sterile filtration system, returning through the return line to the CIP tank closing the CIP loop. Circulation of hot water is maintained for a minimum of 55 minutes. With the water still circulating, the heat exchanger is shut off and the cooler started. Thus the same water used for sanitization is now used to cool the sterile filtration system. When the water has cooled to 5°C (41°F), the CIP pump is shut off and the system beer pump is started to establish normal flow. Following cooling, the filter is charged with fresh beer from the cellar and the sanitization water is pushed to waste. All this is done without interrupting the circulation flow and with proper attention to prevention of pressure shocks.

Pulp filter pads are normally used through one packing and cycle of operation and then are unpacked for reprocessing. Sheet filters, however, can be back flushed, sanitized, and run for two or more cycles before needing to be unpacked and replaced. The back flushing and resanitizing are accomplished using the same CIP system. The beer is pushed from the system with fresh water to the purge beer tanks. For back flushing, water from the CIP tank is heated to 55°C (131°F) and directed through the back flush line to the filter outlet. Some filter sheet manufacturers recommend an initial cold water flush prior to or in place of this warm flush. It then flows backward through the filter to the CIP return line and to waste; it is not recirculated. The back flush continues for 20-30 minutes. After back flushing is completed, a normal sanitization operation is carried out as described earlier and the system is charged with beer in preparation for the run.

Advantages and Disadvantages

Sterile filtration has some advantages not found in other processes for achieving microbiological stabilization. The most important is the gentle treatment of the beer itself. There is no heating and subsequent cooling of the beer, so off-flavors from this source are totally eliminated. Nothing in the entire process, with the possible exception of the pumping action, is detrimental to the beer itself and the additional filtration should actually improve clarity and nonmicrobiological stability. Sterile filtration works extremely well in conjunction with sterile filling and refrigerated marketing to get the freshest tasting beer possible to the consumer. It also has many of the same advantages attributed to flash pasteurization: lower capital and operating costs, low energy use, space savings, mechanical simplicity and lower container weights, shipping costs and headspace requirements.

On the other hand, sterile filtration has some disadvantages. Like flash pasteurization, sterile filtration must be followed by sterile filling which has its own set of problems. In order for sterile filtration to be effective, the beer supplied to the filter must be low in numbers of organisms and suspended particulate material. The degree of organism removal is dependent upon the grade and quality of the sheet and the care and expertise of those packing and sanitizing the filters; the process cannot be changed or improved during the run. There are no quick, effective biological test methods to assure a microbiologically stable beer prior to filling or shipping the product. Other less critical disadvantages are shortened production run times because of the

time needed for repacking and sanitizing of the filter and finally the unscheduled downtimes due to the filter blocking out.

Operational Pitfalls

Operational problems are minimal because of the system's simplicity. Once
the filter is packed, sanitized, and loaded with beer, it is a matter of maintaining a constant flow and avoiding pressure shocks. Flow rates and filler
speeds must be controlled so that the surge tank maintains a desired level for
control purposes. The pressure drop across the filter should be monitored and
maintained below a previously agreed upon maximum. Pressure drops of 2.1
kg/cm^2 (30 psi) are considered reasonable. Switching of beer tanks or low
levels of beer in the tanks can cause gas bubbles at the beer filter pump which
will give sudden undesirable drops in pressure to the filter and usually cause
loss of the sterile integrity of the system. While the control system is not
complicated, it must be kept in adjustment and the pressures and flows must
be monitored periodically by operating personnel.

Equipment maintenance is limited to proper maintenance of the filter,
pumps, valves, and controls and presents no particular challenge. A periodic
chemical cleaning to prevent buildup of deposits in the system is normal
practice.

The importance of maintaining biological control of organisms throughout
the system was mentioned earlier. To do this, the brewer needs to have one
or more persons (depending on the size of the operation) responsible for
making routine biological checks. Normally, biological sampling is done in
the fermenting, lagering and finishing areas in order to know the biological
condition of the beer at each point.

Sterile filtration would probably not add significantly to the level of sampling
done in the early portion of the brewing process. However, it would definitely
add to the level of cleanup activity in response to the problem areas revealed
by the positive samples. This additional cleanup is required to reduce the
numbers of organisms present in the beer, particularly at the outlet of the
finishing filters. Additional sampling is necessary in the remainder of the
process from the finishing filters through the fillers and is discussed in greater
detail under the sterile filling section.

OTHER METHODS

Theory and Principles

General inquisitiveness and dissatisfaction with various aspects of existing
methods for microbiological stabilization have led brewers to seek better methods. Their search has taken them down many avenues and led them to try
many unique approaches such as chemical preservatives, irradiation (including
x-rays, ultraviolet rays, cathode rays) and ultrasonic waves. (Kringstak, H.,
EBC Proc., 1949). To the best of the author's knowledge, only one of these,
chemical preservatives, ever reached the commerical application stage in the
brewing industry. The use of chemical preservatives will be dealt with here
in greater detail, since it is currently being used commercially and because
work continues on finding newer, improved chemicals and acquiring governmental approval for their use in beer. The other methods did not progress to
the commercial stage because of their adverse effects on the beer flavor and
non-microbiological stability.

The principle underlying the effective use of chemical preservatives as a means of microbiological stabilization is simple and straightforward. If chemical compounds known to be capable of inhibiting the growth of organisms are added to the beer prior to the packaging operation, their presence controls the growth of organisms originating in the beer supply itself. Also, because their antimicrobial action continues in the package, the problem of introduction of organisms during the filling and closing operations is no longer a matter of concern as well.

The difficulty in making chemical preservatives a commercially viable alternative has been in finding a compound which inhibits the growth of organisms, which is approved for such use by the government, and which has no adverse effects on the beer flavor or physical characteristics.

At the present time, there is only one preservative agent approved by the U.S. Food and Drug Administration as an additive to beer. This is n-heptyl-p-hydroxybenzoate or heptylparaben. (Strandskov, F.B., *ASBC Proc. 1965*). Laboratory and commercial uses of this compound have shown it to be effective in controlling organisms. Despite the fact that it was proven effective and had government approval, it has not achieved widespread use for philosophical and practical reasons. Many brewers, particularly the larger ones, avoid it purely on the grounds that it is an additive. Those who did try it found some practical problems as well.

The limit of solubility of the compound in beer is nearly the same as the minimum concentration necessary for antimicrobial action. It is necessary, therefore, to precisely meter a solution of the compound into the beer since an excess will precipitate out in the lines and tanks. The compound is also surface active and has adverse effects on foam retention and foam cling. Also, its use increases the rate of chill haze development. A final deterrent is that it is extremely hydrophobic and is removed from the beer by certain can linings and by plastic crown liners. This diminishes the antimicrobial activity and results in a loss of stability. The adverse effects on foam and chill stability can be largely overcome by the addition of another compound to the beer, propylene glycol alginate, but the other problems have not been satisfactorily solved. Consequently, use has declined from a high in the early 1970's to a relatively limited application today.

Advantages and Disadvantages

The use of chemical preservatives has some unique advantages when compared to other existing methods of microbiological stabilization. First of all, their simplicity should reduce capital and operating expenses as well as save space in the packaging area. Secondly, their antimicrobial action continues in the container after filling and protects the beer against growth of organisms introduced during that operation. They also have obvious energy saving advantages over the heat pasteurization methods.

Unfortunately, chemical preservatives have some disadvantages as well. The main one is the incompatibility between the preservatives and the beer; any additive presents the risk of altering the flavor or physical characteristics of the beer. A second disadvantage is increasing consumer awareness of, and resentment toward, the use of preservatives in food products. In the United States, this problem is made worse by proposed labeling legislation which, if enacted, will require disclosure of ingredients on the label by 1983. Other countries, including Germany, France, Belgium and Holland, may have laws or regulations concerning the use of any additives in beer.

It should be mentioned that efforts have continued to find a compound which will not have the adverse effects on the beer that heptylparaben has demonstrated. A new compound, polyhexamethylene biguanide hydrochloride (P.H.M.B.) has been tested and found to be effective as a microbiological stabilizer in beer. The tests have also shown that it does not adversely effect the other properties of beer. A direct food additive petition has been submitted to the F.D.A., but a regulation for its use has not yet been issued. (Strandskov, F.B., *Brewers Digest*, 1978). For the time being, we find ourselves in the United States limited solely to the use of heptylparaben with its inherent deficiencies, should we choose to use this method of stabilization.

STERILE FILLING

Theory and Principles

Two of the microbiological stabilization methods discussed earlier, flash pasteurization and sterile filtration, require a sterile filling operation in order to produce a microbiologically stable filled package. There is no doubt that organisms can and do enter the beer during the normal filling and closing operation. Applying sterile filling techniques and procedures can effectively control the frequency and numbers of organisms introduced. We again benefit from the fact that beer is a poor microbial growth medium and supports the growth of only a few of those organisms which might be introduced during filling and closing. These two factors explain why sterile filling in combination with sterile filtration and flash pasteurization have proven effective and continue to be used.

The objective of any sterile filling process is to eliminate or prevent, to the greatest degree practical, the introduction of organisms into the beer during the filling and closing operation. The use of the word sterile to describe the operation is not strictly accurate since organisms are present, but it does adequately describe the conditions the brewer is trying to achieve.

Sterile filling is not a single, well defined process; it is more a commitment to filling the container under special conditions and using special methods and procedures than it is a defined process.

The key elements in the success of any sterile filling operation are:
1) a commitment to make it work
2) understanding by operators of what is being done and why
3) strict attention to the details of housekeeping, cleaning, and sanitization
4) detailed procedures and training for critical parts of the operation
5) a system of quality cross checks to demonstrate that control is being achieved.

Of lesser importance, but still a matter of concern, are such things as equipment design, the environment surrounding the filler, and the biological condition of packaging supplies such as bottles, crowns, cans and ends. Of course, the beer itself must be free of organisms or the sterile filling operation will be useless.

The first requirement for success is a statement from management of its plans to proceed with a sterile filling operation and its commitment of the resources needed to make it effective.

Next comes the requirement to develop some broad operating philosophies and practices in such areas as minimum downtimes for cleaning and sanitizing, maximum run lengths, making time available during runs for equipment sanitization and determining how long a line can be down during a run for mechanical problems before it has to be resanitized. Although experience has shown that there is considerable latitude in making these decisions, the fact remains they must be made at the onset. Changes can be made later after a successful operation is established. A myriad of other decisions need to be made relating to the specifics of the operation: What type of external clean up will be used on the equipment? What chemicals, if any, will be used externally and what is the best method for sanitizing the internals of the equipment, steam, hot water, or chemical sanitizers? What specifically is to be done during the runs to maintain a sanitary condition? Does one use continuous application of iodophors or stop the filler and apply them periodically? The list is lengthy, but each of these details must be addressed.

Once it has been decided what must be done, it is important to prepare written procedures defining in detail exactly how every critical part of the operation is to be carried out. These procedures initially provide the basis for training, and later for consistency of performing the job on a daily basis. Finally, they provide the basis for supervisory control and cross checking by the quality control function.

The need for consistency and close control becomes obvious when one realizes how dependent the sterile filling operation is on both people and equipment. The objective becomes one of creating a high level of understanding and awareness on the part of the people. Through training and education, everyone involved must be made aware of the need and reasons for doing the special operations faithfully and according to procedure. They must be fully aware of the fact that they have only one chance to do the job and to do it right, and that the success of the entire run absolutely depends upon their performing their jobs faithfully.

It should be readily apparent that the job to be done is first and foremost one of prevention, not correction. This means doing the right things, in the right manner, and at the right frequency to prevent an out of control condition from ever occurring.

The final key element of success is a system of quality cross checks. Anyone contemplating a sterile filling operation must be resigned to the fact that he will need a system to tell him where he is at all times in terms of biological control. For smaller operations, this may require only one person. For larger, multi-line, multi-shift operations, it can mean from 1-2 people per million bbls., particularly if they must also check a flash pasteurization or a sterile filtration operation as well.

Any well designed biological control system will have these basic elements: 1) a professional staff of trained microbiologists, 2) a sampling plan or matrix outlining which samples will be taken where and at what frequency, and 3) a modern laboratory with facilities for preparing media, cleaning sampling equipment, processing of samples into media and onto plates, incubation of samples, and reading of results. There must also be a record and reporting system which can track trends as well as spot isolated short-term problems and report them to operations personnel for correction in a timely fashion.

It is recommended that a variety of samples be taken at different points in the system. A basic sampling plan is outlined below, but it should be altered to fit the needs of each particular operation. The number of combinations of sample types, size, frequency, location, sampling equipment, and media is virtually unlimited. Each brewer must decide which ones will give the most information about the conditions of key areas for the time and effort spent and concentrate on these.

The main focus is on the packaged beer. One or two packaged beer samples should be taken off each filler every two hours to be held at room temperature or in warm storage 30°C (86°F) for 4-6 weeks. An additional 1-2 samples should be taken at the same time for processing with a membrane filter. After incubating anerobically for 3-7 days, these plates can be read giving information on the numbers as well as the types of organisms present. Grab samples of 100 ml. each are commonly taken ahead of the filler and processed in the same way to give an idea of the types and numbers of organisms in the beer entering the filler as compared to those in the package.

It is also recommended that more than just beer samples be taken. This would include plant water supply near to the point of use, can and bottle final rinse waters, and sanitization water samples following that operation on tanks, lines and fillers. All of these would be processed through a membrane filter. It is also common practice to take swab samples of machine surfaces following each clean up and sanitization to control that part of the operation as well.

Equipment

The design of sterile filling equipment does not appear to be nearly as critical as might be expected as evidenced by the variety of makes and models operating successfully. Sanitary design should be considered in making the choice and fillers must be capable of heat sanitization, preferrably with circulating hot water. Special filler designs for sterile filling were developed in the 1960's which isolated the air or air/carbon dioxide mixture that was vented from the package as it was being filled. It was kept isolated and not returned to the top of the beer in the filler bowl as was normal practice in standard designs. This isolation feature appears to be a good design concept, but not an absolute necessity. Standard design fillers without this feature are performing satisfactorily. CIP caps are a worthwhile option and facilitate circulation of hot water. External materials should be stainless steel where practical, and the use of rough castings, welds, and cracks and crevices should be avoided where possible. The design should keep everything open and accessible for ease and thoroughness of cleaning.

All piping and tanks should be stainless construction and have a good internal surface finish free of scratches and pits. Valves and fittings should be of sanitary design and construction as well. Most importantly, they should be capable of being sanitized by heat; 80°C (176°F) for 30 minutes is reasonable. Steam can be used, but a continuous flow of recirculating hot water is preferred because its temperature and flow path can be more readily controlled and it offers a scrubbing action as well. Effort should be made during design and construction to eliminate dead legs and air pockets from piping runs.

Conveyors, particularly those near the fillers and carrying open containers, should be of stainless construction with an open design for cleaning. Cable type conveyors are ideal in this respect.

One very important aspect of a sterile filling operation is the method used for sanitizing the internal portion of the filler itself prior to a run. In some installations, this is handled simply by flushing hot water through the filler at the same time the flash pasteurizer is being sanitized. Although this approach works, it is not ideal. It is better to provide a separate system to sanitize the filler by itself.

Figure 16-9 is a schematic of a typical filler CIP system. It consists of a CIP tank, a circulation pump, a heat exchanger and a cooler. Water is added to the CIP tank and is circulated through the system by the pump. In the system shown, the flow of water is in a direction which is the reverse of normal beer flow. The filler shown is one of the types mentioned earlier which has a separate annular tank which receives the vent gas from the cans as they are filled. The design also allows for the reverse circulation of the CIP water. The water is heated to 80°C (176°F) and is circulated for a minimum of 30 min. The same water is then cooled by shutting off the steam to the heater and opening the chilled water valve to the cooler.

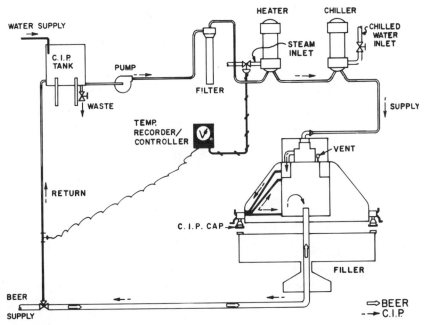

16-9. Filler CIP system schematic.

As additional protection, a 25 ppm iodophor solution can be made and circulated by adding iodophor to the water after initial cool down. The iodophor solution can be drained or left in the system, depending on when the next run will occur. Ideally, sanitization should occur within 2 hours of scheduled start up of the line.

It is also necessary to consider the rinsers for new bottles and cans or the washer for return bottles. A simple in-line rinser with internal and external sprays and adequate drain time is satisfactory for new bottles and cans since they have not been found to be a biological problem. The rinse water should be clean and contain a chlorine residual of 1.0 ppm minimum.

Standard bottle washers have been found to be capable of delivering sterile bottles out of the hot caustic section. The final rinse should be fresh water and have a chlorine residual of 1.0 ppm, minimum. If this is done, the bottles should not present any biological problem.

The need for sterile room enclosures around filling operations has been the cause of much debate. Since there are many operations running successfully without an enclosure, they appear not to be a necessity. When properly designed and constructed, however, an enclosure can be a definite benefit. It provides a separation from the rest of the operation, allows control of air quality, temperature and humidity, and permits the use of materials which are more readily cleanable in the area of the filler. Perhaps more importantly, a sterile room enclosure implies, *"There is something special, different, and critical going on in here—pay attention to what you're doing."* When poorly designed, however, an enclosure is probably more of a detriment than an asset. Figure 16-10 shows the most recent enclosure design which utilizes stainless construction in the floors, walls, and ceiling and is pressurized with sterile, dehumidified, and temperature controlled air.

Packaging supplies are a matter of minor concern. As mentioned earlier, bottles and cans are not a problem if cleaned and rinsed properly before being filled. This is basically true of all other supplies providing they have been

16-10. Sterile filler enclosure (Courtesy Adolph Coors).

properly stored and have not become wet or otherwise soiled. Crowns and ends can be run without treatment of any kind if they are kept clean from manufacture to use. Some breweries like to use a chlorinated flushing spray on the crowns; this is acceptable, but not absolutely necessary.

Operational Parameters

Long continuous runs should be avoided. Runs of 8-24 hours are ideal and it is practical to go as long as 48 hours. Success of the sterile fill process probably depends more on sanitation techniques applied during the run than on the actual run duration. Some sort of sanitation maintenance program during the run is an absolute necessity and must include general housekeeping items such as picking up scrap cans and broken glass and periodic flushing of beer from the equipment, floor, and surrounding areas. This should be done when necessary, but no less frequently than every two hours.

Equally important is some form of treatment with an iodophor. This has been carried out on a continuous basis with sprays directed at critical areas and also on a periodic shutdown basis. Both approaches seem to work. If a periodic shut down is used, it should be done at least every 2 hours during a run. The effectiveness of the iodophor solution is greatly enhanced if the equipment is flushed off first with hot water to remove beer residues. Emphasis should be given to key areas such as filling tubes, crowner platforms, closer heads, and undercover gasser turrets. Additionally, if production ceases during a run for mechanical or other reasons, periodic flushing with an iodophor solution should be carried out. If the downtime exceeds one hour, consideration should be given to shutting down and resanitizing the filler completely. The importance of sanitation maintenance during the run cannot be overemphasized.

Another important aspect of cleaning occurs at the end of the run. No filler should be left soiled after a run. It should be drained and flushed with clean water internally and at least be given a hot water flush down externally to remove the food source for organism growth. A good external cleaning and subsequent CIP sanitization can then be done just prior to the next run. If the downtime between runs is going to be more than a few hours (8 hours maximum), the filler should be given additional internal flushing and extensive external cleanings at shutdown and prior to start up.

Advantages and Disadvantages

Sterile filling has few, if any, advantages over the standard filling operation, but it is the only alternative for the brewer who intends to flash pasteurize or sterile filter the beer. A sterile filling operation is generally more tightly run from a quality standpoint and there are secondary benefits from that. Its disadvantages require definite consideration. First of all, a sterile filling operation is difficult to control, and it depends to a large degree on the human element for success. In addition, biological results come after the product is shipped, too late for any immediate change to the process during the run. Success comes only through total prevention of problems; failure, even for limited periods of time, will result in a product of questionable stability.

An extensive quality cross check program is needed and adds to the operating expenses and housekeeping; clean-up and sanitization costs are higher as well. Equipment utilization is less than normal because the line cannot be run as many hours per week because of necessary downtimes for cleanup and sanitization. Special design, construction, and equipment requirements can add as much as 25-30% to costs. Operation is more critical and training more time consuming and expensive. There is the problem of cold wet bottles to label and cold sweating containers to warehouse unless package warmers are utilized. Finally, it is reasonable to assume additional maintenance will be necessary due to the extra emphasis on cleaning and the adverse effects of cleaning chemicals on equipment and plant.

This rather formidable list of disadvantages does not make sterile filling either impossible or impractical. The hundreds of successful sterile filling operations presently in use throughout the world attest to this fact. Nevertheless, it is also obvious that the inherent problems cannot be taken lightly and that sterile filling requires a greater commitment on the part of the brewer in order to be successful.

FUTURE

Predicting the future course of any activity is a risky endeavor but not totally without merit. Its virtue comes from helping the reader consider the factors of change and their impact on present day practices.

When making predictions, it is often beneficial to look first at the past. The process of microbiological stabilization has changed very little in the last eighty years. From 1880 through 1960, it was exclusively a heat pasteurization process in the package. The changes that did occur were mostly equipment refinements and did nothing to alter the basic principle. The progression of refinement took us from the early "steaming tanks" to basket pasteurization and finally to our modern tunnel pasteurizers which remain the most universally accepted and practiced method of achieving a stable packaged beer.

It was not until the late 1950's and early 1960's that we saw the first real efforts made to develop effective alternatives to pasteurization in the package. In a brief flurry of activity, the industry succeeded in commercially applying the other methods we presently have: flash pasteurization, sterile filtration, and the use of preservatives. The last 15-20 years have seen subtle changes in the existing methods, but nothing new or revolutionary.

The second step in making predictions should be to look at the factors of change. Those factors controlling change within the microbiological stabilization methods include intense competition within the brewing industry, technological advances, and governmental regulations. The competition factor includes both quality and cost considerations. Recent major increases in the cost of basic energy are causing brewers to review their entire operation for ways of saving energy.

With the past and the factors of change in mind, it is possible to speculate on the next few years. The future of microbiological stabilization will reflect the past in that change, when it does occur, will be slow. It is not likely that any new methods will be made available to the brewer over the next few years since new technologies, such as irradiation, have been tried and found unacceptable because of severe adverse effects on beer flavor and physical characteristics.

Heat pasteurization in the package will continue to be the most widely practiced in the western hemisphere and it will gain popularity in Europe as the level of their export market picks up. This method will continue its dominance because of the assurance it offers the brewer of a totally stable packaged product. Energy costs are highest for this method but efforts will continue to find ways of recovering more of the heat through better regeneration techniques within the tunnel pasteurization system. It is not likely, however that regeneration will reach anywhere near the 90% level of flash pasteurization.

The competitive elements of quality and cost will probably cause some brewers to turn to other methods of microbiological stabilization in the interest of avoiding the loss of flavor which occurs any time a beer is heated or even stored at warm temperatures for a period of time. New methods also will be sought by those who wish to cut costs and improve energy utilization.

Flash pasteurization with sterile filling will gain some converts, since it offers a quality product and low costs while removing the need for strict biological control of the beer ahead of the filling operation. Since it virtually guarantees a biologically stable beer at the filler, the brewer need only contend with the problems of the sterile filling operation. Even though it is a heating process, its energy requirements are lower and the flavor impact less than pasteurization in the package because of low oxygen levels and uniform treatment. It can work equally well with a refrigerated marketing approach or with warm marketing by using either a cool or hot fill and eliminate the need for package warmers.

Sterile filtration with sterile filling offers the same quality and cost benefits of flash pasteurization but it is not likely to gain many additional followers because of its stringent requirements for biological control throughout the entire brewing and packaging operations.

The increased use of preservatives has to be considered as a future possibility. It is by far the simplest approach; it requires minimum space, the lowest installation costs, zero energy use and low per barrel costs for the compound. It also provides protection in the package after filling. Increased use of this stabilization method depends upon finding a new compound with fewer adverse effects on the beer and then obtaining governmental approval for its use. If this happens, there may be an increase in the number of brewers who turn to this method in an effort to trim costs and remain competitive. However, the number changing will be limited by the offsetting possibility of negative consumer reaction to the use of a preservative as well as by regulations on content labeling.

Acknowledgements

Creation of this chapter was by no means a singular effort. The author wishes to acknowledge the work of Messrs Borris Miller, James Heuling, Val Mayer and Donald Duncan of Barry-Wehmiller in providing a basic text for Pasteurization in the Package. Mr. Richard Walz of APC and Mr. John Brzezinski of Lone Star Brewery contributed vital information to Bulk Pasteurization. The personnel in the Packaging Process Control Department of the Adolph Coors Company deserve mention and credit for their insight into Sterile Filtration and Sterile Filling.

REFERENCES

1. BASELT, F. C. *Comm Mstn Brew*, Vol. 10, No. 11 (1949)
2. BENJAMIN, H. A. *American Can Lab Report* (1936)
3. BLOCK, B. E. *MBAA Tech Quart*, Vol. 1, 191 (1964)
4. BLOCK, S. S., DISINFECTION, STERILIZATION, PRESERVATION, 2nd Edition, Phil. Lea Flbiger, (1977)
5. BRENNER, M. W.; IFFLAND, H. *MBAA Tech Qtly* Vol. 3, 193 (1966)
6. BUNKER, H. J. *E. B. C. Proc.*, 330-340, (1955)
7. DEL VECCHIO, H. W.; DAYHARSH, C. A.; BASELT, F. C. *ASBC Proc.*, 45 (1951)
8. KING, L. M.; EGAN, L.; SCHISLER, D.; HAHN, C. W. *J.ASBC*, Vol. 36, 144 (1978)
9. KRINGSTAK, H. *EBC Proc.*, Vol. 1, 171 (1949)
10. LIEBERMAN, C. E. *Brewers Assoc. of Amer. Bulletin 2045* (1979)
11. POSADA, J.; GALINDO, J. G.; PALOMERO, F. L. *EBC Proc.*, 399-415 (1973)
12. RAINBOW, C., Proc. *Biochem.*, April, 15-16 (1971)
13. RUNKEL, U. *MBAA Tech Qtly.* Vol. 12, 28 (1975)
14. STRANDSKOV, F. B.; ZILIOTTO, H. L.; BRESCIA, J. A.; BOCKELMANN, J. B., *ASBC Proc.*, 129 (1965)
15. STRANDSKOV, F. B.; BOCKELMANN, J. B.; ZILIOTTO, H. L.; BRESCIA, J. A., *Brew Digest*, Sept., 52 (1978)
16. WALTON, O. *Brewers Guardian*, Vol. 106, No. 8, 20 (1977)

CHAPTER XVII

PRODUCT PACKING

BY GARY C. GEMINN and JAMES HIRSCHY

INTRODUCTION

The choosing of packages and packaging machinery in a brewery depends upon economics, management preference and customers' acceptance; however, in some areas the style of packaging is dictated by legislative action. In general, there are basically three types of containers available for the brewing industry. They are returnable glass, non-returnable glass and metal cans. Of course, there are many dream packages around, such as plastic bottles, plastic lined composite cans, etc., but these are still in the research and development stage and are not ready for general use in the western hemisphere.

Since the cost of packaging material is far greater than the cost of product and labor, it is important to select the most efficient packaging machinery and the most economical materials. There is no cut-and-dried method for choosing machinery and material for the packaging operation. Material and style of packaging is generally a marketing function based on cost and consumer acceptance. Machinery is generally chosen by the packaging department after much discussion of the pros and cons of what is available at the time of purchase.

RETURNABLE GLASS PACKAGING

Style of Cases

Returnable glass is usually packed in some type of case that can make several round trips. On the North American Continent the standard returnable beer case is generally made from laminated kraft; either the Bliss "C" style case or the Gaylord ("Whalley") style case, and in a few instances the regular slotted corrugated carton (RSC) is used. In Europe the standard beer case is plastic, and in some sections of the world the wooden case is still used.

The difference between using corrugated and laminated kraft is price and the number of times that the case can be reused. The corrugated case costs about one fifth of what a laminated kraft case costs; however, corrugated cases are good for only one or two trips, while laminated kraft cases are good for fifteen to twenty trips. The main advantages of the corrugated case are that the package always has a "fresh look" and is easily recycled. With laminated kraft the main advantage is that it is a durable case and will withstand damp basements and other unfavorable conditions.

Commonly used style of beer cases showing assorted types of flaps are shown in figures 17-1 through 17-5.

Partitions

To keep the bottles from breaking in transit, some type of partition is required to protect the bottles from glass to glass contact. Partitions are common

17-1. Single tuck lids, Multiple roll-over ends and Regular style hand hold.
Courtesy Union Camp

17-2. Double tuck lids, Multiple roll-over ends and Regular style hand hold.
Courtesy Union Camp

17-3. Single tuck lids, Multiple roll-over ends and "Blind" style hand hold.
Courtesy Union Camp

17-4. Full BOH lock lids, Full roll-over ends and Regular style hand hold.
Courtesy Union Camp

17-5. Butterfly lids, Multiple roll-over ends and Regular style hand hold.
Courtesy Union Camp

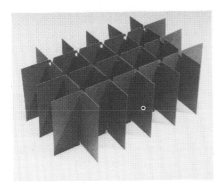

17-6. Shoulder Height Partition. Courtesy CLEVEPAK

with both returnable and non-returnable glass. Shoulder high partitions are the most popular.

The partitions are usually made from chip board from .040″ to .055″ thick and frequently are wax impregnated. They can also be made from other materials such as corrugated or rag paper, and in some instances plastic is being used.

Case Handling

On returnable glass lines packaging actually begins with the cases being returned from the field or warehouse, and the uncasing is covered in Chapter VII. The cases are cleaned and inspected, if not new, prior to packing with filled bottles.

17-7. "S" Style Case Cleaner. Courtesy Genesee Brewery

Case Cleaning and Reconditioning

In some operations the cases are sent to a case cleaning area or room. Here the cases are removed from the line manually, dumped upside down over a waste receptacle, brushed off and cleaned up in general. The partitions are checked and replaced with new ones if necessary. There is also a stock of new cases stored in this area for replacements as required.

In other operations the cases are transported directly from the uncaser to the packer. In these operations automatic case cleaners are placed in the line somewhere between the uncaser and packer.

There are two styles of case cleaners in general use: the "S" slide cleaner as developed by the Heilman Brewery several years ago and the conventional 360° loop case cleaner. The advantage of the "S" slide cleaner is that it requires no power or timing; however, it has a disadvantage in that the case must drop at least 12 feet for it to work effectively. The 360° loop cleaner receives the case, turns the case upside down for rubbish removal by revolving it around a vertical curve and returning the case to a discharge conveyor. Some case cleaners are equipped with air for blowing the inside of the case while the case is upside down to assist in rubbish removal.

When automatic case cleaners are used a case inspector should be stationed just ahead of the packer to assure that the partitions are properly placed, the case is clean and the general condition of the case is satisfactory.

Returnable Multipacks

Most returnable products are packed in case lots; however, there are a few exceptions wherein returnables are packed in multipacks. Since multipack equipment is the same for returnables as non-returnables, multipack equipment is discussed under non-returnables (NR).

Packers

Returnable glass is normally packed with some type of vertical packer, commonly known as drop packers, see figures 17-8 to 11. There are three basic types of drop packers available. In one, the bottles are accumulated into a group above the case, and then some type of bottom slide or bomb bay door opens, which lets the bottles fall directly into the case. The second type of drop packer is the soft drop or lowering head packer. On these packers the bottles are either clamped or gripped around the neck and are lowered into the case. The straight drop packer is considerably faster than the lowering head packer; however, the lowering head packer causes less breakage. A third version is the continuous or rotary motion packer. These packers look like a rotary uncaser, except working backwards. The grippers or fingers clamp onto the bottles and lower them into the case while the case travels under the bottles at the same rate of speed. The continuous motion packer is faster than the standard drop packer; however, keeping it in a good operating condition can be a problem.

Case Formers

Wherever returnable cases are used; a certain number of cases, about five percent, are damaged beyond repair after each trip, and these cases must be replaced. In some breweries the replacement cases are made up manually with a single head stitcher. In other breweries they are made up with machinery that is especially designed for forming and assembling returnable cases. One example of such a machine is the Huntington Box Maker, see figure 17-12.

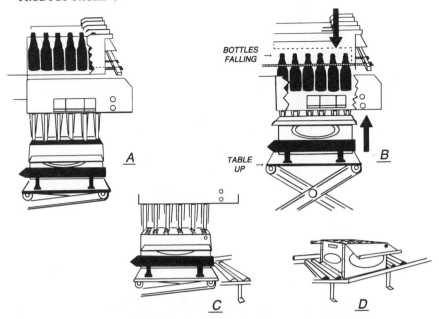

17-8. Basic drop packer operation.

A. The beginning of a packaging sequence for a drop packer. A case is placed under a packaging head which is loaded with bottles ready to drop.

B. The case is raised and the head has shifted permitting the bottles to drop through the guide fingers into the case.

C. The case is lowered and the head is ready to receive another load of bottles.

D. The case is completely filled and on its way to the flap closer and warehouse.

17-9. Standard Knapp Drop Packer Model 950 dual head. Courtesy Standard Knapp

17-10. Standard Knapp lowering head packer Model 930. Courtesy Standard Knapp

17-11. Continuous motion rotary loader Model "Konti-Pack". Courtesy ABC Packaging

NON-RETURNABLE GLASS PACKAGING

Style of Multipacks

N R glass is usually packed in multipacks with the six, eight and twelve packs being the most common. There are many different styles of multipacks available but some of the common ones are: the neck thru, the wrap around with or without add panels, the totally enclosed and the basket carrier, see figures 17-13 to 15. Six, eight and twelve pack NR glass are generally wrapped with fiberboard. In some instances shrink film or plastic clips are used for six and eight packs. Basket carriers are also generally made with fiberboard; however, solid plastic baskets have been used. Another multipack that has

17-12. Huntington Bliss style box maker. Courtesy Mead Packaging

become quite popular is the plastic or paper clip for attaching two quart or two one-litre bottles together.

Multipack Machinery

In order to get the bottles into multipacks many types of packers are available. Six and eight packs are generally packaged with some type of wrap around machine; such as the "Mead Cluster Pack". Of course, if the six or eight packs are in basket carriers, then some type of drop packer is required.

Twelve packs are assembled or packaged in three different ways, using either wrap around machines, end loaders or drop packers.

Mother Containers

In order to transport the multipacks from the brewery to the consumer some type of mother container is required. For breweries that use reshipper cartons, the glass is received in the mother container. It can be a partial tray, full depth tray or an RSC carton. If the multipack happens to be a basket carrier; then the basket is also enclosed in the mother container.

For breweries that are in bulk glass the mother container must be set up or formed in-house. In conjunction with the mother carton set-up equipment, basket set-up and stuffers are also required.

In a few instances no mother containers are used. For example, when the 12 pack is in an RSC carton, it is sometimes shipped without any additional protection.

Mother Packers

There are several styles of packers available for packing multipacks into mother cartons. One style is the continuous motion packer, such as the Nigrelli

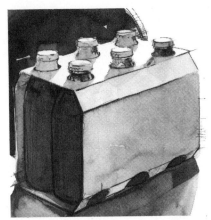

17-13A. *Neck thru carton.* 13B. *Bottle enclosed carton.* Courtesy Mead Packaging

17-13C. *Totally enclosed carton.* Courtesy Mead Packaging

17-14. *12-Pack totally enclosed.*   17-15. *6 pack basket carrier.*

Courtesy Mead Packaging

17-16. Dacam Tray Packer Model TP IV. Courtesy Dacam Corp.

packer. Other styles of mother packers are the ordinary drop packers and slide packers, such as a Dacam, see figure 17-16.

The Dacam packer is the most economical and satisfactory for limited applications and has a speed range from 0 to 55 trays per minute. The drop packers, because of their intermittent operation, are limited in speed and perhaps contribute to some breakage. Drop packers operate at speeds up to 25 cases per minute per head. The Nigrelli packer probably has the least breakage and is excellent where speed is required. Nigrelli manufactures continuous motion packers that have speeds up to 80 trays per minute.

In operations where the NR glass is received in bulk, the mother packing is the same as for cans. These packers are discussed under "Can Packaging".

24 Pack Glass

The packaging equipment used for 24 pack glass (case lots) is the same as that used for cans except where a tab lock case is used. In addition to the packer and gluer required for a standard RSC carton, a slitter is also required to free the tab lock flaps on a tab lock case.

17-17. Tab Lock Case Flaps are held down for ease of uncasing and packing. Courtesy Thatcher Glass

17-18. Standard Knapp Model 160 Tab Slitter. Courtesy Standard Knapp

CAN PACKAGING

Six-Packs

Over 50 percent of the cans sold on the North American Continent are in six packs. The majority of these are packaged with a Hi-Cone machine in conjunction with some type of tray packer. There are other options available for six pack cans such as, a fiberboard wrap, shrink film or plastic clips; however, none of these options are widely used. The Hi-Cone pack is widely preferred by the consumer since it is economical and one of the most efficient machines used in the brewing industry.

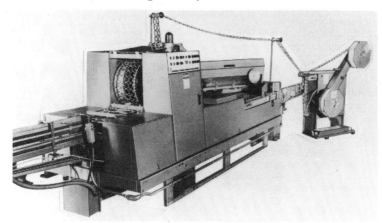

17-19. Model 260 Series Hi-Cone Applicating Machine for 6-packs. Courtesy Illinois Tool Works Inc., Hi-Cone Division

Twelve-Packs

Packaging equipment for a twelve-pack line usually consists of some type of end loader used with or without a tray packer. There are many operations where the 12-pack is shipped directly to the consumer without a mother

17-20. Jones Traypacker Model TP-IV. Courtesy R.A. Jones

17-21. Model HSP-12 Can Packer. Courtesy R.A. Jones

container. Another option for 12 packs is a drop packer and a gluer using an RSC carton; however, a drop packer is slow, approximately 25 cases per minute, while an end loader operates around 150 packages per minute.

24 Loose Packs

Packaging equipment for 24 loose cans and 24 loose bulk NR glass have many similarities. One option for packing 24 loose is using some type of RSC set-up machine with a drop packer and gluer. If the loose pack is glass, then some method for putting a partition into the case has to be added, and this

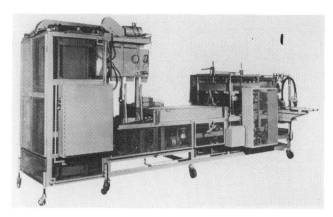

17-22. Case set-up and bottom sealer. Courtesy R.A. Pearson Co.

17-23. R.A. Pearson Partition Inserter. Courtesy R.A. Pearson Co.

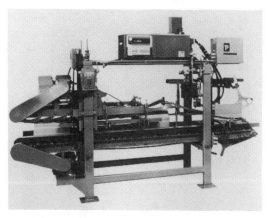

17-24. Top Gluer Model N401. Courtesy R.A. Pearson

17-25. Five flap wrap around carton Model PMI. Courtesy Pak-Master Mfg. Co.

17-26. 24 Pack End Loader Model CMP-HM. Courtesy R.A. Jones

is usually done either manually or automatically with a partition inserter. Another option is some type of wrap-around carton such as a Pak-Master. Still another option is an end loader. End loaders are expensive; however, they are the fastest with an operating speed around 90 cases per minute. The RSC carton set-up machine-drop packer-gluer operations cost less than end loaders; however, they are also slower, around 50 to 60 cases per minute. The Pak-Master is the cheapest; but, its speed is limited to 30 cases per minute.

Shrink Film

Some breweries use shrink film for mother packaging in both NR glass and metal cans. These films that are used for packaging are made of a special thermoplastic material that has been oriented or stretched during manufacture. When wrapped around a package the film will shrink tightly when it is subjected to the proper degree of heat. The main advantage of shrink film is that it is cheaper than other mother packaging materials such as corrugated

17-27. 24 Loose shrink film operation. Courtesy Mead Packaging

or paper board. The disadvantage is that it entraps moisture which leads to mold growth and an unsightly looking package.

Its versatility in use is shown by the following examples. Four six packs, either glass or metal, are placed on a corrugated sheet and formed into a tight block with shrink film. Another example is using four 12-packs (48 count), either glass or metal, which are placed with two 12-packs on top of the first two 12-packs so that, almost a square block is formed when the shrink film is applied. Still another example is 24 loose cans placed in a shallow tray surrounded with shrink film.

CONCLUSION

Packaging material represents the largest single cost element in the Bottle Shop operation. It is important to use the most economical material available which will transport the product from the brewery to the consumer and still meet with the customers' acceptance.

ADDITIONAL INFORMATION
PACKING EQUIPMENT SUPPLIERS

CASE FORMER
ABC Packaging Machine Corp.
General Corrugated Machinery Co.
R.A. Pearson Co.
Huntington Systems
Standard Knapp

CASE SEALERS
ABC Packaging Machine Corp.
Bemis Company Inc.
Elliot Mfg. Co., Inc.
General Corrugated Machinery Co.
Marq Packaging Systems
R.A. Pearson Co.
Standard Knapp
Simplimatic Engineering Co.

DROP PACKERS
Geo. J. Meyers
Standard Knapp
ABC Packaging Machine Corp.
Simplimatic Engineering

MULTIPACK EQUIPMENT
Mead Packaging
Gantz Bros.
Olinksoft
R.A. Jones
Largen
FMC Corp.

TRAY FORMERS
ABC Packaging Machine Corp.
Dacam Corp.
Huntington Systems
Marq Packaging Systems
R.A. Jones

TRAY PACKERS
Nigrelli, Inc.
Huntington Systems Inc.
R.A. Jones
Standard Knapp Inc.

SHRINK FILM WRAPPERS
Anderson Brothers Mfg. Co.
Mead Packaging

Huntington Systems
Weldotrom Corporation
Great Lakes Corp.
Packaging Machinery Co.

UNCASER
Geo. J. Meyer Co.
R.A. Jones
Climax Product Div.

WRAP AROUND CASE FORMERS
Compacker Inc.
Douglas Machine Co.
Clevepack Corp.
Pak-Master Mfg. Co.

PACKING EQUIPMENT SUPPLIERS ADDRESSES

ABC Packaging Machine Corp.
P.O. Box 1285
811 Live Oak St.
Tarpon Springs, Fl 33589

Anderson Brothers Mfg. Co.
1303 Samuelson Rd.
Rockford, Il 61101

Clevepack Corporation
Clevepack Machinery Div.
925 Westchester Avenue
White Plains, N. Y. 10604

Climax Products Div.
Lodge and Shipley Corp.
3055 Colerain Avenue
Cincinnati, Oh 45225

Compacker, Inc.
3030 Hickory Grove Road
P.O. Box 2026
Davenport, Ia 52804

Dacam Corporation
P.O. Box 680
Madison Height, Va 24572

FMC Corporation
Canning Machinery Division
Hoopeston, Il 90942

General Corrugated Machinery Corp.
269 Commercial Avenue
Pallisades, N. J. 07650

Geo. J. Meyer
Packaging Division
1556 Akron Peninsula Rd.
Akron, Oh 44222

Huntington Systems Inc.
830 Welsh Road
Bethayres, Pa 19006

Nigrelli, Inc.
Sheboygan Falls, Wi 53085

R.A. Jones
P.O. Box 485
Cincinnati, Oh 45201

H.J. Langen & Sons
2357 Devon Avenue
Elk Grove Village, Il 60007

Marq Packaging System
P.O. Box 9063
3800 W. Washington Avenue
Yakima, Wa 98909

Mead Packaging Machinery Div.
999 Lee St. SW
Atlanta, Ga 30310

Packaging Systems Corp.
P.O. Box 526
Stanford, Fl 32771

Pak-Master Mfg. Co.
31800 Hayman St.
Hayward, Ca 94544

R.A. Pearson Co.
W. 8120 Sunset Highway
Rt. 4 Box 65
Spokane, Wa 99204

Simplimatic Engineering Co.
P.O. Box 644
Lynchburg, Va 24505

Standard Knapp Inc.
Main St. P.O. Box 313
Portland, Ct 06480

Weldotrom Corporation
1532 S. Washington Avenue
Piscataway, N. J. 08854

CHAPTER XVIII

PRODUCT IDENTIFICATION

BY JOSEPH A CISZEWSKI

INTRODUCTION

Due to increasing Federal and local labeling requirements and the growing emphasis on the need to protect against liability claims, the subject of this chapter takes on added significance. When we add the obvious need for inventory and quality controls, plus the demands of marketing, we can see the complexity of the problem.

In this chapter we will try to deal with the reasons for, and the methods used, to meet with these needs. Since there are so many ways of accomplishing the coding, we will be unable to cover them all; however, we hope to concentrate on the most popular methods.

Coding as used in packaging is a means of condensing into a limited space a great deal of valuable information either in plain language, such as dates, or encoded in alpha-numeric language or other computer readable symbols, such as Universal Product Code (UPC).

A good deal of the information needed for coding is usually preprinted on the package itself. The rest is generally added during the actual packaging operation. This is the ideal situation, as it provides greater flexibility in package utilization and it reduces the possibility of having to discard large amounts of material due to sudden changes in laws or market demands.

We will also cover the Universal Product Code commonly referred to as UPC. Several years ago the grocery industry decided to establish this system of code marking and pricing through the use of a scanner at the check-out counter. The reasons for adopting this system were to expedite check-out time, to provide customers with a more detailed sales slip, to decrease errors and to simplify inventory controls for the stores. Utilization of this system has been expanding not only within the grocery industry, but in other industries as well. Such requirements can be expected to increase in future years as the highly sophisticated systems of distribution multiply and the need to hold down operating costs become and more important.

Lastly, we will discuss labeling regulations, both Federal and State.

REASONS FOR PRODUCT AND PACKAGING CODING

Legal Requirements—FDA and other Regulatory Agencies.

Quality Control—When necessary coding permits an off-specification lot to be identified quickly and isolated, thus saving the remainder of the product. Methods of coding each lot vary from company to company, but such coding is important.

Shelf Life—This is required to ensure product freshness and rotation. Since beer, like all food products, has a finite shelf life, the use of coding containing the date of packaging permits proper rotation of inventory both at the wholesale and retail levels.

Customer Complaint Check—Coding permits identifying and locating suspect material and it can provide for checking validity of the customer complaint.

Efficiency Checks—Personnel and machine codes can identify personnel working on specific product lots, as well as the particular equipment involved.

Time Check—When a complaint involves any failure or defect on the part of the container or package, coding allows the manufacturer of the container or package to isolate the complaint faster and determine its extent.

METHODS OF CODING—PRODUCT

The various combinations of packages, packaging materials, line speeds and packaging plant layouts require different types of coding applications.

Table I lists the location of coding applications, the most commonly used coding method and some advantages and disadvantages of each. While there are additional applications in use in the industry, those listed are the most widely used and fulfill the requirement of coding containers and packages.

The methods used in applying the code have, like all packaging innovations, progressed from hand stamping the code to the use of high speed, non-contact programmable equipment. A description of the methods in use in the industry today follows:

Contact Printing

Contact printing of the code is the oldest and most widely used coding method. The code is applied by contact with rubber or metal type that has been pre-inked. The subject to be coded can actuate the coding device. A simple corrugated case coder is one such device and is illustrated in Figure 18-1.

As the case passes the coding wheel the code is rolled on. The ink rolls in this unit are precharged for longer and cleaner service. Changing of codes causes some line downtime. Downtime can be minimized if dual units can be installed along the conveyor with pre-set codes.

For coding containers (cans and bottles) operating at somewhat higher speeds it becomes necessary to mechanize the coder. One such device is shown in Figure 18-2.

The can is controlled and driven through the coder by the two side belts. For smaller lightweight containers a top hold-down is added.

The coding wheel is timed with can progress to imprint the can properly through the opening shown in the lower plate.

Ink supply is by means of a reservoir and transfer roll. Code changes are made by replacing the coding wheel with a pre-set spare. Line downtime, therefore, is low.

For some companies, the backs of bottle labels provide a convenient place for codes. For limited production runs, the backs can be preprinted. Some labelers permit the use of coding devices.

The coding of finished products on pallet is sometimes overlooked in the overall coding plan because the individual containers and packages on the

TABLE I

APPLICATION	METHOD(S) USED	ADVANTAGES	DISADVANTAGES
Bottle Crowns	Contact printing.	Simplicity; meets line speed requirements; relative low cost.	Codes over crown, litho, poor legibility; water on crown and variations in height affect clarity.
Labels	Labeler machine coding (debossing, perforating and printing).	Legibility.	Requires individual equipment attachments; high maintenance.
	Pre-coding: A. Debossing, perforating and printing.	Legibility.	Slow speed; high manpower, label restacking problems.
	B. Slotting	Simple and rapid application.	Minor tearing and difficult to decode in most cases.
	Non-Contact (laser; ink jet).	Clear sharp print; high speed; programmable.	High cost and technology; requires bottle orientation.
Cans	Contact.	Simplicity.	Not consistent; clarity is hard to maintain.
	Non-Contact	Clear, sharp print; high speed; programmable.	High cost and technology.
Keg Bungs	Hot stamping for plastic only.	Only method available; varied coloring.	Limited lettering size.
	Branding for wood only.	Permanent, clear.	Limited visibility; no color variation.
Plastic 6-Pak Carriers	Debossing.	Simple operation.	Code limitations; difficult to read.
Fibre Wrap-Style Carriers	Debossing.	Simple operation.	Poor Visibility.
	Contact printing.	Clear, simple.	Ink smears.
Corrugated Shipping Cartons	Contact printing.	Clear, simple; low initial cost.	Ink smears.
	Non-contact printing.	Clear, programmable.	High initial cost and high technology.
Pallet Loads of Finished Goods	Labels/Tags.	Identified pallet loads; can be pre-printed.	Manual application; can be lost.

18-1. A simple coder for corrugated cases.

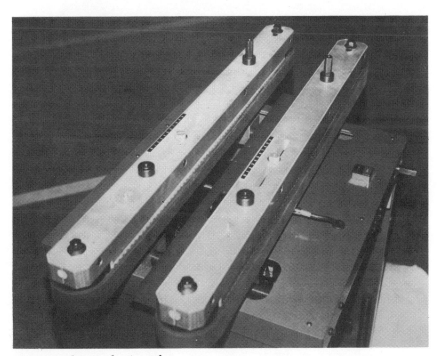

18-2. Mechanized can coder.

pallet have been coded. Pre-stamped pallet tags are applied to individual pallets that identify the product, package line number, packaging date and, even in some cases, the palletizer. This not only provides warehouse people with a quick method of determining inventories, but is useful for quality control.

Non-Contact Printing

Non-contact coding has come into being within the last decade. It appears to be the coding method of the future since it has flexibility and high speed. Ink jet was the first entry with lasers becoming available recently.

The ink jet system forms the ink into charged droplets that are then controlled in their trajectory to the code surface. The system will print on irregular or curved surfaces at high speeds. It can be programmed to automatically change time of day or entire codes during operation with no line downtime. Friar covers the subject in more detail in his paper "Non-Contact Coding by Video Jet Printer" in the *MBAA Technical Quarterly*, Vol. 17, p. 125, 1980. An illustration of one of the systems is shown in Figure 18-3. The cans are dated with waterproof ink in a can track which is usually located before the filler or can rinser.

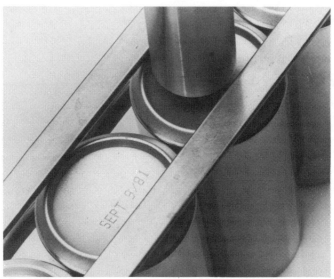

18-3. Ink jet coding.

The laser directs an energy beam through a series of masks forming the code desired. Codes are changed by changing masks. As with the ink jet system, the codes can be changed automatically with no line downtime. Lasers, too, will print on irregular or curved surfaces. Wilson discusses the advantages and disadvantages of this system in "Laser Code Dating", *MBAA Technical Quarterly*, Vol. 17, p. 43, 1979.

Debossing

Debossing a code is done by pressing a sharp, hard faced type against the surface to be coded. It works with plastic items such as six pak can carriers on hard faced fiber cartons, i.e., can or bottle paks. With the advent of higher speed coding of individual containers the use of debossing has declined.

Slotting

Slotting or slitting is the most prevalent method of coding labels. Label coding is accomplished by sawing a series of slots in one or more of the label edges to effect the code desired. Decoding is accomplished by position on the label whether visually or with decoding guages. The labels can be coded prior to production, thereby keeping line downtime to a minimum. One of the machines used for coding labels is shown in Figure 18-4.

18-4. Label slotter.

The labels are clamped in the vice-like holder and are pushed across the rotating cutting blades. All cuts should be kept shallow and are made to one label edge with one sweep. Cutting blades should be kept sharp to prevent label damage.

Hot Stamping—Branding

Hot stamping is used to code plastic bungs. Colors, as well as codes, can be imparted into the bungs.

Branding is the burning of a code into a wooden bung by applying heated metal type into its outside surface (see Figure 18-5). Branding is done by hand, mechanically in a separate branding station or on the racking machine. The branding location is, therefore, dependent on racking speed and equipment. Additional coding can also be achieved using pre-colored bungs.

METHODS OF CODING—CONTAINER/PACKAGING

Packaging manufacturers use the following methods for coding:

18-5. Branded bung.

Glass—On bottom of bottle—date, location, mold number.

Cans—Generally date and time and line number printed on can.

Multi-Paks—The date of manufacture is printed or debossed. The name of the manufacturer and plant location is also shown.

Crowns—Generally only the manufacturer's name is printed on the skirt. Other pertinent information is printed on a label affixed to the box containing the crowns.

Labels—In each bundle the manufacturer usually encloses a tag identifying the type of label, customer's code, etc.

Cartons—The boxmaker's certificate is printed on the bottom panel showing specifications, name of manufacturer and location. Carton manufacturers can also print special information required such as for export or military shipments as well as construction information if requested by the customer.

Bungs or Keg Valve Covers—Information is either printed or stenciled on a label affixed to cartons containing material with customer's identification number, color code (if applicable) and date.

Universal Product Code—As explained earlier, this is for the retailer's benefit. It is preprinted on individual containers, as well as on labels, multi-paks and cartons. The UPC is a 12-digit bar code (see Figure 18-6) with eleven (11) of the digits printed in normal numbers. The number on the far left is the number systems character determined by the kind of merchandise being labeled. The next five (5) digits at left are the manufacturer's number; the next five (5) digits represent the package number designated by the manufacturer. The last digit is not necessarily printed in human-readable form and is a modulo check digit providing an arithmetic check to the scanner. At present, only the UPC number is being shown on the master cartons since the art of printing on corrugated has not been perfect to the degree needed for dependable scanning. This is expected to change in the near future. Further details can be obtained from the pertinent suppliers.

18-6. *Universal Product Code.*

LABELING REGULATORIES

Labeling of malt beverages for use in interstate commerce in the U.S. is regulated presently by the Federal Alcohol Administration Act of 1935 which evolved from the repeal of national prohibition.

Although alcoholic beverages are subject to the Federal Food, Drug and Cosmetic Act, jurisdictional control is currently exercised by the Bureau of the Treasury responsible for enforcement of the Federal Alcohol Administration Act and various revenue laws which relate to alcoholic beverages.

The 21st Amendment to the Constitution, which repealed national prohibition, also gives to the individual states exclusive right to regulate the importation and use of intoxicating beverages within their borders. In addition, various Federal and State revenue laws also regulate labeling for the purpose of revenue protection.

The basic mandatory label information required by Federal and most state laws includes the designation of a brand name and malt beverage class, name and location of producer and a statement of net contents. In addition to the basic information, there are numerous state and foreign regulatory provisions that require state or country identification, container deposit designation and alcohol content statements.

A short reference to Canadian label requirements at this point is also in order. The beverage class, i.e., beer, ale, wine, etc., must appear on the label in both English and French. The net contents must be stated in the metric system. Alcoholic strength must be indicated as percentage by volume. The name and address of the producer and country of origin must be shown in either English or French and the address must be sufficiently complete to insure mail delivery. All label copy on products for Quebec must be predominantly in the French language. Labels must be approved by the Canadian government.

The various regulatory requirements and their applications are far too numerous and complex for a comprehensive inclusion in this chapter. Accordingly, those who are responsible for label content are urged to review their product labeling with appropriate legal counsel or control agency. The U.S.B.A. has available a "Special Information" book in binder form which summarizes state malt beverage regulations by category. This includes labeling and can be obtained from the United States Brewers Association, Inc., Legal Department, 1750 K Street, Washington, DC 20006.

SUMMARY

We cannot emphasize enough the need for flexibility in labeling, coding and quickness of reaction to meet the changing demands that increased competition puts on the product and packaging. It is very important that the various interested departments work closely together. Proper understanding of label content and coding systems will help expedite execution of solutions to these problems.

CHAPTER XIX

WAREHOUSING & SHIPPING

BY JAMES C. ZIEGLER

INTRODUCTION

The warehouse and other facets of physical distribution in the modern brewery are of crucial importance. That importance has never been more evident than today.

Distribution, a term used to identify all activities associated with the warehousing, loading and shipping of final product, represents a significant factor in beer cost. The cost is higher for beer than for many other consumer goods. In addition to the brewery costs, the wholesaler operating costs are a major part of the total distribution cost. The cost factor alone dictates the need for careful planning and administration of the distribution function. As brewers compete with other industries for the best possible freight rates, the maintenance of tightly scheduled loading becomes paramount. Trucks and railcars not loaded on time represent significant costs in terms of idle time and demurrage.

In the recent history of packaging equipment evolution, greater and greater speed has been attained. Can line speeds in excess of 100 cases per minute are now common. This speed requires a parallel speed of activity in the distribution operation. The requirement for this increased pace has also contributed to more emphasis on the warehousing and associated operations.

Inventory represents working capital that is not working. The ever increasing competitive nature of the brewing industry has caused greater scrutiny to be placed on non-earning uses of capital. Inventory, therefore, must be held at a lower level than is sometimes convenient. This creates another pressure for efficient operation of the warehouse.

The factor that has had the greatest impact on warehousing and distribution has been the increasing number of identifiable packages. Marketing techniques and consumer purchase decisions have created the need for increased product segmentation which has resulted in more labels, more beer types, and more package types. In addition, tax requirements and the various deposit legislations have developed requirements for special lids and labels which add more packages to the distribution operation. Each "package" requires some sort of isolation in the warehouse. In this chapter, the term "package" will be used to mean identifiable type of packaged goods (e.g., 24 12-ounce, 3.2 Light beer in aluminum cans with ring-pull lids with an Oklahoma tax identification would be a "package").

TYPES OF WAREHOUSES

Brewery warehouses in the Americas vary greatly in size, shape, and function. Some are built using the latest state-of-the-art technology while others occupy buildings which may be over a hundred years old. They may be single- or multiple-story structures. Some are refrigerated; most are not. They are constructed of a wide variety of building materials. The list of variables is very long but the key to the successful, lowest cost operation is to ensure that the operating plan for the warehouse is carefully integrated into the physical plans of the facility.

Purpose

The purpose of the normal brewery warehouse is essentially to load the output of the brewery into vehicles for shipment to the customers. Within this extremely broad description, a series of complex interactions must be accomplished. The product must be received in the warehouse at a rate that avoids packaging line downtime. Adequate space must be provided to hold enough product to allow a smooth loading operation. Internal scheduling of product must be such that the right package is available at the right spot at the right time. The warehouse, in short, is far more than a simple repository for finished goods.

Building Configuration

Warehouses may be single or multiple story in design. Horizontal product movement is normally faster, more flexible, and less complex to plan than vertical movement, and where the brewery has the option, warehouses are usually built on a single level.

For many reasons, single floor operations are not always the appropriate configuration for the warehouse. Often, the brewer uses an existing older building which may not have been designed as a warehouse. Many breweries are located in places where the land for a single story warehouse cannot be obtained. The existence of multiple story packaging operation may also dictate a multiple story warehouse.

Multiple story warehouses use less land. Distances traveled in the loading process are relatively short. Product inventory may be isolated. In the refrigerated warehouse, the product in storage may be kept in cold storage while the loading area is kept at a more nearly ambient temperature.

The chief drawbacks of the multiple story warehouse have to do with product movement, normally by elevator or lift (which is simply a specialized elevator). This process is slower than horizontal movement by forktruck and/or conveyor. Since the beer is stored on one floor and loaded on another, multiple handling of the product is required, and each time the product is picked up, the potential for damage exists. In addition, the amount of labor required in the multiple level operation is greater; someone has to send the product from one level, and someone else has to receive it on another level.

The single story operation is simpler to run, due largely to the flexibility of operation of the forktruck (elevators obviously can only be operated where they are installed.) Product can be put into storage and taken out by the same people although this is frequently a specialized operation. The beer is normally only handled once as it is put into storage and once as it is taken out to be loaded. The loading area tends to be spread out much more than in the multiple story operation, adding complexity and cost to the operation; however, it allows more loading spots to be built, improving flexibility.

The "front-end cost" of the single level operation is greater than that of the multiple story building. More land is required and this is often a major consideration. The adage "it is cheaper to build up than out" also applies to warehouses.

Layouts/Method of Operation

Theoretically, the warehouse should conform to a specific plan for the loading of vehicles but in actual fact, the scheme for that activity is frequently dictated by the available warehouse configuration. While this may seem to be like the chicken-egg problem, the germane point is that the layout of the warehouse and the plan of operation are highly interrelated; the lowest cost operation will only be achieved when the plan and the layout are completely integrated.

Figures 1a-1c show how the typical layout of the warehouse supports the logic of loading. Figure 1a shows the most common and the most straight forward approach to brewery warehousing. In this approach, virtually all product is loaded from the storage area. No attempt is made to load directly from the packaging lines. The palletizers are grouped in one area for convenience of operation. Product flows from the packaging lines to that area and is assembled into unit loads on pallets. These units are then moved into the storage area. The loading area is located adjacent to the storage section of the warehouse for ease of access to the product.

The chief advantage in the flow-through-warehouse is the simplicity of operation. Communications are simple, direct, and subject to little error. This type of warehouse typically operates with a substantial amount of product in inventory.

Figure 1b shows a different approach. In this operation, the palletizers are more spread out. This facilitates the preassembly of the loads which is the basis of the operation. The design of this warehouse allows the appropriate product to be palletized near the loading area where it will be used. The product may be preassembled in the form of specific loads or (and more commonly) as rows of various segregated products in the necessary quantity to actually form the specific trailer or railcar loads.

This type of operation typically runs on about one day's inventory. The beer loaded on a given day is replaced in basically the same time frame with beer for the next day's schedule loading. The chief benefits are that the product is available where it is needed and that a relatively small inventory is required. Cross traffic in the loading operation is minimized as shown in the illustration. Scheduling is more critical in this operation, as the inventory level is not large, and specific quantities of the various products must be palletized in certain areas to correspond to scheduled loads. Packaging runs on individual products are typically shorter due to the fact that the inventory is smaller than in Figure 1a.

In Figure 1c another scheme is shown. In this plan, the goal is to load beer directly from the palletizers into the vehicles. This type of warehouse contains the smallest inventory. In theory, beer in storage represents a failure of the direct loading approach; however, some inventory is required to keep the loading operation functioning smoothly during machine breakdowns and to make available low volume packages. The palletizers are located at strategic points throughout the warehouse usually in close proximity to the loading area. Vehicles to be loaded are spotted as close as possible to the appropriate palletizers. This system maximizes the amount of beer that is handled only once. The need for warehouse space is cut to the minimum. Beer freshness is assured by having the absolute minimum time from packaging to loading.

The task of product flow scheduling is immense. The coordination of loading

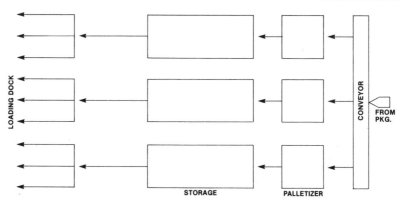

19-1a. Flow-through warehouse.

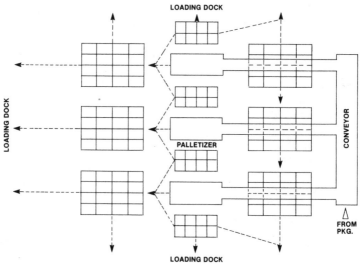

19-1b. Pre-staging warehouse.

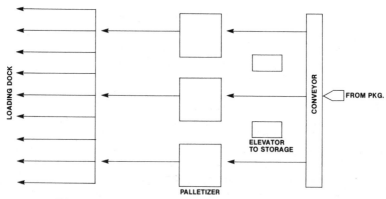

19-1c. Off-line loading concept.

vehicles resembles an air traffic control system at a busy airport more than anything else. The communications system has to be highly sophisticated and has to function very well. Each additional package type adds noticeably to the difficulty of matching vehicles, orders, and the appropriate product. Any variation in the schedule—such as packaging lines running faster or slower than planned, or trailers or railcars being late—or any mistakes in scheduling can spell disaster for a system that so closely ties the packaging and loading operators.

While there are other ways to run a warehouse, and other variations of the chosen examples certainly exist, these layouts illustrate the point that both the design of the warehouse and the logic of operation have to be considered in planning and developing a modern brewery warehouse. These examples also illustrate the diversity of approaches used today.

Refrigeration

Age and high temperature are the enemies of beer. The degradation of flavor that is associated with oxidation is accentuated by high temperature. Figure 2 shows the degree of oxidized flavor notes as perceived by a panel of trained beer evaluators on beer stored at 38°F and on the same beer stored at 70°F.

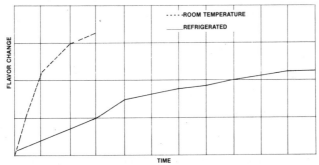

19-2. Effect of temperature and time upon perceived flavor changes.

Most brewers do not consider it necessary to refrigerate their warehouses, but if the brewer does decide to refrigerate the beer warehouse he will obviously incur greater operating costs. Thus he will want to minimize the size of the warehouse with insulation becoming a critical factor in the design of such a warehouse. While the amount of insulation required varies depending on prevailing climatic conditions, a reasonably well designed refrigerated warehouse will have an insulation value of at least R30.

GENERAL CONSIDERATIONS FOR WAREHOUSE DESIGN

A successful warehouse must be constructed with full consideration of many factors. The building should be big enough to support the plan of warehousing operation and the packaging operation. If the future plans for the brewery include expansion, room for expansion should be provided. The current trend toward package proliferation must be considered. The warehouse should be planned considering human factors: it should be light enough for safe easy operation, and ventilation should be good (if propane forktrucks will be used, extra ventilation capacity should be planned).

The layout of the building must support the scheme of operation. To that end a detailed material flow plan should be developed. In this material flow plan, all stops, changes of rates, changes of transportation modes, etc., must be planned for. The priority and method of internal communications should be included in the plans. In short, as nearly as possible, the entire operation of the warehouse should be carefully considered and, if possible, simulated in the planning stage of the development of a new warehouse.

The technology of physical distribution is changing rapidly. The long-term success of a warehouse may be increased by including flexibility in the design to allow the inclusion, as they develop, of new methods of beer handling and storage. For example, storage equipment that increases cube utilization is being developed and refined, providing high density storage. Computer adaptation can also supply significant aids in scheduling, inventory control and loading. Careful consideration of anticipated technological changes in the warehouse design will pay dividends in the future.

Loading Dock Configuration

The dock is the terminal point of the beer loading process. The importance of the dock layout and location is sometimes not considered, resulting in a poorly laid out dock which compromises the total warehouse operation.

In an operation that is designed to maximize the effectiveness of the warehouse, the loading dock must be as carefully designed as the rest of the facility. A great range of possibilities for dock design exist and a thorough examination of the operating plan for the warehouse will allow the brewer to select the most appropriate combination of the alternatives for his use.

Access to the loading area must be considered. The truck dock should be located as near as practical to either the road that serves it or, in the case of a hostling operation, as near the staging area as practical. The entry to the loading area should be large, clear and as straight as possible. For drivers who are not familiar with the loading areas it is important that the route be clearly marked.

A second consideration that is often overlooked is in the staging area adjacent to the dock. Trailers must be backed up to the dock and this maneuvering is often done by the over-the-road drivers. These tractors may be considerably less maneuverable than those designed specifically for the hostling operation. An extremely tight dock and staging area may also present a difficulty not commonly encountered by the over-the-road driver.

The type of dock employed has an impact on the difficulty of staging trailers at the dock. Brewers frequently use the sawtooth dock arrangement shown in Figure 3a. This arrangement allows the staging area to be smaller without the above mentioned maneuvering problems. The straight dock arrangement shown in 3b is also commonly employed. Its chief advantages lie in the ease of approach from inside the warehouse and in the efficient use of loading dock area.

Some method of communicating with the drivers must be developed. A check-in point is normally used. It should be accessible from the staging area to avoid confusion.

Dock ramp design is often not given adequate attention. The slope of the ramp is frequently too severe. If the ramp slopes away from the dock, special

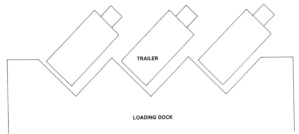

19-3a. Saw tooth trailer loading dock.

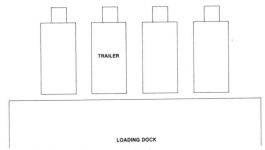

19-3b. Straight truck dock.

measures should be taken to avoid trailer rollout (particularly under icy conditions). The slope is sometimes toward the dock resulting in occasional damage to the trailers and in the problems associated with loading uphill. These problems are also made worse by damp cold weather. The slope toward the dock also creates drainage problems. A properly designed ramp has a slight slope toward the dock from the "dolly" wheels of the trailer to the rear wheels. From the rear wheels to the dock, a slight upslope is added. Some form of drainage is installed at the low point. If the ramp design is not proper, it will be a constant source of difficulty.

Rail dock design also can be done in more than one way. The plan must consider the method and frequency of switching, who will do that switching, the fit of rail cars into the loading scheme, the method of loading and the number of rail cars to be loaded.

Figure 4a shows a typical rail dock layout. In this system, rail car movement may be reciprocal (cars moved in and out on the same track) or it may flow through the loading area. The cars are pulled in, in a string, loaded, and pulled out as a string. Dock plates are movable to allow for less precise spotting and to permit loading cars of different lengths. The dock should be covered. A single track spur may be used, or a whole series of spurs with loading islands may be used.

A variation of the loading operation is the use of parallel spurs accessed from a single dock area as shown in 4b. In this operation, cars are staged on the two spurs so that the doors on the cars on the outer spur align with those on the cars on the spur nearest the dock. Both doors on the inner cars are opened and the doors that are nearest the dock on the outer cars are opened. Dock plates are first installed between the dock and the inner cars, and then

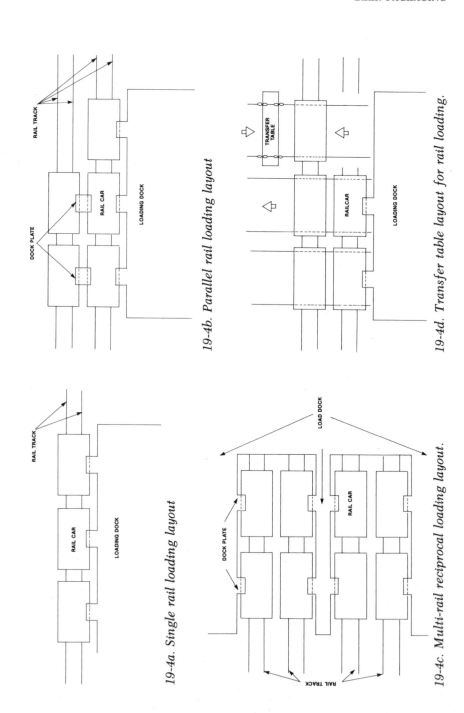

19-4a. Single rail loading layout

19-4b. Parallel rail loading layout

19-4c. Multi-rail reciprocal loading layout.

19-4d. Transfer table layout for rail loading.

a second set of plates is installed between the two parallel rows of cars. The outer cars are loaded first and the plates between the cars are removed. The doors on these cars are then closed as are the outer doors on the other cars. The inner cars are then loaded and closed. Both strings are then pulled and replaced with other cars.

Figure 4c shows another variation of this same approach. It allows the staging of many rail cars. Access to the cars is as shown, and two strings of cars can be loaded from one island dock area. This layout also lends itself to the use of fully covered loading areas.

In Figure 4d, a different approach is shown. This system is designed to support an operation for loading beer directly from the palletizers. Since a package that is part of an individual load may not be in inventory, its availability for loading is dependent on line efficiencies and on scheduled changes in the packaging lines. These variables combine to make it essential to switch out single cars in order to prevent down time at any individual loading spot.

Cars to be loaded are positioned on the inner rail of the pair shown. The car must be positioned precisely on the section of rail, as the dock plate is fixed in place and can only be adjusted vertically. The car is then uncoupled, and the "transfer table" is run into the dock using the electric motor on the table. When the car is run completely into the dock, the outer rail fits into the spur, again making it complete. The train can then access the rest of the spur. When a car is loaded, the table is run out, leaving the car sitting on an again complete rail spur. The car is then switched out, another put in its place and the whole process begins again.

While the first three illustrations show common and essentially generic approaches to rail dock layout, the fourth is obviously a highly specialized approach. It is designed to support an unusual loading scheme.

Climatic Consideration

The warehouse operation is exposed to the weather, and must be adapted to the prevailing climate. A great deal of inventive effort has gone into the development of doors that seal out the weather but do not impede forktruck traffic. There are pass-through doors, automatic opening doors, air curtains and many different sub types. Each of these approaches has its strong points and its drawbacks. The key element in the choice is matching the equipment to the needs.

Many loading docks are completely roofed. Vehicles are moved into place for loading and conventional outside doors are then closed. This approach offers the most complete solution to inclement weather. In some cases, when the warehouse is roofed, the whole loading dock area is heated. In other situations, the actual dock area is not heated and some sort of weather doors between the dock and warehouse allow the latter to be kept at an appropriate temperature.

While completely enclosing the dock offers an excellent solution to weather considerations, it is also expensive to build and maintain. Many brewers, therefore, opt for lower cost methods. A frequently used approach is to use door seals. These provide a seal between the loading dock and the vehicle to be loaded. This allows easy access to the vehicle with only minimal loss of heat (or refrigeration) around the door of the vehicle. These seals may be simple curtains, padded compressible seals, inflatable seals, or they may be adjustable fabric "walls" that bridge from the building to the vehicle. Equipment exists to fill virtually any need for this approach to weather isolation.

Another approach frequently used in conjunction with door seals is to install a partial roof over the door area of the dock. This roof may be no more than two or three feet wide or it may stretch out to nearly the full length of the vehicle. The purpose of the roof is to deflect precipitation from the doorway. When coupled with the door seal, this method provides excellent weather protection at a relatively low price.

Another factor to be considered in weather-proofing the dock is the placement and type of heaters. Breweries frequently have a great deal of relatively low grade steam available for heating; if not, other heat sources can be used. Such heaters are frequently placed above the loading door and provide a maximum of operator comfort at a minimum cost.

Ventilation

In addition to the requirements for heating, the warehouse must be adequately ventilated for employee comfort. The warehouse itself does not generate much heat as there is relatively little heat generating machinery employed. The dock layout may contribute markedly to the air movement in the warehouse. Elaborate systems are, therefore, seldom necessary but wall fans are often a welcome addition to the warehouse. The ventilation system should be designed so that an adequate volume of air is expelled from the warehouse so as to keep the air fresh and relatively cool without strong drafts in the area where people are working.

Propane-powered forktrucks create a more specific need for ventilation. The exhaust is nauseating and toxic; conditions can become intolerable in short order without adequate air flow.

Internal Communications Systems

Some means of communications throughout the warehouse is desirable. Various approaches are used. Systems range from having telephones located at strategic points throughout the warehouse to the use of highly sophisticated two-way radios. The nature of the loading operation dictates the sort of system employed.

If the loading operation is oriented to loading from inventory with only occasional direct off-packaging line loading, the communication system can be relatively simple. Loaders will normally be assigned one vehicle at a time and given a list of items to be put in a vehicle. The list normally tells the loader where to locate the pallet. When one order is completed, the loader will pick up another list and begin loading it. There is no need for electronic communications in this type of operation; it needs only face-to-face contact for direction.

As the scheme of loading seeks to couple a highly dynamic packaging operation to loading, a higher level of communication is required. Since most brewers deal with many different packages, orders frequently call for more than one beer or package type. The loader, therefore, will frequently have to distribute the output of a packaging line out into several different vehicles. As the size of the operation and the number of packages goes up, the need for constant communications goes up also. In a very large operation dedicated to a degree of off-packaging line loading, the communications system used will have to employ either two-way radios or two-way loudspeakers (a paging system).

As with most other decisions about equipment selection in the warehouse, there is no standard approach to communications. The system will be adequate only if it is integrated into the overall loading plan.

Regional-Warehouses

The brewer may develop a requirement for more warehouse space than is available on the plant site, and this need may be satisfied by the addition of a regional warehouse. Since this sort of facility adds a step to the distribution system, it also adds cost to that operation. That fact will usually make the use of regional warehouses temporary. However, since this sort of approach to distribution is often utilized, it is worthy of discussion.

In essence, a regional warehouse functions as a distribution center for a specified territory. The product is loaded at the brewery in the most expedient manner and sent directly to the regional facility where it is unloaded, held briefly in inventory and then used to make up specific orders for the customers of the brewery. The cost of the regional operation is partially offset by allowing very efficient loading at the brewery; beer orders can be assembled into single (or nearly single) package loads. This fact may allow direct, off-line loading to be done, permitting the regional warehouse to augment the capacity of the brewery warehouse.

Multi Plant Scheduling

The process of scheduling is complex even in a single plant operation. If the brewer operates more than one plant, the scheduling program becomes far more involved, and optimum performance requires the careful balancing of the factors of production and distribution from all plants. The constants assumed in scheduling of a single plant become variables when considering the output of several breweries.

On the plus side, the brewery operating more than one plant can utilize that situation to add flexibility to the entire operation. An alert, creative beer order and scheduling system can optimize the output of each plant. Plants can be scheduled to operate in such a manner that they compensate for each other's maintenance shut-downs and other production outages.

In application, the most practical approach to multiple plant planning is that of a central scheduling function. This system requires accurate input from all plants and from brewery customers. Armed with this input, the scheduling operation can generate a production plan that takes into consideration the variables of production, orders, maintenance, transportation availability and cost, as well as other factors.

In some systems, the market area served by a given brewery is essentially fixed. In other programs, the whole scheme is flexible with changing sources for a given product; in which case, the increased cost of scheduling must be evaluated carefully against the potential savings.

Canadian System

Product distribution in Canada is regulated by Provincial governments which differ somewhat in their attitudes: but in general the rules are formulated to control consumption and to protect tax revenues.

Quebec is the most liberal authority and permits sale for off-premise consumption in licensed grocery stores as well as liquor stores. Most other provinces allow off-premise sales through licensed hotel vendors and government liquor stores only.

Ontario has a system of Brewers' Retail Stores, which is operated by the Brewers Warehousing Company and owned co-operatively by the breweries in the province. This system is very cost effective and is particularly efficient in maintaining a high rate of glass return, greatly helped by the standard Canadian compact beer bottle. Brewers Warehousing also distributes beer to on-premise licenses. So do industry organizations in several other provinces, but they do not have retail operations. Nondomestic beers (including out-of-province brands) for home consumption are available only from government stores.

Brewery warehouses maintain inventories of packaged beer, palletized for shipment. Almost all shipments are by truck. In Quebec and Newfoundland where there are licensed distributors, their trucks may pick up loads. In most other provinces loads are moved either by the brewery's own trucks or by the provincial industry organization's trucks to warehouses for local distribution. The major breweries in Quebec maintain satellite warehouses of their own, but in Ontario this is done by the Brewers Warehousing organization.

In the western provinces, the system is similar to Ontario's, with each province operating its own industry co-operative trucking fleet to move beer to and from distribution warehouses. Some brewery trucks are operated in British Columbia in addition to the industry system.

Cost Control

The control of cost in warehousing and distribution is as important as it is in manufacturing areas. Chapter IV covers this subject in considerable detail, and the concepts of setting of standards of performance, reporting and follow-up developed there apply equally well to warehousing and distribution.

BEER ORDER SYSTEM

The beer order system is the method by which the customers communicate their product requirements to the brewery. It is extremely influential in the determination of the method of operation of the warehouse.

Most systems are oriented around a specified lead time with orders received on a pre-arranged day and time. The lead time between receipt of the order and actual shipment of the beer may be fixed or constant. An example of this is a system where orders are received on Friday of week 1 to be shipped beginning in week 3. This fixed lead time allows packaging schedules to be built up to an efficient operating level. It also requires customers to maintain enough inventory of each package to allow business to go on while the beer is in transit.

This system is very delicate but can be effective if the terms of the schedule are adhered to. The critical factors are customer inventory, brewery inventory, schedule accuracy, and the degree to which the schedules are met.

If the customer inventories are not held at the planned level, stockouts can be anticipated which can mean loss of shelf space and commensurate loss of sales. Efforts to avoid such stock-outs on an individual customer basis will result in the compromising of the brewery schedule, causing added cost and possibly shorting other customers.

The brewery inventory of packaged goods is an important part of the beer order system. If it is not developed properly, various packages will not be available at the appropriate time. This may force product substitution in order to allow vehicles to be loaded on time, or vehicles may have to be held until the packaging schedule is modified to provide the needed product. In either case, the customers and, in fact, the whole distribution system suffer.

The realistic scheduling of activities from packaging through distributor is of paramount importance. If the loading schedule and the packaging schedule do not match, the system will be compromised. This factor is far more important in a brewery operating with a small inventory than in one with a relatively large amount of stored product. The careful matching of schedules is a key element in the maintenance of a low cost operation. Each time the schedule must be changed, added to or subtracted from, cost is added and the system is disrupted.

Impact on Warehouse Operations

If inventory policies are established at reasonable levels and adhered to by both the brewery and its customers, the distribution of product can be accomplished at a scheduled pace at the lowest possible cost. If the customer lets the inventory drop, planning to have the brewery become the safety against stock-outs, the whole system is compromised. In this situation, the brewery finds itself in the position of trying to respond, on very short notice, to specific "emergency" situations for a great many customers. Schedules have to be changed frequently. The brewery can not be geared efficiently to this sort of activity as the size of its operation is so large. The economical operation of a packaging line is predicated on maximizing the length of time between beer and/or label changes; otherwise product runs may be very short and the operational costs may soar.

Another deterrent to the effectiveness of the beer order system is that resulting from last minute changes. If accurate orders are given high priority by the customers, they will be as accurate as possible and require few changes. This facilitates the best operation of both the brewery and its customers. If, on the other hand, orders are placed in a perfunctory manner, they will require constant last minute adjustments. As mentioned above, the brewery size of operation is simply not geared to constant, relatively small changes. On the other hand, to the degree that the beer order system represents a positive input to the orderly sequencing of brewery activities, the cost of operation can be minimized for both the brewery and its customers.

Beer Scheduling

Once the beer order is in, agreed to and finalized, it must be translated into an action plan. That plan is the packaging or beer schedule. The purpose of this plan is to give the necessary direction to the packaging and warehousing operation. This schedule details the beer type, label, volume, date and time of runs. When properly developed, this schedule will provide the right product at the right time to meet the beer orders and to maintain the appropriate brewery inventory.

Consideration is given in the beer scheduling process to transportation as well since vehicle availability is a very important facet of the overall loading scheme. From the standpoint of flexibility, the "from inventory only" loading plan has a clear cut advantage in that whatever vehicles are available, the necessary product is available also. In the line loading operation, however, both the vehicles and the product must be available at the right time, adding to the complexity of scheduling.

Breweries frequently find it necessary to maintain traffic or transportation departments to handle the negotiation for and coordination of vehicle supply. This dynamic activity is critical to efficient operation and is increasingly specialized.

Distributor Activities

Although some brewers deal directly with retailers, most of the output of the brewery is handled by distributors whose activities can be beneficial to their joint operation. A good relationship between the brewer and the distributor is essential to the smooth operation of the warehouse. The first area of impact is that of beer ordering. The brewery must compile all of the beer orders and develop the most productive packaging/distribution schedule that it can from them. Changes in that schedule, once it is set, can be very disruptive. Careful forecasting and accurate ordering are essential to a smooth, economical process.

The distributors are an important facet of the marketing effort. They provide detailed input on a great many questions pertaining to the marketing of the product. The constant contact that distributor personnel have with the retailers can provide essential information on product problems, package problems, customer attitudes and many other marketing related issues. As this information is collected, summarized and transmitted to the brewery, important decisions can be made with better data.

The distributor system can also be invaluable in trouble shooting and identification. Many problems with package appearance and function are difficult to predict at the brewery. Problems in the loading process are often not apparent until the product has been shipped. Package design is an area of major importance to the brewer, since packaging materials cost is the largest single item in the cost of goods. Unfortunately, packages that look good and seem to perform well at the brewery sometimes turn out to be less than adequate when subjected to transportation, changes in temperature and humidity and normal handling in the distribution system. Accurate and prompt feedback from the distributors is the first step to solutions of such problems.

PRODUCT MOVEMENT

Conveyors, a Common Approach

A major factor in warehouse operation is that of product movement within the facility. This movement may be categorized by its direction (either horizontal or vertical), and the methods to achieve this movement are varied and, again, should be tailored to the needs of the operation.

Warehouse operations generally favor a conveyor system for the movement of cased product to, and movement of palletized product from, the palletizing operation. These conveyors are critically important. Their configuration and design should be carefully developed to match the overall distribution system design. Several types of equipment are available.

Belt Conveyors

Belt conveyors are commonly used in the movement of cased and palletized product. This type of conveyor is simply a belt, held on either end by rollers. One of these rollers is normally driven by a motor through a gear box. Between these two end rollers, some sort of support is installed to carry the load. This support, normally, is furnished by either a solid plate or by other rollers.

The belts used on conveyors are designed to handle a variety of loads. The underside of these belts is normally rubber or rubber-like as a high coefficient of friction is required to allow the drive pulley to move the belt under a load. The bearing surface of the belt can be covered with many materials. The various "toppings" or outer surfaces of the belts allow matching the belt to its application. Canvas toppings, for example, are frequently used in full case conveying systems as they afford an adequate but relatively low coefficient of friction. This characteristic minimizes case damage in the event of a jam. Rubber grip toppings offering higher friction allow belt conveyors to be used for case goods on relatively steep inclined sections of conveyor.

In a brewery warehouse, belts are commonly found in widths from four inches to nearly four feet. The lengths can vary from around a foot to one hundred feet, the practical maximum length.

In general, belts require little or no maintenance once installed. They must be kept clean and the alignment (or training) of the belt is of critical importance. When a new belt is installed, its training is accomplished by adjusting both the head and tail pulleys until the belt runs absolutely true when in operation.

The solid plate supported belt type is called a slider bed conveyor. This sort of conveyor is very simple in design and, therefore, is generally quite reliable. The cost of the conveyor is low, due to the simplicity of design. The noise level of this conveyor is also very low. The application of this particular conveyor configuration is limited due to friction between the support plate and the belt. That friction results in moderately high belt wear and limits this type of conveyor to fairly short lengths and light loads.

The addition of support rollers instead of the solid plate allows a substantial increase in the capacity and longevity of the belt conveyor. The rollers facilitate higher speed operation than the slider bed conveyor. The rollers are equipped with bearings and these bearings are the first limiting factor in this type of conveyor. The use of precision bearings allows speeds of up to 400 fpm. Before that point is reached, the second limiting factor, case damage, is encountered. At these very high speeds, jams become catastrophic in very short order.

Gravity Roller Conveyors

Roller conveyors are also frequently found in brewers' warehouses. Many different sizes and configurations are available.

The simplest and lowest cost type of roller conveyors is the so-called grocery store type. In this design, the package is supported on a series of small wheels with ball bearings and uses gravity for motivation. This type of conveyor has long been used in operations that utilize hand loading. The chief advantages are low cost and flexibility.

A more commonly used roller conveyor incorporates full width rollers, usually with ball bearings. They may be driven in many different ways or they may be used in a simple gravity system. The rollers may be straight or may conform to other shapes. They may be used in complete roller systems or in combination with other types of conveyors.

The gravity application of this type of system is very straightforward. The rollers are supported in a framework and when enough drop in elevation is built into the system, the product is moved by gravity. This approach provides obviously a low cost operation once it is installed. While many applications can be found, this approach to conveying is limited to places that afford adequate elevation changes and is normally used in conjunction with other types.

Live Rollers

This conveyor system is an application of the roller conveyor design that is motorized. Live roller conveyors are more expensive to install than belt types. They are also noisier in operation than belts and require more maintenance. The life expectancy of these conveyors is very high. They cause little package damage in case of jams. They are capable of conveying heavy palletized loads reliably and when designed to do so can accumulate a great deal of product without allowing the units to touch each other.

Various types of timing belt drive rollers are commonly found in brewing operations. In this design, the drive rollers are connected by belts. The belts are mounted on pulleys attached to the appropriate rollers. In some designs, the pulleys are mounted alternately on both sides of the conveyor. A more concise design puts dual pulleys on the same side. The belts are then alternated on these pulleys. While this approach results in a narrower conveyor with less safety guards, maintenance costs are increased as belt changes on the inside pulley require the removal of three belts.

A second approach to live roller conveying uses a belt to drive the rollers. The belt is installed under the rollers and is held in contact with the rollers. As the belt is driven, it turns the rollers. This method incorporates a belt with a high coefficient of friction on both sides.

A third approach employs chains and sprockets to provide motive force to the rollers. In this system, the rollers to be driven have sprockets installed on one end. Chains, similar to bicycle chains, connect these sprockets so that all rotate at the same speed.

Chain Conveyors

In addition to the belt and roller conveying systems, chain conveyors are frequently used, generally on heavy duty applications such as palletizer outfeeds and for the movement of full pallets.

The chain conveyor is of rugged simple design. It normally employes two or three chains. The chains are supported and driven by sprockets. The chain itself is in contact with the pallet and as it is driven, it moves the pallet. This conveyor is normally used in relatively slow speed applications.

Turns

A conveying system is frequently required to make turns. The types of conveyors described above require specialized turns to be installed at the appropriate points in the system. While many types of curves are available, the use of tapered roller turns for cases is, by far, the most common in the brewing industry. These turns are normally formed by rails on either side with rollers machined to an appropriate taper between the rails. The taper provides for continuous support of the packages through the turn and also supplies a degree of "bank" to the turn. The continuous support prevents package damage while the "bank" helps keep the package on the conveyor.

Diverters or Derails

A specialized turn that is of great importance to the brewer is the derail. These devices are used to transfer product (normally cased product) from one conveyor to another. They are commonly employed to move cased product from some sort of express or general conveyor to an infeed conveyor on the palletizer.

Various types of gate derails are used. These are relatively simple pieces of equipment that can be moved across the conveyor, deflecting the case of product from that conveyor to a turn and then to another conveyor. These derails can be manually positioned or can be remotely actuated.

The gate type of derail is a very simple device that requires little or no maintenance and is reliable once positioned. Since the gate is inserted across the conveyor, package damage is a concern. This type of derail is not fast in operation and is used for continuous derailing only.

A second type of derail that is utilized in brewery conveying systems consists of a series of pop up wheels installed between the rollers in a section of roller conveyor. The wheels are set at an angle to the rest of the conveyor. When activated, they move up into the path of the product, and divert the cases off the roller conveyor. The wheel type derail minimizes package damage although it is dependent on friction to cause the package directional change. A high-speed system can be designed to selectively derail packages. This feature, coupled with case height sensing devices, allows the conveyor to be used for two different height packages at the same time.

The wheel derail system requires an exacting timing system to ensure that the proper packages are diverted. If light sensitive timing equipment is utilized, foil packages can cause malfunction by their reflective nature. The sophistication of this system makes it somewhat less reliable than the mechanical gate type of system.

Vertical Product Movement

Elevation changes are frequently necessary in any operation, especially in a multiple story facility. Lifts, designed specifically for palletized products, are frequently utilized in the warehouse for vertical product transfers. These are usually either continuous or reciprocating types. Freight elevators are sometimes used but these are unnecessarily expensive to install specifically for beer movement.

Continuous motion lifts offer relatively high rate of operation and are, therefore, attractive but are fairly complex in design. This complexity results in slightly higher maintenance cost and downtime than a conventional hydraulic recriprocating beer lift but the higher speed of operation offsets these drawbacks.

The more commonly used telescoping hydraulic beer lift is normally an extremely reliable piece of equipment. It is, in reality, simply an elevator tailored to the size and shape of the pallet and stripped of all unnecessary walls, doors, etc. It should be designed so that its capacity encompasses the range of pallet sizes and weights that the brewery anticipates handling with it.

The hydraulic lift is relatively expensive to install and is normally slower in operation than the continuous lift. When properly installed, the hydraulic lift is very reliable. An appropriate maintenance program will help to ensure trouble-free operation of the lift.

The Future

The technology of physical distribution is constantly being improved. Product movement equipment that will aid flexibility, speed and reliability to the warehouse in non traditional methods is finding its way into the brewery warehouse.

The automatic, wire-guided vehicle is in current use in other types of warehousing. This machine can be adapted to handle virtually any type of product assembled on slip sheets or pallets. The vehicle can be used to transfer product from point to point without any operator interface. Marrying the vehicle equipment with some existing sonar technology could result in a vehicle capable of actually loading beer automatically.

The heart of this system is a computer. Information about product flow and availability as well as destination and routing is stored in the computer and relayed to the vehicles through cables embedded in the warehouse floor. These cables are easily installed in any concrete floor. A saw cut is made in the floor, the cable installed and the cut is then sealed with an epoxy.

The wire guided vehicle can be adapted to many sorts of service, but perhaps the most attractive application for the brewery warehouse is the potential for replacing long conveyor runs with vehicles. This approach can be made to be very flexible. A cable network can be designed that incorporates many modes of operation and can be installed in sections or as a complete system. It can be added to as new needs are identified. The usage of the network is then controlled by the programming of the computer.

Air flotation is an approach to produce transfer/vehicle loading that may represent considerable savings to the brewery. While this approach is not practical for replacing conveyor systems, it does present some attractive possibilities for the loading of vehicles. In application, the load is assembled on the dock or a plate nearly the size of the trailer. When the assembly is completed, the whole plate with its load is driven into a waiting trailer. Air is then applied to the bottom of the slip sheets or solid pallets, raising the product slightly. The assembly plate is then withdrawn, leaving the beer in the trailer. (It is necessary to provide a continuous surface under all of the assembled units of product so that enough surface area is provided to facilitate the elevation of the product with relatively low pressure air.)

The advantages of this system include very high speed loading (the actual time that the trailer is required to be at the dock is only five minutes). The load can be assembled on the dock with very low amount of product damage and this assembly can be done very quickly outside of the trailer. This approach would also facilitate fully automatic loading as various existent conveying methods could be adapted to assemble the load on the plate according to some sort of programming.

Fork Trucks

Fork trucks are the backbone of the modern brewery warehouse. They are used for horizontal transportation in most cases in which flexibility of direction and activity are valuable. Because of the importance of these vehicles to the warehouse, they are described in more detail later in the chapter.

PALLETIZING

Pallet Assembly

The U.S. brewing industry warehousing is designed almost entirely for the use of palletized products. The packages may be assembled on various forms of pallets or on slip sheets. Assembled units may range from less than 60 to 234 cases per unit. These units are usually developed in a certain size to minimize the cost of loading, the amount of product damage, and/or the cost of transportation.

Packages are assembled into preset configurations on specialized machinery known as palletizers. This equipment is available in several configurations and functions, with capacities ranging from about 45 cases per minute to 120 cases. Various methods are employed to orient cases so that the assembled rows of cases on the pallet overlap each other to minimize case separation. In operation, the palletizer receives cased products from the packaging lines. This product is assembled into layers in a specific sequence. Each assembled tier is placed on top of the previous one on the pallet. When the correct number of tiers are reached, the palletizer accumulates incoming cases of product while the finished pallet is removed (usually automatically) from the machine. A new empty pallet is inserted and the process begins again.

A noteworthy variation of the palletized product/palletizer approach is illustrated by the use of slip sheets. This highly specialized system uses a high speed palletizer to assemble the unit of beer on a slave or captive pallet. The completed unit is transferred from the slave pallet to a belt conveyor and from there to a live roller conveyor. At the transition point between conveyors, a slipsheet is inserted completing the assembly of the unit. From this point on, the beer is handled by forktrucks equipped with specialized attachments.

Cases of beer stacked into pallet configuration without bridging to interlock the cases are very unstable. Movement by forktruck will cause the stack to separate and fall causing a great deal of damage; overlapping adds to unit stability. Palletizers are equipped with a variety of hardware that turns and orients each case in a preplanned fashion so that each case overlaps cases on the tier below. Figures 5a-5d shows various configurations in current use in the brewing industry. Figure 5d shows a configuration that is not solid all the way through. This pallet design fits the need for a specified size of pallet at a slight cost in terms of unit stability.

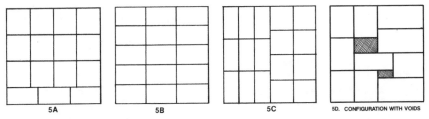

5A   5B   5C   5D. CONFIGURATION WITH VOIDS

19-5. Pallet configurations.

Unit design is very important. The way the units fit together has a great deal of influence on the amount of damage incurred. A tight fit across the width of a railcar, for example, will result in lowered damage from transportation but if it is too tight, the damage may be caused in loading. The ideal system permits just enough working space with a tight fit.

The height of the unit is of critical importance in the design for rail units. Rail rates are normally based on maximum gross weights, and the key to minimum rail rates is the maximum utilization of the railcar volume. Pallet or unit design must consider the planned loading method. If the product is to be loaded two high, the pallet height will have to be lower than if the units are to be loaded at a single height. Loading two high, may increase the opportunities for damage.

Pallet or unit height is also critical at the truck dock. Trucks typically are restricted to maximum gross and axle weights. The design of the unit must also consider the restriction in truck loading. The units must be light enough to fill the trailer as nearly as possible without exceeding the allowable weights. In some systems, pallets are designed separately for rail and truck. This, of course, allows maximizing the effective loads into both vehicles but also adds another level of complexity to the operation.

Unit Integrity Techniques

To the degree that the unit remains intact, damage to the product will be minimized. A great deal of effort and significant amounts of money have gone into the development of methods and equipment to improve the degree to which the unit remains intact in shipment. While the maintenance of the integrity of the whole unit is desirable, the control of as little as the top tier only may be adequate. There is little point in incurring the cost of full unit security if all that is needed is control of a single row. In some cases, simply tying a piece of string around the top row in the unit is adequate. This is sometimes done by hand but ingenious devices are available which automatically place the string around the unit, tie the knot and then cut the string.

Pallets may be strapped to prevent shifting. The straps are usually plastic and can be applied around the pallet either vertically or horizontally or both. The application of the straps may be done manually, semi-automatically, or put on with fully automatic equipment. The straps are applied under a reasonably high tension and provide excellent pallet stability.

Shrink wrap has found limited application in securing beer pallets. A plastic film is applied to the unit and then it is heated, causing it to contract. The degree of security provided is excellent but most shrink wraps are manually applied. As such, the use of this method is compromised by the high cost and low productivity.

Glue dots show great promise. These are simply small dots of special glue that are applied between cases of product on the pallet. The degree of security is variable since many different glues can be used. Some are so strong that the shifting of cases could be absolutely defeated. The main problems with the glue dot approach are that paper transfer occurs when the cases are separated and the glue holds dirt, spoiling the package esthetics. The use of non-skid varnish or coatings on cartons helps lateral stability without some of the problems of glue dots.

Stretch wrap is finding increasing application in the brewing industry. The resiliency of the wrap is controlled by the tension under which it is applied. The two most common methods for the application of the thin plastic film are the pass-through and the rotary methods. In the former, the film is stretched across the pallet and then seamed behind the pallet. An example of equipment for the automatic application of pass through wrap is shown in Figure 6a.

In the rotary approach the wrap is again a thin film. Figure 6b shows a semi-automatic rotary wrap system. In this approach the loose end of the roll of plastic is slipped between two rows on the unit. The whole unit is then rotated while the film is fed in at a controlled rate to ensure adequate stretch of the film. The roll of film normally moves up and down while the pallet rotates to cover the desired portion of the pallet. This sort of wrap may be applied in a fully automatic or in a fully manual method.

Other methods are available but are not commonly found in the brewing industry. The future will undoubtedly bring significant improvements to the technology of load stabilization.

STORAGE METHODS

Compatibility With Packaging Operations

The brewery warehouse is simply a buffer between the loading operation and the packaging lines. If packaging lines could deliver the required number of beer/label changes as needed, and if vehicles could be counted on to be available whenever desired, there would be no reason to have any product

19-6a. Pass through wrapper.   *19-6b. Rotary wrapper.*

in inventory. Since changes in the packaging operation are extremely costly, it is desirable to run as long as possible between changes. Vehicle availability is also a constant problem for most brewers. Breweries, therefore, maintain inventories varying from 30% of a day's production to nearly four times the output of an average day.

With a twelve-fold variation in inventory policy, it is obvious that any rule of thumb will have to be fairly broad. The policy concerning inventory is developed to minimize the cost to the brewery. With the extremely high cost of packaging operations as a major factor in that decision, this policy is typically developed to support the economical operation of that area.

Inventory Storage Methods

The physical limitations of the warehouse are, obviously, a factor in the determination of inventory policy but they can be partially offset by careful utilization of the available space. The height to which the stored product is stacked is a major determinant of the capacity of the facility. Most operations stack beer at least two pallets high, but many increase the utilization of their warehouses by stacking packaged goods three or more pallets high.

Floor loading may be a major consideration in the adaptation of an existing warehouse to a new storage plan. If the floors of the warehouse are not adequate to allow multiple pallet stacking, rack structures tying the major loading directly to main building columns may provide a partial answer.

Damaged Beer

In any beer handling operation, some degree of damage will occur. If the brewery conscientiously attempts to absorb its own damage before the packages pass to its customers, a certain amount of damaged beer packages will be generated. This damage is usually the result of breakage or leakage of containers resulting in the contents wetting and staining adjacent containers and cartons. This is often overlooked in a large beer warehouse but the annual value of damaged product can be very significant.

Damaged cases should be removed from inventory so they will not be passed on to customers. Examination of the volume of products so affected may reveal that repackaging of the undamaged portions of various packages may well be worth the cost. If the brewery maintains a program of selling beer to employees at reduced prices, a perfect outlet exists for the recovered undamaged product.

Inventory Control/Turnover

The brewery normally establishes an inventory policy that defines the maximum amount of time that beer can be held in that warehouse. A plan of product rotation as well as an inventory monitoring is also normally used. Policies on maximum age range from a low of seven days to over four times that long. Some breweries use different time allowance for different products and some have different policies for different times of the year. These policies are usually developed empirically based on perceived changes in beer flavor with age. The policy takes into consideration the amount of product necessary to support the loading plan as well as the economics of packaging scheduling and distributor inventory policies.

Product rotation is based on a plan of first-in, first-out. Some method of product dating is usually used, and careful monitoring of the package dates will keep product from becoming "lost" in the warehouse. This effort to ship oldest product first is extremely important in the maintenance of product freshness.

Inventory is checked in most breweries at least once a day. This process is usually done on a form to ensure that all necessary information is supplied each time the inventory is taken. The use of a form also aids in the interpretation of the information supplied. The inventory sheet is an important scheduling planning tool as well as the key to maintaining proper product rotation.

Product Segregation

Breweries in the United States face the problem of handling an increasing number of identifiable packages or shipments. Since as many as 700 of these packages may be held in a single warehouse, a system must be devised for the separation and retrieval of products.

1. Dedicated area storage

In some operations, this product segregation is accomplished by dedication of certain areas to certain products. This approach has the advantage of simplicity. Very little communication is required as the people moving beer know where it is to go all the time. A disadvantage of this approach is that space utilization is not at its best. Each product type requires some working space which may be anywhere in the warehouse. No attempt is made to put the product near the place where it will be loaded, causing extra forktruck traffic.

2. Semi-dedicated storage

A second approach might be dubbed semi-dedicated storage. In this method, major beer types are assigned sections of the warehouse. Within that assigned area, all labels associated with that beer type are stored. For example, light beer might be assigned a certain section of the warehouse, and that area is then subdivided further into sections for 3.2% and for "high" alcohol. Each label and container requirement creates new packages and each of these must be kept separate. In this approach, these separations are made within the dedicated area.

Since the floor space is available for whichever labels are produced under the given product type, less idle space is employed. This method retains most of the simplicity of operation of the fully dedicated warehouse. The utilization of cubic capacity is compromised as the sales ratios between major beer types vary, changing the required amounts of product types in storage while the floor space allocation is not flexible. Working space for each beer type is also required. The same problem with the travel distance in the loading process that the fully dedicated warehouse exhibits is still present in the semi-dedicated one.

3. Semi-random storage

A third, commonly used, approach is based on semi-random storage. In this technique, the warehouse is generally marked off in rows which simply indicate the places that beer can be stored. The assignment of rows is fully flexible and will change frequently. For ease of relocation, the rows are usually given some sort of alpha-numeric designation. Row A-22 might contain premium, 3.2%, pull-tab, 12-oz. cans on a certain day. Until that beer is shipped, it will remain in A-22. When it is shipped, the row may be reassigned to a completely different package.

This system has the advantage of excellent utilization of warehouse space. With its high level of flexibility, this warehouse layout lends itself to the storage of beer near the dock section where it will be needed for loading. This approach requires a higher level of coordination of loader activities and beer placement. Loaders have to be instructed as to where to get each pallet of beer necessary for each load. Several loaders may well be taking beer from the same row at the same time. A continuous updating of the warehouse inventory is essential if periods of loader inactivity are to be avoided. Proper package date rotation is also dependent on the continuous inventory update.

4. Fully Random Storage

A fourth approach to warehousing that has not yet found much application in the brewing industry is that of fully random storage. This method is not practical without special equipment that facilitates the inventory and retrieval of stored product. The tendency toward greater and greater numbers of "packages" will make this high density random storage approach more attractive in the future.

Although manual entry systems can be developed to utilize random storage, the full value of this system can best be realized through the use of an automatic storage and retrieval system. In general, the warehouse in this system consists of steel racks for storage for full pallets, resembling a honeycomb. The rack forms the substructure of the warehouse, and the exterior walls of the building are framed by simply covering the racks. The control of inventory is accomplished through the use of a sophisticated computer system. The structure of the building and the nature of the computer program facilitate a plan for fully random storage.

5. Block storage

The placement of aisles within the beer storage area in a conventional warehouse is of significant importance. Access to both the dock and the pallets must be ensured. Improper aisle location can add greatly to the cost of warehouse operation through extra travel and congestion.

The warehouse normally has designated routes through the storage areas and these routes define the area available for beer storage. The high number of "packages" has tended to cause storage to be in rows of palletized product inserted into and withdrawn from the end of the row. Where relatively large volumes of individual products are warehoused, the product is stored in solid blocks with no working space between rows of pallets. One aisle is kept open and product is withdrawn either from the front of the row or from the side. As product is removed, the aisle moves through the block of product. As beer is removed, more is placed in the area vacated. The aisle, thus, moves through the block and then returns to the starting point to begin again.

STAGING/LOADING

Types of Vehicles

Beer is *generally* transported in railcars and in closed (van) type trailers. Within this basic description, there are many variations of length and height. Some beer is shipped in insulated railcars, some is not. Some trailers are refrigerated, some are not. Despite the wide variety of equipment used, problems and methods are very similar for the industry, overall.

Trailer/Railcar Staging

Some method of getting the full trailers pulled from the dock and empty ones staged must be provided. In any size operation, this requires a schedule. The absence of such a schedule results in a very uneven loading effort, unnecessarily increasing the cost of loading. This schedule, once developed, is also useful to the truck line dispatcher in planning driver schedules and backhauls. A mutual good effort on the part of the trucking companies and the warehouse will help ensure trailer availability when it is needed.

Some breweries maintain full time hostling operations with remote trailer drop lots. Others have all trailers staged at their dock by the driver of the truck. Still others use a combination of the two. Once again, the system has to be designed to meet the needs of the individual brewery.

Railcar staging is also critically important. Normally, agreements with railroad companies are developed whereby car inventories are maintained and switched into the loading dock by the railroad. In at least one case, the brewery maintains its own rail switching operation. In this operation, the railroad simply brings in empty cars and picks up full ones from the brewery marshalling yards. The details of this operation are tailored to the requirements of the brewery.

The first step in loading is to open the doors and insert some sort of dock plate. Figures 7a - 7c show various approaches to entry to railcars. Figures 8a - 8c show docks used for trailers.

Movement of Product to Dock

Once the vehicle is staged and the method of access established, it is necessary to get the beer to the loading area. The most common method is to use the forktruck to pick the beer up in the storage area and transport it directly into the vehicle. A variation of this approach seen in breweries that load beer directly from the packaging lines is to convey the cased product to palletizers located on or near the dock. The beer is then taken from the palletizer outfeed and loaded directly by forktrucks.

Load Security

The units of packaged beer are subjected to enormous forces during its movement to its destination especially beer shipped by rail. It is therefore, essential that the units be loaded well and held securely in the vehicle. Many methods are used to accomplish this task.

Railcars used for beer transportation normally have bulkhead doors as shown in Figure 9a. These are moveable partitions that can be secured against the load to prevent movement. Various types of filler material are often inserted into voids in the load to prevent shifting. Inflatable bags are sometimes put into gaps and inflated to hold the beer stationary. Some railcars are equipped with side panels, as shown in Figure 9b, which can be positioned to take up

19-7c. Extension type dock plate.

19-8c. Hinged truck dock plate.

19-7b. Dock plate for transfer table.

19-8b. Hydraulic lift used at truck dock.

19-7a. Removable rail dock plate.

19-8a. Removable truck dock plate.

19-9a. Bulkhead doors.

19-9b. Side panels.

19-9c. Floater panels.

the empty spaces in the car. Figure 9c shows that moveable end panel in an air pack car. This equipment is known as a floater panel. In this car, the beer is loaded against this floater panel and secured with the bulkhead doors. Air pressure is then applied to the bladder behind the floater panel causing it to expand against the load. When this is done, the product is held very securely. An air reservoir holds high pressure air and releases it through a regulator into the low pressure bladder to compensate for minor leaks or changes in altitude. In another application of this type car, a battery powered compressor keeps the air panel expanded.

Beer is commonly loaded into railcars two or three pallets wide and one or two pallets high. The tighter the load, the less damage from transportation. Pallet configuration is often designed to fit the car as tightly as possible and to minimize the amount of space that must be taken up by filler material. Lengthwise voids cannot be allowed, and side voids must be kept to a minimum.

Load security in trailers is accomplished by less exotic measures as trailers are not normally subjected to the severe handling that rail shipments are. The most common means of securing loads in trailers is by installing load locks. The beer is loaded tight to the front of the trailers and when the last pallets are placed in the rear, the load lock is installed across the vehicle, about ¾ths of the way up the pallet and in contact with the beer. The load lock will then help prevent the beer from shifting to the rear of the trailer, and little or no damage will occur.

In addition to load locks, various types of filler material are used to fill voids in trailers. This material may be in the form of specially made sandwiched cardboard spacers, knocked down cardboard cartons, inflatable bags or other materials as in railcars.

Methods of Loading Beer

While handloading is still a viable option in some applications, the forktruck is truly the workhorse of the brewing industry in terms of beer loading. With the appropriate attachments, palletized beer is loaded into cars and trailers efficiently and with a minimum of damage.

The brewer should examine the vehicles that will be used to transport beer with an eye toward obtaining the lowest possible cost of transportation. This effort will mean loading as near as possible the maximum weight that the vehicle can legally hold without significant product damage. Some sort of diagram is frequently used to show the beer loader where to put which packages. These may be sophisticated diagrams showing the exact location of each pallet or they may be simply a list of all commodities in the vehicle. The important factor is that the loader knows how to put the product in the vehicle and what types of product are required to complete the load.

Rail Loading

Different brewers have found different solutions to rail loading. Beer is commonly loaded two or three pallets wide. It is sometimes stacked two high, but is more commonly loaded at single height. Special height rail pallets are sometimes utilized to allow loading the beer in a manner that facilitates maximum usage of the railcar's cubic area. By carefully planning the rail loading process, the brewer can load the car to its maximum allowed weight. Loads of over 7,000 cases of 12 ounce cans can be loaded into 60 foot railcars in some applications.

Truck Loading

Truck loading requires a somewhat different approach. Trucks are governed by maximum weight regulations. In many locations, maximum weights per axle are established. Special diagrams can be developed empirically to allow the maximum amount of beer to be loaded without exceeding the legal limits prevailing over the planned travel route. If many different vehicle types are routinely loaded, a computer program can be developed to design load schemes that will maximize the beer volume but avoid overweight trailers.

Beer is normally loaded two units wide and single height in trailers. Depending on pallet weight and other factors, it may be necessary to put single pallets in certain places in the load to avoid excessive axle loading. The voids created require dunnage.

Kegs

Kegs present special problems in beer loading. They are less stable than other packaged goods. Because of their shape, pallets of kegs do not interface with other packages as securely as desired.

Keg load security can be accomplished through the use of keg boards. These are normally thick plywood sheets, often cut to conform to the curve of the keg, that are intersticed between rows of kegs. Kegs can also be stabilized by tying, wrapping or strapping them. In vertically stacked kegs, this is more important than in the horizontally assembled keg pallet which is inherently more stable.

Wholesalers frequently require less than full loads of kegs. When these loads are assembled, the problem of interfacing kegs with other packages must be addressed. Some sort of stiff partition is normally inserted between the kegs and the packaged beer to keep the load intact. Heavy cardboard bulkheads do this in an acceptable manner.

Kegs in mixed volumes in trailers add a degree of complexity to the development of an acceptable loading diagram. Since the weight per cubic volume of palletized kegs includes substantial empty space, kegs weigh less than packaged beer at the same height. Kegs are frequently loaded first in the mixed trailer load to provide maximum security and to minimize the need for separators between kegs and other packages. Another factor to be borne in mind is that the inertial forces developed in braking are greater than that of acceleration.

Beer Loading by Forklift

The operation of the forktruck in the beer handling/loading system requires a significant amount of awareness and skill. The potential for product damage is high. If slipsheets are utilized instead of pallets, this potential is made even greater.

The operator of the forklift is the key individual in the loading system. He must maintain alertness in the face of a highly routine job. He must also be aware of several important safety/quality rules and must have a highly developed skill level in the operation of the forklift and its hydraulic system.

When an operator arrives at the loading area, several checks should be made prior to entering the vehicle the first time. The dock area must be clean and well lit. The floor must be dry and free of oil. The dock plate must be checked to ensure that it is installed properly. If the vehicle to be loaded is a trailer staged at the dock, it must be chocked and jacks or other emergency support must be positioned to catch the trailer in the event of dolly collapse.

The inside of the vehicle should be inspected as a vehicle in poor repair can cause enormous product damage.

The next step is to review the order or load diagram. The loader must be aware of how the mixed beer type pallet sizes will fit together in the vehicle. In the absence of a detailed diagram this skill can become very important.

Once the sequence of product is determined, the loading can begin. As each pallet or unit of beer is picked up, the loader must verify that the product is what the order calls for. Failure to do this step will result in the wrong packages being shipped, and that can often be a costly mistake.

As the operator approaches the pallet to be loaded, he must ensure that his forktruck is square with the unit. The attachment can then be inserted under the unit. Once this is done, the unit should be raised slightly. A momentary pause will assure control of the pallet of beer. The forktruck can then be driven to the loading area with the attachment only high enough to avoid hitting anything with it. In most warehouses, 3-4 inches is about the correct height.

If practical, the forklift should be driven in reverse to afford the clearest possible view. The loader must be careful not to exceed a prudent speed and must be particularly cautious when turning corners. When the forklift is carrying a full pallet of beer, its center of gravity is altered and it is much less stable than when it is unloaded.

Entry into the vehicle must be smooth. If the operator doesn't consider this fact, he may "drop" into the vehicle, dumping the product. As the entry is accomplished, the load should be shifted to the side away from the vehicle wall to avoid scraping the packages as the forklift moves down the vehicle.

As the loader approaches the area where the pallet is to be deposited, he must square the unit up and carefully align it so that it fits exactly where it is supposed to. If the loading is being done two high, the attachment should now be raised to the appropriate height.

The next step is to deposit the pallet in its designated place. As the operator backs away from the unit, caution must be exercised to ensure proper positioning of the attachment. Too steep an angle on the attachment will cause the pallet to be moved and possibly damaged.

The final step is the loading process in the securing of the product. This may be done in many ways. The operator must be aware of how the load security equipment is installed or activated and must conscientiously install or position it. The various methods of load security were discussed earlier in this chapter.

Vibration Damage

In some cases, despite the most careful loading effort, the beer still arrives at its destination with substantial damage. This can be an enormously frustrating problem for the warehouse. Rough handling in transit is usually blamed for this mysterious damage. In many cases, the beer *has* suffered from rude handling but in others, the operation of the railroad is blameless.

Fairly subtle vibrations incurred while the railcar is in motion have been demonstrated to cause significant can damage. This is particularly evident in the relatively new thin wall aluminum cans. The lower column strength of these cans renders them particularly susceptible to this form of damage.

· This type of damage is most commonly seen in the bottom rows of cans. In theory, the vibration experienced in transit causes the cans to separate and come together thousands of times while the car is in motion. This movement and contact eventually causes fatique in the can walls, resulting in failure. Since this damage occurs most often in the bottom of rows, this failure creates the potential for the collapse of other packages in the unit, adding to the damage.

SUPPORT OPERATIONS

Beer Availability/Coordination

Within any warehouse, some means must exist to ensure that beer required for each load is on hand when it is needed. Beer packaging schedules must be developed and altered to provide this desired volume of each product when it is needed. Schedules are developed some time before the need, showing which beer types and packages will be run and when. These schedules are normally based on customers' orders.

A second portion of scheduling concerns itself with the coordination of vehicles to carry the scheduled product to its destination. Loading must be spread out so that it occurs at a pace that avoids major periods of inactivity when loaders are available. Failure to do so results in loaders having periods of nothing to do, followed by periods when more vehicles are available than can be loaded. Both of these situations are costly.

Even in its simplest form, this package/vehicle/loader scheduling function is complex. In a system that attempts to maximize the amount of beer loaded directly from the packaging lines, the scheduling function can be a major effort in itself.

In cases where loading is from inventory, a significant amount of beer must be held in inventory. Experience generally dictates this volume, although it can be calculated (various types of computer simulations are available to determine desired inventory levels).

Orders from customers are generally received a specified number of days in advance of the time the beer will actually be loaded. Orders are then consolidated into the total required for each package for the time covered by the order period (frequently a week). Once the number of each package type required is known, and how much on hand, a preliminary packaging schedule can be developed. This consolidation allows maximizing the lengths of packaging runs and improving the overall efficiency. In the determination of packaging runs for each type of product during the schedule interval, care must be taken to ensure that adequate product is available for loading between runs of that package. The inventory of a package should cycle from a point approaching no inventory while it is being produced to whatever must be available for shipping during the periods of no production.

Packaging lines and their ancillary equipment occasionally break down or run slower than anticipated. If this happens and an adequate safety margin in inventory has not been planned, the loading plan may be seriously disrupted. On the other hand, too large a safety margin results in a need for excessive warehouse space and keeps unnecessary capital tied up in finished goods. A prudent inventory plan falls between the two extremes.

If the variable of some direct loading from the packaging lines is added to the beer scheduling function, the complexity of that function goes up sharply. If it is deemed desirable to develop the entire loading systems around the concept of direct off-line loading, the scheduling becomes even more complex.

In such a system, the warehousing area becomes smaller and is used primarily for low volume packages, overruns, and other packages that cannot be loaded directly.

Scheduling for the off-line loading deals with each vehicle as a separate piece of the schedule. Times must be assigned to the vehicle so that the components in the load will be running on packaging lines while the vehicle is at the dock. When this is impossible the schedule must be arranged to pre-run part of the load, and then fit the vehicle into the loading schedule when the rest of the packages are running. Obviously, to the degree that pre-running is done, the concept of direct loading is defeated. Just as obviously, with today's large number of packages, it is frequently impossible to match the packaging and loading schedules exactly.

Where the individual vehicle is pre-assigned for a certain destination, another level of complexity is added since the specific trailer has to have a specific load that can be assembled and loaded only at a designated time. Any delay in the arrival of the truck creates a major difficulty for the warehouse. This precision of scheduling requires exceptional cooperation between the trucking companies and the warehouse.

In off-line loading, it is imperative to have a number of unassigned vehicles available to load. These unassigned vehicles (railcars and trailer pools) allow continued adjustments of the loading schedules. If a package type is available before the assigned vehicle is, then unassigned vehicles can be loaded with that product, thus loading ahead of schedule. Without this flexibility, every deviation in any of the many factors influencing package or vehicle supply would force product to be stored in a warehouse not designed to hold it.

Order Communication

In a warehouse designed to load only from inventory, the packaging operation is essentially decoupled from the loading operation. Barring major problems in the packaging area, the inventory acts as a buffer allowing the two operations to function independently. In this system, order communication is normally kept as simple as possible. The loader may simply pick up an order that tells where the vehicle is located, what packages go into the vehicle, and where those packages are located. The order will often specify the sequence in which the commodities are to be loaded and may also indicate the placing of single units in the vehicle to avoid axle overweight. Scheduling can be controlled in a fairly straight forward manner. The control of the flow of beer to the loading dock is essentially a clerical function wherein load orders are developed as vehicles are available and, as much as possible, should coincide with the preplanned loading schedule. As one order is completed, the next one is begun.

In a warehouse that seeks to maximize its off-line loading, the communications with beer loaders is more complex. With several beer loaders working at the same time, a system must be defined that either ties the loader to a packaging line, having him load the output of that line into as many vehicles as require it; or it ties him to one vehicle at a time, requiring him to pick up whatever packages compose the load. In the latter case, the loader must travel to the output station of the necessary packaging lines and then to his vehicle. In the former case, the loader travels from one line output station to any loading spot in the warehouse. In either case, communication with loader must be very dynamic and it must be of high quality as a myriad of mistakes are possible.

In the off-line loading scheme, the coordination of the flow of product is more complex. Since there is little inventory to serve as a buffer, even minor changes in packaging line speeds, equipment failure anywhere in the system, late trailers and many other problems must be compensated for. The scheduling of product loading has to be updated on a continuous basis. The people handling product flow must constantly juggle these factors. The communications system has to be capable of handling the moment-by-moment decisions that this system requires. Voice communication is essential in this system due to the complexity of the messages that must be exchanged, and the most practical approach is using two-way radios.

In practice, most warehouses off-line load only the product that can be loaded without the extreme effort described above. This plan cuts the labor and required inventory somewhat. However, the amount of beer that can be loaded this way is normally quite small relative to the total amount scheduled.

Supplies Handling

Another responsibility often assigned to the warehouse is the receipt of incoming supplies. There are variations in which Packaging handles incoming cans and bottles while Purchasing receives the rest of the supplies, but in many breweries the warehouse handles both these responsibilities.

If the can plant is an integral part of the packaging operation then the warehouse has little to do with incoming cans. In many plants however, incoming cans are received in bulk and depalletized in the warehouse. In this operation, palletized cans are received by truck, and the pallets are placed by forklift on the depalletizer. The tiers of cans, separated by cardboard sheets, are swept off the pallet and conveyed to the can line.

New bottles are often received in bulk in the same manner as cans. The depalletizing is accomplished in the same way. Bottles may also be received in pallets of reshipper cases and after depalletizing are conveyed to an uncaser which separates the bottles from the cases prior to the bottle rinser. The empty cases are then conveyed around the packaging operation to bottle packers for refilling.

In some breweries, the pallets of incoming glass and cans are received on trailers equipped with motorized beds. These trailers use a special receiving dock near the depalletizer that has a fixed automatic conveyor that matches up to the one in the trailer, and the pallets of bottles or cans are then moved by use of these conveyors from truck to depalletizer. A variation of this system uses a retractable conveyor that connects the depalletizer with the trailer. This feature allows forktruck traffic to use the dock when bottles or cans are not actually being unloaded.

Power Outages

Power outages can occur and do occur with some regularity in certain geographic areas. The warehouse, due to a generally low level of natural light, can become extremely dangerous at the moment the lights go out. If precautions are not taken, jam ups and other problems occur when power is lost and then regained. If the packaging line operation is on separate power source and continues to run, for even a few minutes, while the warehouse is shut down, the results could be very serious. If the power is distributed so that lights are lost but equipment continues to run, the outcome could be catastrophic.

Due to the above and other possibilities, warehouses are often equipped to at least allow an orderly shutdown in the event of a power failure. The provision for this safe cessation of activity is usually in the form of emergency lighting. These lights are either battery powered or fed from an auxiliary power source.

In some operations, extreme measures are taken to avoid the problem caused by a power outage. These may include high speed power switching equipment and prioritized load dropping schemes. In the prioritized load dropping or shedding process, key equipment and lights are kept operational while less essential equipment is shut down to lessen the load. Effort is commonly made to ensure that if the lights go off in an area, the machinery there will stop also. Fork trucks are normally equipped with headlights. Packaging line operations and warehousing functions are often supplied power from the same source.

FORKTRUCKS/ATTACHMENTS

Nearly any discussion about warehousing turns, at some point, to forktrucks. These machines are used in nearly every application of material handling. Their small size and relatively great lifting capacity coupled with their mobility makes them essential in the day-to-day operation of the warehouse.

Forktrucks come in a large variety of sizes, shapes, and capacities. In addition to this variety of standard features, many of the manufacturers and dealers will do custom work, tailoring the unit even more closely to the needs of the purchaser. Some units are ridden while others are controlled by a standing operator. Several types of walking units are also used. Forktrucks with four wheels are most commonly used but three-wheeled vehicles are also employed. Most brewery warehouse operations use lifts with two or three stage masts. These masts are commonly available in 100- to 150-inch raised lengths although masts are found with raised lengths of up to 200 inches.

Capabilities/Capacities

A wide range of lift capacities are available. Since increased capacity costs more and because higher capacity trucks are longer and less maneuverable, care should be exercised in matching warehouse requirements with forktruck capacities. Maneuverability can be particularly critical in the loading of beer in railcars. Heavy pallets of beer demand larger trucks while narrow doorways make the size of the forktruck very important.

Forktruck capacities are measured in terms of the weight that can be lifted to full extension. The weight of the attachment that will be used must be considered as part of the weight that will be lifted. This can be critical as some attachments weigh up to 1,500 pounds. The capacity is normally specified at a defined load center which is measured from the face plate out (normally 24 inches). Forktrucks with capacities from 2,000 to 5,000 pounds are commonly used in brewery warehouses. Capacities of up to 8,000 pounds are used for some special applications.

The turning radius of the forktruck is another very important consideration in the selection of a forktruck. Extremely sharp turn angles have been engineered into the modern forklift; in some the steering wheels can be turned to angles of more than 80 degrees. The effective turning radius of the lifttruck is influenced by the overall vehicle length. For this reason, it is prudent to try a new type or model of forktruck before buying.

Power Sources

Forktrucks are commonly powered by gasoline, propane or batteries. (Pallet jacks are also used occasionally and these are normally manually operated.) Each type of truck has some advantages, and the warehouse operation should be considered when determining the power source.

Gasoline powered forktrucks have an obvious drawback for warehouse operations. The exhaust of these units is toxic and beer loading requires a high level of forktruck activity. The use of this power source would require a great deal of ventilation of the warehouse. Since this is very costly, the gasoline powered truck is not normally found in an indoor warehouse operation. Beer warehouses are normally served by propane or electric units only.

Propane trucks are also internal combustion engine operated but are frequently chosen for use in beer warehouses. The exhaust is less toxic and moderate ventilation is adequate for operation. The major advantage of propane units is lower initial cost than electric units as no batteries or chargers are necessary.

Electric forklifts are used extensively in the brewing industry. They are ideally suited for operation in an enclosed warehouse from the standpoint of noise and exhaust. They require expensive batteries and chargers must be installed. Labor is required to change the batteries. Battery life greatly influences the economics of electric truck operation. Five years of use is fairly normal but carefully maintained batteries can last seven years and longer, greatly reducing the cost of operation.

Electric forktrucks use a wide variety of battery configurations. Voltages range from a low of twelve (on some small walkalongs) to seventy-two on the very large trucks, but most batteries are either thirty-six or forty-eight volt. These batteries are normally rated for 500 to 675 amperehours.

Forktruck batteries can be recharged from a fully discharged state to fully charged in approximately six hours. The discharged battery will have an electrolyte specific gravity of 1.15. When the charge cycle has been completed, that reading will be 1.25. Battery life can be greatly enhanced by ensuring that the batteries are not charged more times than necessary. It is, therefore, a prudent practice to have the battery charged only when the appropriate specific gravity has been reached.

Forklift Hydraulic Systems

Forktrucks have great flexibility of operation, and much of this flexibility is due to the range of motion afforded by the various hydraulic systems. The mast can be moved to either side (side shifting). The mast can be tilted forward, backward, extended, and the attachment raised and lowered on the mast. This all important movement is normally hydraulically actuated.

The hydraulic system commonly used consists of a hydraulic reservoir, at least one pump, hydraulic plumbing, control valves and various slave cylinders. A simplified schematic of a typical hydraulic system is shown in Figure 10.

When slip sheets are used instead of pallets for handling beer, the hydraulic system is required to perform the additional functions of gripping the slip sheet and activating the push-pull unit. (A push-pull unit is shown on Figure 11c.) Because of this additional load, experience has shown that a second hydraulic pump is advisable. Without the second pump, the hydraulic fluid simply gets too hot.

Forklift Attachments

Attachments for forktrucks are available in an extremely wide range of designs and capacities. The brewing industry uses many of the available attachments. Figures 11a-11f show six types that are used most commonly.

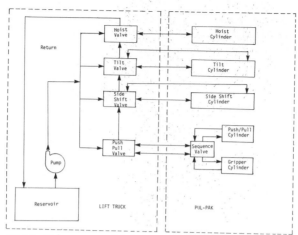

19-10. Schematic of lift truck hydraulic system.

Speed Of Operation

Warehouse efficiency is heavily influenced by forktruck speed. It is imperative that these trucks be able to move and lift at a rate to match or exceed the requirements placed on them by the loading scheme. It is also obvious that there is no point in paying for capacity that will not be needed.

Rates or speeds are normally expressed for several different functions. The speed at which the truck will move is normally expressed in miles per hour loaded and unloaded. The layout of the warehouse influences the requirements in this area. A single story warehouse with long runs from the beer supply to the loading area will require more speed from the truck than will a multi-story operation with concise runs from elevator to dock. Operating speeds in the 8-9 mile per hour range are commonly specified. The units will normally be about a half a mile per hour slower loaded than unloaded.

The rate at which the unit lifts is also specified. Trucks can be expected to lift empty in the 100 to 115 feet per minute range. Adding a full load to the forks will cut that rate by about 40 percent.

The unit will normally be constructed so that it lowers more slowly than it raises. Rates 70-85 feet per minute are common if the forks are empty. That speed can be expected to increase due to the additional pressure on the hydraulic system if the truck is loaded. Loaded lowering speeds are about 15 percent faster than empty.

Reliability

A forklift in the shop is not contributing anything to the operation. In fact, a vital part of the loading scheme is missing whenever unscheduled maintenance is required. The key elements in maintaining good service on forktrucks are proper equipment selection and appropriate periodic maintenance. Properly selected equipment should require very little unscheduled maintenance. Considering breakage and periodic maintenance, the warehouse should expect the fork truck to be operational approximately 95% of the time, and scheduled maintenance should not exceed 3%.

Tires

Tires are obviously very important to the operation of the forktruck. They

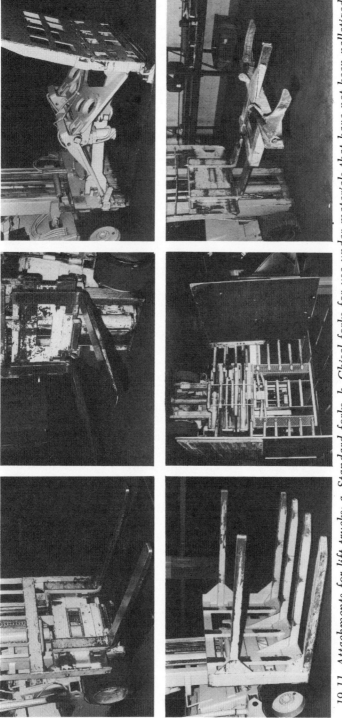

19-11. Attachments for lift trucks: *a*. Standard forks. *b*. Chisel forks for use under materials that have not been palletized. *c*. Push-pull unit for handling product assembled on a slip sheet. The flat, solid blade is called the platen and the vertical pusher plate is called the pantograph. The hydraulic gripper bar is used to secure and pull the lip of the slip sheet. In the hands of a skilled operator, this unit permits very precise handling of loads. *d*. Kegs forks to handle vertically stacked kegs. The fork shown can handle 18 kegs at a time. *e*. Bale clamp *f*. Barrel or drum clamp used in support operations permitting easy gripping, transportation and dumping of containers.

are the means of movement of the truck and transmit the load weight to the floor. Both pneumatic and solid tires are used in the brewing industry. A general preference for solid tires is seen in the actual beer loading function. They have proven to have adequate shock absorbing qualities and tend to have a greater life expectancy than pneumatic tires. With available steel or fabric impregnation, solid tires stand up well to the rigors of rough floors, heavy loads, and the abuse of driving over dock plates.

Tires that have been properly matched to the application can be expected to give excellent service. Tire life can be greatly extended by observation of a few simple rules:

1. Keep floors clean. Debris is a basic enemy of tires. Running over solid objects with solid tires on a heavy lifttruck can severely cut the life of tires. There are many types of powered sweepers and scrubbers to keep floors clean and free from debris.
2. Keep the tires away from excessive heat. Abnormal heat breaks down the tire compound and must be avoided.
3. Keep the truck wheels properly aligned. Tires can be worn very quickly if they are not properly aligned. Improper alignment causes a scuffing of the tires that wears them out very rapidly.
4. Avoid contact with oil, grease, etc. Many chemicals can damage rubber. Prolonged contact with these substances can cause a breakdown of the tires.
5. Operate within the load rating of the tires. Severe damage can occur when overloading is allowed. Tires will split, separate and be cut by the wheel rim when they are overloaded.
6. Don't leave the forktruck standing loaded. Severe "squaring" of tires can result if the truck is left standing with a load on for long periods of time. This can result in abnormal stresses on the tire and cause a bumping at each tire revolution.
7. Ensure adequate periodic maintenance on the trucks. Many problems will be discovered by the P.M. inspector. In addition, regular P.M.'s will ensure proper lubrication which should avoid the tire drag associated with improper lubrication.

These fundamental notes on avoidance of tire damage, coupled with a high level of driver awareness can contribute markedly to extended tire life. It is easy to overlook this aspect of lift truck operation as being of minor importance. A program that results in minimized operational costs for forklift operation is, however, a series of minor items carefully monitored and controlled.

Although forklift tires come in a wide range of sizes, brewery warehouse truck tires usually are 18″ diameter for the drive wheels. The width of these tires is chosen to properly distribute the weight of the load and to lend stability to the truck. The steering wheels are normally smaller, about 12 inches in diameter and are narrower than the drive wheels.

Safety

No discussion of forklift operation is complete without a mention of safety. The very nature of these vehicles makes them so potentially hazardous that unusual care must be taken in their operation. Complacency is the cause of most forktruck accidents, and yet the repetitive nature of operations done with them lends itself to that complacency.

These machines operate at a relatively high rate of speed and are enormously heavy (a 5000 pound electric unit with battery will weigh about 10,500 pounds.) These factors combine to provide extremely high inertial forces. Since the vehicles are unsprung, the full force of that inertia is expended in a collision.

The attachments utilized with forktrucks tend to be relatively sharp. With the force for the truck behind these attachments, they can easily be driven into and through many things that might cross the path of the truck.

For these reasons and other obvious ones, it is imperative that some fundamental safety rules be followed. The following list outlines some basic rules:

1. *Don't overdrive* the vehicle. It is often capable of going faster than its brakes and the driver's reflexes can handle safely.
2. *Don't* use the seat brakes or hand brakes to stop the vehicle. These are emergency brakes, designed to hold, not to stop the vehicle.
3. *Don't* drive with the load elevated. Pick the load up just enough to allow it to be moved. This keeps the unit much more stable and allows maximum visibility.
4. *Drive backwards* as often as is practical. The view through the masts, over the load is always obscured to a degree. The view the opposite direction is always clear.
5. *Never* operate the vehicle with more than one person on it. Forklifts are designed to carry just one operator. Allowing the vehicle to be operated with more people on it is asking for trouble.
6. *Stop the truck with the attachment on the floor.* This practice will ensure that you know what is under the attachment.
7. *Keep the warehouse floors clean and dry.* Wet, slick floors are enormously dangerous to forktruck operation. Skids and loss of control will result if the floor is not properly cleaned.
8. Ensure that adequate periodic maintenance is performed. In addition to improved performance, a good P.M. program will uncover problems before they result in accidents. Periodic maintenance will also help to keep oil leaks under control and that will aid in the effort to keep the floors clean and dry.
9. *Never* operate the truck with more weight on it than was designed to carry. Serious instability can result if overloading is allowed. It is also possible for the unit to fail mechanically under severe overloading.

Electrical forklifts require that special care be taken of the batteries:

1. Avoid overcharging the battery. A serious explosion hazard can exist where proper care is not taken in the charging of the battery.
2. Avoid short circuiting the battery. The greatest danger of explosion of the battery exists if the battery is shorted out. If that explosion occurs, its force is considerable, but the greatest hazard comes from the acid which is thrown all over.
3. Don't drop the battery. The battery is very heavy (2800 pounds for a 48 volt battery). This weight alone can do a great deal of damage. The danger of released acid also exists in the case of a dropped battery.

MAINTENANCE OF THE WAREHOUSE

Cleaning and Sanitation

The brewery warehouse is part of a food plant. Sanitation has to be considered as important in the operation of that facility as in the rest of the plant. Warehouse activities can supply enough nutrients to allow the growth of a substantial number of insect pests if beer spills are not taken care of.

Routine clean-up can be overlooked in the rush to load beer, but the successful warehouse operation includes details such as sanitation. Cleanliness promotes safety in the operation. The warehouse is highly dependent on the forktruck for its successful operation, and the forktruck is vulnerable to damage from debris as well as from wet or oily floors. A wide variety of power sweepers or scrubbers are available, frequently battery powered with voltages ranging from 12 to 36 volts. They can be controlled by either a rider or walking operator.

Too often, clean-up is relegated to a specialized crew and is done only once a day. While the once-a-day clean-up needs to be done, spot clean-up is also important. If the warehouse people are made aware of this importance and are instructed to clean up immediately, the potential for accidents will be reduced, and the overall pride of the workforce will be enhanced.

The warehouse is usually a relatively large area with many low traffic spots, and if a concerted clean up/inspection program is not maintained, the low traffic areas will soon become storage spots for everything imaginable.

Lighting/Visibility/Painting

Warehouses tend to be large buildings with few windows since sunlight is harmful to beer. Most of the lighting is artificial. Unless a conscious effort is made to ensure a brightness, the floors, walls, and equipment will absorb the available light resulting in a dim, dungeon-like effect and the potential for accidents is increased. The dimness also detracts from the mental alertness of the people working in the area, adding to the potential for accidents.

In an effort to combat the problems associated with poor lighting, warehouse managers frequently have routine inspection programs to ensure that the lights are kept functioning. Walls and columns are often painted white or light yellow. Columns are frequently striped to increase their visibility. Forktrucks are commonly painted bright colors to add to their visibility.

PERSONNEL

The key element in any operation is the people that perform the work and the supervision that directs that activity. The selection of people to fill these jobs is of paramount importance. If the process of selection is left to chance, the consequences could be very serious. A detailed treatise on the employment process is beyond the scope of the chapter. A few generalizations are worthy of note, however.

Since the warehouse operation is frequently spread out over a significant area, the supervisor will have to control the crew and the operation without being able to observe much of the process at any one time. This fact argues for supervisors that have excellent communication skills. Because of the nature of the operation they must also be able to handle many types of activities simultaneously and it is essential that they be able to make decisions quickly and competently.

Once people are hired the task of training begins. It is imperative that this facet of employment not be left to chance. The employees in the warehouse may operate high speed palletizing machinery and most of them will drive forktrucks at least part of the time. Improper handling of this equipment represents enormous potential for serious accidents. The quality of the product can also be compromised, and considerable cost added to the price of doing business by carelessness in the handling and loading phases of the operation.

Although many approaches to training are used, the successful ones have several factors in common:

1. The program identifies the objective of the training and the necessary skills for the operator. It evaluates the needs of the individual trainee and is structured to fulfill those needs.
2. A standard set of references (such as procedures,) is used to ensure that training for all people is done on a uniform basis.
3. Progress is monitored and documented carefully. Reasonable standards for performance are established and the trainees are measured against those standards in an objective manner.
4. The training includes a mix of hands-on training and theoretical information. The trainees must gain adequate skills through the training but must also receive insight into the whys of the operation and the equipment used.
5. Adequate reference material should be provided to the operators to answer questions and to allow further study.

SUMMARY

The warehouse function in the modern brewery is an extremely important part of the operation. It utilizes a significant portion of the money expended in the production and packaging of the product. A serious effort to maximize the effectiveness of the operation can result in the judicious employment of these allocated resources.

From the enormous number of potential approaches and the equipment possibilities, the combination that best meets the needs must be selected. To the degree that this decision considers and blends the operational aspects of the distribution program with those of ordering/scheduling and the actual equipment design, the warehouse operation will be successful. Where these factors of production do not match, the entire operation will be compromised.

In the process of determining how the variables will fit together, consideration must be given to not only the type of facility to be run, but the impact of the beer order system and product quality considerations on inventory policy as well. Once these most basic determinates are clear, the loading scheme can then be carefully defined.

The activities of movement of product, palletizing, and storage are supported by various specialized types of equipment. The careful analysis of the details of the warehouse operation will reveal the most appropriate equipment. Continued monitoring of changes in requirements and technology will allow operation of the warehouse in the long run in the most cost effective, quality maintaining manner possible.

Within the warehouse operation itself, activities to control and update the inventory and match loading schedules with packaging schedules are required. The manner in which these operations function must be in concert with the capabilities of the warehouse system and with the overall plan of operation. Where the fit of efforts and capabilities is good, the operation will be the beneficiary.

The workhorse of beer warehousing is the forktruck. Many types are available. Each has some strong points and some drawbacks. Careful attention to the many factors at play in this critical equipment selection area will result in a smooth, reliable loading operation. The forktruck offers extreme flexibility through the many available attachments. These must be evaluated and matched to the operation to maximize their benefit.

Attention to detail is essential in the operation of the warehouse. By its nature the facility is prone to become a catch-all. Its highly repetitious nature of operation can cause its people to fall prey to habit, resulting in failure to adapt to changes in the overall operational plan. If all of the factors of production are not integrated fully, the operation will always be slightly "out of focus." Only through continued effort and objective evaluation of the operation can this highly dynamic part of the brewery serve its function in the best possible manner.

ACKNOWLEDGEMENT

The author wishes to acknowledge the contributions of Andrew Leith and his associates at Carling O'Keefe Breweries of Canada for the section on the Canadian system of beer distribution.

In addition thanks are due to William Rammes, Joseph McDevitt, Henry Zarnichi, John Peluse and Norman Kuhl for helpful discussions and for the suggestions they made during the preparation of the manuscript.

Section 6

CHAPTER XX

SOFT DRINK OPERATIONS
BY ROBERT F. RISLEY

INTRODUCTION

Both breweries and soft drink plants make use of common or similar technologies. The science of package handling is a common technology. Beverage filling is a similar technology in the two industries. The factors that must be considered in the design of a soft drink facility are shown in Figure 20-1.

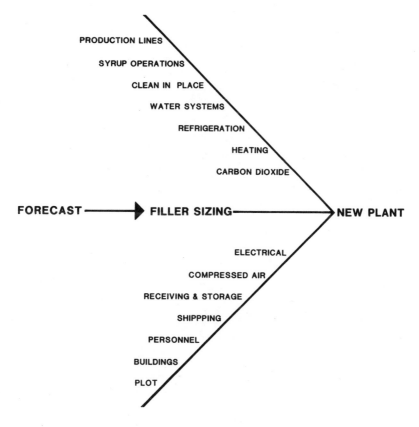

20-1. Factors in a soft drink plant design.

449

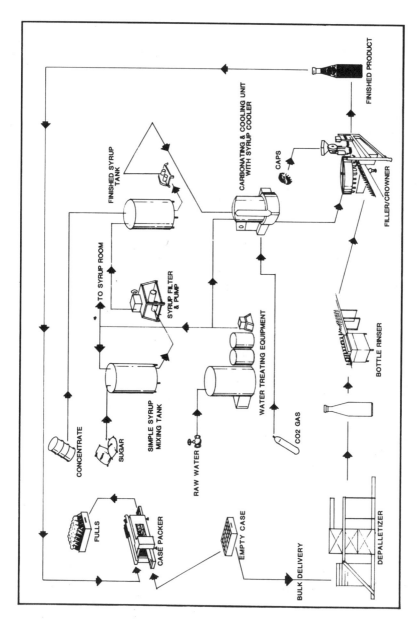

20-2. Process flow chart.

The differences between the beer and soft drink industries lie in the area of ingredient processing. The prime ingredients of soft drinks are water, sugar, carbon dioxide gas and flavorings. This chapter contains discussions covering these prime ingredients, with the exception of flavorings. Flavor concentrate preparation is proprietary throughout the soft drink industry.

The manufacture of soft drink carbonated beverages is a complicated procedure comprised of several steps as shown in Figure 20-2. These steps require special care to assure that the product is clean and sanitary. Various ingredients are gathered together to make the finished product. The ingredients for carbonated soft drinks are syrup, made from sugar and water, to which a small amount of suitable acid and flavor is added. This mixture is blended, carbonated, cooled and packaged. Purified water and purified carbon dioxide gas are used in the process.

WATER TREATMENT

Water treating methods are selected to suit the specific needs of the location of the soft drink facility. Water quality is of utmost importance and consequently much effort is put into analyzing the local water and designing/selecting the best water treating methods to assure good quality water. Typical water quality standards are:

Appearance	Clear
Organic Matter	None
Taste	None
Odor	None
Color	5.0 ppm (max.)
Turbidity	1.0 ppm (max.)
Total Dissolved Solids	500 ppm (max.)
Chlorides (as Chloride)	250 ppm (max.)
Sulfates (as Sulfate)	250 ppm (max.)
Iron (as Fe)	0.1 ppm (max.)
Total Alkalinity (as $CaCO_3$)	50 ppm (max.)
Free Chlorine (as CIO)	0.0 ppm
Nitrates (as NO_3):	25 ppm (max. bottles)
	5.0 ppm (max. cans)
Fluoride	1.0 ppm (max.)
Manganese	0.05 ppm (max.)
Zinc	5.0 ppm (max.)
Copper	0.05 ppm (max.)

Bottling plants draw their water supplies from many different sources. Deep wells, shallow wells, reservoirs, rain catchment systems, lakes and even the oceans themselves are potential sources of useable water. Whether the bottling plant has its own well or whether the water supply comes from a modern municipal treatment plant, each individual water supply presents its own particular problem. Deep well water is usually constant in chemical and bacteriological characteristics, but has a tendency to pick up mineral salts from the underground strata through which the water passes. Shallow wells and surface supplies such as rivers, lakes and streams are usually the easiest sources to tap but are affected by weather conditions and are more easily contaminated or polluted. Rain water collected in catchment systems is relatively pure. The

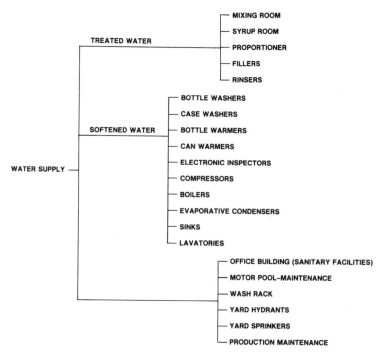

20-3. Water systems in a soft drink facility.

only dangers lie in the pick-up contaminants, such as airborne bacteria, wind blown debris and factory combustion materials in the air.

Municipal treating plants cannot be depended upon to supply properly treated water that could be considered suitable for bottling use. The main reason is that municipalities treat the water so that it is safe to drink. They cannot afford to produce water of the outstanding quality needed for producing high quality soft drinks with good shelf life. There is also the possibility of further contamination of city water as it passes through the pipes from the municipal treating plant to the bottling plant. This is particularly true with respect to organic matter and iron content.

Potential Problems

The potential problems presented by these water sources along with general effects on the finished beverage can be broken down into three main groups:

Physical

Physical discrepancies in the water such as turbidity, color, odor or taste have an almost immediate effect on beverage flavor or appearance. All turbidity, color, odor and off-taste must be removed. Turbidity in the water can also cause foaming problems, either at the filler while the beverage is being bottled or later when the bottle is opened by the consumer.

Sanitary

Harmful microorganisms or conglomerations of organic matter in the water can have an effect on the taste and odor of the product and can cause unsightly sediments to develop.

Chemical

There are many chemicals and minerals present in water supplies which have an adverse effect on the beverage. When they are present in large quantities, they must be removed. High alkalinity, for example, can neutralize the delicate acidity of the beverage, lessening its tang and making it susceptible to spoilage. High salt content can change the taste of the beverage and cause appearance problems.

Treatments

To safeguard against these problems, all water used in preparing syrup and beverage must be treated. The extent of treatment will depend upon the analysis of water samples and consideration of the water source.

Bacteriological standards demand that the water is free of all coliform and other pathogenic organisms. The general water treating processes for bottling and syrup making water include superchlorination, coagulation with alkalinity reduction, treatment for high solids water and demineralization.

Superchlorination

With established water supplies of outstanding quality, treatment consisting of superchlorination with two hours retention, and sand filtration, carbon purification and final polishing can prove sufficient. This system has very limited application, however, and is only used where extensive history shows a low solids water with excellent physical and microbiological quality. These conditions must be present in the water as it is received in the bottling plant.

The incoming water flows into a retention tank holding a minimum of two hours supply of bottling and syrup making water. Here it receives super-chlorination (dosage sufficiently high to yield 6 to 8 parts per million free available chlorine at the outlet of the sand filter). After the rentention tank, the water flows through a sand filter, carbon purifier and polisher.

This type treatment can handle simple bacteriological contamination and partial iron removal. Taste, color and odor are also removed by the carbon purifier.

As a measure of security, it is advisable to construct the retention tank in such a fashion as to allow it to be converted to a coagulation tank should a water problem develop at some time later.

Coagulation With Alkalinity Reduction

With most water supplies, a complete coagulation treatment plant is necessary. The plant consists of a coagulation tank allowing alkalinity reduction and superchlorination with two hours retention, a sand filter, carbon purifier and final polisher. Experience has shown this to be the most acceptable treating system for bottling water. It cannot, however, treat brackish water or water high in chlorides or sulfates.

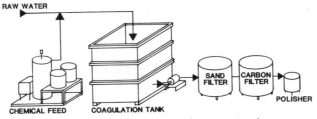

20-4. Schematic for coagulation treatment of water.

The water flows into a coagulation tank holding a minimum of two hours supply of water, where it receives a dosage of chlorine, coagulant and lime. The coagulation tank is followed by a sand filter, carbon purifier and final water polisher.

Water treating chemicals normally used are ferrous sulfate or alum (as coagulant), lime (for pH adjustment and alkalinity reduction) and chlorine (for sanitation). Calcium chloride is added when the water contains sodium alkalinity.

This equipment, when suitably sized and correctly operated, is capable of handling such diverse conditions as excessive alkalinity, iron and manganese removal, turbidy, color, off-taste, oil traces, hydrogen sulfate and the destruction of organic matter. The limitation is that coagulation systems cannot be used for removing chlorides and sulfates.

Treatment For High Solids Water

For water with exceptionally high solids or brackish water with high salt content, either demineralization, distillation or electrodialysis equipment is usually recommended. All three methods are costly and in most cases must be accompanied by supporting equipment.

Demineralization

Demineralization equipment usually consists of two pressure tanks each containing a different ion exchange resin. These resins have the ability to remove ions such as sulfate, chloride, calcium and sodium depending on the type used and the method of regeneration.

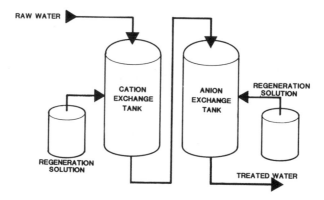

20-5. Schematic of water demineralization.

The first tank normally contains a cation exchange resin which uses a strong acid for regeneration. This cation exchange resin removes calcium, manganese, magnesium and sodium. The second tank holds anion exchange resin which uses caustic or another strong alkali for a regeneration. The anion exchange resin removes alkalinity, chlorides, sulfates, nitrates and free carbon dioxide. The most common use of demineralization plants is with water moderately high in solids.

The demineralization plant can only remove salts and cannot be considered complete water treating equipment. It should normally be supported by a coagulation type water treating plant as used with normal water supply.

PROPORTIONING/CARBONATING/COOLING

Following the establishment of treated water of satisfactory sanitary, physical and chemical character and finished flavored syrup, the next step in soft drink production is proportioning/carbonating/cooling.

Proportioning is the term used for blending finished syrup and treated water in the correct ratio as directed by product standards. One common method of proportioning is by use of the flow control system proportioner. The unit consists mainly of two equally large glass reservoirs, one for water and one for syrup. Proportioning is based on the fixed head over orifice principle. Pre-cooled water is delivered to the proportioner through an air operated valve. The infeed rate is controlled by a float. Syrup is introduced through an air operated valve and controlled by float. Water and syrup are accurately proportioned by maintaining fixed heads over water and syrup orifices. The water orifice is adjustable to provide convenient and fast Brix changes. Syrup orifices are available in a wide range of fixed sizes and are interchangeable for specific ratios and flow rates. A third reservoir maintains a level of proportioned mix prior to the carbonator.

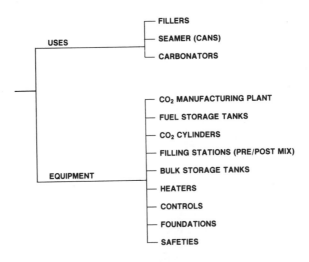

USES
— FILLERS
— SEAMER (CANS)
— CARBONATORS

EQUIPMENT
— CO_2 MANUFACTURING PLANT
— FUEL STORAGE TANKS
— CO_2 CYLINDERS
— FILLING STATIONS (PRE/POST MIX)
— BULK STORAGE TANKS
— HEATERS
— CONTROLS
— FOUNDATIONS
— SAFETIES

20-6. Carbon Dioxide distribution system.

The next phase of this operation is the carbonation and cooling of the proportioned product. Carbonation is the act of dissolving carbon dioxide gas in water under conditions of favorable temperature and moderate pressure. The carbon dioxide in the beverage, or carbonation, furnishes an identifying characteristic. The amount of carbonation most desirable in beverages depends on the type or flavor of the beverage. It is a generally accepted fact that suitable carbonation is important because of the sharp acidic taste it imparts to the beverage, plus its beneficial physiological effect on the digestive system.

General standards for carbon dioxide:

Compressed CO_2 Gas

Gases:	% by weight
Carbon dioxide	99.87 (min.)
Nitrogen	0.05 (max.)
Oxygen	0.009 (max.)
Sulfur dioxide	None
Hydrogen sulfide	None
Carbon monoxide	None
Water vapor	0.070 (max.)
Odor	None
Yeast	None

The amount of carbon dioxide used is expressed in volumes. One volume is the amount of gas that a given quantity of water will absorb at atmospheric pressure and a temperature of 60°F. Since the carbonation of a beverage provides sparkle and life, maintenance of the correct volume of gas is important and brings out the flavor. A well carbonated beverage should contain from three to four and one-half volumes when bottled, depending on the type of beverage.

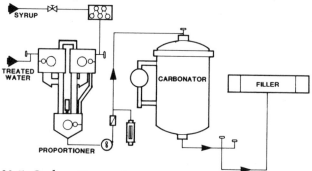

20-7. Carbonation system.

The cooling of the carbonated beverage takes place in the carbonator tank which contains refrigerated plates under a carefully controlled atmosphere of CO_2. During operation the syrup mixture enters the tank and is evenly distributed over the refrigerated plates by distributing troughs. Product level in the tank is automatically controlled by probes located in the sight glass. Product transfer to filler is effected by high carbonator tank CO_2 pressure working against a lower filler bowl pressure.

SYRUP OPERATION

The manufacturing of syrup is one technology that differentiates the soft drink industry from the brewing industry. The syrup contains the sweetening agent, the flavoring ingredients, essential oils and fruit juices. The syrup is diluted to the final desired concentration by adding water in a unit called a proportioner to yield the finished beverage. This mixture of syrup and water is carbonated and placed into bottles or cans to go directly to the consumer.

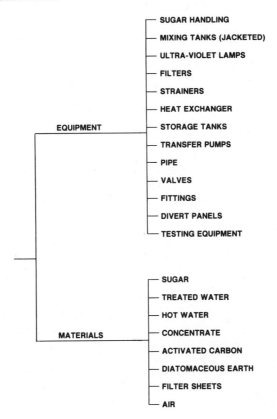

20-8. Syrup operations.

Syrup is manufactured in steps, the number and complexity being dependent upon the nature of the product (regular or diet); the type of sweetener (granulated or liquid); and the quality of the sweetener. The basic mixture of water and sugar (granulated sucrose, liquid sugar, inverted dextrose syrup or high fructose corn syrup) is referred to as *simple syrup*. To this mixture is added all the flavoring, oils, ingredients and fruit juices to form the *finished syrup*. Finished syrup is the final product of the operations in the syrup room. The quality of the beverage produced is dependent on the quality of the finished syrup.

The rest of this chapter will cover the most important considerations of syrup room operation, starting with the different sweeteners used in the soft drink industry, the occasional need for sugar treatment, the treatment methods, and a discussion on the sizing of a syrup room facility.

Sweeteners

Two categories are used:

Natural

—Granulated sucrose

—Liquid sucrose

—Liquid medium invert
—High fructose corn syrup
—Inverted dextrose syrup
Low Calorie
—Saccharine
—Aspartame
—Cyclamate
Standards For Sugar

The first requirement of sweeteners is that they in no way adversely affect the flavor or appearance of the product or products manufactured. Where a sugar causes a beverage discrepancy, the supply must be rejected.

In international markets, if no other supplier exists, the production facility will have to consider special treatment. These treatment methods are covered in a subsequent section. Table I lists the suggested standards for sugars, in regards to physical, chemical and microbiological properties. In addition to the standards listed, all sweeteners must be delivered in clean, sterile containers which will not impart any flavor, odor, foreign particles or metallic or non-metallic contamination to the sugar.

TABLE I
SUGGESTED STANDARDS FOR SWEETENERS

Property	Granulated Sucrose	Liquid Sucrose	Liquid Invert	HFCS 42
Purity, Minimum	99.85%	99.8%	—	—
Percent Solids	—	66.3 - 67.3	76.0 - 77.2	70 - 72
Invert, %	None	0 - 2	32 - 42	
Higher Saccharides, %	—	—	—	7 Max.
Ash, Maximum	0.01%	0.025%	0.1%	0.03%
Fructose, %	—	—	—	42 - 43
Color, RBU Max.	35	35	35	35
Turbidity, RBU Max.	20	1	1	1
pH	—	6.5 - 7.0	4.5 - 5.5	3.0 - 4.0
Taste	No molasses or any other foreign flavor			
Odor	No molasses, storage musk or other odor			
Insoluble Matter	None	None	None	None
Viable Yeast, Max.	10 Per 10 Gram	4 Per 10 Gram*	4 Per 10 Gram*	
Bacteria	200 Per 10 Gram	200 Per 10 Gram*	200 Per 10 Gram*	
Molds	10 Per 10 Gram	4 Per 10 Gram	4 Per 10 Gram	

*Weight expressed in terms of dry solids equivalent (D.S.E.)

Sanitary in-plant handling of liquid sugar is a must. The storage tanks must be made of stainless steel and must be equipped with ultraviolet lamps to maintain a microorganism-free syrup on the surface. Filtered air ventilation is also a must to cut down on moisture due to condensation.

Granulated Sucrose

Is obtained from either sugar cane or sugar beet. Raw sugar must be properly processed to result in a product that meets Bottler's standards for granulated sucrose.

The main advantages of using granulated sucrose lie in its resistance, during storage, to spoilage by contaminating microorganisms (such as yeast or mold) and minimal expense in storage equipment. Disadvantages involve the complexity and cost of handling as opposed to liquid sucrose.

Liquid Sucrose

Is a solution of granulated sucrose and water and delivered in bulk to the bottling plant or manufactured on site. The advantage of liquid syrup is ease of handling. Also, the amount of time and energy required for making the desired syrup is kept at a minimum since the sugar is already in a solution. A disadvantage is that liquid sucrose does not offer resistance to spoilage microorganisms.

Liquid Medium Invert

Is a syrup of sucrose sugar solution, glucose and fructose. Glucose and fructose are produced by inversion by acid hydrolysis of the sucrose molecule.

The advantages of liquid medium invert are its resistance to spoilage organisms and the minimum storage space required because of high solids concentration.

High Fructose Corn Syrup (HFCS)

Is made from corn by means of an enzyme. The enzyme breaks the building blocks of the starch present in the corn and yields a sweetener very high in quality and degree of sweetness.

In recent years bottling facilities have started to use more HFCS in their formulations mainly because a pound of HFCS can provide the same level of sweetness as 1.2 pounds of sucrose, therefore, saving in direct manufacturing costs. HFCS is also gaining acceptance in the low calorie soft drinks because of its ability to "mask" the flavor of saccharin.

Saccharin

Is a non-caloric sweetener derived from phthalicanhydride and most commonly used in its sodium salt form. The soft drink industry is by far the heaviest user of saccharin, and O'Brien[*] mentions that 61% of the saccharin consumed in the United States is used in soft drinks. Saccharin is approximately 300 times sweeter than sucrose.

Aspartame

Is a non-nutritive sweetener made by coupling two naturally occurring amino acids: L-phenylalamine and L-aspartic acid[*]. Aspartame's sweetening power is about 200 times that of sucrose. It breaks down in solution; however, the pH/temperature dependent rate of hydrolysis is slow enough to permit use in soft drinks. At the present, aspartame cannot be used in soft drinks in the United States for lack of F.D.A. approval.

Cyclamate

Has only one-tenth of the sweetness of saccharin but about 30 times that of sucrose[*]. The use of cyclamate in soft drinks in the United States is not approved by the F.D.A.

Other Sweeteners

O'Brien[*] lists other lesser known sweeteners such as Acesulfame K, Talin, Monellin, etc. For the reader interested in this subject, this article provides a lot of information and a good bibliography.

Syrup Formulation

Definition of Terms:

Brix (or Degree Brix)—Written °Brix, it represents the concentration of

[*]O'Brien, L. and R.C. Gelardi, Chemtech. May, 1981.

sugar solutions. The Brix scale is defined in terms of the relative weight of pure sucrose in a solution of sucrose and water, expressed as a percent. A 20 °Brix solution, therefore, is one that contains twenty pounds of sugar and eighty pounds of water for a total of one hundred pounds of solution.

True Brix—Since the Brix scale is defined in terms of sucrose, a correction factor must be added (or subtracted) to the reading obtained with other sweeteners. This correction factor would give us the actual percent solids in any given solution.

Baume (or Degree Baume)—Written °Be, it represents a number in an arbitrary scale that relates the reading to the specific gravity of any given solution. The definition is:

$$°Be = 145 - (145/\text{specific gravity})$$

Specific Gravity (sp. gr.)—A dimensionless number obtained by dividing the density of a syrup, at a given concentration and temperature, by the density of water at that same temperature.

Syrup Formulations:

The syrup manufactured has to be prepared following some technical and economical considerations:

- Concentration of sugar must be high to help preserve the syrup against microbial attack.
- A highly concentrated syrup occupies less space than a dilute one, therefore saving in the number and size of tanks needed for storage.
- Concentration of the syrup must not exceed solubility of the sugar at the lowest syrup room temperature in a given day to avoid crystallization.
- Bottling equipment must be designed to handle high Brix.

In general terms, a Brix between 55 and 60 will satisfy these three requirements when room temperature is 20°C (68°F).

Weight, volume and temperature come into play in all syrup formulations. The formula for a given product will give us both the volume and concentration of the syrup needed to prepare the final beverage. This is the starting point for all our calculations.

Simple Syrup Made With Granulated Sugar

Precise weighing of the sugar is of foremost importance.

For a given batch of syrup, the amount of sugar specified by the formula is added slowly to a tank containing a pre-measured volume of water while the tank agitator is in operation.

After all the sugar has been added and completely dissolved, the syrup so prepared is checked for concentration with either a Brix refractometer or a Baume or Brix hydrometer. If the reading is above or below that specified by the formula, either the sugar has not dissolved completely or an error has been made. Agitate the simple syrup for an additional 10-15 minutes and test the syrup again.

The following example illustrates not only the corrections required but the use of the sugar tables[*].

Example 1

A batch of syrup must be prepared using granulated sugar. The formula calls for adding 2,500 pounds to 230 gallons of treated water to produce 450 gallons of simple syrup of 30.75 °Be.

[*]Tables used in this example are those published by the Geo. J. Meyer Manufacturing Co., Milwaukee, Wisconsin, W.C. Cooper, author.

TABLE II
Characteristics of Various Baume and Brix Sugar Solutions

Brix	Baume	Pounds Solids Per Gallon	Pounds Water Per Gallon	Total Weight Per Gallon
54.0	29.38	5.637	4.802	10.439
54.04	29.4	5.642	4.799	10.441
54.1	29.43	5.650	4.794	10.444
54.2	29.48	5.663	4.785	10.448
54.24	29.5	5.668	4.782	10.450
54.3	29.53	5.676	4.777	10.453
54.4	29.59	5.689	4.769	10.458
54.42	29.6	5.692	4.767	10.459
54.5	29.64	5.702	4.760	10.462
54.6	29.69	5.715	4.752	10.467
54.62	29.7	5.718	4.750	10.468
54.7	29.74	5.728	4.744	10.472
54.8	29.8	5.741	4.736	10.477
54.9	29.85	5.754	4.727	10.481
55.0	29.9	5.767	4.719	10.486
55.1	29.95	5.780	4.710	10.490
55.2	30.0	5.793	4.702	10.495
55.3	30.06	5.807	4.694	10.500
55.38	30.1	5.817	4.687	10.504
55.4	30.11	5.820	4.685	10.505
55.5	30.16	5.833	4.676	10.509
55.58	30.2	5.843	4.670	10.513
55.6	30.21	5.846	4.668	10.514
55.7	30.26	5.859	4.660	10.519
55.77	30.3	5.868	4.654	10.523
55.8	30.32	5.872	4.652	10.524
55.9	30.37	5.885	4.643	10.528
55.96	30.4	5.894	4.638	10.532
56.0	30.42	5.899	4.635	10.534
56.1	30.47	5.912	4.627	10.539
56.16	30.5	5.920	4.622	10.542
56.2	30.52	5.926	4.618	10.544
56.3	30.57	5.939	4.610	10.548
56.35	30.6	5.945	4.606	10.551
56.4	30.63	5.952	4.601	10.553
56.5	30.68	5.965	4.593	10.558
56.54	30.7	5.971	4.589	10.560
56.6	30.73	5.979	4.584	10.563
56.7	30.78	5.992	4.576	10.567
56.74	30.8	5.997	4.572	10.569
56.8	30.83	6.005	4.567	10.572
56.9	30.89	6.018	4.559	10.577
56.92	30.9	6.021	4.557	10.578
57.0	30.94	6.031	4.550	10.581
57.1	30.99	6.045	4.541	10.586
57.12	31.0	6.047	4.539	10.587
57.2	31.04	6.058	4.533	10.591
57.3	31.09	6.072	4.525	10.596
57.32	31.1	6.074	4.523	10.597
57.4	31.15	6.085	4.516	10.601
57.5	31.2	6.099	4.508	10.606
57.6	31.25	6.112	4.499	10.611
57.7	31.3	6.125	4.491	10.616
57.8	31.35	6.139	4.482	10.621
57.9	31.4	6.153	4.474	10.626
58.0	31.46	6.165	4.465	10.630
58.08	31.5	6.176	4.458	10.634
58.1	31.51	6.179	4.456	10.635
58.2	31.56	6.193	4.448	10.640
58.28	31.6	6.203	4.441	10.644
58.3	31.61	6.206	4.439	10.645
58.4	31.66	6.220	4.430	10.650
58.48	31.7	6.231	4.424	10.654
58.5	31.71	6.233	4.422	10.655
58.6	31.76	6.247	4.413	10.660
58.67	31.8	6.256	4.407	10.664
58.7	31.82	6.257	4.405	10.665
58.8	31.87	6.274	4.396	10.670
58.86	31.9	6.282	4.391	10.672
58.9	31.92	6.287	4.387	10.674
59.0	31.97	6.300	4.378	10.678
59.06	32.0	6.309	4.373	10.681
59.1	32.02	6.314	4.370	10.684
59.2	32.07	6.328	4.361	10.689
59.25	32.1	6.335	4.357	10.692
59.3	32.13	6.342	4.353	10.694
59.4	32.18	6.355	4.343	10.699
59.44	32.2	6.360	4.340	10.701
59.5	32.23	6.368	4.335	10.703
59.6	32.28	6.382	4.326	10.708
59.64	32.3	6.388	4.322	10.710
59.7	32.33	6.396	4.317	10.713
59.8	32.38	6.409	4.309	10.718
59.84	32.4	6.415	4.305	10.720
59.9	32.43	6.423	4.300	10.723
60.0	32.49	6.436	4.291	10.727
60.02	32.5	6.439	4.289	10.728
60.1	32.54	6.451	4.283	10.733
60.2	32.59	6.464	4.274	10.738
60.22	32.6	6.467	4.272	10.739
60.3	32.64	6.478	4.265	10.743
60.4	32.69	6.491	4.256	10.747
60.42	32.7	6.494	4.254	10.748
60.5	32.74	6.505	4.247	10.752
60.6	32.79	6.519	4.238	10.757
60.62	32.8	6.522	4.236	10.758
60.7	32.85	6.533	4.230	10.762
60.8	32.9	6.546	4.221	10.767
60.9	32.95	6.560	4.212	10.772
61.0	33.0	6.574	4.203	10.777
61.1	33.05	6.588	4.194	10.782
61.2	33.1	6.602	4.185	10.787
61.3	33.15	6.616	4.177	10.792
61.4	33.2	6.629	4.168	10.797
61.5	33.26	6.643	4.159	10.802
61.58	33.3	6.654	4.152	10.806
61.6	33.31	6.657	4.150	10.807
61.7	33.36	6.671	4.141	10.812
61.78	33.4	6.682	4.134	10.816
61.8	33.41	6.685	4.132	10.817
61.9	33.46	6.699	4.123	10.822
61.98	33.5	6.709	4.116	10.825
62.0	33.51	6.712	4.114	10.826
62.1	33.56	6.726	4.105	10.831
62.18	33.6	6.737	4.098	10.835
62.2	33.61	6.740	4.096	10.836
62.3	33.67	6.754	4.087	10.841
62.36	33.7	6.762	4.082	10.844
62.4	33.72	6.768	4.078	10.846
62.5	33.77	6.782	4.069	10.851
62.56	33.8	6.790	4.064	10.854
62.6	33.82	6.796	4.060	10.856
62.7	33.87	6.810	4.051	10.861
62.76	33.9	6.818	4.046	10.864
62.8	33.92	6.824	4.042	10.866
62.9	33.97	6.838	4.033	10.871
62.96	34.0	6.846	4.028	10.874
63.0	34.02	6.852	4.024	10.876
63.1	34.07	6.866	4.015	10.881
63.16	34.1	6.874	4.010	10.884
63.2	34.12	6.880	4.006	10.886
63.3	34.18	6.894	3.997	10.891
63.34	34.2	6.900	3.993	10.893
63.4	34.23	6.908	3.988	10.896
63.5	34.28	6.923	3.979	10.902
63.54	34.3	6.928	3.975	10.904
63.6	34.33	6.937	3.970	10.907
63.7	34.38	6.951	3.961	10.912
63.74	34.4	6.957	3.957	10.914
63.8	34.43	6.965	3.952	10.917
63.9	34.48	6.979	3.943	10.922
63.94	34.5	6.985	3.939	10.924
64.0	34.53	6.993	3.933	10.926
64.1	34.58	7.007	3.925	10.932
64.14	34.6	7.013	3.921	10.934
64.2	34.63	7.022	3.915	10.937
64.3	34.68	7.036	3.906	10.942
64.4	34.74	7.050	3.897	10.947
64.5	34.79	7.064	3.888	10.952
64.52	34.8	7.067	3.886	10.953
64.6	34.84	7.078	3.879	10.957
64.7	34.89	7.092	3.870	10.962
64.72	34.9	7.095	3.868	10.963
64.8	34.94	7.107	3.860	10.967
64.9	34.99	7.121	3.851	10.972
64.92	35.0	7.124	3.849	10.973
65.0	35.04	7.135	3.842	10.977
65.1	35.09	7.150	3.833	10.983
65.12	35.1	7.153	3.831	10.984
65.2	35.14	7.164	3.824	10.988
65.3	35.19	7.178	3.815	10.993
65.32	35.2	7.181	3.813	10.994
65.4	35.24	7.193	3.805	10.998
65.5	35.29	7.207	3.796	11.003
65.52	35.3	7.210	3.794	11.004
65.6	35.34	7.221	3.787	11.008
65.7	35.39	7.236	3.778	11.013
65.72	35.4	7.238	3.776	11.014
65.8	35.45	7.250	3.768	11.010
65.9	35.5	7.264	3.759	11.023

All figures have been rounded to the third decimal point

When checking the Brix of the simple syrup, however, a reading of 58 °Brix was obtained. Find:

a) Do we need to add water or syrup?
b) What volume of water or weight of sugar will be added?
c) What will be the final volume?

Solution:

a) From the sugar tables (sucrose) we find that 58 °Brix corresponds to 31.46 °Be. Therefore, the syrup is too concentrated and water must be added.
b) From the same sugar tables, we see that 30.75 °Be is not listed. We will have to interpolate between two values given to find the exact Brix:

$$30.73 \text{ °Be corresponds to } 56.6 \text{ °Brix}$$
$$30.75 \text{ °Be corresponds to } X \quad \text{°Brix}$$
$$30.78 \text{ °Be corresponds to } 56.7 \text{ °Brix}$$

Therefore, by linear interpolation:

$$X \;=\; 56.7 \;-\; \frac{(30.78 - 30.75)(56.7 - 56.6)}{(30.78 - 30.73)}$$

$$X \;=\; 56.64 \text{ °Brix}$$

Enough water must be added to lower the simple syrup Brix from 58 to 56.64 degrees.

Since the quantity of sugar will *not* change, we will base our calculations on this key component.

From the sugar tables, we find that a 58 °Brix solution has a total weight of 10.630 pounds of syrup per gallon. Since we have a total volume of 450 gallons, the total weight of syrup will be:

$$10.630 \text{ lb./gallon} \times 450 \text{ gallons} \;=\; 4{,}783.5 \text{ lb. syrup}$$

And the total weight of sugar present is:

$$4{,}783.5 \text{ lb. syrup} \times 58 \text{ lb. sugar}/100 \text{ lb. syrup} \;=\; 2{,}774.43 \text{ lb. sugar}$$

And the amount of water present will be:

$$4{,}783.5 \text{ lb. syrup} - 2{,}774.43 \text{ lb. sugar} \;=\; 2{,}009.07 \text{ lb. water}$$

The "corrected" syrup will have the same weight of sugar and, from the definition of Brix:

$$\text{°Brix} \;=\; \frac{\text{weight of sugar}}{\text{weight of syrup}}$$

Then,

$$\text{weight of syrup} \;=\; \frac{2{,}774.43 \text{ lb. sugar}}{56.64 \text{ lb. sugar/lb. } 100 \text{ lb. syrup}}$$

$$= 4{,}898.36 \text{ lb. syrup}$$

And,

$$\text{weight of water} \;=\; 4{,}898.36 \text{ lb. syrup} - 2{,}774.43 \text{ lb. sugar}$$

$$= 2{,}123.93 \text{ lb. water}$$

Water to be added is:

$$2{,}123.93 - 2{,}009.07 \;=\; 114.86 \text{ lb.}$$

Finally, from a water density table we find that, at 20°C water has a density of 8.34 lb./gallon and therefore the volume of water to be added is:

$$\text{volume} \;=\; 114.86 \text{ lb. water} \times \frac{1 \text{ gallon}}{8.34 \text{ lb.}}$$

$$\text{volume} \;=\; 13.77 \text{ gallons}$$

c) Total volume of syrup:

$$450 + 13.77 \;=\; 463.77 \text{ gallons}$$

In the case of a syrup to which sugar must be added, corrections can be made using the same approach, only water is taken as the key component and all calculations based on it.

Simple Syrup Made With Liquid Sucrose

For this case, the calculations are made as if we want to correct a syrup for high Brix and are straightforward. To determine the volume of liquid sucrose needed, it is only necessary to divide the total weight of the liquid sucrose by the density (lb. per gallon).

When we want to mix two syrups of different concentrations to obtain a third one of a definite concentration we must solve for the total volume desired.

The results will be erroneous if we add up the volumes, as the following example illustrates.

Example 2

We have 300 gallons of 62 °Brix syrup and we want 500 gallons of 56 °Brix syrup, using the necessary amount of a 50 °Brix syrup to dilute the first. Find the number of gallons needed of the 50 °Brix syrup.

Solution:

List the three different syrups that come into play:

	1	2	Desired
Brix	62	50	56
Volume, gal.	300	Unknown	500
Density, lb./gal.	10.826	10.252	10.534
Total weight, lb.	3,247.8	Unknown	5,267
Total sugar	2,013.63	Unknown	2,949.52
Total water	1,234.17	Unknown	2,317.48

Step 1: List the density (lb./gallon) from the sugar tables. They are, respectively, 10.826; 10.252 and 10.534.

Step 2: Calculate total weight for syrups 1 and desired,

Weight = volume × density

For syrup 1: $300 \times 10.826 = 3,247.8$ lb.

For desired syrup: $500 \times 10.534 = 5,267.0$ lb.

Step 3: Calculate weight of the sugar in each,

lb. sugar = total weight × °Brix/100

For syrup 1: $3,247.8 \times 0.62 = 2,013.63$

For syrup 2: $5,267.0 \times 0.56 = 2,949.52$ lb.

Step 4: Calculate sugar to be added:

$$2,949.52 - 2,013.63 = 935.89 \text{ lb.}$$

We have our first unknown solved.

Step 5: Calculate the total weight of the syrup 2 to be added by dividing by the Brix:

$$\frac{935.89}{50.0} \times 100 = 1,871.78 \text{ lb.}$$

We have solved for our second unknown.

Step 6: Calculate the total volume by dividing the total weight by the density:

$$1,871.78 \div 10.252 = 182.58 \text{ gallons}$$

We have solved for our final unknown.

Since we have chosen to base our calculations on the sugar solids, the amount needed in the desired syrup is fixed and therefore we add *only* the necessary amount of syrup at 50 °Brix to give us 2,949.52 pounds of sugar.

We can see that the volumes *do not* add up (300 + 182.58 = 482.58 gallons).

Therefore, we have 482.58 gallons of syrup that has 6.112 lb. sugar/gallon, value that does not match with the one given in the tables for 56 °Brix (5.899). The syrup is more concentrated than the one we want and therefore we will need to add more water if we want to have 500 gallons.

Step 7: Calculate the water in syrup 2 by subtracting the sugar weight from the total weight.

$$1,871.78 - 935.89 = 935.89 \text{ lb. water}$$

Step 8: Calculate the amount of water to be added by subtracting the water in syrup 1 plus the water in syrup 2 from the water in the desired syrup:

$$2,317.48 - (1,234.17 + 935.89) = 147.42 \text{ lb.}$$

Step 9: By using the value of the density of water at 20°C (68°F), calculate the volume of additional water:

$$147.42 \div 8.34 = 17.67 \text{ gallons}$$

The total volume of syrup will therefore be:

$$300 + 182.6 + 17.67 = 500.27 \text{ gallons}$$

And, checking with the tables, it has 5.896 lb. sugar per gallon, close enough to the value given of 5.899.

If we had simply added the volumes we would have had:

300 gallons of 62 °Brix syrup contain	2,013.63 lb. sugar
200 gallons of 50 °Brix syrup contain	1,025.2
Total 500 gallons of unknown Brix syrup contain	3,038.83

So, the sugar content will be 3,038.83/500 or 6.077 lb. sugar per gallon, corresponding to approximately 57 °Brix.

Syrup Made With Invert Sugar

The use of liquid invert is more complicated since it is hard to determine the exact degree of inversion that has taken place.

It is imperative that the manufacturer supplies the bottling plant with the information needed to properly formulate the syrup:

• Exact percent inversion to correlate to Brix readings.

• Pounds of sugar and total pounds per gallon of invert.

The degree of inversion changes the properties of a syrup, both in terms of the sugar solids weight per gallon and the density, total weight per gallon. Mixtures can only be made using syrups of the *same* degree of inversion to keep errors at a minimum.

For example, we can mix a 50 °Brix medium invert syrup with 35 °Brix medium invert syrup and calculate very accurately the final weight, volume and concentration of the resulting syrup, since in all points in the calculations we will use the tables for medium invert. However, we cannot mix liquid sucrose and medium invert and get an accurate value of the properties of the mixture *unless* we have a table for the mixture.

Syrup Made With HFCS

Again, since HFCS is a different sweetener, we will need the appropriate table of properties for each syrup. In most cases, the supplier will provide the bottling plant with the table adequate for each concentration. HFCS 42 is one type that contains 42% fructose, HFCS 55 is another type with 55% fructose and HFCS 90 has 90% fructose. Each type has its own different set of properties.

As in the case of liquid invert, we can mix two syrups of different Brix and *still* use the same table only if we mix HFCS 42 with HFCS 42. Or HFCS 55 with HFCS 55. We cannot mix HFCS 55 with HFCS 90 without incurring formulation errors. Once we have the table for each sweetener, we can calculate all the properties for mixtures in the same manner as we did for sucrose.

Syrup Quality and Treatment

In-plant treatment of sugar becomes necessary when the supply does not meet the standards previously set and an alternative source is not available. This situation is especially prevalent in third-world countries where the only sugar available is solid sucrose in either raw or plantation white grades.

Depending upon the impurities present (insoluble solids, lint, bagasse, color or odor), the methods range from simple filtration to flocculation and flotation using polyelectrolites.

Simple Filtration

In this method, the simple syrup is passed through a filter (commonly a plate and frame type filter) employing filter sheets as the filtering media. The filter acts like a polisher only, to remove bag lint, dust or any other debris that might have come in contact with the sugar or the package.

This method should be used only with bottler's grade, refined sugar that does not yield any extraneous odor or color in solution.

Filtration Using Diatomaceous Earth (D.E.)

Some sugar supplies contain materials that, when the sugar is dissolved, cause colloidal matter to form in the syrup. These particles either clog the filter media or pass unfiltered to the syrup storage tank. Addition of diatomaceous earth to the simple syrup continuously creates a new surface as the syrup is being pumped and this porous cake traps the suspended matter without any sizable reduction in flow.

Two steps are necessary when using this method. First, the filter sheets are coated with diatomaceous earth to a thickness of 1/16" to 1/8" by recirculating a slurry made with D.E. and water. This is known as the pre-coat.

Second, D.E. is added to the syrup tank before the syrup is pumped to the filter. This is called the "body feed" and the D.E. adds itself to the pre-coat, maintaining a surface that does not clog.

In general terms, the amount of D.E. to be used is between 0.1% and 0.5% of the weight of the sugar to be filtered. This number, however, depends upon the quality of the sugar and the correct amount to be used has to be determined by a trial-and-error procedure at the plant.

A limiting factor in the use of D.E. is the sludge space in the filter. This space must be of the adequate size to hold the D.E. in the pre-coat and in the body feed in order to give satisfactory results.

Diatomaceous earth is manufactured in various grades (particle size). For every application, the manufacturer of the filter must be contacted as the proper grade of D.E. to be used for best results.

Treatment With Activated Carbon and D.E.

When the sugar contains impurities that remain in solution and therefore cannot be filtered out, such as color- and/or odor-producing bodies, treatment with activated carbon will generally yield a syrup acceptable for manufacturing soft drinks.

In this process, powdered activated carbon is added to the syrup in the mixing tank, agitated for a given period of time to provide intimate contact between the syrup and the carbon, and then the syrup is filtered. To allow for better filtration rates, D.E. is also added to the mixing tank as in the D.E. filtration method.

The amount of carbon to be added to achieve the desired degree of impurities removal is dependent upon various factors, namely:

• Amount of impurities present in the untreated syrup.
• The amount of impurities that can be accepted in the treated syrup.
• The temperature at which the syrup will be treated.
• The type of carbon used.
• The contact time between carbon and syrup.

Again, a limiting factor is the size of the filter. The sludge space available to hold both the D.E. and the carbon must be enough to accommodate the mass added to the syrup.

The approach must be to size the filter to provide for the syrup that we need, both in terms of quality and quantity and with the optimum filtration time. If a filter cannot hold the necessary weight of carbon plus D.E., a bigger filter must be procured.

As a general rule, the proper amount of carbon to be used in achieving the desired reduction of impurities is determined at the bottling plant by a trial-and-error procedure. In some cases, a manufacturer of activated carbon will advise the proper carbon dosage for a given sugar by conducting laboratory-scale experiments.

Most sugars will need between 0.1 and 1.0 percent of carbon, based upon the dry weight of the sugar to be treated, to yield sugar of satisfactory quality.

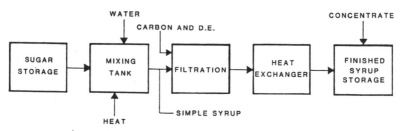

20-9. *Simplified flow diagram for hot carbon treatment.*

Treatment With Activated Carbon and D.E. at High Temperature

There are some sugars that will not be satisfactorily treated with carbon at room temperature. Increasing the temperature will not only permit better impurities removal by the carbon but will also kill—to a great extent—yeast and bacteria that could be contaminating the sugar.

One added advantage of hot carbon treatment is that the viscosity of the syrup will be reduced with increasing temperature and filtration times will be drastically reduced. The one key disadvantage of this method is its relatively high cost of operation. In most existing plants where the syrup room operation must be modified to accommodate the hot carbon method, retrofitting involves buying a new boiler, steam piping, new jacketed tanks, refrigeration, etc. Additionally, more fuel must be purchased to generate the steam needed to heat the syrup.

The steps involved in this method are:

First: Add the sugar to the mixing tank. Keep heating the syrup at 170-180°F while mixing.

Second: Add the correct amount of activated carbon after all the sugar has been added. Allow at least ½ hour contact time. Keep the agitator on and the temperature at 170-180°F.

Meanwhile, pre-coat the filter with D.E.

Third: Add diatomaceous earth to the syrup in the mixing tank. The amount used here will generally be the same (by weight) as the amount used to pre-coat the filter.

Fourth: Once the ½ hour period (or the desired contact time) is over and the filter has been pre-coated, the syrup can be filtered.

Fifth: The filtered, hot syrup must be cooled down to below 90°F as rapidly as possible. This is generally done in an on-line heat exchanger located between the syrup filter and the storage tank.

Other Methods

Recently, a number of companies have come into the market with other processes to treat sugar of extremely poor quality. Most of these processes use a liquid polyelectrolite that attaches itself to the color and/or odor producing impurities, forming an insoluble compound that is removed from the syrup by either filtration or flotation. For example, the Talofloc° process was originally designed for refineries and has been adapted to in-plant sugar treatment in various countries.

In every case, the bottling facilities' management has to weigh the advantages

---

°Talofloc is a registered trademark of Tate & Lyle Ltd., London, England.

and disadvantages of in-house treatment of its sugar supply versus the procurement of a better quality raw material supply, even if it means paying higher prices.

Syrup Operations Equipment and Facilities

The basic requirements of any syrup room are:

1. The floor area should be large enough to accommodate all the syrup tanks plus adequate space for the persons who will be working in the area.

    Ceiling height should be a minimum of 6 meters (19.7 feet). Enough clearance should be given to vertical tanks for shaft removal, maintenance, etc.

2. The syrup room must provide a sanitary environment.

    Positive air pressure is a must, using filtered air. Air intake ports must be located as far as possible from sources of contamination and odors. A level of 20 air changes per hour can be considered satisfactory. Temperature in the syrup room should be kept at 64-68°F.

The general building specifications for the syrup room can be divided into three key areas:

Interior walls: Ceramic tile is the preferred material. Epoxy painted concrete can also be used but oil painted concrete or wood panels should be avoided.

Floors: Quarry tile with epoxy grout gives the best protection against floor deterioration and pitting by product spills. Epoxy flooring is also accepted for this purpose but concrete, vinyl and ceramic floors must be avoided.

Ceilings: Painted gypsum or plaster is the most suitable material. Sanitary tile can also be used. Leaving the building structure exposed is definitely unacceptable.

Proper lighting is also important. Fluorescent or mercury vapor lamps are best for this area. High pressure sodium vapor lights are not recommended (although they can be used) because the intense yellow light distorts color perception.

All the equipment used in the syrup room must be of sanitary construction. All gaskets, seals and lubricants must be food grade F.D.A. approved.

All metal parts that come in contact with the syrup must be of stainless steel, polished to a finish of 2B.

A key requirement for the equipment in the syrup room with regards to cleaning and sanitizing is that all components in contact with the product must be suitable for sterilization with:

• Water at 85°C (185°F) for 30 minutes.
• Caustic soda solution at 2.5% by weight at 85°C (185°F) for 20 minutes.
• Chlorine solution at 200 ppm at ambient temperature for 15 minutes.

Syrup Room Equipment

The equipment needed for syrup room operations depend upon various factors, namely:

• Type of sweetener used. Liquid sucrose or HFCS calls for storage tanks. HFCS also requires heating in cold areas. Granulated sucrose calls for mixing tank(s) and adequate storage facilities.
• Type of treatment. Hot carbon treatment calls for processing tanks, heat exchanger, refrigeration equipment, filters to handle hot syrup, plus separate storage space for activated carbon, diatomaceous earth, sugar, etc.
• Number of flavors. The more flavors produced, the more tanks the plant will need.

• Aging requirements. Some products require a minimum aging period before the syrup can be bottled. The longer this period, the more tanks will be needed.

Selection and Sizing of Syrup Tanks

Simple criteria for sizing syrup tanks:

A. Larger tanks are chosen over several smaller tanks of the same volume for reasons of cost and improved operation.

B. Two tanks are preferred over one for reasons of flexibility. One is used while the other is sanitized, filled or in some other way out of operation.

C. Tank size must be large enough to provide the volume of syrup required for continued line production between scheduled breaks (such as lunch, coffee breaks).

Since percentage of syrup yield loss increases in inverse proportion to batch size, tanks must not contain less than two hours of production.

D. Tank size should accommodate integral multiples of concentrate units for reasons of operation convenience and product quality.

E. Tanks are sized for the fifth year requirements, but also taking immediate needs into account. That is, large enough for the fifth year but not too large for the first year. Tanks must not have a capacity of more than twice the volume of a batch to prevent aeration of the syrup.

F. The number of tanks must be sufficient to permit adequate sanitation cycles between batches.

G. For reasons of cost, standard size tanks are chosen over custom-made special tanks.

H. Strong flavors (such as root beer) may require dedicated tanks to prevent flavor carry-over to other products.

Example 3

Assume that a bottling facility will produce 260,000 cases of an orange flavored drink per month.

The product is bottled in 12 ounce bottles, 24 bottles per case and the ratio of syrup to water is one part syrup to five parts water.

The operation is one line, one shift (8 hours the first), 23 days per month.

One unit of concentrate makes 230 gallons of finished syrup.

Determine the number and size of the storage tanks.

Solution

To find the total storage required per day, calculate the syrup draw per day, add a safety factor and then test against the criteria for size.

Step 1:

Calculate the cases produced per day:

$$260,000 \; \frac{\text{cases}}{\text{month}} \times \frac{1 \text{ month}}{23 \text{ days}} = 11,304 \text{ cases/day}$$

Step 2: Calculate the gallons of product bottled per day:

$$11,304 \; \frac{\text{cases}}{\text{day}} \times 24 \; \frac{\text{bot.}}{\text{case}} \times 0.355 \; \frac{\text{lt}}{\text{bot.}} \times \frac{1 \text{ gal.}}{3.785 \text{ lt}} = 25,446 \; \frac{\text{gal.}}{\text{day}}$$

Step 3: Calculate the gallons of syrup consumed per day:

$$25,446 \; \frac{\text{gallons}}{\text{day}} \times \frac{1 \text{ gallon of syrup}}{6 \text{ gallons of product}} = 4,241 \; \frac{\text{gal. syrup}}{\text{day}}$$

Step 4: Add a 10% oversize factor. Total storage requirements are:

$$4,241 \times 1.1 = 4,665 \; \frac{\text{gallons}}{\text{day}}$$

Step 5: Find the number of concentrate units:

$$4,665 \; \frac{\text{gallons}}{\text{day}} \times \frac{1 \text{ unit of concentrate}}{230 \text{ gallons}} = 20.28 \text{ units}$$

Step 6: Correct the total storage required (criterion D):

$$230 \text{ gallons/unit} \times 21 \text{ units} = 4,830 \text{ gallons}$$

Step 7: Weigh each alternative against selection criteria:

      Alternative 1: One 5,000 gallon tank.

             Meets criteria A, C, D

             Violates criteria B, F, G

      Alternative 2: Two 2,500 gallon tanks.

             Meets criteria B, D, F, G

             Violates criterion A

      Alternative 3: Three 2,000 gallon tanks.

             Meets criteria B, D, F, G

             Violates criterion A

Since we have calculated the total storage capacity in terms of units to be 21, choosing alternative number 2, one of the tanks will have to hold 10 and the other 11 units. In gallons, this translates into 2,300 and 2,530, which exceeds the holding capacity of at least one of them.

We therefore consider that the best alternative for this case is three 2,000 gallon tanks. This way, the maximum number of units that one tank will have to hold at any given day is 21 ÷ 3 = 7 units or 1,610 gallons. This will also allow for additional capacity in the future, since each tank can hold one more unit for a maximum capacity of 1,840 gallons per tank, without exceeding the holding capacity.

Mixing Tanks

Once we have determined the syrup storage tanks, we can calculate the size of the mixing tank. Mixing tank capacity must be in a fixed ratio (1/1, 1/2) with the storage tanks. The alternatives are:

Alternative 1: One-to-one ratio means that one 2,000 gallon mixing tank will fill one 2,000 gallon storage tank. One mix per tank will be needed, three mixes per day.

Alternative 2: One-to-two ratio means that one 1,000 gallon mixing tank will fill two 2,000 gallon storage tanks. Two mixes per tank will be needed, six mixes per day.

Alternative 3: Two 1,000 gallon tanks feeding the 2,000 gallon storage tanks (1/2 ratio). Still two mixes will be needed per storage tank, six mixes per day.

In order to choose between the three, we must consider the time required for preparing the syrup. Assuming a minimum time of one hour and 45 minutes for mixing, contact with carbon, filtering and cleaning, the total time required will be:

Alternative 1: $\dfrac{1 \text{ mix}}{\text{tank}} \times 3 \text{ tanks} \times 1.75 \dfrac{\text{hours}}{\text{mix}} = 5.25 \text{ hours}$

Alternative 2: $\dfrac{2 \text{ mixes}}{\text{tank}} \times 6 \text{ tanks} \times 1.75 \dfrac{\text{hours}}{\text{mix}} = 10.5 \text{ hours}$

Alternative 3: A total of 6.75 hours will be required using two tanks, since while one tank is being emptied the other is being cleaned and brought back into service.

In this case, alternative number one provides the best solution since it takes less time. Furthermore, one big tank occupies less floor space than two smaller ones. Since there are only three mixes, cleaning and pre-coating the filter will have to be done only three times so less time, less labor will be required. Syrup losses will be kept to a minimum and the operation will be run more efficiently.

Sugar Handling System ·

The equipment used to take the sweetener from the storage area to the mixing tank depends upon the sweetener and the process with which it will be treated.

As a general rule, liquid sucrose, medium invert and HFCS require only simple filtration or straining. Syrup can be mixed in the storage tank since the sweetener is already in liquid form. In this case, nothing more than a pump, a filter press and a meter will be needed.

When granulated sucrose is used, it becomes necessary to provide for an elevator of the capacity to feed the mixing tank.

The basic parameter for sizing the elevator is the time required to load the sugar needed by the mixing tank. Generally this time is taken as 30 minutes.

For our example, since we have sized the syrup mixing tank at 2,000 gallons, to prepare up to eight units (1,840 gallons) of syrup and, assuming that the syrup will be 57 °Brix, the amount of sugar needed will be:

$$1,840 \text{ gallons} \times 6.031 \ \frac{\text{lbs. sugar}}{\text{gallon}} = 11,097 \text{ lbs. sugar}$$

And, since our time required for loading is 30 minutes, the capacity of the system will be:

$$11,097 \times 2 = 22,200 \text{ lbs./hour}$$

Syrup Filter

The type and size of the syrup filter is also dependent upon the sweetener and the treatment given to it. Liquid sweeteners of a high degree of purity require only simple filtration or straining while granulated sucrose must be carefully evaluated to determine appropriate treatment.

Three key requirements:
• Flow rate
• Filtering surface
• Sludge space

Sizing of the filters is done on the following recommended bases:

Simple filtration	$60 \frac{\text{gallons}}{\text{hr. ft.}^2}$
Filtration with D.E.	$60 \frac{\text{gallons}}{\text{hr. ft.}^2}$
Hot carbon with D.E.	$12 \frac{\text{gallons}}{\text{hr. ft.}^2}$
Cold carbon with D.E.	$9 \frac{\text{gallons}}{\text{hr. ft.}^2}$

Based on the volume of syrup to be treated and the treatment method, we can use the data in example 3. Consider the diatomaceous earth density (when wet) of 18 lb./ft.³, carbon at 30 lb./ft.³, with 45 minutes to filter the batch:

	Area	Sludge Space
Hot carbon with D.E.	153 ft.²	2.35 ft.³
Cold carbon with D.E.	205 ft.²	2.35 ft.³

The area was calculated for each case as follows:

$$\text{Area} = \text{total flow} \div \text{recommended flow rate}$$

And the sludge space assuming a dosage of 0.2% D.E. and 0.3% carbon:

$$\text{Volume} = \frac{\text{pounds carbon}}{\text{density}} + \frac{\text{pounds D.E.}}{\text{density}}$$

It should be stressed at this point that the size of the filter must be tailored for each application. The guidelines given above are only to get a "ballpark" estimate of the size and capacity of the filter that will probably meet our needs.

For the reader interested in filter design and scale-up, the book by Peters[*] provides an excellent treatise on the subject.

Water Meters

In order to provide for accurate formulation of both the simple and finished syrup, water meters are needed for measuring the amount of water required

[*]Peters, M.S. & K.D. Timmerhaus, "Plant Design and Economics for Chemical Engineers." Mc-Graw Hill Book Co., 3rd Ed.

in the syrup room operations. The water meters can be sized based on the water required for mixing and the time for the delivery of the water to the mixing tank. For our example, since we will prepare a batch of 1,840 gallons of a syrup 57 °Brix, the amount of water required by the batch will be:

$$1{,}840 \text{ gallons} \times 4.55 \ \frac{\text{lbs. of water}}{\text{gallon}} = 8{,}372 \text{ lbs. water}$$

Assuming that this water will be added to the tank in 15 minutes, the flow rate will be:

$$\frac{8{,}372 \text{ lbs. water}}{15 \text{ min.}} \times \frac{1 \text{ gallon}}{8.34 \text{ lbs.}} \times \frac{60 \text{ min.}}{1 \text{ hr.}} = 4{,}015 \ \frac{\text{gallons}}{\text{hour}}$$

Syrup Pumps

The syrup pumps can be sized based on the flows we have already determined.

Since we require 45 minutes to filter the syrup and we designed the mixing tanks to hold eight units of 230 gallons each, the pump capacity will have to be:

$$1{,}840 \ \frac{\text{gallons}}{45 \text{ min.}} \times 60 \ \frac{\text{minutes}}{1 \text{ hr.}} = 2{,}453 \ \frac{\text{gallons}}{\text{hour}}$$

The finished syrup transfer pump (for transferring the syrup to the line) must be sized for the greatest demand. For this example, since we will bottle 260,000 cases per month, we will assume that a maximum of 12,000 cases per day will be bottled. In eight hours 1,500 cases per hour will be needed. The requirements in terms of syrup will be:

$$1{,}500 \ \frac{\text{cases}}{\text{hour}} \times 24 \ \frac{\text{bottles}}{\text{case}} \times \frac{0.355 \text{ lts.}}{1 \text{ bottle}}$$

$$\times \frac{1 \text{ gallon}}{3.785 \text{ lt.}} \times \frac{1 \text{ gal. syrup}}{6 \text{ gal. product}} = 563 \text{ gal. per hr.}$$

Piping and Accessories

The final step in the design of the syrup room is the diameter of piping needed to interconnect the mixing tank, heat exchanger, filter and syrup storage tanks.

Pipe lengths, bends, valves and location of pumps can be determined once the layout of the syrup room has been finalized.

PLASTIC BOTTLES AND CASES

Traditionally, packages and package handling have been comparable in breweries and soft drink plants. Production line equipment, conveyor design and package handling are similar, filling is accomplished in much the same manner, and most soft drinks are packaged in glass bottles or cans and packed in cardboard cases or trays, as is beer. However, in recent years there has been increasing use of plastic for both bottles and cases for soft drinks.

Plastic Bottles

The use of PET (polyethylene terephthalate) bottles in the soft drink industry has gained popularity due to the numerous advantages to both the consumer and bottler. Consumers have expressed a preference for PET bottles over glass because they are lightweight, shatterproof, safe and non-returnable. This consumer preference has created significant market demand. Advantages to the bottler include virtually noise free filling and safer processing of shatterproof packages, often resulting in reductions in insurance rates.

PET bottles are manufactured by an injection blow molding process. First, a "preform" is made from polyethylene terephthalate resin. This preform is tubular in shape, the open end is shaped with the flange and threads for capping (see Figure 20-10). During the second stage the preform is heated, and stretched inside a bottle mold by high pressure compressed air. PET bottles are formed in two configurations, the free standing petaloid base and rounded bottom, which requires a base cup. The molding and application of base cups, when required, are the third and fourth steps of plastic bottle manufacturing.

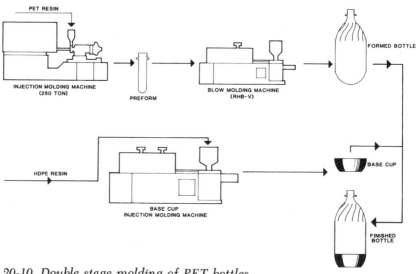

20-10. Double stage molding of PET bottles.

PET bottles are delivered to bottling plants palletized in bulk or in reshipper cartons. It is often economically feasible for large plants to acquire molding machines and self-manufacture PET bottles. The technology involved is usually within the capabilities of a bottling operation. Several systems are available. The alternatives include small, single stage machines in which the injection and blow molding functions are combined (see Figure 20-11) and high speed, double stage systems in which the preforms are injection molded separately and can be stored prior to blow molding (see Figure 20-10). Base cups, composed of polyethylene, are molded separately and affixed to the bottle when warranted by base design.

Plastic bottles are handled similarly to other non-returnable packages. They are bulk depalletized or uncased and rinsed prior to filling. The light weight of empty PET bottles creates conveying and handling problems, often compounded by the instability of the petaloid base. Neck guides can be installed on the conveyor to prevent bottle tipping. However, filled plastic bottles, again due to their light weight, facilitate material handling and warehousing.

Shelf life of beverages packaged in plastic bottles is somewhat diminished,

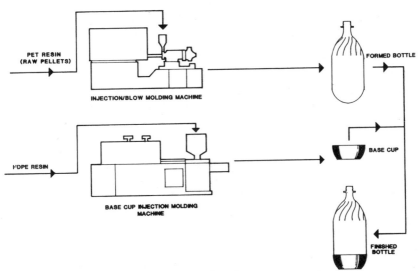

20-11. Single stage molding of PET bottles.

depending on product and package size. The popular two liter cola package has maximum shelf life of 16 weeks. The reduced shelf life is due to the permeation of CO_2 gas through the bottle, and the leaching of acetaldehyde (a harmless natural by-product of citrus fruits) into the soft drink, which produces an off-taste. The off-taste is not considered to be a significant problem in beverages containing citric acid.

The tremendous market response to the PET bottle has proven to be sufficient incentive for the soft drink industry to overcome any problems encountered in the handling of plastic bottles.

Plastic Cases

The soft drink industry often uses plastic cases with returnable bottles. The cases are injection molded, high density polyethylene, with screen printed artwork. They are manufactured in full and half depth, and are available with or without pockets. Plastic cases are attractive, lightweight, durable, and cost-efficient. They are, in themselves, effective point-of purchase displays. Additionally, their uniform size and shape facilitates stacking and material handling, and eliminates the potential for uncaser and packer jams caused by wood cases.

Case washers should be installed on lines running plastic cases. Plastics, due to their tendency to generate static electricity, attract dirt and dust. Since maintenance of the appearance of the case is crucial to consumer appeal, plastic cases must be cleaned prior to each use. Case washers are usually installed in-line, between the uncaser and case packer. They should be supplied with an inverter to spill out loose debris, high-pressure detergent jetting with a liquid temperature of 160°F, a rinse/drain section, and a re-inverter.

Ultrasonic case cleaners are an alternative to hot detergent jetting. They are particularly useful in areas where air pollution discolors cases or where heavy soils (cement, packed sand) are a problem. Ultrasonic cleaners are available as in-line units or as separate tanks in which the cases are immersed by hand.

SUMMARY

In conclusion, we have seen how water treating, proportioning/carbonating/ cooling, and syrup preparation technologies differentiate soft drink and brewing processes.

All process water is treated to assure product quality and uniformity. The water treating method selected is dependent upon the raw water analysis. Treated water is blended with finished syrup, in specific ratio, by the proportioning unit. This mixture is carbonated and cooled prior to filling. Syrup preparation is the most complex component of soft drink technology. Natural and artificial sweeteners, which must comply with bottler's standards and government regulations, are used. Simple syrup is formulated by blending precise amounts of sugar and treated water to achieve the desired °Brix (concentration of sugar solution). This simple syrup is filtered, and treated if necessary, to remove any impurities which may have been present in the sugar. The sugar and water mixture is usually transferred to a storage tank, where flavor concentrate is added to produce the finished syrup which is pumped to the proportioner.

Packaging technologies are similar in both industries; however, the plastic bottle has become a popular soft drink package. The soft drink industry frequently uses plastic cases with returnable bottles.

ACKNOWLEDGEMENTS

The author gratefully acknowledges the collaboration of Harry DeLonge, Frank Norton, Rob Slaymaker, Alex Yaeggy and Peggy Lyons. Their contributions made this chapter possible.

Section VII: Related Packaging Functions

CHAPTER XXI

SAFETY

BY PAUL T. MOORHOUSE

INTRODUCTION

Maintaining a safe and healthful workplace is desirable and necessary. It requires dedication and continual vigilance on the part of everyone to ensure that safe conditions are maintained. Supervisory personnel should set an example and be scrupulous in their observation of safe and healthful practices. Workers who are properly trained and who understand reasons for the established controls and work practices will cooperate in their proper use. The rewards for such policies will be in the form of lower compensation rates, less down time due to accidents and illnesses, and usually, a more dedicated and contented workforce.

A health and safety program, reinforced by employee safety training, will make unsafe acts and conditions become more readily apparent. Through the elimination of such unsafe practices, injuries to employees will be minimized, and the frequency and severity of accidents in plants will be greatly reduced.

ACCIDENT ANALYSIS

What is an accident? An accident may be defined as "an unexplained or unintended occurrence that interrupts or interferes with work activities." Obviously, accidents and injuries are not the same. An accident is a mishap. It need not result in injury to anyone or result in damage to anything. It is well to bear this thought in mind because if preventive measures are delayed until an accident recurs or an unsafe act is repeated, injuries cannot be eliminated.

An accident, whether resulting in injury or not, is an interference with production and thus can possibly affect the quality of product. The loss of productivity and effect on quality are costly and must be avoided—but not by sacrificing the safety of personnel. Therefore, it is imperative that safety be an integral part of production with no over riding priorities.

Frequency and Severity

Until the early 1970's safety was measured in the United States and in many foreign countries by the American National Standards Institute (ANSI). Standard Z 16.1 (1967) titled "Method of Recording and Measuring Work Injury Experience," was based primarily on the frequency and severity of accidents.

475

Frequency was defined as the number of disabling injuries per million man hours of exposure, and severity was defined as the number of days lost or charged per million man hours.

A third measurement included in the standard shows the average day charged for disabling injury.

Frequency rate formula: $\dfrac{\text{Number of disabling injuries} \times 1,000,000}{\text{Employee hours of exposure}}$

Severity rate formula: $\dfrac{\text{Total days charged} \times 1,000,000}{\text{Employee hours of exposure}}$

Average days per disabling injury formula:

I. $\dfrac{\text{Total days charged}}{\text{Total disabling injuries}}$ or

II. $\dfrac{\text{Severity rate}}{\text{Frequency rate}}$

The Occupational Safety and Health Act of 1970 (OSHA) required the use of an incidence rate based on doctors' cases and on 200,000 man hours instead of 1,000,000 as in Z 16.1. A very simple method for calculating the OSHA incident rate is to divide the ANSI frequency rate by five.

The above are all ways of measuring frequency and severity of accidents. This can be done departmentally, by groups or on a plant-wide basis. An accurate measurement of safety performance will provide the severity and frequency rates and total plant accidents. It will also indicate where the emphasis should be placed in the safety program.

Causes of accidents or injuries, such as hazardous conditions, or acts performed or omitted by individuals, should be identified. Oftimes singly, or in combination, any of the above may result in an accident or injury. When an accident or near miss does occur, an analysis of the conditions at the time of the incident should be undertaken. By so doing, the possibility of a recurrence will be eliminated.

Common Types of Industrial Accidents

• *Struck Against:* An accident in which the person accidentally runs into equipment, another person, or some object.

• *Struck By:* An accident in which the person is struck by moving vehicles, flying or falling object, swinging door, etc.

• *Fall From Elevation:* An accident, including a fall from a ladder, platform, staging, etc. in which the individual falls to a lower level.

• *Fall on Same Level:* An accident, for example, in which the person slips or trips and strikes the floor.

• *Caught In, Under, Or Between:* Accident caused by squeezing, pinching or crushing between a moving object and a stationary object, between two moving objects, or between parts of an object.

• *Rubbed Or Abraded:* Accidental injury produced by pressure, vibration or friction.

• *Bodily Reaction:* Applies to injury produced by body motion which imposes stress or strain upon some part of the body.

• *Overexertion:* Applies to injuries resulting from excessive physical effort, as in lifting, pulling, pushing, etc.

- *Contact With Electric Current*
- *Contact With Temperature Extremes:* Applies to burns, heat exhaustion, freezing, frostbite, etc. resulting from contact with, or exposure to, hot or cold objects, air, gases, vapors, or liquids.
- *Contact With Radiation, Caustics, Toxic and Noxious Substances:* Applies to the inhalation, absorption (skin contact) or ingestion of harmful substances. Includes chemical burns, allergic reactions, exposure to the sun's rays or other radiations.

Accident Factors

According to the ANSI the following are essential points that are classified as Accident Factors, and these points should be covered in the accident analysis.

- *Agency*—That most closely associated with the injury: machine, conveyor, working surface, hand tools.
- *Agency Part*—*Particular part:* chuck on a hand drill, gears on a conveyor, belt, etc.
- *Unsafe Condition*—No guards, slippery surface, hazardous arrangement of material.
- *Accident Type*—*Manner of injury:* striking, caught by, fall, etc.
- *Unsafe Act*—*Violation of safe working practice:* not shutting down equipment for repair or adjustment, not using ladders properly, using hands rather than equipment, a personal factor.
- *Unsafe Personnel Factor*—Attitude of personnel, eye sight, knowledge or skill training.

As indicated, there are many reasons why accidents occur. Therefore, the analysis of each accident is a very important part of a safety program. Without proper analysis (accident investigation), the chances of recurrence are not only possible, but greatly enhanced.

CONTROL FACTORS

Management's Role

There are many controls that may be exercised to achieve accident elimination. The first, and most essential, is the full cooperation of management. Without this full endorsement, the task is almost impossible. Management must be convinced that safety is to be accorded first priority, even over productivity. It is vital that management be convinced that quality and productivity can go hand-in-hand with safety. Only with the full understanding and support of management can a successful safety program be achieved.

Engineering

OSHA states that engineering is the first method of hazard removal in the work place so there must be a good working relationship between the Safety Department and the Engineering Department.

The ultimate goal is to design equipment and to set up job procedures so that employee exposure to injury will be either eliminated or controlled as completely as possible. When a high degree of safety is incorporated into the design of the equipment or the planning of the process, the need for training and supervision to control unsafe acts is reduced.

Company policy should specify that safety must be designed and built into the job before it is executed. To add safety after work on a job or process has begun is usually more costly, less efficient, and less effective.

The most efficient time to engineer hazards out of the plant, process or job is prior to building or remodeling, before a change in a process is put into effect, or before a job is started. Every effort, therefore, should be made to find and remove potential hazards at the blueprint or planning stage.

At each level, engineering should be given the responsibility for building safety into the job, right through to the production phase. This responsibility should extend to package design, machine design, plant layout and conditions of premises, selection and specification of materials to be used, time study, methods study, and the work of employees assigned to a maintenance, re-modeling or new installation job.

If an engineer, whether he is a design engineer, a methods engineer, a production engineer, or other, has processed a job and has left an avoidable hazard in it, he has not fully met his responsibility.

Method Change

Problems may also be eliminated through a method change. When an accident or near miss occurs, and the cause is either an unsafe condition or unsafe act, it is reasonably certain that a deficiency exists in equipment or procedure.

An analysis of that process should be done with the final result being the elimination of the problem by a possible change of method for the operation.

Machine Guarding

Machine guarding is important. Personnel cannot always be relied upon to act as safely as they should around machinery in motion. The same person will react differently at different times to the same environment because of physical, mental or emotional changes—sometimes reacting safely, sometimes not. It follows that even the well coordinated and highly trained individual may at times perform unsafe acts that could lead to injury and death. The proper guarding of machinery is generally considered to be most effective in safeguarding the employee. In fact, it could be said that the degree to which machines are guarded in an establishment is a reflection of management's interest in providing a safe workplace.

Employee Safety Training

The prevention and/or correction of unsafe acts requires employee training. A safe operation depends largely upon employees who are properly informed and aware of potential hazards. Training needs will vary according to the complexity of the operation and the potential hazards. Employee training is a responsibility of plant management. Some suggestions follow.

• *Familiarize employees through initial training and with periodic up-dating, as necessary, with the standard operating procedures and appropriate precautions to be taken. Employees should be totally familiar with plant safety measures (e.g., what to do in case of fires or other emergencies such as shut down of equipment). These procedures should be promulgated and rigidly enforced and be readily available to employees.*

• *Educate employees so they are knowledgable about the toxicity and hazards of all the chemicals with which they will be working.*

• *Thoroughly train employees in the proper use of all protective equipment, particularly respiratory protective devices for each individual chemical for-mulation, preparation and process to which exposure is anticipated.*

• *Thoroughly train and rehearse employees in emergency procedures for* accidents, such as chemical spills and leaks, and to eliminate hazardous exposures or conditions.

• Train each employee in good personal hygiene practices, and instruct them to report all injuries, no matter how minor.

• Have at least one person trained in first aid on each shift. First aid training should include emergency measures (e.g. eye wash) to be taken in the event of acute exposure to specific chemicals.

• Impress upon the worker the need to be constantly aware of the operations about him, even when such operations are automatically controlled.

• Develop and maintain check points to be observed during each shift as a part of the standard and emergency procedures.

• Post appropriate warning signs and operating procedures.

• Instruct employees in the use of portable and fixed fire extinguishing systems.

• Be sure that employees who are authorized to use or work in the vicinity of any motorized equipment (including fork lifts, cranes and trucks) are thoroughly trained as to use, safety precautions, signals, etc.

• Develop a "good housekeeping" awareness that will reduce accidents and develop the employees' sense of pride in their surroundings. A house-keeping schedule should be established, and an individual should be assigned the responsibility for the clean up.

• Be sure machines are appropriately guarded and employees are aware of guarding requirements.

• Impress on each employee the importance of the use of personal protective equipment.

• Be certain that employees know that they have a responsibility to report unsafe conditions.

• Develop an understanding that the employee's safety is also his responsibility and that he understands his role in the safety program.

Enforcement of safety rules is actually a matter of education. To set a good example for employee education, top management and supervisors must know and believe in the rules, and must scrupulously follow them.

Education often succeeds where discipline fails, and it is usually used when supervisors find violations. Some companies, in addition to instruction, give a warning on the first violation. The second offense may be followed by a stronger warning or a short layoff. The third offense often results in an extended layoff or, in extreme cases, discharge.

Where labor bargaining groups represent employees, they should be consulted on proposed methods of enforcing rules. Such an agreement should prevent later misunderstandings.

Administering reprimands for the violation of rules demands tact and good judgment. When management feels the worker is deliberately disobeying the rules, and where he continues through unsafe acts to endanger his own life and lives of others, prompt and firm action is justified. It is far better to use extreme measures than to allow accidents to happen because of laxness in the enforcement of safety rules. However, many companies feel that a spirit of cooperation, or mutual understanding and agreement, makes drastic measures of enforcement unnecessary. Indeed, this philosophy should be the goal of safety rules.

Safety Committee

The basic function of a Safety Committee is to create and maintain an active interest in safety and to reduce accidents. Although the make-up of a Safety Committee varies with the company size, organization and corporate policy, it commonly consists of an equal number of representatives of hourly employees and management. The organization and responsibilities of an effective Labor/Management Committee in one company are covered in detail by Schoof in *MBAA Technical Quarterly* Vol. 14, No. 4, p 214, 1977.

The committee set-up helps to fix responsibility, to uncover executive qualities in plant subordinates and, in the course of time, to give many people direct contact with the safety programs. Without careful development and pursuit of the committee set-up and proper control of committee activities, much of the potential value of the committee can be lost. It should not become a gripe session or an arena for manpower discussions, nor should it attempt to take over authority of responsible production supervisors. Ideally, at least, a safety committee will function well only after the need for it is recognized and the services are welcomed.

PERSONAL PROTECTIVE EQUIPMENT

Quite often it is necessary for a worker to wear specially designed protective equipment. When personal protective equipment is supplied, it should be worn by each and every worker exposed to danger. The supervisor should demonstrate his leadership qualities by setting the proper example and wearing the personal protective equipment required on any job or operation in his department. It is well for the supervisor to bear in mind that even though he may not be qualified to select and purchase the most efficient type of personal protective equipment, his responsibility does include the recognition of hazards. Personal protective equipment is designed specifically to prevent injury, but it should be remembered the equipment in itself does not prevent accidents. It does insure, however, that if a mishap occurs the injury will be eliminated or reduced. Because there often is misunderstanding concerning such equipment, the following is a list of common types of personal protective equipment and the occasions for its use.

Safety Glasses

Should be worn in all areas of the Packaging Department. All trade people should be issued a pair of safety glasses. This type of protection is for flying hazards only (i.e. piece of steel, glass, hard objects, etc.) and should not be used for chemical hazards. They should be fitted with side shields. If employees require prescription glasses, a program should be set up to supply prescription glasses to assure control over the quality of the glasses being used in the program. A record should be kept of the employees receiving glasses.

Goggles

Goggles should be worn on all chipping, grinding, caulking jobs, and those operations where caustic or acid solutions are being poured, or in any area where such solutions are apt to be spilled, or where objects are apt to fly and strike the worker. Where harmful rays exist, as in the case of arc welding, the worker should be protected with a welding helmet equipped with a high density welding plate and the arc welding area should be separated by screening to protect the eyes of fellow workes. A lighter lens shade can be used for eye protection during brazing operations. The value in adding coloring materials to the welder's lens is that the goggles then also remove some of the glare, making the worker more comfortable.

Face Shields

This type of eye and face protective equipment has become popular within the past few years. Under no circumstance is it considered to replace the goggle. It can be used in exposures where light, small particles are apt to fly without force. It may be used, too, in some cases where the pouring or handling of caustic is done in small amounts.

Cartridge Type Respirators

Fundamentally, there are two types of face respirators of the cartridge type. One is intended to screen out dust particles of a harmful size, and the other is intended to absorb dangerous chemical vapors. The dust respirator cannot be used in an exposure where there is a chemical vapor hazard. The respirator should be fitted to the man's face according to the manufacturer's instructions, should be a type approved by the United States Bureau of Mines for the operation it is to be used on, and should have its cartridge replaced when the worker begins to smell the odor of the material from which he is being protected. Each worker requiring this equipment should have his own respirator which should be cleaned regularly. Respirators should not be exchanged by the men.

Air Line Respirators

In some cases an air line respirator is recommended. This is a special type of equipment permitting the worker to enter a hazardous atmosphere by equipping him with a hood and individual air supply under positive pressure. It is used when going into an environment that has no oxygen or contains poisonous vapors, such as when cleaning trichlorethelyne and petroleum tanks.

Gloves

Gloves are recommended on many material handling jobs. They should never be worn when working on or around moving machinery unless their use is approved by some responsible person.

Safety Toe Shoes

In the newer designs of safety toe shoes, the construction of the toe will protect the wearer from ordinary heavy impacts, and yet be comfortable while he is wearing them. In many cases, the design is such that they are difficult to distinguish from ordinary dress shoes. Their reasonable economy and long wearing quality should make them desirable to every employee, in addition to the advantage of being protective.

Safety Hats

Every man working in an area where rocks or tools or other small but heavy objects are apt to fall should wear a safety helmet. These can be ordered in various sizes and shapes so that the comfort of the worker is assured, as well as his safety.

Lift Truck Operator Training

The objective of a lift truck training program is to prevent injury and minimize property damage through accidents involving lift trucks. An OSHA regulation states that only trained personnel may operate lift trucks (Standard 7105.3): "Operator training. Only trained and authorized operators shall be permitted to operate a powered industrial truck. Methods shall be devised to train operators in the safe operation of powered industrial trucks."

Lift trucks cost as much as a fine passenger car, sometimes considerably more. They are expensive and vital pieces of equipment and when operated recklessly or with lack of know-how, their operation can and has caused loss of life, permanent injury and extensive damage to property and product. Their safe use is covered in detail in Chapter XIX, Warehousing.

COMPLIANCE WITH REGULATORY AGENCIES

There are many governmental agencies at the local, state and federal levels that are interested in making the work place an environment free of work hazards and health hazards. Local and city agencies have codes that control building construction and installation of equipment which must conform with their safety standards. These standards also include codes for fire safety and life saving and are enforced by inspectors checking work places periodically.

OSHA

The Occupational Safety and Health Act of 1970 provides for the establishment of standards of safety in the work place. It also provides for inspection and enforcement to insure compliance with such standards. Failure to comply can result in a citation.

In The Elements of Safety Brewing Operations, *MBAA Technical Quarterly* Vol. 14, p 209-217, No. 4, 1977, Robert I. Schoof states that all department supervisors should be familiar with the OSHA Act. (Summaries of the act are available from many sources.) His chapter on safety in the *Practical Brewer* is a valuable reference.

Examples of OSHA Citations

—(T8) 4051. Employer failed to install and maintain a guard over the pump coupling, such as a mixing pump (2).

—29CFR 1910.134 (b)(1). Failed to assure that written standard operating procedures governing the selection and use of respirators be established, exposing employees to respiratory hazards.

—8 CAC 3273. Failure to keep permanent floors reasonably free from water and also to maintain drainage system properly, where wet processes are used.

Occupational Noise Exposure

Excessive noise is one of the more common hazards encountered in the packaging operations and may cause hearing damage. To protect employees it is management's responsibility to make certain they are not exposed to noise levels in excess of the standards. The U.S. standard (1982) is 90 decibels A-weighted (dBA) for an eight-hour exposure; in some countries it is 85 dBA. Even at this level, hearing damage can be expected in some individuals. It may soon be a requirement, (and it is considered good practice), to have hearing checked (audiometric testing) on an annual basis for all employees exposed to 85–90 dBA noise levels for eight hours daily.

At greater than 90 dBA exposures (eight hours per day) or for higher noise levels in excess of the allowable time (e.g. 100 dBA for more than two hours), a continuing, effective hearing conservation program MUST be administered. Table I gives various noise levels and the maximum allowable exposure times: If exceeded, it is REQUIRED that either engineering controls, such as enclosing noisy equipment, or administrative controls, such as limiting time of exposure, be utilized to reduce noise level or the exposure time to comply with the standard. If these control measures are not feasible, then effective personal protective equipment is REQUIRED. There are many forms and types of ear protection that can be considered, from ear muffs to ear plugs. Some are more useful than others, depending on the noise level, the frequency of the noise, and how well they fit the individual. It is necessary to provide protection that is effective and reasonably comfortable to the wearer.

Table I is provided to assist in the evaluation of the noise levels in the workplace. If referral to the table indicates that levels and time of exposure are such that corrective action is needed, it is recommended that professional help be sought to correct the problem. A noise survey by adequately trained personnel should be made before implementing engineering and administrative controls, and/or setting up a hearing conservation program with the following program objectives:

1. Prevent increased noise induced hearing loss for employees.
2. Comply with State and Federal regulations (OSHA).
3. Minimize/stabilize workers compensation liability arising from hearing loss.

TABLE I
Permissible Noise Exposures

Duration per day, hours	Sound level dBA, slow response
8	90
6	92
4	95
3	97
2	100
1½	102
1	105
½	110
¼ or less	115

SUMMARY

H.W. Heinrich noted in an analysis some fifty years ago, "An accident resulting in the occurrence of a lost time injury was preceded by 329 similar accidents caused by exactly the same unsafe act or mechanical exposure. Of these preceding accidents, many of which were sustained by the very same person who finally was seriously injured, 29 were minor first aid cases and 300 were narrow escapes from actual injury."

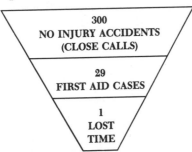

This concept has stood the test of time. Its use can help to concentrate accident prevention activity in the right area.

Many "loss control" specialists say that most accidents are the result of more than one cause. Usually there is an unsafe act of the person or persons involved in addition to an unsafe condition. However, if each individual is taught to understand that he should work and think safely, he can eliminate the unsafe personal factor that is partially responsible for the occurrence of an accident and thereby save himself from accidental injury. In other words, if the individual does the job properly, even though a situation may be hazardous, the chances are no accident will happen to him. Accident records of jobs where extremely hazardous machines are being used show that most often the number of accidents that occur in such situations is less than in those jobs where less hazardous equipment is being employed. This undoubtedly is because the worker takes particular care to act safely and thus protects himself.

When it is stated that all accidents are the result of unsafe acts or unsafe conditions, it should be borne in mind that the analysis of any particular mishap will probably disclose one or more unsafe acts and one or more unsafe conditions. Usually, however, in the list of specific accident causes it will be recognized that either one particular act, or one particular condition, was the principal cause and that the others were more or less contributing causes.

Honest investigation of all accidents discloses first of all that they are all *caused*. This simple statement needs a great deal of emphasis in order to overcome such faulty notions as: "if your number is up, it's going to get you," "Accidents are bound to happen," and so forth. Such beliefs, in regard to the occurrences of mishaps, do not admit the possibility of preventing accidents.

Actually, every accident is caused by some personal or mechanical failure. The supervisor who recognizes very clearly that all accidents are caused, and that their causes may well be expressed as unsafe acts or unsafe conditions in his department has crossed an important threshold in his thinking and has entered the area that permits him to seek out and correct the accident causes. Supervisors can never do a "top notch" job of improving accident experience until such time as they direct their thinking along these lines and persistently search for the common unsafe acts and conditions which may cause accidents to their men.

In conclusion, we have focused on a few facts that pertain to the packaging areas and have given some idea of where efforts may be put to eliminate accidents and unsafe acts.

It is evident that most brewery accidents do occur in the packaging department, and it is easy to understand why: the exposure is certainly greater since there is more moving machinery in addition to the obvious glass hazards. However, with a concerted effort on the part of everybody, accidents in the packaging department can be eliminated; as many as 80% of all injuries are caused by unsafe acts.

REFERENCES

Schoof, Robert J. "The Elements of Safety—Brewing Operations" *MBAA Technical Quarterly,* Vol. 14, p 209-17, No. 4., 1977

Schoof, Robert J., "Safety", Chapter XXI, *The Practical Brewer,* Second Edition, Broderick, H.M. (Edit.), Master Brewers Association of the Americas, Madison, Wisconsin.

National Safety Council. *Accident Prevention Manual for Industrial Operations.*

Blaile, R. P. *Industrial Safety.* Prentice Hall—Third Edition.

CHAPTER XXII

PACKAGING QUALITY ASSURANCE

BY ROGER B. PETERSEN

This chapter is not intended to be a cookbook of methods or procedures, nor does it pretend to be the definitive presentation of all concepts of Quality Assurance. It attempts to present the philosophy and concepts of a system developed and successfully functioning for a large multi-plant operation.

QA (Quality Assurance) is conceived to be a system of controls for the purchasing, manufacturing and distribution processes to assure that the ultimate consumer receives a product that uniformly conforms in all respects to the intent and specifications of the producer. Quality and Process Controls are important parts of the assurance system, but only parts. Quality Control, in general, involves the acceptance evaluation of all the components of the package, including the product, and an outgoing quality inspection of the packaged product to make certain that all package and product specifications are met. Process Control is the system used to insure that all aspects of the production operation function to produce a finished package meeting all specifications. Nominally, information feedback from the outgoing quality inspection is used to verify or modify the process controls in use.

The introduction of QA into an operation must originate with top management recognizing the need for and value of the tool. It must then determine exactly what it wants the system to accomplish. This normally develops over a period of years with many modifications, changes and additions to adapt to new problems and needs.

SPECIFICATIONS

When management has established what it needs from QA, it must then develop and publish specifications, operating instructions and procedures that define and quantify the above objectives.

A specification is quite simply an appropriate way for management to describe in detail what characteristics it wants items purchased or produced to possess. Most of these characteristics must be assigned a numerical value together with the amount of variation in it that is acceptable (tolerance). There are several general rules to be followed in setting up a specification:

1. Establish why it is needed and that the industry standard or practice will not suffice. For example, specifications that are not intended to be the basis for action should not be issued.
2. Do not set tolerances any tighter than the process requires. Excessively tight tolerances, if obtainable, usually cost more to maintain than the value of the benefits derived.
3. Make certain the specification is within the capability of the process involved. All specifications must be based on a complete knowledge of the process and its needs.
4. To be effective, all specifications must be written clearly and made available to all concerned. Verbal understandings rarely maintain any

uniformity of operation or supply.

5. Set up a periodic review program to verify their continued validity.

When a specification is issued, directives and procedures must be developed to instruct QA as to its application. These include the methods of measurement, the frequency, the sampling and sample size, the acceptance or rejection process, and the record and reporting system. All this becomes an integral part of the total written specification.

RISK

One of the most difficult concepts for management to accept is that of "risk" as applied to quality. Regardless of the desire for "zero defects" in the product, this can only remain an objective never to be achieved. QA can determine and control the normal level of defects in the process, but it cannot guarantee that portions or "lots" will not contain levels above those specified. Risk of accepting defects can be reduced by increasing the sample size, or making multiple inspections, but an economic limit is quickly reached in terms of cost and interference with the operation. Management then must accept the degree of risk it can afford.

The factor of risk is no different for quality than it is for loss or destruction of property and the amount of "insurance" coverage must be based on the economic balance between the costs of protection and the potential damages.

COST

Whatever the level of QA specified by management, its operation requires funding. This would appear to be so obvious as to require no discussion. It is surprising, therefore, to find that management will on occasion demand an extension of coverage without recognizing its cost. It is the responsibility of QA to avoid this by providing, without delay, their assessment of the added cost with respect to the budget.

Management must accept a budget of QA costs adequate to provide the operational, product and material coverage it has established.

RESPONSIBILITY—AUTHORITY

The final, and possibly the most important, requirement of management is that responsibility for QA be clearly assigned. This is best done using a chart of reporting responsibility and will be discussed in the following section of Organization. With responsibility must go authority, again clearly defined. For example, can QA shut down an operating line or the use of defective material on its own authority or must it only recommend?

ORGANIZATION

Corporate

The ultimate responsibility for Quality must be placed at the highest level of authority in the company. This may be retained by the president or his vice-presidential designate. This level of authority is needed to insure that the frequently conflicting needs of production and quality may be resolved in a manner that best serves the company. A large multi-plant QA operation may require a vice president whose duties are entirely related to quality, while smaller or single-plant operations may require only that quality be part of a vice president's duties.

As in most operations, quality has both administrative and technical requirements which in a small operation may very well be handled by one man and his staff. Large multi-plant operations generally require that the corporate technical requirements of both Brewing and Packaging Quality Assurance be handled by a single person in order to make certain that all plants enforce the quality specifications uniformly, using the same techniques. Personnel and salary administration and manning of the separate plant quality staff are, on the other hand, best handled by the local plant manager reporting to the corporate operations vice president or equivalent.

Local or Single Plant

The basic organizational divisions of QA in a single plant are those of function. The size of the operation again dictates how each of these functions is supervised and manned. It is important only that each is covered adequately to execute management's mandate.

The prime functions are as follows:
> Packaging material testing and acceptance
> Production operations
>> Process controls
>> Product inspections
> Technical services
> Ancillary services

The performance of these functions are discussed in detail in the following sections.

PACKAGING QUALITY ASSURANCE OPERATIONS

Objectives

The ultimate objective and obligation of the packaging quality assurance program is to protect the quality of the finished product and to maintain it at the level prescribed by management. To fulfill this responsibility, QA coverage requirements are established to provide total protection of the product, including all areas of incoming materials, operation of production equipment and finished product in the most effective and economical manner possible.

Principles

Assuming prior knowledge that supplier and process capabilities permit operation meeting all specifications, the QA system is based on the periodic inspection of small samples sufficient to serve as a continuing measure of the average level of defects and other quality factors in material and production, and at the same time to detect the possibility that an adverse change in quality is occurring. If such a change is detected, immediate action in the form of increased inspection, production holds, etc., is taken to determine whether the observed change is significant. The affirmation of a significant change then requires the use of formal statistical sampling and control plans until the problem is eliminated when the coverage reverts to the normal mode.

In other words, the basic program is an alarm system which detects the development of a serious problem at nominal cost and permits costly, concentrated inspection to be confined to the material, times and production lines where real trouble exists.

PACKAGING MATERIAL TESTING AND ACCEPTANCE

The acceptance of packaging materials ideally would provide for inspection and evaluation of each shipment *prior to use*. Unfortunately, this is rarely physically or economically practical especially for those materials used in large quantities. It is difficult to justify scheduling, receiving, unloading, providing space for storage and rehandling to reject or to place in service, while QA samples and runs its laboratory and functional tests on materials, the vast majority of which will prove to be acceptable.

Material quality control is the responsibility of the supplier, as certified by his contractual agreement to meet the users' specifications, which should include the proviso that regardless of all else the material will function satisfactorily. Thus QA can concentrate its efforts on instances of real or suspected poor performance, as detected by production, or as the result of its own functional observations.

The QA program can be outlined as follows:

SUPPLIER QUALIFICATION

The purpose of qualification is to insure that the supplier is capable of producing specification material and to assist him in so doing.

The first step requires that the supplier be fully instructed in, and understands all details of, the specification and the sequence of steps to be followed in the qualification procedure. This often involves other departments other than QA:

Brewing, for any taste qualification needed.

Package Engineering, for specifications.

Merchandising or Creative Services, for any color or art work.

Production, for any special requirements or problems.

Procurement, for the procedures involved in scheduling use and bringing material into the plant.

Packaging Quality Assurance, for the details of the qualification procedures and material evaluation tests.

Next the supplier submits preproduction samples for checks to verify that his basic setup is satisfactory. These checks are usually laboratory measurements. Obviously, any errors should be corrected before production begins.

These being acceptable, production may begin, from which a large sample is submitted for both laboratory and line function evaluation followed by a series of production runs. The quantities used in these evaluations are dictated by the nature of the material and the needs of the user. In the case of bottles or cans, these are truck or carload quantities. If failure occurs prior to final qualification, the procedure reverts to the last satisfactory step of the qualification procedure.

When qualification is achieved, no further intensive acceptance work is done by QA unless a quality or a production problem occurs.

ROUTINE OPERATIONS

When functional problems occur, they must be investigated to determine their probable cause. In particular, is the problem the material, the packaging equipment, or both?

If the material proves to be the source, the supplier is called in and advised of the defect. He is provided with appropriate samples and allowed to observe the effect on line operation if at all possible. If the defective material results in the production of a product lot that is suspected of failing to meet specifications, the lot must be held. At the same time the material involved is embargoed from use pending the investigation. A random sample of the production is inspected to determine whether the product defect tolerance has, in fact, been exceeded. If the random sample fails, the held production is then 100% inspected to remove the defective material. If it passes, the product is considered salable and the material embargo is lifted.

THE DEFECTIVE MATERIAL REPORT (DMR)

If the investigation proves the material to be at fault, all costs of labor and product loss are accumulated in the form of a DMR for backcharge to the supplier in accordance with the contractual agreement. In addition, all embargoed material is returned to the supplier at his expense, for possible rework and resubmission if he so desires. Only one resubmission is allowed. Should this fail, the material lot is rejected for further use.

Repetitive receipt of defective material from a supplier may disqualify his product and force a repeat of the qualification procedure prior to any further use of that product.

VENDOR RATINGS

The DMR's, reports of production downtime and customer complaints resulting from defects in a vendor's product are accumulated over a fixed period of time, usually semiannually and annually, and used to prepare a "Vendor Rating". This compares each supplier with all others supplying the same material on the basis of a ratio, weighted for the quantities purchased. None of the various possible forms of vendor ratings will be considered fair by all suppliers, but if all are judged on the same basis in accordance with published rules, the desired result of competition between vendors will be achieved. The net effect is to improve material quality and service, and to favor the better ones with increases in the quantities purchased from them. An example of one form of Vendor Rating is based on the number of DMR's issued against a supplier during a designated six-month period. This is divided by the quantity in standard units, received during the period and the resulting ratio used to rate the vendor. For example, a bottle supplier receives six DMR's for defective 12-oz. NR ware during the first half of 1981. During this period he supplied 284,000 gross. The standard unit is 10,000 gross; thus, 6/28.4 yields a ratio of 0.21. Similar calculations are made for the other suppliers of this bottle and ranked by ratio. Further weighting of the ratio might include service complaints which pertain to proper loading, use of correct pallets in good order and similar factors. Also the minutes of downtime per standard unit resulting from supplier defects can also be considered. The Vendor Rating is a valuable tool for QA, Production and Material Procurement. They are required by Material Procurement to assist in determining who shall receive future orders and what quantity each will provide.

QUALITY IMPROVEMENT

A major and continuing responsibility of QA is to work with the packaging material suppliers, to maintain and improve the quality of their products. This is accomplished by means of regular and frequent contact with the supplier to discuss all problems and possible ways to reduce or eliminate them. Since it is not uncommon for a supplier's production people to fail to realize the effect a defect has on the user's operation, visits are made to his plant and in turn his operators are encouraged to return the visit and observe their product in use.

The Vendor Ratings also assist in quality improvement since they result in competitive pressure between suppliers, in addition to their effect on potential orders.

Frequently a supplier will propose a modification in his operation which may result in a quality improvement. QA should assist in this by running any production tests required to establish the merits of the change.

There is no question that the above, in addition to the back-charges and rejected material, results in steady quality improvement of packaging materials with a corresponding improvement in production line efficiencies and product quality.

MAJOR ITEMS COVERED

Bottles

During the qualification or whenever new molds are placed into service, a double mold set sample is measured to verify that fabrication, especially finish, and all dimensions meet specification. These include height, diameter at shoulder and heel, label panel depth, roundness, rocker bottoms, perpendicularity and overflow capacity. The glass color is also measured to insure product protection and to maintain package appearance.

Line function is measured by running a 10,000 bottle sample through a production line with a breakage count after the washer-rinser, filler-crowner, pasteurizer, labelers and packers. Delayed breakage may be checked by holding the test lot for three days after palletization, followed by inspection for wet cases. All broken glass is collected for examination by the supplier to determine the cause of breakage. In addition to breakage, the test is observed for bottle mobility and any leakers resulting from a finish defect.

It is desirable to audit shipments occasionally for missing and damaged bottles, and to spot check carriers and cartons for printing quality, color and makeup, especially gluing.

Cans

Laboratory examination of cans is normally confined to color, lithography and overflow capacity on small samples (12 cans). Periodically, cans are filled and their effect on taste evaluated. If steel cans are used, iron pick-up measurements[1] may be required after one week storage at 43°C (110°F) together with checks for metal exposure using the Wilkins-Anderson enamel rater.

Functional tests require that large samples, generally a truck-load, be run on a production line under observation for count, damage, mobility and leakers.

As with bottles, periodic audits of shipments for missing and damaged cans are useful. The audit is based on the direct observation of random pallets as the cans are being mechanically unloaded and fed to the operating line. Damaged and missing cans on the exterior of the pallet are counted on the pallet infeed conveyor. Those found in the interior of the load are counted on the unloading table. Damaged cans are removed and made available to the manufacturer to assist in locating and eliminating the source of the damage. The audit can be used as the basis for backcharges to the supplier if desired.

Bottle Closures

By specification, each shipment of closures should contain a random sample box. This is available for periodic checks for count, damage, lithography, liner placement, height, diameter and dirt or debris. Previous production problems may dictate a line function run of the random box prior to use of the shipment. This may also include a taste evaluation and a CO_2 retention test[2]. Storage for one week at 43°C (110°F) can be substituted for the 24 hours at 60°C used by the ASBC procedure.

Can Closures

Other than for periodic checks of tube counts, there is little direct acceptance work on lids except when a new sealing compound or other modifcation is proposed, or when there is a serious production problem when various dimensions, plate thickness, compound weight and tab or ring pull measurements may be useful. Most lid quality information is obtained from the routine can seaming analysis, examination of leakers and line tab function checks. It is desirable to have the supplier select a random sample, as the lids are tubed, sufficient to fill a specially marked tube placed in the top layer of each pallet. These samples are valuable when selection is necessary because of a defect.

Cartons and Carriers

For the most part, on-going carton and carrier quality is judged in use and as part of outgoing quality inspections. Part of the line quality checks, in addition to basic functionability are count, damage, color, printing, makeup and gluing. When production problems are investigated or a supplier qualified, detailed laboratory measurements are made of board quality, blank dimensions, cutting, scoring and printing rub resistance. Bottle suppliers are required to evaluate all materials used in packing their ware for compliance with the user's specifications and report their findings to QA in the plant receiving their ware.

Labels

Periodically, or when requested by production, sample bundles of each label type from each supplier are evaluated for count, dimensions, uniformity of cut, printing quality, color and correctness of packaging. Additionally, paper weight and stiffness may be checked.

Draught Kegs

Since these are high-unit-cost items, they warrant close control until confidence in the supplier is established. The interiors should be inspected for proper welding with no gaps or slag inclusions. In the case of stainless steel, the presence of carbide lines around the welds may indicate the loss of stainless properties which will result in iron pickup in the product. Exposing the weld to a salt solution, with resulting rust or stain, will confirm this.

Height, diameter, valve and bung bushings and capacity are important to line function and must be verified against the specification. Any defects found should be reported immediately to the manufacturer to prevent further production of defective units.

Bungs

A random sample box should be specified for each shipment. This is inspected for wood defects which can result in breakage or leakers and for dimensions controlling the fit and drive. Effect on taste is checked by inserting split segments of the bungs in filled bottles which are then recrowned and tasted after 24 hour storage at room temperature.

Miscellaneous

Though lesser in magnitude than the above, there are a number of other packaging related items of importance to the operation. Some of these may be adhesives, keg valves, draught beer dispensing equipment, valve covers, sealing tape and pallets. These also should be covered by appropriate acceptance programs.

PACKAGING OPERATIONS

In general, all tests, sample sizes and frequencies are nominal and may vary with the type of equipment, the specific needs of an operation and management policy. Some items may be considered process controls and covered by production personnel. When this is policy, audits should be made by QA.

While QA is assigned the responsibility for maintaining the packaging quality standards, the role of operating personnel must not be overlooked. QA inspections are periodic, while observations by the operating personnel are nearly continuous, which, if encouraged and acted on, can greatly improve the net quality result.

DRAUGHT BEER

Keg Washing (Bunged types only)

Twice per shift check the temperature and concentration of washing solutions, and function of external brushes and jets as well as the equipment required to clean the Hoff-Stevens and Perlick tap units if these are used. Cycle time should be verified at startup. Interior spray checks require the use of a transparent or windowed package.

Washed kegs should be 100% inspected by production personnel to detect and reject for rewash any improperly cleaned packages. QA audits the performance of these inspectors and checks for water and alkali carryover in 4 packages at shift startup.

Racking

At each startup or beer change, verify beer identity by color[3] or specific gravity[4] and check for clarity, CO_2 content[5] (pressure-temperature) and DO (dissolved oxygen) level (Hayes, IL 540, Beckman or other meter). Monitor racking technique (filling, bunging) visually several times per shift and observe for excessive beer wastage. This is the most practical way to control fill; however, as additional coverage and for the record, pre-tared packages should be racked, weighed and gravimetric fills calculated.

Outgoing Quality Inspection

Several packages should be checked periodically, after the racker for correct beer identification, production date coding, valve covers, properly driven bungs and external appearance. Detection of leakers is best done in the cold storage room or during loading after 24 hours. Since short fills are almost always the result of operator error, they do not occur when the operator can see that a test is being made. Thus any checks of fill in full goods must also be made in the cold storage room. Rapid checks of gravimetric fill can be made by using the average tare weight of empty kegs. This has more value as a monitor of operator performance than as a verification of outgoing quality.

Occasionally, it is desirable to determine the oxygen pickup during racking. This is measured with a meter using beer withdrawn from a filled package and compared with the DO of the bulk beer used.

BOTTLING AND CANNING OPERATIONS

Packaging Cellar

At startup, especially after line cleaning, and as each tank group is released by brewing, the beer is checked for identity, clarity, CO_2[5] and dissolved oxygen or "air" content. A problem detected at this point will prevent a much more serious one in the packaged product.

BOTTLING

Returnable Bottles

If these bottles are not washed on return from the trade, but are stored before use, they may develop internal residues which exceed the cleaning capability of the washer. Tests or experience can indicate what this capability is and a storage policy established that insures that the capability is not exceeded. In general, bottles that are not warehoused more than 6 months can be washed without difficulty.

When operating with warehoused unwashed bottles returned from the trade, it is desirable to check their "age" as indicated by the label code. If it is found to average more than 9 months, the production should be placed under statistical control with holding of the product until it is accepted or rejected based on the results of the inspection of a random sample. This will avoid shipping product containing foreign matter.

Washing—Rinsing

Alkali concentration (titration), fill level and temperature of each compartment is checked at least once per shift. If an alkali reclaiming system is in use, its contents should be checked daily for alkali content. Twice per shift the mechanical functioning of the rinser should be checked for brush height, rinse water pressure and the bottle-jet alignment.

Washed returnable and rinsed NR (non-returnable) bottles should be sampled daily and checked for water and alkali carryover as well as for any debris.

EBI (Empty Bottle Inspectors)

These should be checked for detection and rejection of test bottles at startup and at two hour intervals. The test bottles should be prepared as recommended by the EBI manufacturer. If, during operation, the EBI is found to be non-functional, production for the period affected must be held and checked for foreign matter.

Filling

At each startup and beer or tank change, verify beer identity by means of color or specific gravity and check for clarity at the filler. In addition, "air" and CO_2 content of the filled bottles from the first salable round are checked. During the run, six packages are run for "air" content and three for CO_2[5] every two hours. It is desirable to warm the samples to about 20°C (68°F) prior to testing since this helps gas evolution in the "air" measurement and permits more reliable CO_2 values.

The "air" measurement requires some discussion. The prime purpose of the measurement is to control container headspace air removal during filling and crowning, and the most rapid and effective way of doing this is to limit "air" measurement to the first 100 ml of gas drawn from a package using 45% commercial KOH as the CO_2 absorber in a multi-burette Orsat (Figure 21-1). Total "air" shakeout does not improve control and requires much more time.

22-1—Multi-burette Orsat for "Air" Measurement

When package DO meters become available, it is expected that these will replace all gasometric "air" measurements. Additional "air" control is based on visual checks of the operation for pressure, speed and foamover. These checks are made 4 times per shift alternating with the above "air" measurements. When there is a problem with "air" control it may be desirable to measure DO at the base of the filler for comparison with values obtained in the supply cellar.

Fill is checked using the samples taken for "air" and CO_2 measurements. Six filled bottles are tared together prior to the tests and drained and weighed empty afterward. The average weight difference per bottle is converted to fluid ounces at 20°C (68°F) using a chart of weight versus specific gravity of the beer involved. Combined weighing reduces weighing error and test time. Fill is also checked visually during the "air" control above.

Crowning

Crimp is checked at each startup or after crowner adjustment using a standard steel bottle or the average of a sample of five crowned bottles from each head.

Additional crimp checks are made as part of the outgoing quality inspection discussed later.

Capping (Twist E-Z Capper)

One bottle per head is checked for removal torque and visual defects (incomplete threads, broken pilfer-proof ring, etc.) at pre-startup and startup and one per head per shift thereafter. Additional coverage is part of the outgoing quality inspection.

Torque (Crowns and Caps)

Select a sample of 24 bottles weekly after the pasteurizer. Store one day at room temperature and one day at 4°C (40°F) prior to testing. Use the Owens-Illinois torquemeter.

Low Fill Detector

Before test bottles can be prepared for use in setting and checking the function of the low fill detectors, a low fill must be defined. Legal requirements for fill are the first to be considered. The U.S. Federal regulations are quite loose in that they allow a maximum variation of ± 0.5% of stated fill based on *plant* average fills over three consecutive calendar months. They do not apply to singles, lots, production lines or container types. Thus, while continual fill control is required, the low fill detectors can be set to eliminate only the visually obvious low fills and thus minimize process loss. Management must establish what the rejection fill should be. Where state or local regulations differing from the federal are enforced, the detectors must be set to comply with them. The test bottles themselves should be prepared in accordance with the recommendations of the manufacturer of the detector.

The detection and rejection functions of the device are checked at startup and at the midpoint of the shift using test bottles for standard fill, low fill and missing crown. Each type is passed through the detector five times and adjustment made immediately if acceptance or rejection fails on any pass.

Pasteurization

There are several systems in use with the objective of eliminating the growth of beer spoilage organisms in packaged beer. The most widely and reliable method used is the heat process called pasteurization. The only off-set of pasteurization, other than economic, is the possible adverse effect of heat on taste and shelf-life. Thus it is necessary to control it closely; first, to insure that biostasis is achieved; and second, to avoid exposing the product to any higher temperature than is necessary and for minimum time. A second method uses chemical bio-inhibitor additives and a third, "sterile" packaging procedures. The latter requires that the beer itself be bacteriologically "clean", that the filler be essentially sterile and operated in a separate filler room ventilated with filtered air. Beer so packaged should be stored and shipped at a temperature below 16°C (60°F).

The usual requirements for a biologically "clean" product specify that it reach a minimum temperature of 60°C (140°F) and that it be held at this temperature or higher until it has received a minimum total of about 6 PU's (pasteurization units). One PU is defined as one minute at 60°C (140°F). PU's are accumulated at a slower rate in the zone 52°C (125°F) to 60°C (140°F) and at an increasingly faster rate above 60°C (140°F)[6]. To minimize heat exposure, the pasteurizer must be adjusted to raise the product temperature to 60°C (140°F) as rapidly as possible and to cool it as quickly as possible after receiving the required PU's.

If the cooling water permits, the product-out temperature should be 27°C (80°F) or less, but not lower than the ambient dewpoint since condensate interferes with labeling and damages the packaging material.

Control is based on the pasteurizer cycle time (product in—product out) and the temperature settings of the various heating and cooling sections. There are several devices to measure the time-temperature exposure of the product for a given cycle time. Until recently the best device used a traveling thermocouple connected by cable to a potentiometric strip recorder. This was cumbersome and required the presence of the operator during the entire run. Currently, a new electronic device, the "PU Computer-Monitor"[7], is available that records time and temperature for the product and the external water. It records these magnetically and, at the end of the test, calculates and displays digitally the PU's received. When a complete time-temperature chart is needed, as when adjusting the time or temperature setting, the device is plugged into a strip recorder which is activated by the magnetic memory. The operator is needed only to insert and remove the monitor and other work can be done during the cycle.

It is obvious that PU measurement is not an operating control. It is a method of determining what time-temperature settings should be to insure that biostability is maintained in the outgoing product. Periodic checks are made to determine if other factors such as weakening pumps or plugged nozzles are changing the results. These should be run once per week on the side of the pasteurizer furthest from the water inlet and include both decks of double deck units. These are supplemented by weekly startup checks of cycle time and visual checks of each nozzle for plugging. Hourly visual checks are made of water flow or spray coning and compartment temperatures.

Operating Control of Pasteurization

Bacteriological tests for the operational control of pasteurization of the product are not useful since they require three days to complete. Thus a rapid technique has been developed, based on the fact that the invertase in the beer is destroyed at approximately 6 PU which in turn assures minimum pasteurization[8]. One gram of pure sucrose is added to a five ml beer sample and, after 30 minutes, tested for the presence of glucose using a commercial test tape or strip of the type normally used for the detection of glucose in urine. This test is made twice per shift on samples from both sides of the pasteurizer.

If the beer normally contains glucose, this test cannot be used.

Water Treatment

The concentration of additives for biological and corrosion control in the pasteurizer water should be checked periodically in accordance with supplier or engineering instructions.

Labeling

Visual checks are made four times a shift by QA supervision for such obvious labeling defects as missing, flagging, inverted, incorrect, misplaced, askew and glue smears. In addition, label damage occuring on the line (fold-backs, tears and scuffs) are watched for as well as errors in notch coding.

Packers

Observations of carrier and carton makeup are made by QA supervision four times per shift. However, most functional problems, especially jamming, are reported by production personnel to QA for investigation.

Electronic Inspection

The carrier check weighers and carton inspectors for empty, broken or missing bottles are tested once per shift for detection-rejection function using standard packages made up by QA.

Outgoing Quality Inspection (OQI)

The preferred sampling point for OQI is after the sealer, as the cartons enter the conveyors to the palletizers. At this position all packaging operations, including sealing and coding, are complete and the cartons are ready for sale. The quality of most packaging operations has already been screened, thus OQI is an audit of prior inspections and controls, for the most part.

Several important items are best inspected at other locations, since this decreases reaction time and the size of holds when a problem is detected. The OQI for foreign matter and glass should be made as close to the filler as possible at the pasteurizer infeed. The OQI for crown crimp and leakers is made at the pasteurizer discharge, since the time and pressures of pasteurization are often needed to make the defect detectable.

The sample size and frequency of making the OQI depend on how well the line inspection functions are performed and the action taken to correct any defects found. Also, any operational abnormalities or equipment problems require a large increase in the OQI for their duration as compared with the normal coverage.

Nominal OQI requires a 24 bottle (1 case) sample per hour on lines operating at 600 bpm or less and 48 (2 cases) on higher speed lines. When a line has established a low risk record, inspection can be made at two hour intervals, but at the same sampling rate. The inspections for foreign matter and glass, etc., which are not checked after the sealer, require the same sample size and frequency.

The items visually checked in OQI after the sealer are:

Bottles—missing or broken, correct count.

Labeling—placement and proper gluing, damage, missing, incorrect.

Label code—clear, correct.

Fills—compared with a standard bottle.

Bottle defects—excessive scuffing, chipped locking rings or heels, cracked necks and external foreign matter.

Cap defects—broken bridges, fractures, untucked pilferproof ring.

Crowning defects—off center, incorrect logo, bull nose.

Cartons (re-used)—appearance, function, partition, interior and exterior foreign matter, tape seal and code.

Cartons (new)—appearance, color, bottom seal, tape or top seal and code, correct manufacturer's code on bottom flaps.

Carriers—printing, color, tear strip function, missing partitions, end flap or botton tuck or gluing defects.

CANNING OPERATIONS

Can Coding
Verify function of the coder and correctness of code at the start of each shift.

Rinsing
Once per shift, visually check for nozzle function, mechanical operation, water pressure and cleanliness.

Rinsed Can
Once daily, select a sample of ten cans and measure water carryover and check for debris.

Filling
Identity—verify beer by color and specific gravity at each startup, beer change and tank change.

"Air" and CO_2—test one package per closer head for "air" and three packages total for CO_2 during the first salable round, at startup, beer change, tank change and every two hours during a run. Use the same technique as described for bottles.

Fill—"Air" Control—alternating with the above, make four visual observations per shift of pressures, speed, bubble breakers, quietness of fill and general filler operation including valve function.

Fill (valve control)—during one shift daily, measure the fills gravimetrically, of one full round by valve using the average can-lid tare weight. This test is not practical unless the line after the closer is equipped with a sampling gate and sample run large enough to hold a complete round in the order filled. Valve identity is established from the position of a marked can in the sample observed to have filled on a specific numbered valve. The fill data thus obtained is tabulated by valve to observe variability and trends.

Fill (outgoing quality average)—four times per shift at intervals of two hours, check a sample of ten random cans selected after the closer (unit in normal operation). More frequent checks may be required if unusual fill control is needed, as when producing for certain states.

Use the average tare of the can and lid in use for the gravimetric fill measurement. These are reported as the shift average fill measurement. The effect of scale and tare error can be minimized and weighing and calculating time decreased by weighing ten cans as a unit. Modern electronic weighers with digital readout further reduce error and test time.

Check all samples for dents, damage, leaks and lid defects.

Closing

Seaming—check the seam produced by each head at the beginning and middle of each shift using the standard techniques developed by the manufacturers of the closers. Even when this is not done by QA, it should be responsible for analyzing the results and recommending any action required to maintain the seaming at the specification values adopted. Failure to control seaming closely can result in the production of microleakers that may not be detected until the product is consumed and found low in CO_2 (flat).

Oil and Grease Contamination—it is possible to contaminate the product during the seaming operation if the lubrication is not done carefully, with proper wipedown afterward, or should seals fail. It is desirable, therefore, to take occasional samples at startups after lubrication, pasteurize them and evaluate the taste, aroma and foaming characteristics of the beer. Detection of contamination warrants investigation to find the source and to eliminate it.

Pasteurization—see Bottling.

Low Fill Detector

See Bottling for a discussion of defining a low fill.

Function—check each unit for detection and rejection of low fills at intervals of 2 hours using selected filled cans or special plastic test slugs. Correct the equipment if the test containers are not accepted or rejected 5 of 5 passes.

Check Weigher—once per week at startup, verify the accuracy of the weighers used to screen rejected cans for properly filled cans falsely rejected.

Leakers—the low fill detector is also an excellent leak detector, thus the rejects should be checked visually each hour for any leaking cans or lids.

Tab Function—open all rejects during leaker check.

Packing

Make four visual checks per shift of carrier and carton operations for material related problems. Verify correctness of carton codes.

Outgoing Quality Inspection (OQI)

At intervals of one hour, select four cases at random after the sealer and visually inspect for the following: missing cans, incorrect cans-lids, can and package codes, leakers, buckles, dents, damage, lithography, low fills, missing or turned tab rings, external foreign matter, carton and carrier makeup and sealing.

AUDITS AND REPROCESSING

During production operations, it is often necessary to hold certain portions or lots because they are suspected of containing defects above the level acceptable for shipment. This is done by advising the palletizer foreman of the time period containing the defect, isolating the pallets as they are made up and tagging them for identification. The pallets are then moved to the inspection area where a random sample is taken in conformance with the standard, statistical, single sampling plan (see "Statistics") designated for the defect. The sample is then audited for the defect. If the number of defects exceeds the acceptance number, the lot is retained for reprocessing by removing all the defects during a 100% inspection, after which the lot is returned to salable inventory. If the audit passes, the lot is immediately returned to salable inventory.

Occasionally the audit will show that the defect level is very high. In these instances, since 100% inspection rarely results in 100% removal of defects, it is advisable to select a second random for audit before releasing the product. If the audit fails, a second 100% inspection is required. Usually this is adequate even for the lowest tolerance defects.

The procedure above applies to items that are inspectable, such as leakers, foreign matter and glass, labeling defects, etc. For those defects that can only be found by destructive testing, as "air" or CO_2 content outside the acceptable limits, it is necessary to sample and test each pallet on a non-statistical basis, attempting to find acceptable ones. Those pallets not released for sale should either be consumed or dumped in accordance with company policy.

If, as in some operations, the reprocessing work is considered part of the production operation, QA must audit the inspected lot before release.

WAREHOUSE AUDITS

Overage Beer
The full goods warehouse is audited daily for any product which has passed the time limit for in-plant storage. Any "overage" product found is recorded, tagged and moved to a designated area for disposition. It is important to continue these "age" audits at the branches, distributors and on the retailers' shelves to prevent the sale of packages that no longer are representative of the original quality product because of age. Field audits are not normally made by plant QA, but by the field sales personnel.

Miscellaneous
Other audits may occasionally be required to spot check for delayed leakers, delayed bottle breakage or container damage, as well as to compare a defect level with that indicated by the production line testing.

BACTERIOLOGICAL TESTS[9]

Since beer is both food and beverage, sanitation in handling and packaging it is essential. Gross contamination is visually obvious and can be controlled by inspection and cleaning. This cannot be done for microbiological contamination and the special techniques of Bacteriology must be used. The results of these tests indicate sources of contamination, when special cleaning and sanitizing are needed and whether these procedures are effective. In addition, pasteurization can be confirmed. Fortunately, bacteria, molds and yeasts that will grow in beer are not harmful to humans, but can have a gross effect on beer clarity and reputation.

To conduct appropriate tests in packaging, the laboratory should be set up to culture 4 types of organisms: aerobic bacteria, anaerobics (pediococci and lactics), yeasts and molds, and operate under the supervision of a trained bacteriologist. A minimum operation should concentrate on those packages which are not pasteurized and do not contain bacteriostatic additives; for example, draught beer. Coverage would include the beer as delivered to racking and from the keg after filling, together with checks of the washed kegs.

A simple microbiological stability test is useful and does not involve plating, incubation or counting. Samples of the beer before and after racking are transferred asceptically into sterile flasks stoppered with cotton. These are allowed to stand at room temperature, with daily observation, for the development of turbidity. A stable product should remain essentially clear for 10 days. When turbidity develops or after 10 days, the beer is examined microscopically and the types of organisms seen, reported as none, very few, few, moderate or numerous. Pediococci, lactic rods and yeast may be found.

More extensive coverage would include testing of the beer as delivered to the packaging department and standard plate counts of aerobic bacteria, yeast and mold for washed or rinsed bottles and cans, and verification of the pasteurization of the packaged product.

The rinse water and city water should be checked for bacteria, coliforms and residual chlorine. If jetters are used to eliminate headspace air in bottles, the water used should also be monitored.

The frequency and number of samples tested depend on the space, equipment and staff allowed.

SERVICE FUNCTIONS

Technical Services

One of the more important functions of QA is to provide plant management and production with technical assistance in finding the solution to operating problems, particularly those related to quality. To do this, one or more selected individuals should be assigned to this work only and relieved of any responsibility for the routine tasks. This permits undivided attention to a problem for considerable periods of time, which operating personnel cannot do.

In addition to operational problems, this function could, for example, investigate additives for improved bottle washing, techniques for descaling rinsers, procedures for cleaning fillers and other production equipment, the reduction of beer and packaging material losses, additives for control of corrosion and slime in pasteurizers, performance of proposed or operating electronic inspection devices, new filling valves, etc.

Experience has proven that this service more than pays for its cost in terms of operating efficiency and quality.

Inspections

Since QA is concerned but not directly involved, management may assign it the responsibility for periodic inspections of the sanitation and pest control of the plant and its equipment. In what is legally a food packaging plant, sanitation is very much an important factor affecting product quality.

QA personnel should also make similar periodic inspections of the plants producing all the materials used in packaging both for sanitation and to verify their quality control.

When packaging materials are stored in outside warehouses, these should be inspected by QA to verify their suitability in terms of cleanliness, pest control and physical condition.

CUSTOMER COMPLAINTS

The best available measure of the effectiveness of the QA operation is the complaints received from distributors and consumers. They constitute a "report card" of sorts and deserve the closest attention for numeric trends and type. They are indicators of areas where improved controls may be required and constant reminders of the fact that "zero defects" is an objective not to be achieved. Some may indicate the need for a change in packaging or in the handling of the product, but since it is not possible to please everyone or to control all aspects of distribution, reaction may not be desirable.

Regardless of the type or validity of complaint, all should be responded to promptly and honestly as the facts permit. Management should establish a policy and system for doing this.

STATISTICAL METHODS IN THE QUALITY FUNCTION

Anyone involved in the packaging of beverages as well as the administration of QA would be well-advised to become acquainted with the concepts of basic SQC (statistical quality control) since these are essential "tools" for obtaining, handling, presenting and interpreting the masses of data involved. This does not imply that it is necessary to become a statistician or, for that matter, to have more than a minimum understanding of the mathematical principles on which the "tools" are based. One does not have to understand computer technology to use one. The American Society for Quality Control routinely conducts training courses in SQC in all areas of the country and also published a large number of books covering specific applications. Most of these are designed for practical use and do not require advanced mathematics or knowledge of statistical theory. In his "Statistical Analysis of Plant Data", P.E. Dakin[10] presents a general discussion of many of these tools and also lists various source references. The most useful and comprehensive of all the SQC publications available is J.M. Juran's "Quality Control Handbook"[11].

Sampling and Sampling Plans

The quality aspects of modern high speed packaging operations can only be controlled by means of the inspection of relatively small samples of the production. As previously indicated in the Operations section these are often minimal and serve only as "alarms" to indicate when statistical samples are required. Experience has proven that single sampling plans for attributes[12] are ideal for controlling packaging problems since they are simple to apply and administrate. In single sampling plans, acceptance or rejection is based on the defects (attributes) found in a single group of individuals (sample) selected at random from a production unit or lot. The lot size is arbitrary and is often the number of units produced in a given time. A large hold of production may be divided into sub-lots in order to reduce the risk of rejecting portions that will pass if sampled separately. In general this has proven to be a profitable practice, even though the total lot sample is increased.

Before a sampling plan for attributes can be selected or derived, several parameters must be established.

What is the LTPD (Lot Tolerance Percent Defective)? For a critical defect

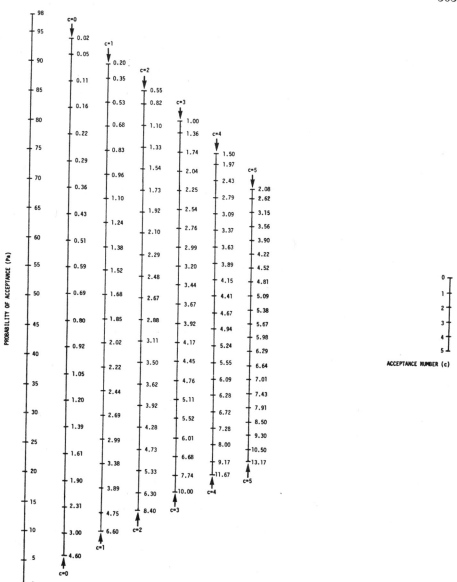

22-2. Nomograph for Determining Sample Size for a Single Sampling Plan. Copyright © 1978 American Society for Quality Control, Inc. Reproduced by permission.

such as glass inclusions in bottled product the LTPD might be set at 0.2% defective.

The next parameter needed is the acceptable risk or P_a (probability of acceptance) of a lot having a higher defect level than the LTPD. When making this decision it must be remembered that the lower the risk the larger the sample to be inspected. In general, a 20% risk has proven to be a reasonable compromise though 10% is common.

An appropriate plan may be found in MIL-STD-105D or Dodge-Romig tables[13], or may be derived very simply using a nomograph (Figure 22-2) developed by R.E. Schulze[14] as follows.

With an LTPD of 0.002, a P_a of 20 and acceptance number (c) of 1, the sample size (n) can be determined by laying a ruler connecting 1 on the right hand scale of acceptance numbers and 20 on the left hand scale of P_a, then reading the intersection on the middle c = 1 scale. A value of 2.99 is found. When this is divided by the LTPD (0.002) the sample size (n) is obtained, 2.99/.002 = 1495. Thus, if a sample of 1495 bottles is inspected and no more than 1 defect is found, the lot is accepted and released for sale. If 2 or more defects are found, the lot is rejected for 100% inspection to remove all defects before release.

If a smaller sample size is desired the same procedure is followed using c = 0. Thus the intersection for c = 0 is 1.61 and n = 1.61/.002 = 805.

A smaller sample has been achieved, but at the cost of an increase in the risk of rejecting a good lot. In general, sampling plans having an acceptance number of zero are undesirable.

The middle scales represent LTPD $\times$ n, thus knowing their values and c, the P_a can be estimated (0.002 $\times$ 805 = 1.61). Placing the ruler on c = 0 and 1.61 in the c = 0 column, P_a is found to be 20%.

Process Capability

In the section on Specifications, rule 3 requires knowledge that a specification be within the C_{PR} (capability of the process). There are several methods of measuring it, but only one, the $\bar{X}$ and R control chart method[15], is absolutely correct since it verifies that the process is evaluated when the operation is free of non-normal sources of variation (assignable causes) as, for example, a defective valve on a filler. The method to be outlined here is an approximation, but is simple to use and yields generally valid information.

In beer packaging the most useful process to study is the performance of the filler. Experience indicates that the filler normally operates "in control" and its C_{PR} can be readily calculated using the fill measurements accumulated during routine control operations. A minimum of 50 values obtained in groups of 3 to 5 packages at 1 or 2 hour intervals is adequate. Calculate the average fill of the sample and its standard deviation[16] by means of the formula:

$$s = \sqrt{\frac{n\Sigma(X^2) - (\Sigma X)^2}{n(n-1)}}$$

where s = sample standard deviation; X = measured fill values;
Σ = "sum of"; n = number of measurements.

Presently, it is unlikely that the above will be used since electronic calculators are so readily available. These are usually programmed to produce the $\bar{X}$ and s simply by entering the X values and pressing 2 keys.

C_{PR} is defined as 6s, thus for a filler with s = 0.05 fl. oz., the C_{PR} is 0.30 fl. oz. For any given normal average fill, 99.73% of all individual fill values will be distributed in a zone ± 0.15 fl. oz. (± 3s) from the average.

Many other examples of the application of statistical procedures to QA could be given, but it does not seem appropriate, since they are readily available in the references cited.

CONCLUSION

All of the foregoing comprises a quite successful QA system. Much of the success stems from the cooperation that has developed over the years between production management and QA. There is mutual understanding that both have the same objective, to produce a quality product at maximum efficiency. Without some degree of this relationship, no QA program can be really successful. This is not to imply that a utopia exists. QA still interferes periodically with production's desire to increase numerical productivity and production still argues occasionally with the apparent rigidity of QA's enforcement of a specification, but overall there is a basic understanding. Management's consistent and continuing emphasis and support of QA is the backbone of this relationship.

QA makes a direct contribution to production efficiency by means of its successful programs to improve the quality of packaging materials, to find and eliminate operating problems and to reduce product losses by finding and eliminating sources of defects.

One area having great potential for quality improvement has been neglected. This is in the quality consciousness of the hourly worker. If every person in the packaging operation could be convinced that the detection, reporting and, in some cases, correction of any quality problem is beneficial to him and a real part of his job, virtually no defects would reach the customer and many would not even be generated.

In recent years, management has made a determined effort to improve the workers' safety consciousness, and the program has greatly reduced all forms of injury. A similar program for quality would yield benefits for both labor and management.

•

REFERENCES

1. KNEEN, E. (Ed.) METHODS of ANALYSIS, 7th Rev. Ed., St. Paul, ASBC (1976) Beer, 19A.
2. *Ibid.*, Packages and Packaging Materials, 1.
3. *Ibid.*, Beer, 10.
4. *Ibid.*, Beer, 2.
5. *Ibid.*, Beer, 13.
6. DEL VECCHIO, H.W., DAYHARSH, C.A., and BASELT, F.C., ASBC Ann. Proc. (1951), p. 45.
7. PCAS, Inc., 5800 Corporate Drive, Suite A-1, Houston, TX   77036
8. HAAS, G. and FLEISCHMAN, A. ASBC Ann. Proc. (1956), p. 62.
9. Kneen, E. (Ed.) *op. cit.*, Microbiology.
10. BRODERICK, H.M. (Ed.) The PRACTICAL BREWER, 2nd Edit., Madison, MBAA (1977), Chapter XVI, p. 309.
11. JURAN, H.M. (Ed.) QUALITY CONTROL HANDBOOK, 3rd Edit., McGraw-Hill (1974).
12. *Ibid.*, 24-2.
13. *Ibid.*, 24-19.
14. SCHULZE, R.E. *Qual. Prog.*, Oct., pp. 30-32, (1978).
15. JURAN, J.M. (Ed.) *op. cit.*, 23-8.
16. *Ibid.*, 22-7.

CHAPTER XXIII

PACKAGING MATERIALS AND BEER QUALITY

BY WILLIAM A. HARDWICK

INTRODUCTION

Brewing and Packaging technologists have known for years that packaging materials coming in contact with beer can have a definite influence on the flavor of that beer. Most of the time this influence is adverse and the alteration of flavor can be great enough to render the beer unsalable. Several of the flavorful substances in packaging materials have an extremely potent impact on flavor; when present in beer at concentrations of about one part-per-billion, they exert an undesirable flavor influence. All of these compounds are harmless to health; several of them are found in other foods where their flavor influence is positive and is part of the characteristic flavor of a given food.

This chapter will review those packaging materials and practices that can influence beer flavor. Materials or methods of manufacture of a package or package component will be discussed when they appear responsible for off flavors that ultimately can get into the beer. Since change in beer flavor is the predominant area of concern here, flavor testing is the analytical measurement most frequently made.

Few industries rely on critical flavor evaluation as heavily as does brewing. It is a vital part of several brewing functions: the selection of brewing materials, following of brewing progress or maturation, and the control of packaging variables. It is not done in haphazard fashion, nor is it done on a sporadic basis.

Flavor evaluations are done on an assigned schedule by trained personnel who are at significant levels of employment in their companies. They taste following established formal taste panel procedures that have been proved reliable. Preliminary flavor screening work or tentative investigations frequently can best be done by informal tasting. When large numbers of samples require flavor screening, one or two qualified flavor analysts can work through them quickly while a more formal flavor panel would take entirely too much time and effort. Final judgments, however, must be made properly by flavor panels operating in a formal session.

Although this is a review of packaging *materials* primarily, there are packaging *operations* that can adversely affect beer flavor. Those having to do with cleanliness of the system are discussed elsewhere. Reference must be made here to two enemies of beer flavor that constantly threaten us. One is oxygen and the other is temperature. They both accelerate oxidation and make beer taste old more quickly than it should.

Beers vary in the particular flavor changes they undergo as they age. Changes in flavor occur in all beers, however, and they are hastened by the addition of oxygen (air) or by too warm storage conditions.

A brewer must constantly check his can or bottle filling operation for the amount of air that it introduces into his beer. If it introduces more than one part-per-million of oxygen, his beer will suffer in the market place. Less than half that amount should be the target of a good filling operation.

Anything the brewer can do to reduce the heat dosage his beer receives during shipment and storage will help both flavor and physical stability of his beer. A rule of thumb that illustrates how heavy the influence of temperature is can be simply stated as "beer stored for one week at 100°F tastes as old as beer that has been stored for two months at 70°F or for over one year at 40°F."

BOTTLES

Bottles generally are freer of potential flavor problems than cans. Their composition and manufacture is simpler with fewer organic compounds involved.

The returnable bottle has persisted in the beer marketplace for many years because it is economical and reliable. It stands as mute evidence of the excellent cleaning job the brewing companies have done over the years. Like the bottles, the cleaning equipment is uncomplicated; caustic soaking compartments followed by extensive rinsing sprays render these old soldiers clean and free from inclusions.

The non-returnable bottle has two susceptibilities not shared by the returnable bottle. Both are due to the thinner wall in the lighter non-returnable bottle.

Freshly-blown glass has very high friction and if a new bottle merely brushes another bottle, scratching of the sidewall surface takes place. Such scratches weaken the sidewall resistance to internal pressure and result in explosion breakage of filled bottles in the pasteurizer, or even worse, breakage during shipping.

This tendency to scratch is countered by applying a friction reducing material to the new bottle surface to lubricate it. The material most widely applied is a water emulsion of polyethylene. This material is not without flavor influence, however, and it must be applied so that none enters the bottle. The emulsion is sprayed on the bottle exterior as it is being conveyed upright on a transfer belt, and it is difficult, but not impossible, to prevent any spray from getting into the bottle.

The second susceptibility of the non-returnable bottle is light exposure. The same amber glass is used to make both the returnable and non-returnable bottle. A much thinner sidewall is present in the lighter-weight non-returnable bottle. This results in significantly lighter amber coloration in the sidewall area. Since a reasonable intensity of brown coloration is required if the bottle is to adequately screen out incidental light in the warehouse and the retail outlet, the color intensity of the non-returnable bottles in use today provides marginal protection against light-struck flavor damage. Figure 1 shows why the brown or amber bottle is used. Here we see the ability of various standard

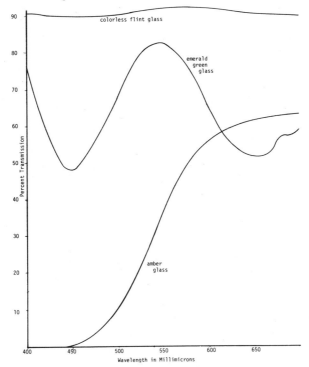

23-1. Transmittance curves for bottle glass

thickness of colored glass samples to adsorb light waves. This shows the brown bottle glass to be relatively efficient at adsorbing light at 400-520 nanometer wavelength, which is the range of the visible light that causes light struck flavor in beer. Curves for the other glass samples show that they do not offer very much protection at this wavelength.

The terms light-struck, sun-struck or "skunky" describe a flavor that develops when beer is exposed to light. An isoprene diene[1] is split from a hop bittering substance, humulon, and reacts with hydrogen sulfide (traces are naturally present in beer) photochemically to produce the same mercaptan that skunks have in their armory, at higher concentrations, of course. This aroma is not considered pleasing in beer either, so brewers use amber bottles and light protective paper cartons in an effort to prevent this photochemical reaction.

Testing Methodology:

It is frequently desirable to set up laboratory tests to determine the ability of bottles and various accessory packaging materials to protect beer against light exposure. It has been found that 50 foot-candles of fluorescent light from standard warm white 40 watt fluorescent tubes is a good light test environment. It duplicates reasonably well the lighting conditions found in midwestern supermarkets. Bottles stored under these conditions should be able to withstand the light dosage for a period of at least five days without any evidence of skunky or light-struck flavor development.

BOTTLE CROWNS

The bottle crown used on most beer packages today is lined with polyvinyl chloride plastisol materials. In addition to polyvinyl chloride resins, these liners contain a plasticizer or softening agent, dioctylphthalate, a stabilizer antioxidant material (generally calcium or zinc stearate) and the twist-off crowns will contain an added fatty amide or paraffin lubricant.

Purity of these various ingredients is essential to the manufacture of crowns having a minimal influence on beer flavor. Some of these materials, like the plasticizer and stabilizer, can contain trace impurities that are very potent in flavor. If these impurities are non-volatile, they probably get extracted into the beer if the bottle is stored horizontally. If volatile impurities are present, they, too, can get into the beer unless they are driven off during curing of the crowns.

Some crowns are lined by placing the creamy plastisol material in the crown shell where it is spread by spinning or by molding and is cured quickly in an oven. Other crowns are lined by melting a powdered plastisol in an extrusion chamber and extruding the molten material into the crown shell where it is kept warm until a tamping tool can form it into the desired shape. If inadequate temperatures are employed in either method of crown lining, volatile material can remain in the liner and find its way into the beer. If this volatile is flavorful, the beer is likely to develop a flavor defect.

Some crowns are made more resilient by incorporating puffing agents into the plastisol formulation; they behave much like leavening agents in baking. They decompose to give off a gas, generally nitrogen, during the curing cycle of the resin. This produces in the plastic film minute bubbles which act as cushioning agents and offer a more flexible surface than the flat resin does by itself. Essentially all puffed crowns exert some adverse flavor influence. Either the puffing agent itself produces off-flavors or the bubbles disrupt the plastic liner surface increasing the amount of exchange taking place between the plastic liner and beer.

Mention should be made of problems that can arise from crown dust. The existence of tiny particulate matter in beer that floats and shimmers in the product is upsetting to the consumer. Most packaging operations try to eliminate the presence of such materials by installing air cleaners or vacuum systems for their crown hoppers so that this dust is removed. Crown hoppers are being redesigned to reduce agitation of crowns and the resultant dust.

Other crown-lining materials are used, although they are used generally for soft drinks, not beer. Polyethylene and ethylene vinyl acetate liners are reasonable substitutes for the polyvinyl chloride liners in soft drinks. Unfortunately, in beer they exert a somewhat greater flavor influence than do the PVC liners. They tend to absorb flavorful compounds from the beer rather than to contribute any off-flavors of their own. Polyethylene formulations especially will literally scavenge many of the esters from beer and concentrate them in the liner material.

Testing Methodology:

Flavor evaluation is the best test criterion for both Quality Control coverage of the crown lining material and for screening candidate formulations. Naturally the crown liners must satisfy other performance tests besides flavor influence. Sealing efficiency and adequate resiliency are two; the other performance tests will be discussed in another chapter.

Flavor evaluations on materials or ingredients being considered for use in crown liners are most generally done by the following methodology:

Liner Components:

If material is not lined into a crown (rolled out as a thin sheet, for example), pieces should be cut to uniform sizes having about three-quarters the surface area of a crown; about ¾ of a square inch is satisfactory. Both sides of the piece will be exposed to beer so total exposure is about 1½ times normal. One piece of this material is inserted into each of several bottles which then can be filled on conventional filling equipment, crowned and pasteurized. Some powders and liquids cannot be formed into films. It has been found satisfactory to merely add the proper amount of such materials to the bottle prior to filling. Filling can be done by hand, but the risk of including too much air (oxygen) during filling is significant. If the air introduced allows more than 1.5 ppm of oxygen to be introduced, then the flavor changes due to oxidation may be great enough to compete with the flavor influence of the packaging variable being examined.

Commercial pasteurized bottled beer (returnable bottles) can be used with reasonable success if the bottles are chilled to 32°F. prior to opening to insert the cut liner pieces. The bottle should then be tapped smartly to induce slight foaming and the resealing crown should be applied just as the foam reaches the bottle lip. Control bottles should be opened, tapped and resealed just as are the test crown; minor differences in carbonation level are tasteable.

Lined Crowns:

If lined crowns are being tested, they should be properly marked so they can be easily identified (sanding the crown down to bare metal is good). This makes recovery of the test bottles easier to make from a busy line or pasteurizer discharge. The test crowns should be mixed in with the proper number of regular crowns (control) in the hopper of a crowning unit so that they get applied to production bottles under production conditions. Control bottles should be taken for measuring air and CO_2 content before they are committed to flavor testing.

A less desirable procedure is to recrown commercial bottles with test and control crowns as described earlier.

Processing Punishment:

Both bottles containing added materials and bottles capped with candidate crowns should be pasteurized if the commercial use of the crown liner is to be on pasteurized beer. The heat of pasteurization accelerates certain flavor changes. Additional storage time is needed to duplicate the shelf life of a commercial package prior to consumption. Storage at elevated temperatures has been found to effectively reduce the storage time required and still permit typical flavor influences to occur. It has also been found that storage of the bottle on its side is a good practice. Sufficient bottles and cans are stored commercially in this manner to justify doing it for flavor evaluation.

The most effective single storage condition has been found to be horizontal storage of the test and control bottles for two weeks at 85°F.

This is followed by overnight cooling to about 38°F., which is the tasting temperature. If there is any interest in checking for changes in physical stability, the beer should be chilled down to 30°F. for 24 hours prior to getting it to tasting temperature. Bottles should be removed at the end of 30°F. storage and examined for change in clarity.

CANS—2-PIECE

The two-piece cans from their inception, almost two decades ago, have grown steadily in volume until today they have virtually displaced the three-piece can. The advent of these cans has added a new dimension to can-making technology. As each new can plant is built, it displays innovations that either improve the integrity of the can or reduce production costs. Although they offer excellent quality and reliability, their use as beer packages has not been without flavor problems.

Considerable changes in can decoration and can interior lining materials have recently taken place and they, too, are accompanied by new flavor problems.

Sources of flavor problems from two-piece cans are:
1) Residues from the can-making process (lubricant residues)
2) Outer can decoration
3) The internal coating system
4) Empty can storage and handling
5) Can lids.

The greatest source of flavor problems arising from can manufacturing is the lubricant materials that were employed either in the can making process or in the final reduction rolling of the can metal stock itself. Under ideal conditions the lubricants are washed away after fabrication in the can washer and there is no problem. Under less than ideal conditions, traces of these potent film-forming materials will survive the washing stage. If potent flavorants are present on the inner surface of the can, the polymer coating applied to its interior will be challenged to cover the material and retain it. Sometimes the polymer coating is unable to do so and the material gets into the beer.

The lubricant material itself can become contaminated with other machine lubes and greases which lubricate the can-making presses or with the protective coating material that has been applied to the aluminum sheet material from which the cans are made. Many of these materials can cause off-flavor problems and must be adequately removed from the can lubricant system. Since the can lubricant system is continually recycled with filtration or centrifugation done at some point in this recycling, it is also susceptible to contaminating bacterial growth. Chemical oxidation occurs and is accelerated by particles of metallic aluminum or iron that are present as residuals from the can body making procedure.

The most common type of flavor problem encountered in two-piece cans has an interesting etiology. The coolant or lubricants being used today in the two-piece can industry are either soluble-oil emulsions made up of both mineral oil and fatty acids and/or esters, or they are made up of fatty acids and fatty esters and other organic compounds which aid in lubricity and cleaning properties but contain no mineral oil. In many instances, both of these lubricant coolant materials contain significant levels of polyunsaturated fatty acids or fatty esters. When traces of such material are left on the can's surface, these unsaturated fatty compounds are oxidized in the can drying oven of the can washer, in the outside decoration ovens or in the can storage warehouse. These oxidation products have been described by Lee and Swoboda[2]. They are potent flavorants as evidenced by 2-nonenal, which is detectable in beer at levels below 1 ppb. 2-nonenal and other fatty aldehydes are not driven off by the oven temperatures. They apparently remain on the can's inner surface. When cans containing traces of these fatty aldehydes are sprayed with the ideal polymer coating (epoxy or vinyl systems), the aldehydes tend to dissolve into the resin system and remain there. Some other interior coating systems are either unable to retain these aldehydes or never dissolve them but merely flux them loose from the can surface so that they end up dried on the inside coating surface, where they are immediately available to the beer. They are detectable in freshly-pasteurized beer. In some other coating systems, after a few days the aldehydes migrate through the coating and get into the beer.

Materials other than free fatty acids in the lubricants can cause flavor problems in a similar manner. The brewer must develop tests and methods for (1) screening the lubricants to select those exhibiting the least flavor influence, (2) selecting those coatings that are most able to retain the contaminants and (3) work with can manufacturers to develop an adequate washing and rinsing system to minimize carryover of these unwanted materials. When these three things have been done, the metal-forming portion of can manufacturing will cease to pose a threat to flavor quality of beer. Other areas of can production and handling present problems slightly different in nature.

Can Outside Decoration:

At today's can making speeds, it may be impossible to prevent some can interiors from becoming contaminated with low levels of the outside decoration materials, such as basecoats, varnishes or inks. It behooves the brewer to make sure that these materials are (1) FDA approved for use in food packaging and (2) substantially free from flavor influence. If this is done, it minimizes the risk that such incidental contamination can cause. Since the cans that get contaminated by these materials get contaminated prior to internal coating application, the ideal internal spray materials should cover the contaminant material and prevent any contact with the beer. We cannot, however, merely rely on an interior coating material to retain the variety of outside materials that are in current usage. We must flavor-screen these potent contaminants themselves.

Internal Coating Systems:

The internal spray coat itself can have direct influence on beer flavor. If it contains traces of low molecular weight impurities, such as unreacted monomer or traces of retained solvent, these can get into the beer and cause flavor problems. If the coating polymer tends to absorb odors, it can alter beer flavor in either of two ways: (1) it can absorb outside odors and present them to the beer, or (2) it can absorb certain flavor substances from the beer, making it taste thinner and less blended.

Some internal coating systems are sensitive to excessive bake oven temperatures. Some epoxies, for example, will exhibit an off flavor influence at temperatures that cause no chemical or physical evidence of heat degradation. The brewer should evaluate cans that have been baked at several temperatures so that the optimum temperature for flavor performance can be established for the inside bake ovens.

The new coating systems which are suspended in water-solvent mixtures demonstrate how a resin system with good barrier properties can still have flavor problems. They tend to loosen contaminant material from the can's interior surface when they are applied. They cannot dissolve this soil, however, because their suspending solvent system is mostly water which offers poor solvating power to many of the substances present as contaminants. This material fluxes to the wet film surface, where it is dried and remains until it is taken up by the beer.

Metal Exposure:

It has been stated frequently that quality of a beer can is no better than the coating inside it. Not only does this apply to quality of the coating itself, but also to the quality of its application. If significant metal exposure exists in a can, beer quality will suffer. The brewer must be aware of the limits of metal exposure that his beer will tolerate, and see to it that his cans do not exceed this limit. Simple tests can be done with either enamel-raters that can be purchased commercially or by the mere filling of test cans with a saturated aqueous solution of copper sulfate (copper plates out on exposed metal areas) to demonstrate the degree of coverage obtained by the internal coating.

Can Handling and Storage

All polymers have some ability to absorb odors. The coating formulators simply select those having the least capacity for doing this and develop coatings with them. Because the can liners will absorb some levels of certain contaminants, the can palletizer and storage environment has some influence on beer flavor. If either of these areas contains significant atmospheric odor, then it can be expected that the cans will exhibit some level of that odor as a result. For example, the divider sheets that are used to separate layers of cans on a pallet can be potent flavor sources. These cardboard sheets are notorious nomads. A divider that is in a pallet of liquid soap or perfumed material today can easily be in a pallet of beer cans tomorrow.

The can warehouse or storage area itself should be free from odors. Although stored cans are in pallets and are layered beneath divider sheets that cover the can openings, they can still breathe due to changes in temperature and pressure in the storage area. The only effective safeguard is to keep odors away from the cans.

Can Lids

At the risk of redundancy, it seems proper here to note briefly the flavor impact that can lids are capable of causing in beer. Both the lids and their end seal compounds are discussed more fully in a later part of this chapter.

Can lids have had some interesting flavor influences in the past. The sealing compound that is applied to the lid is reasonably free of flavor influence itself. This is further kept minimal by placing the compound so that essentially all of it is locked into the double seam, leaving little or none to contact the beer. This material will absorb certain odors readily and, for this reason, care must be taken to keep solvent and odorous compounds away from the kraft paper cylinders of lids during transport and storage. Significant metal exposure on the lids can also cause flavor problems as readily as it will in cans.

The lubricants used on the presses making the tab-top lids can cause flavor problems, turbidity or foam inhibition. They should be screened by the brewer, and only those that do not present these potential problems should be used.

Thanks to the combined efforts by lubricant manufacturers, washer chemical suppliers, can coating suppliers and the can manufacturers themselves, the two-piece can is a highly reliable package. What is emphasized here is that there are routine control measures that should be matched to the unique steps in the manufacturing and processing of these packages to keep them free of flavor problems.

CANS—3-PIECE

The three-piece can for several years has continued to be replaced by the two-piece can in the U.S.A. market place. In Mexico and South America the two-piece replacement is just beginning; in Canada one company has started using 2-piece aluminum cans.

The major reason for a shift to two-piece cans in the U.S. has been economics. Less metal is used and a simpler, speedier manufacturing is possible. The three-piece can calls for manufacture of both a lid and a bottom; it calls for extensive shearing of sheet stock to produce body blanks that must be formed then soldered, glued or welded. The finally completed can has had at least eight applications of organic coating made to one part or another of it. This repeated handling of the can components certainly does not minimize the chances for things to happen which can adversely affect the integrity of the finished can. This is especially true where impact of the can on beer flavor is concerned.

It is really surprising that this package has performed well for so long in the market place. When all manufacturing steps have been properly taken, the final container is relatively free of flavor influence and most of the time the cans are properly made; the instances of metallic or "canny" tasting beer are infrequent. In the U.S., however, *any* frequency of "canny" flavor development in the three-piece can is too great. The consumer no longer must forgive these occurrences if he wants the convenience features of the can. He has discovered that he doesn't have to; he can purchase two-piece cans that stay relatively free of this flavor defect.

In those areas where the two-piece cans are not available, the three-piece cans still provide a good service. They are convenient and useful to the consumer. He buys cans at a steady rate: 7.5% in Canada and 22% in Mexico as compared to 70% of all packaged beer sold in 1979 in the U.S.A.

Perhaps the best test a brewer can use to check for metal exposure in cans is copper sulfate. Filling suspect cans with a saturated solution of copper sulfate and allowing them to stand for a few minutes will result in a dark copper deposit developing over any exposed can metal. A tougher, more probing test is to let it remain in the suspect can overnight. If minute areas of metal exposure are present, the copper sulfate will corrode them nicely to a detectable size.

Can Lids:

In three-piece cans, the lid that is applied to the can bottom poses the greater threat to beer flavor. It is made of iron as opposed to the almost universally used aluminum tab-top lid; iron is almost fifty times as detrimental to beer flavor as is aluminum. The brewer should spot check his can deliveries by the use of an enamel rater or by copper sulfate to make sure adequate coating is present to protect his beer from the can body metal or the can bottom metal.

The aluminum tab-top generally will have some slight metal exposure due to the score line made for the pull tab. This exposure actually protects the beer from slight metal exposure in the iron wall or bottom. When such bimetallic exposure exists, a galvanic current is established, with aluminum being the sacrificial metal. Some aluminum seems to dissolve into the beer and instances have been noted where it actually plates out on the exposed iron (or tinplate) surface. Iron uptake into the beer is greatly reduced in such packages.

Frequent reference has been made here to "iron" can bodies and "iron" can bottoms. The actual metals are either tin plate or iron that has been surface treated to produce a chrome-chrome oxide film. In either instance, the surfaces will not prevent the rapid dissolution of iron into the beer.

Testing Methodology:

Can lids can become contaminated with press lubricants and contribute an oily aroma to beer. This can best be covered in a standard quality control tasting of the packaged beer production. No other coverage is as quickly or as comprehensively done not only for can lids but for all packaging influences on beer flavor. Most experienced flavor panels will not merely identify an off-flavor situation. They will name the culprit material and frequently indicate its source.

End Seal Compounds:

Can lids (and 3-piece can bottoms) are lined with a rubber-based compound that enhances the sealing properties of the seam once the lid is applied and double-seamed onto the filled can. Several suppliers make compounds available to the lid manufacturers. They all are similar in that they contain one or more rubbers, at least one "tackifying" resin, a rubber stabilizer, and an insoluble filler, generally a clay. The soluble components are dissolved in hexane or heptane; the insoluble material is uniformly suspended in the solubles. Viscosity of the compound is carefully maintained so that application and placement in the lid can be properly controlled.

This compound must meet rather rigorous performance standards. It must have sufficient "tackiness" to strongly adhere to both the can body surface and the lid surface. It must have slight mobility so that it will squeeze slightly to fill a void yet it must resist excessive mobility so the pressure exerted by the seaming chucks will not squeeze it along leaving "starved" areas behind. It must not carry any flavor influence to the beer, nor should it absorb any from the beer. There are other requirements which deal with stability under various conditions, etc.

Essentially all the end seal compounds now used for beer can lids are solvent based. Hexane or heptane is employed to dissolve the soluble components and keep the entire formulation in a fluid condition so that it will flow through an application nozzle. These solvents evaporate readily so they quickly disappear from the applied sealant.

Efforts are being made by some lid manufacturers to use end seal compounds that are water-based and free of solvents. Some lids are being produced with these water-based compounds; this usage should increase as the demand for elimination of solvent vapors in manufacturing plants and the general atmosphere increases.

There are also some "high solids" solvent-based compounds being used as substitutes for the regular solvent-based compounds. These compounds, because of their high solids content, have considerably less solvent emission and satisfy existing government agency requirements. These compounds should also enjoy increasing usage.

Testing Methodology:

The sealing compounds in current usage are relatively free from flavor influences, because a few brewers have worked with the formulators of the compounds to select materials that survive flavor testing in beer. The actual compounds can be effectively flavor-screened by coating or smearing a thin film of about 25 milligrams of compound onto a glass rod, allowing it to dry overnight, placing it into a clean beer bottle and filling it on a production line. The pasteurized bottle should be stored for 2 weeks at 85°F. and tasted in comparison to a control sample.

Sealing compounds tend to absorb certain odors readily. It is wise to prescreen the ink that is used to stencil production information onto the kraft paper sleeve that holds the lids until they are used. Naturally, care should be taken that the lids are shipped and stored in a relatively odor-free atmosphere.

PLASTIC CONTAINERS AS POTENTIAL BEER PACKAGES

In recent years, plastic containers have come into widespread use for a number of foods and beverages all over the world. The one food segment that does not have significant usage of plastic containers is beer. With the exception of two or three minor market situations in Europe, beer is not being packaged in plastic.

There are valid reasons for this; up till now the various plastic containers have not been satisfactory alternative beer packages from a flavor, physical or economic standpoint.

Plastic beer bottles have been used in Europe. Polyvinyl chloride (PVC) bottles with conventional crowns have been used in Germany. A spherical bottom container (PVC) has been used in Sweden. It had a paper cylinder skirt attached so that it would stand upright and a plastic closure instead of a conventional crown. A plastic pouch resembling a sausage casing was used in England. These containers can only be used to contain beers that are low in carbonation (to prevent bursting) and they cannot be pasteurized. A relatively short shelf life must prevail for these packages because they have been found to have adverse influence on flavor at standard American storage periods. None of these or similar European containers will meet the American requirements for internal pressure containment, gas barrier properties, flavor stability or (I suspect) cost.

In the following sections an effort will be made to describe the shortcomings that now exist in various candidate materials that have been examined in an ongoing program that has functioned for more than a decade.

Evaluation of a plastic material for possible use as a beer container generally goes no further than the initial flavor evaluation. The development of off flavors in beer discourages further work on many of these materials. Origin of the off flavors seems to vary with the polymer being examined. Impurities in the polymer film, absorption by the film, and poor barrier properties have been responsible.

Another chapter deals with soft drink operations and will deal with the use of plastic bottles for soft drinks. Plastic bottles, especially bottles made from polyethylene terephthalate, are finding some acceptance as containers of one quart or larger volume. Gas permeability of this film limits shelf life of the bottles for soft drinks; it renders them unacceptable for beer. This is due to the extreme damage that molecular oxygen does to beer flavor.

Impurities in the Polymer Film:

Although the polymer systems that form the plastic beer container are insoluble in beer, they can contain certain substances that are soluble and will migrate into the beer. Small-molecular-weight-species of the container polymer can escape complete polymerization and be present; soaps and other processing aids can also be present. Outright impurities, such as mold release agents and any aerosol mist products that might be in the air employed to blow the container can produce spurious flavors.

Competent flavor evaluation, of course, must identify the "correctable" flavor defects, such as the outright contaminants which can be avoided, to permit a better evaluation of the polymer container.

Outright impurities have been found in samples of acrylonitrile, nylon, polyvinyl chloride, polybutylene and some polyethylenes. Needless to say, many of these impurities are residuals from a given manufacturing process and new production techniques bring forth higher purity polymers that merit reevaluation.

Absorbing Polymers:

Perhaps there is a more proper descriptive term for the polymers that fall into this category. These polymers accept certain specific beer components into the polymer film and concentrate them there. An excellent example is polyethylene which will scavenge a significant portion of the beer esters. Polyvinyl chloride plasticized with Dioctylphthalate does this although it has great specificity for only a few of the esters present in beer. Other polymers remove other materials. The result is a beer that is no longer full-flavored and blended in character. Frequently, some of the flavorants removed will have been responsible for the blending and softening of the flavor impact of the hop bittering substances. When such flavorants are removed, awareness of hop bitterness increases significantly. Tasters will describe such beers as being "thin, depressed and having increased bitterness" or "sharp bitterness" or "lingering bitterness."

Both low and high density polyethylene and polypropylenes readily remove aromatic materials, mostly esters, from beer. Nylon also does this, although it appears to specifically absorb larger-molecular-weight-material, such as some hop related material and tannin-like compounds. In fact, all plastics tested were found to do this to some extent.

Poor Gas Barriers:

Few polymers have gas barrier properties that are adequate for beer. Beer and soft drinks must have adequate carbonation levels when consumed or they lose some taste appeal. Beer must be protected from oxygen; the migration of two parts per million of oxygen across a polymer membrane and into the beer harms beer flavor significantly. If the migration rate allows this level of oxygen to get into the beer within a month, market place and shelf-life problems will plague the brewer. The beer will taste aged and dull. The polyethylene terephthalate films lack sufficient gas barrier properties at current beverage bottle thicknesses to be of any use as beer packages although they are satisfactory for soft drinks.

In evaluating polyethylene terraphthallate (PET) bottles for flavor influence, it was found that oxygen permeability of the container side walls allows oxygen to reach the beer and cause oxidation flavors before any flavor influence from the polymer could be evaluated. One technique which allows a longer storage period is to submerge the test container in de-aerated water to prevent oxygen entry through the container wall. Storage in CO_2 chambers, although not tried, should also be satisfactory.

At present, PET appears to offer all required features for a beer package except the barrier properties. This must be overcome by coextruding this material with a better barrier film or by coating the PET container with some suitable material that is more impermeable to oxygen.

Physical Properties:

In addition to flavor defects, the polymer materials, at economic weights, generally lack sufficient cohesive strength and creep resistance to be considered viable candidates for beer packages.

It is possible to produce a beer container from almost any plastic that will hold beer and/or have satisfactory barrier properties. To do so, one would merely use enough material to meet the physical requirements, but such a package would be grossly expensive.

Prior to the commercial development of stress orientation, practically all polymers lacked the strength to be suitable beer container material at economic weights. Some could withstand the pressures called for to contain a U.S. beer at cool temperatures but could not at higher temperatures, such as those reached in pasteurization, where most of them lost cohesive strength and burst. Polyvinyl chloride, polyethylene and some of the acrylonitrytes were failures in this respect. Some sample bottles were made which survived pasteurization yet were not able to stand up under storage of 100°F. for two weeks. They developed sufficient creep to distort in shape and eventually explode.

The polyesters in general demonstrate sufficient strength and temperature tolerance to offer promise as a container for pasteurized beer. However, containers made from these materials show inadequate oxygen (and CO_2) barrier properties and, like PET, they must be treated in some way to be made more impermeable.

There is considerable belief that the rising costs of glass and metal beer packages will eventually become great enough to permit competitive use of plastic beer containers. Certainly more energy is required for glass and metal packages, and energy costs continue to rise. The major reason for the rise in energy costs, however, is increasing oil and natural gas prices which are also direct cost factors for plastic beer containers. This one factor of increasing petrochemical cost would seem to push further into the future the date of cost equalization for plastic and other containers.

DRAUGHT BEER PACKAGES:

Essentially all the beer cooperage employed today in America is metal; either stainless steel or aluminum. Most of these containers are half-barrel capacity, although quarter-barrels and even eighth-barrels are not uncommon.

Stainless steel cooperage need only be washed thoroughly, refilled by the brewer and shipped. Aluminum cooperage must be "pitched" or lined with a flavor-inert material that will prevent the beer from reacting with the aluminum alloy containers. If this reaction is not prevented, reactions of the beer with the container metal will cause turbidity and hydrogen gas will be produced which will react with sulfur compounds in the beer, producing hydrogen sulfide at objectionable levels.

Parafin or microcrystalline wax is the material employed to line the aluminum alloy beer kegs. Only U.S.P. grades of this material are employed and organoleptic tests of it are done as quality checks.

The cooperage is washed, dried and kept hot (70°-80°C F.) until the molten wax is applied over the inner surface of the container. Application is most generally done by atomized spray. A final visual and organoleptic check is made of the unit before it is released for filling. Where wooden bungs are employed for final closure, it is essential that the wax be carefully removed from the bung opening. This insures that adequate friction will exist to retain the bung.

In North America, draft beer is unpasteurized; this means that the filled packages must be kept cold (below 10°C.). The beer must be consumed before brewers' yeast or beer spoilage bacteria, mostly lactic acid bacteria, have time to develop and contribute unwanted flavors to the beer.

The retail outlet must also follow a regular cleaning procedure on its dispensing equipment to prevent the development of spoilage organisms and attendant problems. Most brewers have active sales service programs designed to assist the draft beer retailer keep his dispensing equipment properly cleaned.

GOVERNMENTAL SUPERVISION

Every American brewer operates under the scrutiny of his Federal government. State, province or local governments also get involved, but for the purposes of this section the Federal agencies in the United States that govern brewery activities will be noted. In Canada and Latin America this governmental supervision is carried out by similar agencies well known to the legal representatives of any brewery.

Brewery operations in the United States are generally under the supervision of the Bureau of Alcohol, Tobacco and Firearms (BATF), a branch of the Treasury Department.° Other agencies, such as the Food and Drug Administration (FDA), the Environmental Protection Agency (EPA), the Department of Agriculture (USDA) and the Occupational Safety and Health Administration (OSHA), a division of the Department of Labor, all have areas of concern that reach into the brewing area. There are not clear-cut guide-lines that

°Recent Federal re-organization plans have called for the abolishment of the BATF; however, at present no formal assignment of BATF responsibilities for brewing industry have been made to other agencies.

describe which agency prevails in every brewing area but certain "rules of thumb" have developed that the brewer can follow.

The FDA is concerned with sanitation in the breweries, the substances added to beer and the materials used in packaging that come into contact with beer. The BATF has similar concerns but generally follows the rules laid down by the FDA. The BATF also is concerned with labelling as well as with all aspects of alcohol production and sales distribution. The EPA and OSHA are concerned with the use of chemical substances in the brewery and their disposal. The USDA is concerned with the kinds of fumigants, pesticides and other economic poisons that are being used to protect agricultural materials. There are areas of overlap, naturally, but these result in little friction to the brewer.

The brewer must make sure that every packaging material that comes in contact with his beer is approved to do so by the FDA. This agency has published in the Federal Register a list of those materials that are permitted to contact foods. Limitations of usage and restrictions of food categories are spelled out. The ingredients in a bottle crown liner or internal can coating, for example, must all be approved for such use in Section 121 of the Code of Federal Regulations[3]. The brewer should require a statement from his supplier guaranteeing that such materials consist of FDA-approved substances.

For the most part, other American countries recognize FDA approvals. This is not always so, however.

CONCLUSION

This chapter has given a survey of packaging and has identified those areas that can threaten beer quality. It has also touched upon control measures and precautions that can be used to detect potential problems before filled packages are shipped to the market place. The information in this chapter has come largely from the author's experience; there is little published on this subject.

Any individual who finds himself with a job assignment in this general area should feel no reluctance to the innovative where new tests of packaging materials are concerned. The net result should be better quality integrity for his company's beers.

REFERENCES

1. KURIOWA, Y. and NASHIMOTO, N. Composition of Sun Struck Flavor Substance and Mechanism of Its Evolution. A.S.B.C. Proc. *19*:28-36 (1961).
2. LEA, C. H. and SWOBODA, P.A.T. The Flavor of Aliphatic Aldehydes 1958, 1289.
3. Code of Federal Regulations. Office of the Federal Register. U.S. Govt. Printing Office, Washington, D.C. 1975.

CHAPTER XXIV

PACKAGING LINE INSTRUMENTS AND CONTROLS

BY JOHN J. KIEDROWSKI

INTRODUCTION

In modern breweries, instrumentation and controls are essential to insure the highest levels of productivity, quality, and operator safety. Competition has forced new and innovative methods of keeping costs down, including brewing in larger quantities and packaging at higher speeds. Added emphasis on consumer satisfaction has raised our quality awareness. We must always be concerned with the quality of our product, as well as with the finished package consumer appeal. Government regulation promotes automation to eliminate personnel from potentially dangerous operations and new safety rules continually challenge the creativeness of equipment manufacturers and packaging engineers.

The electronic revolution which has taken place over the past ten years has had a significant affect on industry; and breweries have been no exception. Solid state is a way of life, where traditional mechanical-electrical instruments and controls no longer meet our millisecond expectations. Also, management has come to expect charts, graphs, and reports, all of which require modern techniques to gather and process production data.

In the following discussion on instruments and controls we will,

1. Introduce the reader to the basic measurement devices in the packaging area;
2. Review the concept of instrumentation control loops;
3. Explain basic machine control concepts;
4. Explore some general rules for line design;
5. Show how line design is coupled with controls to maximize line performance, and;
6. Become familiar with "state of the art" control techniques which employ programmable controllers and computers.

PACKAGING INSTRUMENTATION

Instrumentation commonly found in the packaging area generally achieves one or two purposes: it can be used to measure and indicate; or to measure, indicate, and control a physical process. Both of these applications will be reviewed in the following discussion.

INSTRUMENTS TO MEASURE

Using instruments as measurement tools is the most basic and traditional application. When a change in a process is noted, we usually must have a means to measure it. This has been true since sun dials were first used to tell time by movement of a shadow, and is equally true today when laser beams are used to measure long distances with precision and accuracy. Over the years the concept of measuring a process has not changed, only the methods used and the accuracy of our results.

Packaging technology, as in all other industries, has made great advances in its speed, productivity, quality, etc., but the process still remains fairly straight forward from an instrumentation-engineering point of view. There is a need for accurate measurements of the processes which affect our operations; however, these can often be obtained using traditional equipment and do not necessarily require state-of-the-art instrumentation. Therefore a review of some of the most common types of measurement and indicating instrumentation found in the packaging area is in order.

TEMPERATURE MEASUREMENTS

Probably the most popular and widely used device for temperature measurement is the liquid-in-glass thermometer. This device generally uses a liquid, such as mercury or alcohol, to indicate a change in temperature. In using it, the thermometer bulb, or reservoir, is placed in contact with the process to be measured. As the temperature increases or decreases, so does the volume of the liquid in the bulb. By means of a clear capillary tube connected to the bulb, the expansion and contraction of the liquid may be viewed, and with the appropriate scale the temperature read directly. This instrument has the advantage that it is accurate to $\pm$ 1% of full scale, while being low cost and easy to install. Disadvantages, on the other hand, are that the unit is slow to respond to temperature changes and difficult to read, since your line of sight must be directly opposite the liquid level in the capillary to get an accurate reading. Also, this instrument has no means of transmitting its measurements to other more sophisticated pieces of instrumentation equipment or recording for future reference.

A variation of the liquid-in-glass thermometer is the constant volume liquid filled or gas filled thermal sensing system. Here a bulb is connected by means of a capillary tube to a pressure or volume sensitive element. As the process heats and cools, the liquid or gas attempts to expand or contract accordingly, and since the system is sealed the volume or pressure sensitive elements change size or shape. This mechanical distortion is then measured and used to drive a mechanical indicator directly. If a remote indicator is desired—that is, the indicator is to be located at a distance away from the sensing bulb—this system often has the ability to extend the capillary tube from 50 to 100 feet (depending on the manufacturer's recommendations) without special equipment. Beyond this distance, however, special bulbs and capillaries may be required and the cost involved often makes electronic methods of measurement more practical. Filled thermal sensing systems have the advantage of being accurate, generally within $\pm$ .5% to $\pm$ 1% of full scale and are relatively inexpensive to purchase and install. Also, by having the option of liquid, gas, or vapor pressure systems, each has its specific advantages or disadvantages and the optimum system can be selected for your application.

By far, the fastest growing area of temperature measurement has been in the use of electrical signals. Devices which have changes in their electrical characteristics as the temperature changes, fall into two categories: resistance, or thermal electric.

The resistance method of measuring temperature relies on utilizing a sensing element which is allowed to change temperature with the process, and in doing so, changes its electrical resistance in a predictable and repeatable manner. Commonly referred to as "RTD's" (Resistive Temperature Devices), they utilize a sensing element, which is a small wire winding or coil sealed in a probe and put in contact with the process. The coil could be one of several metals, but is usually made of copper, nickle, or platinum, with platinum having the most desirable properties; that is, its resistive change is most linear with temperature change. The RTD is connected directly to an electronic circuit which is basically an automated Wheatstone bridge.

Very simply, it compares the RTD's resistance to a reference resistance and adjusts it to match to the reference. In doing this, a mechanical linkage is operated and temperature indicated on the appropriate scale. Advantages of RTD's include an accuracy of $\pm$ .5% of full scale and ease of remote installation, i.e.; the sensor and recorder may be separated by long distances without special equipment and extra costs.

Thermal couples, another popular form of electronic devices which are used to measure temperature, were discovered by Seebeck in 1821. He observed an electro-motive force (EMF) generated in a closed circuit between two different metals when their junctions were at two different temperatures. The sensing junction, or "thermo couple", is formed simply by connecting together the ends of two dissimilar metal wires, such as iron and constantan or copper and constantan, to form a measuring or "hot" junction. The hot junction is then inserted into the process where the temperature is to be measured. The reference or "cold" junction (at the opposite end of the wires which make up the hot junction) is generally connected to the measuring instrument's terminals. As the temperature of the process increases, so does the difference in temperature between the hot and cold junctions. With this difference in temperatures, an EMF is generated and when connected to a sensitive instrument, the EMF can be measured and the instrument calibrated to read temperature directly. Key advantages of thermo couples include very rapid response to temperature changes, and very high accuracy in the ranges of $\pm$ .3% of full scale.

PRESSURE MEASUREMENTS

The most common instrument for measuring pressure is the simple Bourdon Tube. Patented by Eugene Bourdon in 1841, the instrument is a thin, flattened metallic tube which has been bent to form a partial circle. An increase in the tube's internal pressure tends to straighten out the tube. The tube's tip moves linearly with an increase in internal pressure, and this movement can easily be converted to indicate pressure by a simple mechanical linkage and pointer arrangement. This instrument has an accuracy of $\pm$ 1% of its range value and can be used on virtually all pressurized systems, providing the material from which the tube is made is compatible with the process.

A second type of pressure measuring device is a pneumatic force balance arrangement. This system is commonly used to measure differential pressure (DP) which is used to determine flow through pipes and levels in liquid tanks.

The pneumatic DP cell operates on a force balance principle. A flexible diaphragm, which separates the two different pressures, moves back and forth as the two pressures vary. This movement is transmitted to a pneumatic feedback mechanism by means of a force bar which exerts a balancing force to keep the system in equilibrium. This back pressure force is proportional to the differential pressure being applied to the diaphragm by the process and may be connected to a Bourdon Tube pressure gauge to directly display differential pressure, tank level, etc.

ANALYTICAL MEASUREMENTS

In the packaging area it is not uncommon to require the use of "electrochemical" measurements. Generally referred to as "conductivity", these measurements are based on the current-carrying properties of solutions containing ions to determine the concentration of a specific solution.

The most common use of conductivity measurements in packaging is in determining the concentration of sodium hydroxide (NaOH) commonly referred to as "caustic", in a solution. Used extensively in keg washing, bottle washing, and in process sanitation, it is purchased in a concentrated liquid form, usually 50%, and diluted for use, generally 2 to 4%. In some plants, this is an entirely manual process; that is, a predetermined amount of caustic is added to a certain amount of water and mixed thoroughly. Samples are then taken, titrated, and the concentrations determined. Any adjustments are made by adding more caustic or water. While the caustic is in use in the keg or bottle washer, periodic checks must be made to determine the concentrations and insure proper cleaning. In manual systems this means that samples must be taken, titrated, and the caustic levels adjusted accordingly. Automatic conductivity measuring devices and controllers which adjust the concentrations according to a predetermined set point, are commonly used and are an alternative to the manual monitoring of caustic concentrations.

All electro-chemical measurements rely on the electrical current carrying properties of solutions containing ions. The system used for measuring sodium hydroxide concentrations will measure all ions in the solution and this is called electrolitic conductivity. A liquid which will conduct electricity is referred to as an electrolyte. How well it conducts is determined by the type and the concentration of the ions present and is called the conductance of the electrolyte. The unit of electrical conductance is "mho", the reciprocal of electrical resistance which is measured in "ohms". The conductance of a material varies with the shape of the conducting path. The conductance or ability to pass electrical current for any material increases directly with cross sectional area and indirectly with the length of the sample.

In actual measurement, a conductivity cell is placed directly into the caustic system to be measured. By using two electrodes and passing a current between them, the conductivity is measured and a signal sent to an indicator and/or controller. Generally calibrated in terms of percent concentration or parts per million, the indicator is direct reading. If an indicating controller is being used, a set point is entered and the unit will activate a signal to add caustic and/or water to the system to achieve the desired concentrations. Often, when measuring conductivity, the solution being measured may not be compatible with the electrodes; that is, the probes may be subject to polarization, fouling, or chemical action. In these cases, electrodeless conductivity systems are used. Here, two toroidally wound coils are encapsulated within close proximity in the sensor, which is placed in the solution. An AC signal is applied to one coil and a current generated in the second, which varies directly with the conductance of the solution. Accurate to within ± 2% of upper scale, conductivity controllers reduce the time required to mix cleaning solutions and insure the concentrations are maintained to provide proper cleaning.

A second type of electro-chemical instrument which could be found in the packaging area is a pH monitor and/or controller. Most commonly used to control the pH in process water, it is also used to monitor and control pasteurizer water systems where pasteurizer cooling water is reclaimed and recirculated back to the pasteurizers for re-use. Proper pH is essential to maximize the performance of the chlorine in the water and protect the pasteurizers from corrosion. Similar in operation to the previously mentioned conductivity probe, the pH system measures only the acidity or alkalinity of the solution. The probe, made of a special type of glass which is sensitive to hydrogen ions, is immersed in the fluid to be monitored. The glass probe contains a chamber which is filled with a reference fluid of constant pH. An internal electrode is submerged in this liquid and connected by means of a shielded cable to the pH indicator and/or controller. If the hydrogen ion concentration is greater in the process than it is in the reference fluid inside the tube, a positive electrical potential will exist across the glass tip of the probe. If the process has a lower hydrogen ion concentration than the reference fluid, a negative potential will exist. The relationship between the potential difference and the hydrogen concentration follows the Nernst equation. The signal, which is received from the probe, is processed by an electronic controller according to this equation. As with the conductivity controller, the pH controller can also be set up to record and control to a preset set point.

SANITARY REQUIREMENTS OF SENSORS

In the previous discussion we made a quick review of some of the various instruments which are commonly found in the packaging areas. Among the systems measured by these devices are steam, air, CO_2, water (hot, ambient, and refrigerated), and beer. Each instrument selected to measure a process, should be suited to the application. The operating conditions should be considered; that is, temperature, pressure, speed, accuracy required, etc., and the instrument matched to the parameters of the process. The instrument should be selected to function in its optimum range during normal system operations and be capable of withstanding the maximums of the system without damage.

An important area which is often overlooked when selecting instrumentation is sanitary considerations. In the packaging area of a brewery, there are several systems which require sanitary conditions and are frequently cleaned and regularly monitored for microbiological growth by Q.C. personnel. These include water (process), CO_2, and beer supply systems. These systems all contact the final product and for this reason, must be maintained in a high state of cleanliness. To insure that instrumentation complies with the sanitation parameters, the term "sanitary" or "food grade" has been applied to installations and equipment which meet this criteria. "Sanitary", in terms of instrumentation, refers to the physical characteristics of the sensor's surfaces in contact with the process being measured. Surfaces which permit the collection or entrapment of material supporting microbiological growth and will not be removed during normal equipment cleaning are not acceptable for food. On the other hand, sanitary installations are smooth, non-corrosive, have no pockets for stagnant collection and are cleaned as the system is cleaned.

Probably two of the most common causes of non-sanitary instrumentation are compromises because of cost or time and a lack of sanitation knowledge. To cut costs or to save time, a non-sanitary sensor is used. This is an extremely easy pitfall to be caught in because, generally speaking, sanitary installations are significantly more expensive and require additional time and expertise to install. The second most common cause is the lack of a working knowledge regarding "sanitation". Often instruments, fittings, or piping arrangements are installed on systems with food contact which are inherently unsanitary. Many times this happens because the personnel doing the work have had no exposure to sanitary concepts, and are not aware of the special considerations required. To prevent this, training for hourly personnel, designers and supervisors regarding food grade installations is most helpful.

As previously mentioned, we said that for an installation to be sanitary it had to be cleanable during normal system cleaning. This cleaning can happen in two ways. First, and least advantageous, is cleaning which requires large amounts of operator involvement. This includes equipment dismantling, hose connections, special tools, etc., and relies heavily on the operator to insure that the proper procedures are followed. Often when time is short, tools are misplaced or untrained operators perform the cleaning, steps are missed in the cleaning procedure, and the system's sanitation is compromised. The second, and most popular, cleaning technique is clean in place, or commonly called "CIP". With this, instrumentation is left intact and is cleaned automatically as the system is cleaned. Modern CIP systems generally require little operator input as they are automatically cycled through a series of wash-rinse cycles.

To eliminate the sanitation problems in instruments, special "sanitary or food grade" sensors and adaptors have been developed. These devices, when installed properly (eliminating cracks, crevices, dead legs, etc.,) permit accurate monitoring of the process without fear of microbiological growth.

SANITARY TEMPERATURE MEASUREMENT

In the previous discussion, the temperature measurement devices all required a probe to be placed in contact with the medium being measured. To facilitate this and maintain a sanitary installation, thermowells are used, Figure 24-1. Basically, a thermowell is a hollow metal tube, open at one end and sealed at the other. The sensor is inserted into the tube and allowed to make contact or "bottom out" with the end and sidewalls of the well. It is important that a good contact between the sensor and the well is achieved to insure that the sensor reaches the same temperature as the medium it is measuring. Thermowells offer several advantages. First, the well is usually stainless steel and when installed properly, it is sanitary and is cleaned during normal CIP. Second, the well acts as a positioner, or holder, for the sensor. By varying the

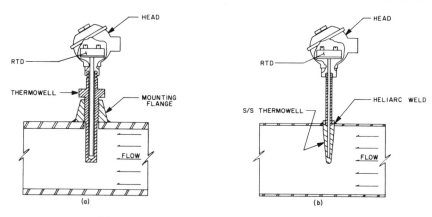

24-1. Diagram of typical thermowell installation: a) Non-sanitary, b) sanitary.

thermowell's length, the sensor can be exactly positioned in the system being measured. Third, since the well penetrates the system and provides a seal between the system and the probe, the probe may be removed from the well without disturbing the medium; that is, the system does not need to be emptied or depressurized to remove the sensor.

SANITARY PRESSURE MEASUREMENT

In discussing pressure measurement, it was stated that the Bourdon Tube is the most popular device. However, from a sanitation point of view, it is obvious the device cannot be used in food contact since the material will travel up and collect in the tube itself. This build-up cannot be removed during normal CIP and would soon become a source of contamination. However, where needed for sanitary pressure measurement liquid filled systems using the Bourdon tube are available. They consist, basically, of a diaphragm and a reservoir which is connected to a Bourdon Tube and the entire system is filled with a non-compressable liquid and sealed. Note, however, that this liquid must always be non-toxic and not have an adverse affect on the process if a leak were to occur, and must be FDA approved for use with food products. A common liquid used in breweries for this purpose is propylene glycol. The diaphragm is made of stainless steel and is mounted in a special gasketed socket assembly. The entire assembly usually fits flush with the wall of the system and lends itself well to normal CIP. As the pressure of the system changes, the diaphragm flexes in and out. This movement attempts to compress the fluid within; however, since the system is filled and sealed, the Bourdon Tube is distorted, just as it was when measuring the system pressure directly.

Another form of sanitary pressure measurement system, which is commonly used to determine levels in liquid tanks, is the sanitary differential pressure or DP cell. With this device, a stainless steel diaphragm is mounted in a gasketed socket and is attached flush to the bottom or lower side of the tank. The pneumatic force balance system is used to generate an air signal proportional to tank level which may be displayed directly, or used as an input to other controls. The diaphragm, if installed properly, will not collect contaminants and is cleaned during normal CIP of the tank.

MEASUREMENT RECORDERS

Many times it is advantageous to record measurements as a function of time. All of the previously mentioned devices can have this ability and it usually comes in one of two forms; circular charts or continuous strips. Each of these has advantages and/or disadvantages and the type chosen is usually determined by the nature of the operation. The charts or strips are preprinted, scaled to the process being measured, and are usually direct reading.

Rotating charts or circular charts are widely used in the packaging area and represent predetermined time periods; that is, one revolution in one shift, 24 hours, one week, etc., see Figure 24-2. Charts of this type are very easy to install and are especially convenient when recording for a constant unit of time. For example, it is convenient to file pasteurizer temperature charts for each day with the production reports for that day, etc.

Continuous strip or "strip charts" are often used when the process being measured is long-term and not interrupted by the changing of a shift or day, etc., and tend to be more common in the Utilities area where continuous services are measured, see 24-2. Strip charts have an advantage over circular, in that their scales are a constant width across the entire length of the chart, while a circular chart, on the other hand, has narrower time scales at the center and wider scales at the outside edge. This may hamper readability in the lower ranges of the circular scale.

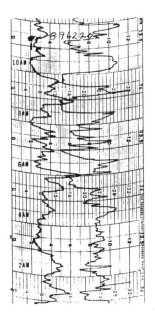
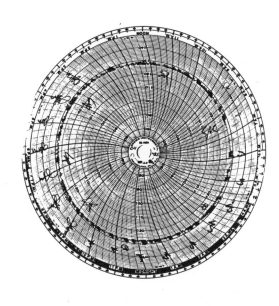

24-2. Examples of charts "two-pen strip" recorder and "single-pen circular" chart.

MULTIPLE PEN RECORDERS

When two or more properties of the same system are measured, such as pressure and temperature, etc., it is often convenient to record both measurements on the same chart at the same time. To do this, multiple pens with different colored inks are used. Both measurements are recorded side-by-side for the same instant of time, making comparison and visual correlation much simpler. Here again, multiple pen recorders are available in both circular and strip configurations.

PASTEURIZATION MEASUREMENTS

Since pasteurization is a critical packaging process in almost all major breweries, we will devote some discussion to the instruments which are used to verify its performance. Usually operated by the Quality Control Department, these instruments measure and record the temperature-time relationship, which is the key to the pasteurization process (See Chapters XVI and XXII).

There are three widely used types of instruments to verify pasteurizer performance. All employ an electrical or mechanical means of measuring and recording temperature as a function of time. First, and probably the oldest and simplest method, is the use of a "traveling clock". Here, a sample bottle or can has a filled bulb inserted in its cold spot, approximately ¾″ above the bottom. The bulb is connected by means of a capillary tube to a rotating chart recorder which is sealed inside a waterproof housing. Driven by means of a spring or batteries, the recorder is sealed and set in the pasteurizer with the sample bottle attached. As the bottle travels through the various pasteurizer zones, its internal temperature will rise and, by means of a capillary tube, the information will be transmitted to the recorder. This information can then be used by Q.C. personnel to calculate the pasteurization units, or "PU"s, experienced by the product. On a more sophisticated unit, a 2-pen recorder is used and the second pen is attached to an external sensor. This external sensor is a sealed bulb which is attached to the outside of the traveling clock which senses and records the temperature of the water sprays that are heating the bottle or can. Consequently, it can be used to verify the spray temperatures and to determine which temperatures to change if adjustments to the pasteurization process are required. Disadvantages of this system include accuracy of only ± 1°F, and it requires manual, time-consuming calculations of the PU's from the recorder chart.

A second, and very popular method, uses RTD's, or thermocouples, and a remote recorder. Here, a RTD or thermocouple is again inserted into the cold spot of the container and connected by means of a waterproof cable to a continuous strip recorder. The container is placed in the pasteurizer, and the cable is played out as the container moves through the machine, with temperature being fed via the cable to the remote recorder. Also, if spray temperatures are desired, a second RTD or thermocouple and cable is attached to the outside of the container to record the water or spray temperature, see Figure 24-3. This system has the advantage of being accurate to .5%; however, the disadvantage is having to handle the cables which connect the container to the recorder. Often up to 100 feet in length, depending on the pasteurizer

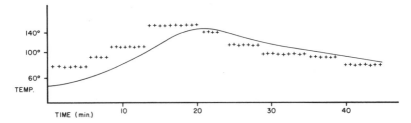

24-3. Pasteurizer PU survey as recorder on a continuous strip recorder. Solid line indicates beer temperature. Asterisks indicate pasteurizer spray temperatures.

length, the cables must be fed and then pulled from the pasteurizer after the test. As with the traveling clock, the PU's must be calculated from the strip recorder.

The most recent method of PU survey is the solid state PU computer. This device has been available for about the past three years and combines the advantages of the two previously discussed instruments. It has the convenience of the traveling clock, the accuracy of electronic sensors, plus the added feature of automatic PU calculation. Basically, it consists of a microprocesser contained in a waterproof enclosure with electronic temperature sensors. As with the traveling clock, the sensors are placed in the container and, along with the enclosure, ride through the pasteurizer. Temperature and time changes are recorded within the processor's memory, where they are stored for future reference. At the end of the survey, the computer displays the total PU's experienced, along with the maximum temperature that the container attained. Also, by use of a plotter, the external spray temperature and internal beer temperature are graphically displayed.

The one failing that all of the previously mentioned instruments have is that they only measure temperatures in a narrow band in the pasteurizer. They cannot indicate clogged nozzles or pans except in the area the instrument passes.

INSTRUMENTS THAT CONTROL

There are two basic types of automatic control: "open loop" and "closed loop", where loop refers to the concept of information continuously traveling from one component to another in a closed circuit.

Open loop control indicates that there is no feedback to the controller from the system being controlled; that is, when a signal is given, a preprogrammed change is made within the system, and the effects of this change are not fed back to the controller for evaluation or adjustment. A prime example of this is an automatic clothes washer, where the cycle is initiated and follows a preprogrammed routine with no feedback, whether or not the clothes are being cleaned, Figure 24-4. The machine follows its cycle, regardless of its results, and can make no corrections to get a cleaner wash. This off-on logic is not used to control critical processes and is generally found controlling water

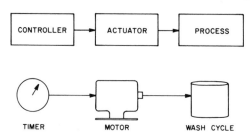

TIMER   MOTOR   WASH CYCLE

24-4. a) Components of an "Open Loop"
control scheme; b) Components of a wash
machine as an example of "Open Loop"
Control.

softener regeneration equipment, clean-in-place systems, etc., where the cycle
length is designed to achieve and insure the desired results.

Closed loop control relies on feedback from the system being controlled as
input to the controller. This feedback is used to further control the process
and, ultimately, achieve the desired results. Figure 24-5 shows a typical schematic of a closed loop system. Here, the three key elements of a closed loop
exchange information to achieve a preselected set point. Basically, the measurement device or sensor monitors the process and sends information regarding its status to the controller. The controller, which is the brains of the
system, compares this status to the set point and decides on a corrective action,
if any is needed to achieve the set point. This action signal is sent to the
actuator which controls the variable being controlled (such as steam), and this
changes the variable (such as temperature) in the process. The sensor device
detects this response in the process and relays the information to the controller,
and the closed loop is completed.

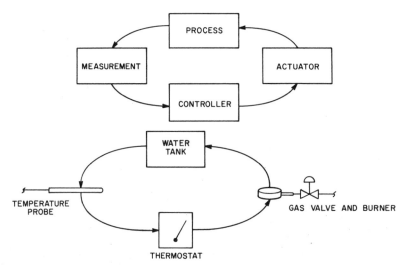

24-5. a) Components of a "Closed Loop" control scheme; b) Components
of a gas water heater as an example of "Closed Loop" control.

Closed Loop Components

Let's take a closer look at the components of a closed loop system:

Process

This is the characteristic which is being measured and controlled. Some common processes that are controlled in packaging include pressure, temperature, flow, and level.

Measurement

This is the job of the measurement device previously reviewed. Its function is identical to that of the indicator devices, with the exception that it has the additional ability to transmit its findings by means of a mechanical, pneumatic, or electronic signal. Such devices are referred to as temperature transmitters, pressure transmitters, level transmitters, etc., and inform the controller about the status of the process.

Controller

This is basically the brains or decision center for the control loop. It has a preset goal, or set point, to meet, and compares this set point to the measurement received from the transmitter. The difference between these two values is measured and, based on its magnitude, a correcting signal is sent to the control element to achieve a set point. Controllers are categorized as electronic, pneumatic, or mechanical and are usually some combination of two or more of these systems; that is, it is not uncommon for an electronic signal to enter a pneumatic controller and, by means of a mechanical linkage, send a pneumatic signal to the control element.

The basis for the control decision process is called "the method of control". Simply stated, this is the logic the controller has been given to use when the process measurement varies from the set point, and will be discussed shortly.

The Final Control Element

This device controls the variable, which changes the characteristic being measured. This is usually a valve, but could be a heating element, motor speed control, or mechanical actuator. In packaging, the most common control element is the pneumatically operated control valve. It consists, basically, of a body or a valve assembly which, when operated, will change the flow rate of the variable in the process. The valve is mechanically connected to an actuator, which is a device that moves, or "operates", the valve according to the magnitude of the output signal it receives from the loop controller. These valves, which vary the variable in the process, are referred to as modulating, or control, valves.

Types of Control

As previously mentioned, the controller is the brains of the closed loop. In the packaging area, its decisions are generally based on what is called "proportional control". This means that the signal, which is sent to the final control element, is proportional to the difference between the measurement and the set point. The ratio of proportional control is expressed in terms of "proportional band" which, simply stated, means "how far will the measured value be away from the set point before the final control element is activated 100%?" For example, a controller with a scale of 0 to 100, 50% proportional band and a set point of 50, means the final control element will be fully closed at a measurement of 25 and fully opened at a measurement of 75, since the difference between these two points on the scale is 50, and 50 is 50% of the 100 scale.

The proportional band is always centered about the set point; that is, in the previous example, the valve would be ½ open when the measurement matched the set point of 50. For any process control loop, only one value of proportional band is best and this can only be determined by proportional tuning of the loop; that is, adjusting the band width until an optimum performance is achieved. If the band is too small, the controller will over-react to small measurement changes and a constant oscillation around the set point will occur. If the band is too wide, the controller will not respond enough and the process control is not as close to set point as possible.

One drawback to pure proportional control is that the controller will rarely maintain set point; it will always be above or below it. This variance is called "offset" and is acceptable in some processes where the process need not exactly follow the set point. If offset cannot be tolerated, we add a second control factor to more closely achieve the set point, and this is called "reset". Simply stated, reset is a corrective action taken by the controller to achieve the set point based on how far the measurement is from set point and how much time has elapsed since the last reset signal.

Perhaps the best way to visualize proportional band and reset is by means of a simple example.

Imagine the tank in Figure 24-6 filled with 10 feet of water. It will be drained by opening the bottom valve and will be refilled by the man opening the water inlet valve. Assume that the man's goal is to keep the tank level at 5 feet, or half full and he has 100% proportional band. When the bottom valve is opened, the tank begins to drain and the level drops. With 100% proportional band, this means the level must drop 100% of scale for the man to open the valve 100%. Therefore, a 10% drop in level and the man will open the valve 10%, a 20% drop and he will open the valve 20%, and so on. Imagine, now, the same situation with 50% proportional band. This means that the level must move only 50% of the scale for the man to fully open the valve. Remembering that proportional band is always centered about the set point, this means that the man will just begin to open the valve when the level drops to 7.5 feet and the valve will be wide open at 2.5 feet. 7.5 feet minus 2.5 feet is 5.0 feet, and this is 50% of the total band of 10 feet. Therefore, this control is 50% proportional band in the system. We can continue to tighten the proportional band to attempt to achieve the desired level; however, eventually, the band will become too tight and the man will overreact to changes in level and continually overshoot his set point. To help in actually achieving the set point, the man can be given another action to take after proportional control, and that is "reset". With reset, he will still open the valve according to his proportional band; however, he now has the ability to compare the tank level with his 5 foot set point and initiate action to achieve set point. He then opens or closes the valve and waits to see what affect it has on the system. Having seen the effect, he will again adjust the valve and again wait to see how close he gets to his set point. He will continue this routine until the set point is achieved. It is important that the man waits to see the effect of his change before he makes another change. This time required for a change in a system is referred to as "lag" or "dead time". In a controller, reset is

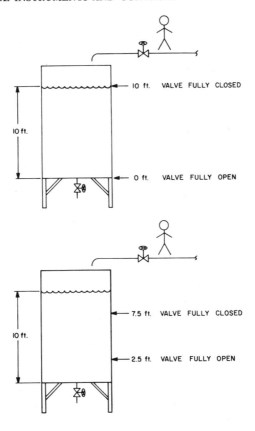

24-6. a) Man and tank as an example of
100% proportional band; b) Man and tank
as an example of 50% proportional band.

measured as minutes per repeat, or repeats per minute. If reset time is less than the lag or dead time, the controller will go into what is called "reset wind-up" where it over-corrects and the process continually oscillates about the set point.

Control Loop Applications

The types of instrumentation loops common in packaging include both pneumatic and electronic installations. In pneumatic control systems, low pressure air is the signal used to communicate between various loop components. These signals are usually 3 to 15 psig, with 3 pounds being 0% and 15 pounds being 100% of full scale reading. Electronic instruments use a 4 to 20 milliamp, 5 volt signal to communicate. Here, 4 milliamps usually represents 0% and 20 milliamps represents a full scale reading. Both type systems have their advantages and disadvantages and, for this reason, many combination installations are often seen; in which, both pneumatic and electronic devices interact in the same loop.

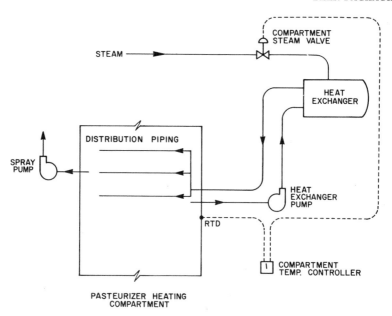

24-7. Schematic diagram of a pasteurizer heating circuit.

A traditional and straight-forward control application in packaging is pasteurizer temperature control, Figure 24-7. Here, the sump temperature is monitored by a RTD which signals an electro-pneumatic controller. The controller compares the measurement to a set point and sends a corrective signal to a control valve which modulates the steam flow to the heat exchanger. The water is heated by the steam in the heat exchanger and is returned to the sump to adjust its temperature. Looking at the control loop for this system, the elements of the control system can be identified: the process is the sump temperature; the measurement device is an RTD; the control is an electro-pneumatic set point controller; and the final actuator is the control valve which modulates the steam to the system.

A similar pasteurizer application, which is slightly more complicated, is the single set point, dual actuator controller. This type control is very common in regenerative-type pasteurizers in which the front zones are used to heat the containers and the back zones cool them. Here, the controller has two methods of controlling the sump temperatures. If the temperature is too low, steam is added, and if the temperature is too high, chilled water is added. By means of a dead band located directly at the set point, we insure that both steam and chilled water are not applied at the same time.

Many breweries control the beer level in their filling bowls by means of a control valve at the inlet to the filler. Two types of systems are most popular. The first utilizes a float or capacitance probe as a measurement device to signal the level directly to the controller. The controller compares this to the set point and adjusts the beer level by sending a pneumatic output signal which operates a control valve and adjusts the flow of the beer into the filler.

This system has the advantage of accuracy and there is never any question as to the level in the bowl. The disadvantage, however, is that the signal from the sensor on the filling bowl must go through a rotating connection to communicate with the controller. This connection point can often be a source of high maintenance and lost production if not properly attended to.

The second method uses the filler bowl CO_2 pressure to indirectly measure the level of the beer within the bowl. Here, the bowl is a sealed vessel. As the beer enters the bowl and the level increases, the gas above the beer, CO_2, will become compressed and the bowl pressure increases accordingly. A sanitary pressure transmitter is placed in the beer line feeding the filler and senses this pressure. A set point controller receives this measurement and operates the valve on the beer line to maintain a preset pressure in the bowl. That is, if the level drops, so will the pressure and the valve is opened. If the pressure increases, the valve is closed to reduce beer flow into the bowl. This system has the advantage of not requiring a rotating connection to transmit the signal from the sensor to the controller, as the sensor can be mounted in the beer line at the base of the machine. On the other hand, it has the disadvantage of not measuring level directly and is very sensitive to other filler variables such as CO_2 counterpressure, operating speed, acceleration and braking speeds.

Other controls in use not mentioned include the use of a float to drive a mechanical to air transmitter or use of a bubble system.

PACKAGING LINE CONTROLS

Before discussing packaging line controls, the term "control" should be defined. Control, in the packaging sense, is the mechanism used to regulate, guide, and coordinate the operation of a machine or machines in a packaging system. This mechanism may be of different types, that is, electro, mechanical, pneumatic; however, the ultimate goal of all is the same, to maximize production while maintaining safety and quality standards.

Packaging lines consist of a series of machines which are interconnected by a network of case, bottle, or can conveyors. Each piece of equipment has its own task to perform. The performance of this task is governed by its own internal logic or control which monitors the operation of that machine and the conditions which affect that machine only. To coordinate these individual efforts on the line and maximize production, a higher logic or control is used; that is, packaging line control. Since both machine and line controls are required on a packaging line, we will review the components of each type individually.

MACHINE CONTROLS

Generally speaking, machine controls for this discussion refer to electromechanical circuits which are confined to an individual machine and regulate the operation of that machine. These circuits are commonly 110 volts AC or 24 volts DC and employ relay logic to achieve the desired response in the machine.

Machine controls are concerned firstly with operator safety. In an age of ever increasing concern for safety, machine controls are designed to reduce the possibility of operator injury. Engineers employ a series of electrome-chanical interlocks which insure that safety requirements are met prior to machine operation. These include insuring that access doors are closed and machine guards are in place. Machine manufacturers often resort to exotic and redundant interlocks to insure the safety system is not bypassed. However, for any interlock system designed, there is always some way to mechanically or electrically bypass it. Unfortunately, if this is the goal of the operator or maintenance personnel, it most certainly will be accomplished. It is the re-sponsibility of management to ensure that employees are trained on the im-portance of machine safety devices. It is only through education and awareness at the operator and maintenance level that the integrity of the machine's safety controls can be preserved and improved.

The second purpose to machine controls is the smooth operation of the machine itself. Generally, all major pieces of equipment on a packaging line are purchased prewired; that is, the control logic has been determined and the electro, mechanical, and pneumatic devices have been assembled to im-plement this logic. This has several advantages. First, the manufacturer, who should have the best knowledge of their machinery, decides on a method of control. This is advantageous from the warranty and service aspect, since manufacturers often void both warranties and performance guarantees if the machine is not operated per their suggested controls. In addition, most man-ufacturer's service personnel use a machine/control modification as an excuse as to why their machines do not perform properly, and if modified, they will no longer service it. To avoid warranty and service problems, it is best to rely on controls as furnished by the equipment suppliers. Modifications to machine control circuits should be made sparingly and always with safety in mind. Control modifications should always be well documented, and the manufac-turer consulted on the change for his concurrence and input on future ma-chines. Also, operators should always be alerted to changes in the controls, since they interface directly with the machine, and should be knowledgeable as to how their machine reacts in any situation.

A third function of machine controls is machine protection; that is, to avoid situations which cause damage to the machine. As packaging line speeds increase, so do the speeds of the individual machines in the line and to avoid machine damage when faults occur at high speeds, manufacturers have de-veloped electro-mechanical sensing devices. These devices sense a problem at its earliest possible state and initiate a reaction, usually shutting the machine off, to avoid serious damage to the equipment. Such controls are especially valuable to the user since they protect his investment and, again, insure op-erator safety. Modifications to machine protection circuits should therefore be scrutinized by qualified personnel prior to implementation. These circuits have always been included by the manufacturer for a reason, that is, to overcome problems that have arisen in the past. Again, if changes are made, good documentation and concurrence from the manufacturer is always rec-ommended.

The fourth function of machine controls is to interface with the line. Gen-erally, machines have a "domain" on a packaging line. This includes their immediate infeed, the machine itself, and its immediate discharge. The ability of the machine to control or sense the condition at its immediate infeed and discharge conveyor is critical to its operation. One common infeed control determines if there is material available to be processed by the machine, and another common control determines how much. The first input often determines whether the machine runs or waits for materials and is referred to as "prime". Prime, in packaging terms, is the accumulation of containers (bottles, cans, or cases) prior to a machine which requires that a minimum supply be maintained to insure proper machine function. The second infeed control tells the machine how fast to run. Often, high speed equipment has the ability to run at multiple speeds. The speed is based on the queue or waiting line in front of the machine; that is, if there is an adequate supply, the machine will run at normal line speed. If there is an excessive supply, the machine will go into high speed, or surge to reduce the excess of containers at its infeed.

There are generally two important discharge controls which are fed back to the machine. The first is the normal "back-up" condition which is caused by equipment downstream not taking the product away. In this case, the machine generally goes into a slow speed, and if the "back up" is severe enough, it will go into a cycle stop—a "cycle" stop being defined as stopping in an orderly manner usually clearing the machine of product.

The second is the downstream emergency back-up, which indicates a malfunction or jam at the machine's discharge area. This is a serious condition and to avoid machine damage, will usually result in an emergency shut down of the equipment. Emergency stops generally do not clear machine of product.

Machine control logic relies on information input to determine its activities. Basically, it must come from one of two sources: automatically, or operator initiated. The first type relies on switches or sensors to provide information regarding a physical condition upstream, internal, or downstream from the machine. These are automatically operated by physical conditions and are usually electronic, metal proximity, or limit switches which sense the presence of product. This presence is relayed to the machine control by completing a circuit which is a part of the overall machine logic. The logic determines what action, if any, is to be taken. Operator input is generally from such devices as switches, push buttons, etc.; operators relay their intentions to the control scheme, which acts accordingly to a preplanned scheme.

In both of these cases, the inputs give notice of a condition and the logic acts accordingly. The logic referred to is actually a well thought out game plan for machine operation. It has been developed by a controls engineer and is actually a series of electro-mechanical devices which are arranged by means of a control circuit and reacts in a predetermined manner. The machine control logic processes inputs according to a preplanned control scheme and initiates outputs which direct both the machine and operator. Signals may be given to automatically start or stop, speed up or slow down, open or close bottles/can stops, etc. Controls aid operators by giving indicator lights to help in troubleshooting. Open machine guards, low materials, product jams, etc., can all be indicated to speed operator correction and to improve machine performance.

Another form of machine control inputs and outputs are "customer contacts". These are simply signals sent between the machine control and the line control to aid in the coordination of the machine with the line. These signals generally indicate conditions or events which are happening outside the machine's domain and allow the machine to perform as part of the line. Customer contacts will be further discussed later in this chapter.

We have reviewed the concept of machine domain; that is, each machine having its own logic and acting accordingly. Let's now discuss how individual machines are tied together to form a coordinated packaging line.

PACKAGING LINE DESIGN

To fully understand line controls, we must first appreciate the objective of the line and its components. As previously stated, a packaging line is a series of machines interconnected by a network of case and/or bottle or can conveyors with the objective of producing a quality product at the highest level of productivity and safety. Obviously, when building a line, certain pieces of equipment are required such as uncasers, fillers, labelers, etc. How these machines are assembled to meet the objective is the challenge of the packaging engineer.

LINE DESIGN AND CONTROL CONCEPTS

On brewery packaging lines, the filler is the focal point. Line speed is based on filler speed, and the line goal is to keep the filler running. How the different machines are interconnected with conveyors and controls is a prime factor in determining how well the line performs. Line design generally varies from company to company; that is, each brewer thinks he has a special combination which makes his packaging lines run faster and more efficiently than the next. Since philosophies on machine speeds, accumulation, and conveyor speeds are as varied as the brewers themselves, no attempt will be made to discuss any particular design, rather some basic steps and general rules-of-thumb in line design will be presented.

Step 1—Equipment Selection

Generally, the filler is the focal point and should be the slowest piece of equipment on the line. The nominal filler speed, which also becomes the line speed, is usually based on a speed guaranteed by the manufacturer and should be a speed at which the filler can operate very efficiently.

After the filler or line speed has been determined, the selection of equipment upstream and downstream can begin. Of prime concern in selecting this equipment is how fast should each piece of equipment before and after the filler run? Again, a general rule-of-thumb is that the minimum speed should be 10 to 15% faster than the filler speed at each succeeding or preceding station. (Obviously, we are assuming the operating efficiencies at the pieces of equipment are very similar to that of the filler. If the efficiency is significantly lower than the filler, an increased speed beyond 10 to 15% would be desired.)

Step 2—Accumulation

Determining the amount of accumulation or container storage space to build in between the various pieces of equipment is not quite as simple as rules for machine speed. Imagine a very short packaging line with pieces of equipment placed end-to-end without accumulation in between. Basically, his is a one-for-one line flow; that is, one bottle is uncased and gets passed to the rinser. The rinser then feeds the bottle directly to the filler, etc. The line would have the advantage of being very compact but the disadvantage of being very inefficient since when one machine has a problem, the entire line has a problem. To eliminate the one-for-one delays mentioned, accumulation, or the ability to store product between work stations, is essential to controlling the line flow and necessary for the efficient operation of the line. Rules for how much accumulation to place between pieces of equipment are hard to come by. This is determined by line layout; that is, the actual physical room available and the amount of capital available to purchase and install accumulation. Generally speaking, the more accumulation, the better, but there is in each situation an economical, idealized amount of accumulation.

Step 3—Conveyor Speeds

Conveyor speeds can be partially based on machine speeds. For example, if a filler runs at 1,000 bottles per minute, the conveyors feeding it must run a minimum of 1,000 bottles per minute just to supply it with empty containers. How much faster should the conveyors run? This question has no one single answer since conveyor speeds must consider factors such as container stability, conveyor damage, (i.e., product denting or breakage), noise, etc. However, a good starting point and rule-of-thumb is the accumulation conveyors should run 40 to 60% faster than the equipment it is feeding. Therefore, for the 1,000 bottle-per-minute filler, the upstream conveyors should run from 1,400 to 1,600 bottles per minute. As mentioned, this is a starting point. We will later discuss methods of optimizing these speeds.

These three steps, when combined with years of experience, are how the vast majority of packaging lines are designed. Draftsmen assemble layouts of equipment and conveyors which will fit within the physical building constraints, and engineers and executives review and modify the layouts based on equipment characteristics, their experiences, personal preference, etc.

Often in designing new lines, in addition to the three steps discussed, it is helpful to review existing installations to determine optimum machine speeds, accumulation, etc. To do this, engineering time studies are made to determine the characteristics of delays experienced between pieces of equipment. Engineers make in-depth studies of a machine or series of machines to determine the causes of delays on the line. Delays are classified as upstream, internal, or downstream, and are used to calculate an overall machine efficiency or reliability. With this information, engineers can make adjustments in machine speeds, accumulation, etc., to minimize these delays in new designs. One main drawback to this method is that it is impossible to look at the entire line at one time; that is, because of the complexity of the machines interfacing with each other, an entire line cannot be manually simulated at one time. Also, this process is extremely time-consuming.

COMPUTER SIMULATIONS

A fairly recent advance in this area has been the use of computer simulations for line design or line efficiency improvement see Figure 24-8. This process combines the rules-of-thumb with the machine delay information gathered and simulates running the line over long periods of time, using only a few minutes of actual computer time.

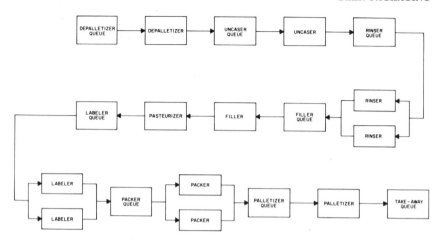

24-8. *Flow chart of a bottle line showing work stations and queues which serve as the framework for computer simulations.*

Basically, the major pieces of equipment, or "work stations" as they are called in some simulation programs, are laid out in a series and/or parallel arrangement to form a flow chart of the actual line. The work stations are connected by lines which represent the bottle or can conveyors, but have no reference to their length or configuration. In front of each work station is the accumulation or "queue" that is possible between that work station and the one directly upstream of it. When completed, the information on the flow chart is coded and entered in the simulation program where it serves as the framework for the simulation. As previously mentioned, this information gives no indication of the physical distances or configurations of the line; it only provides the computer the interaction of the machines and queues in the system.

Information regarding the physical qualities of each component of the line layout is then compiled. For work stations this includes machine speed or speeds—that is, low, medium, and high—and at what population or level of accumulation in the upstream queue will the specific speeds be activated. Also, machine delay information is entered. This has been compiled by engineering studies, as previously discussed, and is basically a profile of that work station's internally generated downtime; that is, the average length of delay, the average time between delays, etc. As previously mentioned, queues represent the accumulation that is available prior to a work station. This is usually measured in cases or bottles or cans of product and represents the total number of containers that can be stored in front of a machine on the actual conveyor.

The final information necessary is the conveyor speeds or travel time; that is, the minimum time it takes a container to travel from one work station to another. When all of these items have been fed into the program, the actual simulation can begin.

In the simulation, the line will be operated using the parameters previously ntered. Bottles or cans or cases, ("transactions" in simulation terminology), will travel from machine to machine and be processed or delayed just as they would be in an operating line. Work centers operate at specified speeds and experience delays which conform to the pattern of the engineering studies made. Queues or areas of accumulation, empty or swell accordingly to line conditions. In fact, the line being simulated is basically identical to an operating line, with the exception that the simulation runs a production shift in a matter of minutes.

The true value of line simulation is in the areas of data analysis and experimental changes. Information regarding queue sizes, average machine speeds, conveyor speeds, machine control, etc., can be reviewed to determine the limiting factor on the line's performance. Then a change, or changes, can be made in the model and the simulation rerun. This trial and error approach is invaluable when trying to optimize the line performance before the first piece of equipment is purchased or when costly line modifications are to be made.

PACKAGING LINE CONTROLS

Line controls are basically a network of electro-pneumatic and mechanical devices directed by a pre-planned logic to interface with machines, accumulation, and operators to minimize filler downtime and maximize line output and quality in the safest possible manner.

The key components of packaging line controls are very similar in concept to instrumentation controls; that is, sensors, controllers, and actuators connected by means of electro-pneumatic signals. The sensors or inputs detect a physical event or situation and relay this information to the control circuit. The control circuit follows a pre-planned logic and sends signals to the actuator in the circuit.

LINE CONTROL INPUTS

The inputs employed are of fairly standard type from brewery to brewery. Generally, they consist of devices which transmit physical conditions on the line by one of three methods. First, and most prominent, are line sensors. These may be one of several types to determine the presence or lack of product. Limit switches are the most common devices used in line control. Here, a mechanical lever is moved by the presence of product and completes an electrical circuit, sending a signal to the control logic. Actuators for the switch can be made to virtually any design, and the switches themselves are available in various mounting arrangements or shapes, making the device applicable for sensing bottles, cans, and cases, empty or full. Advantages of limit switches include low price, usually quick installation, and easy troubleshooting or adjusting.

A second type of sensing device which is gaining popularity is the metal proximity switch. These devices utilize an electrical inductance to sense the presence of metal without physically touching the object. Especially adaptable to cans, they are also used on bottle lines to sense the presence of full bottles by mounting the sensor above the conveyor and sensing crowned bottles below. The advantages to the use of proximity switches is that there are no moving parts. The sensing unit is sealed, watertight, and need only be within ½ to 1 inch of the object being sensed to give a good, consistent result. Also, the sensors are generally available with built-in delay timers; that is, delay the signal on, or delay the signal off. This allows tuning of the control directly without purchasing separate timing devices. One disadvantage is higher cost since basic proximity devices will generally cost anywhere from two to four times as much as limit switches.

The third most popular sensing device is the electric eye. Like limit switches, the electric eye is commonly used in all breweries. Consisting basically of a transmitter and receiver, an electric eye unit emits and receives a beam of visible or invisible light. When this beam is broken—that is, the presence of the product has been detected—a signal is sent to the control circuit. Some electric eyes do not require separate transmitters and receiving devices, but instead use a plastic reflector to return the beam to a combination transmitter and receiver unit. These are referred to as being retroreflective. Still more advanced eyes do not require reflectors but instead rely on the object being sensed to reflect the infared light back to the receiver and, thus, sense the presence of the product. Electric eyes also are generally available with built-in timing devices and are comparable to the proximity switches in price.

A second method for putting information into the control system is through operator inputs. These consist mainly of push buttons and selector switches which when activated by operating personnel send a signal to the control circuit. Consisting mainly of off-on or start-stop type signals, this transmits the operator's desire to stop conveyors, machines, etc., to the line control unit.

The third type of input to the control systems includes machine interfaces, or the "customer contacts," discussed in the machine control section. These signals from the machine indicate the machine's intentions to the line. Commonly, just opening or closing of an electrical contact, the signals allow the machine to function as part of the line in a smooth, continuous fashion. Information transmitted to the line logic may indicate that the machine is ready to accept product and, therefore, the infeed conveyor may be started. Or, it may say the machine is shut down and, therefore, does not need product. These signals are automatically generated by the machine and are important to its functioning properly and as a coordinated member of the line.

COMPONENTS OF LINE LOGIC

The three methods of putting information into the line logic have been reviewed. How this information is used, or the basis for decision making, is called line control logic. The equipment which physically receives these inputs and processes the decision is called line logic hardware.

Again, as in individual machine controls, the logic employed for packaging line control is relay logic. Inputs enter the control by one of three previously discussed methods. Electro-mechanical and electronic switches which have been arranged to a predetermined control plan divert the signal through the circuit to act by itself or to interact with other signals to determine the action or output. Until recently, the principal components of logic hardware were ectro-mechanical in operation. Inputs are wired to relays which interconnect pneumatic or electronic timers and other relays to complete the decision making process. These devices are "hard wired", meaning an actual signal wire connects the devices to the input, output, or next device in the control circuit. This arrangement has disadvantages in that complicated control circuits often get very large physically and require large cabinets to contain the equipment. Circuits often become very complicated and are difficult and time-consuming to troubleshoot, thus extending line downtime. Also, changes in logic are often difficult and expensive to make, requiring additional devices, rewiring, etc. The output from the logic hardware is the signal which directs the events which will take place on the line. Usually at 110 volts, this signal can activate motors, conveyors, indicator lights, alarms, air solenoids, etc., as directed by the control logic to make the line run smoothly.

In the past few years programmable controllers have gained wide acceptance in breweries for controlling individual machines, as well as complete packaging lines. The programmable controller (PC) is designed to control using the same relay logic as used in the previously mentioned electro-mechanical relays. The difference is that the PC is a solid state device, and utilizes electronic switches without moving parts. Inputs are received from the identical devices as previously discussed, that is, limit switches, electric eyes, operator input, etc. These are physically connected to an input card which converts the 110 volt or 24 volt DC signal to a low voltage signal input and sends it to the processor. The processor, or brains of the control, has been pre-programmed with relay logic to make decisions based on these inputs. By using a CRT which displays the logic contained in the program, all of the electro-mechanical logic devices previously discussed can be recreated in the form of a ladder diagram. The PC then interprets the logic of the ladder diagram and arranges its electronic switches to accomplish the desired control. When action is required, a low voltage signal is sent out to an output card, which then converts this signal to 110 volts and operates the appropriate control device. PC's have several advantages over traditional electro-mechanical relays. They have proven to be extremely reliable, with no moving parts; if problems occur, they contain their own diagnostics to quickly locate and display certain faults. They are easily programmed and require no special training, since symbols used are familiar to relay users. If the number of external devices are changed, changes or additions to circuits, which would normally require additional relays and rewiring in a conventional relay system, can be done in minutes by the use of a CRT or programming panel. That is, certain control devices or logic is added on-line with a minimum of line downtime. Documentation, or ladder diagrams, are easily obtained by means of a printer which lists the logic contained in the controller. With this, an updated program is easily available at any time.

LINE FLOW

The term "flow" in the packaging line sense is not simply getting the container from machine to machine and eventually into a case and off the line. Rather, flow is the interaction of machine speeds, accumulation, conveyor speeds, and control to permit line and machine operation in a smooth and continuous fashion. We have discussed how to select these components of a

24-9. Schematic diagram showing accumulation and overspeed prior to the filler.

packaging line; let's now review how they function together to create flow.

As previously mentioned, the filler is the focal point of the line, and the line objective is to keep the filler running. To achieve this, all equipment before or upstream of the filler must provide a continuous line of containers, and all equipment downstream must continually take them away. This is where machine speed, accumulation, and conveyor speeds become critical. Consider a simple situation immediately upstream of the filler wherein a rinser is feeding directly to the filler see Figure 24-9. If the filler speed is 1,000 bottles per minute and the accumulation between the two will hold 3,000 bottles, based on the rule-of-thumb for equipment speeds, the rinser should be 10 to 15% faster than the filler, or approximately 1,100 bottles per minute minimum. Imagine now, the two machines running independent of the rest of the machines on the line; that is, the rinser will have all the bottles needed to run, and the filler will have no downstream delays. As the two machines begin to run, the rinser is producing bottles at a rate of 100 bottles per minute faster than the filler is taking them away. This excess is being stored, or "accumulated", in the area between the two machines. If this condition exists for 10 minutes and then the rinser experiences a delay, what would happen? Since the rinser has been running at a 100-bottle-per-minute advantage for 10 minutes, there must be 1,000 bottles stored in the accumulation area, or queue. When the rinser stops, the filler continues to run by taking the bottles out of the accumulation area. With 1,000 bottles stored and the filler running at 1,000 bottles per minute, the accumulation could absorb up to a 1 minute delay at the rinser before the filler would run out of bottles. When the rinser starts up, it would again begin filling the accumulation at a rate of 100 bottles per minute. These bottles would continue to be stored until the accumulation area is filled or until the next instance of rinser delay, when the filler must again call on the accumulation area to supply it with bottles. This is a basic example of how accumulation and overspeed prior to the filler work to maximize filler efficiency.

Obviously, from this example, we can say that more overspeed and more accumulation is advantageous and this is true. For theoretically, a rinser running infinitely fast with infinite accumulation between it and this filler, would never cause filler downtime because of its delays. However, in reality; there are practical limits to how fast equipment can run and to how much accumulation to provide. Generally speaking, the faster a piece of equipment runs, the more subject it is to delays and loss of performance. And, eventually, a breakeven point is reached between overspeed and reliability, and beyond this point any increase in speed is offset with additional downtime. A similar situation exists in accumulation. Accumulation costs money in additional conveyors or accumulation tables, and in both cases, the physical space to put

24-10. Schematic diagram showing accumulation and overspeed after the filler.

this equipment to store the product. Here again, there is a breakeven point; that is, the point where the cost of more accumulation is not justified by an equal savings of decreased filler downtime.

Consider now a situation after the filler see Figure 24-10. With the same filler running at 1,000 bottles per minute feeding a labeler which by the rule-of-thumb runs 1,100 bottles per minute. Neglecting the pasteurizer between the two machines (since this is actually a slow moving non-accumulating conveyor), there is 3,000 bottles of accumulation between the two units. As the machines are running, bottles are being fed from the filler to the labeler at a rate of 1,000 bottles per minute, and the labeler with an advantage of 100 bottles per minute, easily stays ahead. Let's now say the labeler experiences a 2-minute delay—what would happen? The filler would continue to run and the bottles would be stored in the accumulation area. After the 2-minute delay, the labeler would resume running and the filler would experience no downtime. Also, since the labeler is running 100 bottles per minute faster than the filler, this overspeed would eventually empty out the bottles accumulated during the downtime and make room to accumulate during future delays. From these examples, the two opposite applications of overspeed and accumulation on the same packaging line can be seen; that is, the objective of equipment overspeed upstream of the filler is to keep accumulation full. The objective of equipment overspeed downstream of the filler is to keep accumulation empty. Both are essential to keep the filler running at its maximum efficiency.

The optimum conveyor speeds are also necessary to maximize line performance. Conveyors which run too slowly will extend line downtime, while conveyors which run too fast will actually create line downtime. In the previous discussion, the rule-of-thumb given for conveyor speeds was that they should be 40 to 60% faster than the machine they are feeding. This is referred to as "catch-up" speed and serves to reduce the effect of machine downtime on the downstream machine. In the case of the rinser-filler we previously discussed, the shorter the travel time between the two machines, the longer the rinser can be down and still "catch up" to the filler without interrupting production. However, increasing conveyor speeds to the point of causing tipped containers, broken glass, excessive noise, excessive maintenance etc., will result in more downtime and serve only to reduce filler efficiency. Generally speaking, the 40-60% rule of thumb is a good place to start, but often only by adjusting the speeds in the field can the optimum speeds be attained.

There are two main philosophies or schools of thought on line control, and most lines utilize one or a combination of these to maximize performance. The first method divides the line into control units or domains. Here, pieces of equipment are grouped together based on their interaction with each other.

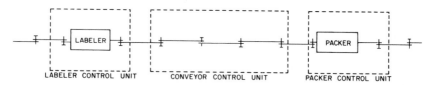

24-11. Schematic diagram of the Control Unit approach to line controls.

Consider the section of line in Figure 24-11. The labeler, along with its immediate infeed and discharge conveyors, are considered as part of one control unit. That is, since the labeler must control these conveyors to function properly, they are in the same domain. The next control unit is the section of bottle conveyor from the labeler discharge to the packer infeed. Here, the conveyors are allowed to control themselves. Based on the number of containers on the conveyor, sensors determine a full condition or a demand for product at the packer and cycle the conveyors accordingly. The packer, along with its immediate infeed and discharge conveyors, is the next unit. Again, the packer must control these conveyors to function properly. Some control unit's sensors may extend beyond their domain for the purpose of controlling that unit. In our example, the labeler will, no doubt, have sensors downstream in the conveyor's domain to warn it of a back-up or jam condition. Also, the packer will have sensors located upstream in the conveyor's domain which will relay speed information; i.e., how many containers have accumulated and, therefore, how fast should the packer run? In each case, sensors cross boundaries; however, the actual control ability of each unit is still limited to that unit's domain.

The "control unit" approach has the advantage of being quite simple to understand and, therefore, easy to troubleshoot when problems occur. Set rules can be established as to how machinery and conveyors will operate and this reduces the confusion which can result from complicated controls. The disadvantage to this system is that it only works on lines where domains are easily defined. On shorter, more compact lines, domains often are not clear-cut and the control scheme becomes more complicated.

The second approach to line control utilizes control overlap. Often referred to as "anticipate and command", it utilizes direct signals to and from pieces of equipment, often in lieu of line sensors, to achieve flow and maximize production. Most often found on shorter lines, this type control generally is used to compensate for a lack of accumulation between pieces of equipment. A common application of anticipation and command is to eliminate machine cycling after a line restart. Here, after a back-up between two machines, the downstream unit signals the upstream that it has restarted. The upstream unit will then neglect its downstream sensors and begin production. This early start will reduce or eliminate the usual gap which occurs in restart and allow the downstream machine to run continuously.

The disadvantage of this type control is that circuits often are extremely complicated, difficult to understand and time consuming to troubleshoot. However, anticipate and command control permits engineers to compensate for physical problems, i.e., conveyor layouts, lack of accumulation, speed limitations, etc., and to achieve acceptable performance.

COMPUTERS AND PACKAGING

At the present time, the "state of the art" in packaging line control is the PC, or programmable controller. Computers are becoming common in the process control areas; however, their value as packaging line controllers is still to be proven.

Computers are being used in packaging to perform what is called "line monitoring". Here, they provide line supervision and management personnel with information regarding the operation of their line. By means of sensors and other inputs, information regarding each piece of equipment is relayed to the programmable controller. This includes machine status, i.e., running or down, and its speed. If the machine is down, the reason for the delay is also transmitted. This could be an upstream, internal, or downstream delay. Once in the programmable controller, this information is read by the computer by means of an interface and transmitted to the computer for analysis.

In the computer, the machine speed data is compared to "standard speeds" which determine if the equipment is running to expectations. Delay information is analyzed by programs which will trace the exact cause of line downtime and assign the fault to the responsible machine.

The computer provides feedback to management in two forms. First, by means of a CRT, performance and delay information is relayed to the line supervisor for his immediate attention. With this, there is no need to wait until the end of the shift to see what your major cause of downtime was, since the computer keeps a running tally and will inform the supervisor when a machine becomes a significant problem. The second form of feedback consists of summary reports. Generally provided at the end of a shift, week, month, etc., this data will provide downtime data to identify problem areas and direct maintenance attention. Also, management may use this to justify machine or layout changes to improve line performance.

Computer applications in packaging are still in the development stages. However, they have displayed their value to both engineering and production personnel and are certain to be a part of packaging lines in the future.

References

Anderson, Norman A., *Instruments for Process Measurement and Control*, Third edition, Chilton, 1972.

Foxboro, *Process Control Instrumentation*, Foxboro Educational Services, 1971.

Gillum, Don, *Automatic Feedback Control*, Plant Engineering Magazine, May and June, 1980.

DeLong, Larry, *Understanding Programmable Controllers*, Plant Engineering Magazine, April, 1980.

CHAPTER XXV

MAINTENANCE AND LUBRICATION
BY ROBERT L. TIEMANN

INTRODUCTION

Readers have already been introduced to some of the approaches to packaging maintenance in comments made in earlier chapters in this book. The intent of this chapter is to present some of the philosophies which exist in the brewing industry today and discuss the organization and methods in use to carry out these philosophies as expressed in effective maintenance programs.

The last 15 years have seen a dramatic change in the relative importance of maintenance and lubrication of packaging operations as a part of the total cost of packaging. We are now in an era where there are more complex and more sophisticated systems in use, where we have more automatic lubrication and where we are faced with an ever-increasing cost of packaging equipment. The installed cost of a new bottle filler today is four to five times the cost of one 15 years ago. A 100-valve filler, with attendant conveyor and inspection equipment, costs at least $1 million to install. While such costs are capital expenditures and are prorated over the expected life of the equipment, it is obvious that this new equipment must run much better than its predecessor in order to reduce maintenance costs by reducing down time and by increasing efficiencies.

While production workers today are still comparatively unskilled, maintenance personnel must have more skills than ever before, especially those who are involved with electrical systems. Most brewing companies separate production and maintenance costs. Therefore, it is difficult to make a comparison; however, we know that maintenance costs today run between $2.50 per barrel and $3.50 per barrel. These are total brewery maintenance costs and are affected by volume. In other words, a plant running at 95 percent capacity would be much more capable of operating close to $2.50 per barrel than a plant running at 70 percent capacity.

But to be effective today, a maintenance program must have as its primary objectives, the constant running of high-speed packaging lines and a minimal amount of down time in brewing. There must be few or no malfunctions of equipment. This will make the program cost effective.

Maintenance expenses have been on the rise as the result of increasing inflation which has brought higher wage rates and higher prices for materials and equipment. Maintenance managers, therefore, must be alert to every opportunity to reduce the cost of maintenance in areas that do not contribute to the effectiveness of the program. This means more advance planning, greater utilization of manpower, better purchasing, and a more complete body of knowledge concerning the cost of maintaining each piece of equipment in the operation.

Thus, the maintenance manager and his staff are becoming more data oriented. It is now necessary to have a data bank of information which tells management when a piece of equipment becomes too expensive to maintain and should be replaced, as well as providing the data concerning the cost of maintaining each segment of a line during the course of a month.

MAINTENANCE PROGRAMS

There are several types of maintenance programs that have attained acceptance in the brewing industry: remedial maintenance, which takes care of breakdowns as they occur; preventive maintenance, which seeks to relieve excessive down time through planned care of troubled areas on a regular basis; and planned preventive maintenance, which is, in fact, a mini-overhaul on a regular time frame using the accumulated data available on each piece of equipment.

There are as many opinions concerning maintenance programs as there are readers of this book. Some say it is best to have a craft person or persons, depending on the jurisdictional set-up in the operation, on each line with back-up people in the shop. These advocates contend that the shop personnel can provide many useful services such as routine repairing of parts, rebuilding, fabricating, and a whole host of other things. There are just as many others who say that there should be no maintenance personnel on the line but have them available in the shop; however, the maintenance shop should do none of the aforementioned fabricating and rebuilding since it is cheaper to use outside subcontractors.

Where do we draw the line? It is impossible to create a single type of maintenance program and organization which will fit the varied operations in the brewing industry. The physical configuration of the plant, the type of union organization which exists, the relationship of supervisory personnel to craft people, and the relationship between maintenance and production are all factors which make it necessary for each plant to gather unto itself the best organization and program for its particular operation.

ORGANIZATION

Maintenance organizations have been discussed in earlier chapters of this book. It is important to realize that the authors of those particular chapters, while dealing with other topics in packaging, set forth only a particular type of maintenance organization to illustrate a point. Historically, a maintenance superintendent with a brewery maintenance supervisor or general foreman, a packaging maintenance supervisor or general foreman, and a general plants maintenance supervisor or general foreman is the most basic organization. There is then to be considered the question of to whom does the maintenance department report. Does it report to the plant engineer; or does it report to the operations manager; or does it report to the plant manager? Each of these approaches has its own merit, but each is dependent upon the particular situation in the particular plant. Historically, again, most maintenance departments report to the plant engineer, who in turn, reports to the plant manager.

In some locations where the historic craft unions are part of the contractual obligation of the company, more supervisors are required since there is a supervisor over each craft.

The craft unions commonly found in a brewery are machinists, electricians, pipefitters, oilers, and laborers. Older breweries may also have iron workers, carpenters, and painters. A few breweries have both machinists and millwrights. There is historically an overlap of jurisdiction between the machinists and the millwrights. Both are concerned with connecting and disconnecting equipment, repair of fillers, labelers, pasteurizers, bottle washers, etc. However, where both machinists and millwrights work in the same plant, the millwrights perform carpentry functions.

The work of electricians is fairly well defined. Many breweries have instrument men to insure that control and recording equipment is operating properly, and in such cases, there is sometimes an area of overlap with the electricians.

Pipefitters or steamfitters work mainly with piping and pumps.

Today there is a tendency to get away from such craft supervision and to place individual supervision in an area of packaging, warehousing or brewing. This approach brings more supervisory expertise to the overall efficiency of each area or each type of equipment, whereas craft supervision is often merely utilized in directing a particular union group as to where it should go next and as to what it should do. However, each plant is different, and each plant must evolve its own organization from the labor contracts it has, from the history built up in that plant as well as the history of maintenance in production operations in other industries in the same area, and from the desire of plant management to achieve maximum efficiency at the lowest possible cost.

LUBRICATION

Lubrication is the core of good maintenance. The beginning point of good lubrication is good planning.

Lubrication planning includes listing all pieces of equipment in the area which must be maintained and therefore must be lubricated. From this list of equipment, one must prepare a frequency chart to make certain that each piece of equipment is properly oiled and greased. The next step is to determine how long it takes to properly lubricate each piece of equipment. From this point, using the most logical route of employee movement from one piece of machinery to the next, and using the time it takes to lubricate plus walking time, develop a schedule which determines the number of people required to do lubrication in each segment of an operation.

Once the schedule has been established, it is important that it be transmitted to the lubrication team. They must be aware of what is expected of them each day and where they are expected to be at each point in time during their work shift.

It is not the intent here to suggest the frequency of lubrication for any particular piece of equipment. This has been mentioned by several authors earlier in this book where they have been dealing with specific types of packaging equipment.

Nor is it the intent here to define the types of lubrication material to be used. Certainly it is necessary that any lubricants which may come in contact with the product and even the package, must have FDA approval, and further that any such lubricants must be tasteless, odorless, and have no ill effects upon the product. Equipmental manuals should be consulted for lubricant specifications.

Each lubrication system requires a schedule of uniform application of each particular lubricant. It is essential that all pieces of equipment be scheduled with the proper frequency. It takes time to develop an adequate lubrication program and one must be certain that it is properly supervised.

Some equipment comes with automatic lubrication systems. These systems permit continuous operation of equipment without stops for lubrication. Experience has shown these systems to be remarkably accurate and reliable; however, one must check to see that they are in good working order and that they continue to be in good working order. Thus, a physical audit of automatic lubrication systems must be made on a regular basis.

Much of today's lubrication is still done manually with a squirt of oil or a shot of grease to a particular bearing, conveyor, or cam. One of the greatest fallacies in the field of lubrication is the idea that if one squirt or one shot is good, then two squirts or two shots must be twice as good. This is not necessarily true. In fact, there are times when all one does with the second shot is create a safety hazard because it goes on the floor or on the grating where employees stand. This is not only a safety hazard, but adds unnecessary additional cost, since it wastes lubricating materials. It is necessary that quantities be built into the schedule so that management knows the anticipated cost of lubrication. The high quality food grade lubricants used today are fairly expensive, and therefore, the usage must be carefully controlled. The frequency and amount of oil and grease used is a very important part of the cost of maintenance.

One of the essentials of a good lubrication schedule is periodic reevaluation to make certain that the schedules are being followed, to correlate the frequency with the cost to see if it is necessary to change any portions of the schedule, and to make certain that all of the lubrication needs of the operation are being met. A periodic reevaluation also becomes necessary because of personnel changes. Vacations, jury duty, and other items which change the work force require supervisors to be more alert to see that schedules are properly followed and that the work is properly completed.

The work force is, of course, an important element in the lubrication schedule. Most plants operate with the historic craft unions including Firemen and Oilers, the latter doing the lubrication work. This is a particularly efficient way of providing good lubrication, since these people are probably more professionally trained and more dedicated than any other group. During the past ten to fifteen years, however, there has been a movement in the U.S. brewing industry toward a single maintenance unit, This has placed lubrication in a peculiar labor situation. In some plants operating with a "wall-to-wall" unit, lubrication is done by maintenance personnel, while in other plants it is performed by production personnel. Most maintenance people assigned to lubrication feel it is demeaning, and they do not like those assignments. On the other hand, production workers like the assignment because it is often not too heavily supervised, and therefore, they are able to get more free time for themselves.

Whatever the labor set-up in a particular plant, it is necessary that management thoroughly understand the advantages and disadvantages of that

ADOLPH COORS COMPANY   PAGE 1458

```
BPM19R02              PLANT MAINTENANCE SYSTEM        PAGE  1 OF  1
DATE: 07-26-82    PREVENTIVE MAINTENANCE TASK SCHEDULE      WEEK 31
DATE COMP 7/31/82 INSP BY  LS              HRS PM 1/2 HRS WORK 1/2


GROUP-MAIN      AREA-BREW      PM TYPE-STATIC    CRAFT-PLB   SHIFT-
TAG# - TG012048 A BREWLINE PRESS                 LOC - 2ND FL SBC


TASK #              DESCRIPTION            FREQ I.C. NUMBER
8000    *****  "A" FILTER PRESS    *******  WK
8005    LOCATED: SBC 2ND. FLR & PRESS FLR.   WK
8010    NORTH END OF PRESS:                  WK
8015    ✓ END PLATE CARRIAGE RLLRS. 4 GFM2   WK
8020    ✓ END PLATE SHAFT SOCKET    1 GFM2   WK
8025    ✓ HYD CYL (NOTE: THIS FITTING        WK
8030               MAY NOT EXIST   1 GFM2   WK
8035    SOUTH END OF PRESS:                  WK
8040    ✓ END PLATE CARRIAGE RLLRS. 4 GFM2   WK
8045    ✓ END PLATE SHAFT SOCKET    1 GFM2   WK
8050    ✓ HYD CYL (NOTE: THIS FITTING        WK
8055               MAY NOT EXIST)  1 GFM2   WK
8060    AUGER:                               WK
8065    ✓ AUGER END BEARINGS        2 GFM2   WK
8070  · ✓ AUGER SHAFT SEALSS        2 GFM2   WK
8075    ✓ AUGER HANGER BEARINGS     2 GFM2   WK
8080    -                                    WK
8085    SOLIDS PUMP (MOYNO):                 WK
8090    ✓ GREASE FITTINGS           4 GFM2   WK
8095    -                                    WK
8100    EXTRACT PUMP:                        WK
8105    ✓ CK OIL LEVL IN SIGHT GLSS OFM105   WK
8110    ✓ CLEAN SCREEN IN COOLING            WK
8115         WATER LINE                      WK
8120    ---ARE ALL BRNGS. & FTTNGS. WIPED    WK
8125         AFTER GREASING?                 WK
8130    IS EXCESS OIL WIPED UP?              WK
8135    ✓ YES  ( ) NO                        WK
```

(handwritten annotations: "— repaired broken grease LINE" / "Editor's note: Type of grease. Four fittings. Check when completed.")

25-1. *Example of computer-generated lubrication schedule. Courtesy Adolph Coors Co.*

labor organization in relation to lubrication and compensate for it by more stringent supervision, more closely knit schedules and by tighter cost control.

Where does lubrication belong? Should it report to operations, that is, to the production people; or should it report to maintenance? Usually the people who lubricate plant equipment are part of the maintenance system and report through maintenance supervision, and historically plants tend to move in this direction. It is essential in any case that whoever directly supervises the lubrication crew sees that it does its work properly, that it maintains the schedules which are set forth for it, and that there is no waste of lubricating material. It is also essential that operating personnel check to make certain that the lubrication schedules have been followed so that they do not unnecessarily incur down time. This double check is important to the continued highly efficient operation of plant equipment.

One final word about lubrication. Perhaps over the years lubrication has not been given the place of prominence which it deserves. While it is a rather innocuous job, its importance cannot be over-emphasized. No automobile runs without proper lubrication nor does any piece of equipment. Therefore, psychological tools to impress upon the lubrication work force the importance of their task can also help improve efficiencies in the packaging plant.

MAINTENANCE

Webster's Dictionary provides one meaning of maintenance as: "the upkeep of property or equipment". While that definition is short and to the point, it does not go on to say that in industry the reason for keeping up property and equipment is to make certain that operating costs are as low as possible. It is essential that the maintenance system work toward creating higher efficiencies and thus lower production costs.

Reports

The object of any reporting system is to properly account for the labor and materials expended. When a piece of paper is generated to cover a breakdown which must be repaired immediately in order to get a unit back into operation, it is for that purpose only. However, the same piece of paper can be used to request maintenance work which can wait until a later time. From those requests which are not immediate in nature, a schedule must be developed to show specifically those jobs which are to be performed on a weekend or some other time, and the priority from which the schedule is developed. It is also necessary to define the approximate number of hours and people required, thus accumulating an estimate of labor costs involved in that type of maintenance.

Monthly reports are then issued which detail the cost for both labor and material as well as the overhead portion of the maintenance operation. These result in the dollars being spent per barrel, and give management a tool to determine whether their maintenance needs some alteration because it is too high in cost, or to show that low efficiencies are the result of insufficient personnel available to do maintenance work, or some combination of the two.

Types of Maintenance

Some companies keep craft people on packaging lines and in various other areas where they anticipate that breakdowns will occur. This type of breakdown maintenance insurance is very expensive, unless one can provide sufficient bench work to keep employees busy while they are waiting for a breakdown. Other companies, while operating a basic breakdown maintenance system, keep craft people in a shop area and assign work which can be done in the shop while awaiting calls for equipment breakdowns.

Most companies use a combination of breakdown and scheduled maintenance work. This means that a number of individuals are assigned to handle breakdowns but are still available to do scheduled maintenance work in a confined area when they are not otherwise engaged. It also means that a more realistic schedule of preventive maintenance can be devised.

Preventive maintenance presumes some knowledge, or data bank information, which shows the frequency with which certain pieces of equipment, or equipment components, break down based on operating hours. Thus, before that critical number of hours is reached, a maintenance effort is made to check

WORK REQUEST

21	03528

COST CENTER   **WORK AREA**   **CRAFT**   **TOTAL MATERIAL COST**

6	1	0	0		2	7		0	5

REQUESTOR. MUST COMPLETE ALL SHADED AREAS BELOW.

TO: MAINTENANCE ENGINEERING

DATE: 6-7-82

FROM: John Bosch - Prod. Mgr.

REQUIRED COMPLETION DATE: 7-29-82

APPROVAL:

COMPLETION DATE: 7-29-82

WORK AREA: Bottle House

FOREMANS APPROVAL: Joe Brown

WORK TO BE DONE:

Revamp inFeed Conveyors To #9 Olin MAchines so thAt drop outs CAN be iNstAlled For down Bottles ANd broken glAss.

MATERIAL USED

QTY.	DESCRIPTION	UNIT COST	TOT. COST
24 ft	1/2" Round S.S.	—	52.00
10 ft	1"x2" Flat Stock		12.00
24 ft	1/2" PlAsTic Wear STRiP		30.00

1 ☐ CARPENTERS   7 ☐ MILLWRIGHTS
2 ☐ LABORERS   8 ☐ PIPEFITTERS
3 ☐ PAINTERS   9 ☐ PLANT MACHINIST
4 ☐ ELECTRICIANS   10 ☐ PALLET BLDG. MACH.
5 ☒ BOTT. MACHINIST

MAINT. ENG. APPROVAL Bill Jansen

DATE ASSIGNED	DATE COMPLETED	TO COSTING	FROM COSTING	TO IBM	FROM IBM
6/10/82	7/29/82	8/2/82	8/5/82	8/6/82	8/7/82

539-P 9-8-72

TOTAL MATERIAL COST ⇨ 94.00

TOTAL LABOR COST ⇨ 240.00

TOTAL COST ⇨ 334.00

25-2. *Example of a Work Request form for all major maintenance work or maintenance changes. The form is sent directly to the Maintenance Engineering Department for evaluation and distributed to the maintenance department directly involved with the work to be performed.*

1 copy is held by Maintenance Engineering, 1 copy by the Requestor and 1 copy is sent to Maintenance Department which will handle the job. Upon completion the Maintenance Department sends the work request back to Maintenance Engineering Department for filing and to Accounting for costing. Courtesy Christian Schmidt Brewing Co.

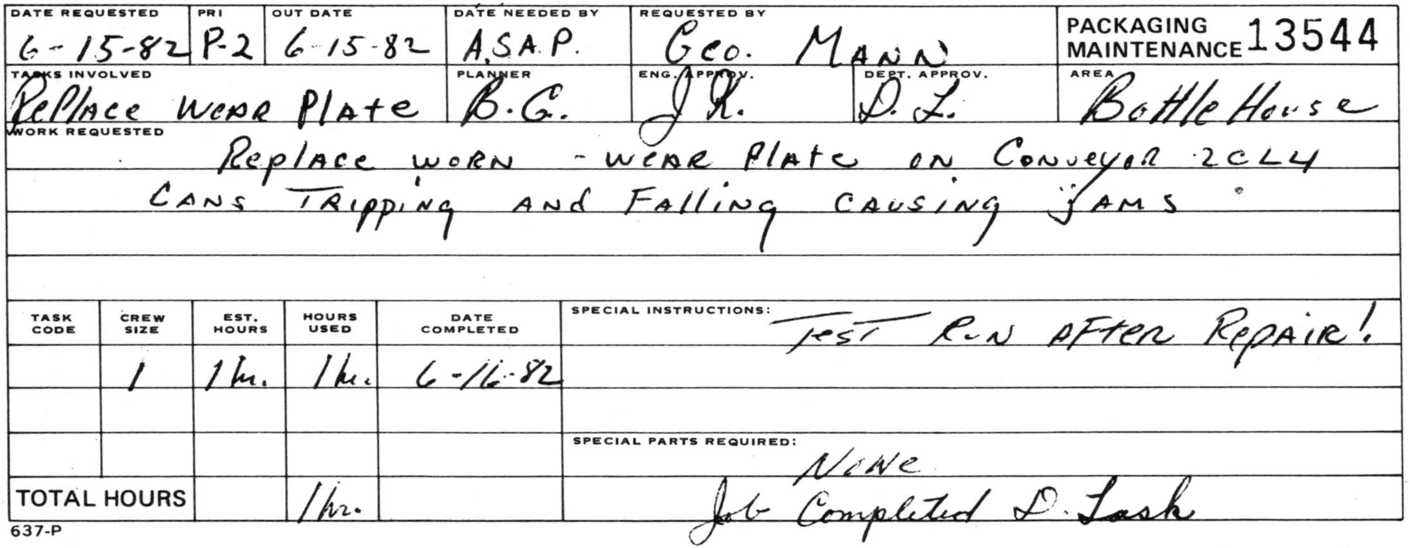
DATE REQUESTED: 6-15-82 | PRI: P-2 | OUT DATE: 6-15-82 | DATE NEEDED BY: A.S.A.P. | REQUESTED BY: Geo. Mann | PACKAGING MAINTENANCE 13544

TASKS INVOLVED: Replace Wear Plate | PLANNER: B.G. | ENG. APPROV.: J.R. | DEPT. APPROV.: D.L. | AREA: Bottle House

WORK REQUESTED: Replace worn - wear plate on Conveyor 2CL4 Cans tripping and falling causing jams

TASK CODE	CREW SIZE	EST. HOURS	HOURS USED	DATE COMPLETED
	1	1hr.	1hr.	6-16-82
TOTAL HOURS			1hr.	

SPECIAL INSTRUCTIONS: Test Run after Repair!

SPECIAL PARTS REQUIRED: None

Job Completed D. Lask

637-P

25-3. *Four part job ticket for normal daily maintenance work, complaints and repairs. No maintenance work is performed without a job ticket; however, an emergency breakdown or a safety hazard is taken care of immediately, and the job ticket is filled out as soon as possible. Procedure code used to assign priorities: R-1 Scheduled work—maintenance when line is down; R-2 Scheduled work—with P.M. work; R-3 Scheduled work—with overhaul. P-1 Top Priority. Must be done whether machine is running or not. a. Safety hazard. b. Machine problem—if kept running will cause further damage. c. Problem—if corrected immediately will improve production. P-2 Top Priority. Must be done at first break or when production line runs out.*

The first copy is kept by the Requestor and the second is returned to the Requestor when the job is completed. The third and fourth copies are used by the Maintenance Department and are filed in the equipment file by the individual machines. Courtesy Christian Schmidt Brewery Co.

TABLE I
LINE CHANGE OVER—N.R. QTS. TO RET. QTS.

MACHINISTS: 12.0 hrs 3 men

1. FLAP OPENER: Set up Flap opener for Returnable case and Test Run.
2. UNCASER: Run Cases through Uncaser. Check timing and height. Adjust as necessary.
3. SOAKER: Check Infeed timing and Check Discharge timing.
4. FILLER & CROWNER: Install proper table equipment to run bottles through crowner: hookup drive for the crowner and disconnect the Alcoa Capper.
5. PACKER: Install hold down rail on lift table. Check Packer with cases. Check all rails through packer.

MILLWRIGHTS:

1. Change Diverter from Rinser to run into Soaker.
2. FLAP OPENER TO UNCASER: Check rails from the flap opener to Uncaser, and set for the Returnable Cases.
3. EMPTY CASE CONVEYORS: From Uncaser to 3RD Floor. Check flap Control rails and the center flap control rail with A Case. Adjust as necessary to control the short flap.
4. OPTI-SCANS: Install proper Stars and rail on both Opti-Scans.
5. FLAP CLOSER: After Packer; Set flap closer with case. Adjust if necessary.
6. DIVERTER: Swing diverter from the gluer slitter.
7. CASE CLEANER 3RD FLOOR: Set to run cases through the Case Cleaner.
8. EMPTY CASE CONVEYOR: Case cleaner to the Packer. Set flap Control rail as necessary to control the short flap.
9. FILTECS: Set rails for proper bottle control on both filtecs.

ELECTRICIANS:

1. OPTI-SCANS: Set up and Check both Opti-Scans. Use the test bottles.
2. FILTECS: Set up filtecs and check out using the test bottles.

UTILITIES DAILY SHIFT LOG
CI-529-B

WORK REQ. NUMBER	AREA OR BUILDING	FLOOR NUMBER	JOB DESCRIPTION	PRI-OR-ITY	COMP. YES	COMP. NO	TIME ON	TIME OFF	CHARGE CODE	TOTAL TIME	MECHANIC'S NAME
E41621	BREW	3	CLEVELAND PRESS	A	X		8	4	42010	8	ROGERS
"										8	WOODS
E416322	PKG	6	#1 STER. PT. LINE	B		X	8	4	42001	8	JACKSON
E4-01	BREW	1	A BREW KETTLE SEAL								

NAME	HRS.	NAME	HRS.	NAME	HRS.	NAME	HRS.	NAME	HRS.	ABSENT	HRS.	VACATION	HRS.
ROGERS	8	JONES	4	NAMATH	8					JONES	4	PHIPPS	8
WOODS	8	JACKSON	8										
SMITH	8	RODRIQUEZ	8										

SUPERVISOR	COST CENTER	AREA	SHIFT	SHEET	MECHANIC HAS PAGER	WEEK NUMBER	DATE
SMITH	42083	BREW	3	1 OF 1	71002	26	7-31-82

25-4. Example of Daily Shift Log. Courtesy Adolph Coors Co.

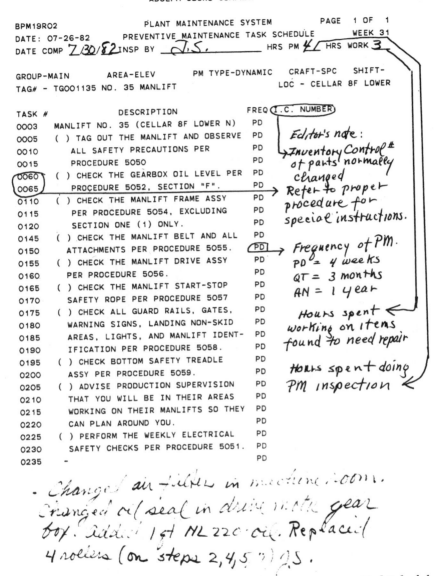

ADOLPH COORS COMPANY   PAGE 1570

BPM19RO2   PLANT MAINTENANCE SYSTEM   PAGE 1 OF 1
DATE: 07-26-82   PREVENTIVE MAINTENANCE TASK SCHEDULE   WEEK 31
DATE COMP 7/30/82 INSP BY _____J.S._____ HRS PM 4 HRS WORK 3

GROUP-MAIN   AREA-ELEV   PM TYPE-DYNAMIC   CRAFT-SPC   SHIFT-
TAG# - TGOO1135 NO. 35 MANLIFT   LOC - CELLAR 8F LOWER

TASK #	DESCRIPTION	FREQ	I.C. NUMBER
0003	MANLIFT NO. 35 (CELLAR 8F LOWER N)	PD	
0005	( ) TAG OUT THE MANLIFT AND OBSERVE	PD	Editor's note:
0010	ALL SAFETY PRECAUTIONS PER	PD	Inventory Control #
0015	PROCEDURE 5050	PD	of parts normally
0060	( ) CHECK THE GEARBOX OIL LEVEL PER	PD	changed
0065	PROCEDURE 5052, SECTION "F".	PD	Refer to proper
0110	( ) CHECK THE MANLIFT FRAME ASSY	PD	procedure for
0115	PER PROCEDURE 5054, EXCLUDING	PD	special instructions.
0120	SECTION ONE (1) ONLY.	PD	
0145	( ) CHECK THE MANLIFT BELT AND ALL	PD	
0150	ATTACHMENTS PER PROCEDURE 5055.	PD	Frequency of PM.
0155	( ) CHECK THE MANLIFT DRIVE ASSY	PD	PD = 4 weeks
0160	PER PROCEDURE 5056.	PD	QT = 3 months
0165	( ) CHECK THE MANLIFT START-STOP	PD	AN = 1 year
0170	SAFETY ROPE PER PROCEDURE 5057	PD	
0175	( ) CHECK ALL GUARD RAILS, GATES,	PD	Hours spent
0180	WARNING SIGNS, LANDING NON-SKID	PD	working on items
0185	AREAS, LIGHTS, AND MANLIFT IDENT-	PD	found to need repair
0190	IFICATION PER PROCEDURE 5058.	PD	
0195	( ) CHECK BOTTOM SAFETY TREADLE	PD	
0200	ASSY PER PROCEDURE 5059.	PD	Hours spent doing
0205	( ) ADVISE PRODUCTION SUPERVISION	PD	PM inspection
0210	THAT YOU WILL BE IN THEIR AREAS	PD	
0215	WORKING ON THEIR MANLIFTS SO THEY	PD	
0220	CAN PLAN AROUND YOU.	PD	
0225	( ) PERFORM THE WEEKLY ELECTRICAL	PD	
0230	SAFETY CHECKS PER PROCEDURE 5051.	PD	
0235	-	PD	

- Changed air filter in machine room.
Changed oil seal in drive motor gear
box. Added 1 qt NL 220 oil. Replaced
4 rollers (on steps 2,4,5?) J.S.

25-5. Example of computer-generated Preventive Maintenance Task Schedule. Courtesy Adolph Coors Co.

the equipment and replace potentially defective parts. Perhaps the easiest way to describe preventive maintenance is to understand that chucks and rolls in a can closing machine are replaced after a given number of cans have been run through that particular closer. This is a number which is fixed by the brewer and the manufacturer and is the basis for taking out of service a particular closer and replacing the chucks and rolls. A similar approach can be developed for other major pieces of equipment.

Some plants have sufficient packaging equipment to allow them the luxury of taking a line out of service during straight time and working it over on a planned, or preventive, or combination planned/preventive maintenance basis. This means that overtime is not necessary or at least, it is minimized. The equipment is checked and defects found before they develop into breakdowns, thus reducing the cost of maintenance and enhancing packaging efficiency. On the other hand, excess equipment requires capital being previously expended to provide that luxury. Certainly, no one can dictate which is the proper system. One can only say that any approach, be it on straight time or on overtime, must be defensible and should be closely supervised. Moreover, such a program must have a basis in fact which shows the number of breakdowns which have occurred in terms of operating hours or cases produced.

Years ago, it was considered proper to strip annually a packaging line to the floor and rebuild it. That day is gone. The cost of doing this is prohibitive and the necessity does not exist. Here, again, the use of data which have been accumulated to show the frequency of breakdowns, the life expectancy of equipment, or parts in a particular piece of equipment, should form the basis for doing any kind of prolonged repair work. The term overhaul has fallen into disrepute because it has become a Parkinson's law type of maintenance, in that, if you take a line out for four weeks for maintenance it will take the people working on it four weeks to get it fixed. Then, when they get it back into operation, start-up problems occur over an additional period of time.

Companies today are looking at doing a number of weeks of repair work in segments of one week each or in segments of less than one week but adding up to a considerable amount of time over a year. Most of this type of work is based upon two principles: (1) that employees will not be thinking of how they can stretch out the job, and (2) that no extra people need be hired. It is important under these circumstances to define exactly what work must be performed and that it be done in as short a period of time as possible. In most cases, these outages do not exceed one week at a time.

There are obvious exceptions. It is sometimes difficult to consider replacing a bottle washing machine chain in one week (and other parts will come to mind), but the principle is to confine the period to as short a number of hours as possible in order to condense the work and to concentrate on it without allowing time for creating other work which need not be done at that time.

Maintenance Contractors

Recently, that is within the last three to four years, outside contractors doing maintenance work have come upon the scene who are able to do jobs at a cost cheaper than using in-house personnel, but they may not be as knowledgeable as in-house personnel. One of the major factors in determining whether to use outside contractors or not is the labor agreement or agreements under which a particular plant operates. Perhaps it is better to go outside; or perhaps it would be better still to insist that you will go to outside contractors unless concessions (in terms of jurisdiction and work rules) to reduce your maintenance costs are granted.

Certainly, those maintenance contractors operating in various plants throughout the country are becoming more efficient in their work, and at the same time they are in a position to be able to transfer to a plant in which they work the benefits of what other companies are doing in terms of better maintenance.

25-7. For all major work such as projects and machine overhauls, a Maintenance Engineering Report is submitted in two sections.

The first part includes: Pre-Inspection Report, Manpower Requirements, Material Audit and Tentative Overhaul Date.

The second part includes: Job Completion Report, Inspection on Completed Jobs, Follow Up and Work Assigned for Backlog, Cost Analysis Report and Parts List for Reordering. Examples follow. Courtesy Christian Schmidt Brewing Co.

MAINTENANCE ENGINEERING REPORT

Overhaul #1 Palletizer	**Tentative Overhaul—2-8**
Type of Overhaul	**Completion Date 2-22**
Complete	Other Depts. Notified
General	Carpenters
Partial	Pipefitters
Section X	Millwrights
	Electricians X
	Painters

PRE-INSPECTION REPORT

After inspection of #1 Alvey Palletizer and Conveyor Systems, the overhaul areas to be done are (3) sections plus a project conveyor change.

The first section: Apron assembly needs the most attention and a complete overhaul.

The second section: Discharge Conveyor System & Elevator

The third section: Infeed Conveyor System from bridge to high speed rollers on palletizer.

The project pertains to the last curve before the palletizer which is also a case turner.

This corner will be completely changed to a high speed case roller turn, work will be handled by the millwrights.

MANPOWER REQUIREMENTS

4 Mechanics	— 2 days work—2 second shift for 2 weeks
2 Beltmen	— 1 week
3 Millwrights	— 2 weeks—corner project.

MATERIAL AUDIT

	IN STOCK	ORDERED
Parts for Apron Assembly	X	
Slats	X	
Tubes	X	
Chain	X	

*Note: Do not know condition of pinion and rack on apron until we tear it down.

	IN STOCK	ORDERED
Parts for Discharge Conveyor System		
Rollers	X	
Bearings	X	
Sprockets	X	
Chain	X	
Case Infeed Rollers High Speed (Urethane)	X	
Parts for Discharge Conveyor		
Rollers	X	
Chains	X	
Sprockets	X	
Bearings	X	

Parts for Elevator

Rollers	X
Bearings	X
Chains	X
Sprockets	X

Note: A list of parts used will be attached to report.
   Reordering of materials will be done in conjunction with this list.

JOB COMPLETION REPORT
INSPECTION ON COMPLETED JOBS

Section I—Alvey Apron Assembly

Apron completely rebuilt—tubes, slats, chain—bearings chain guides, sprockets. The pinion and rack drive for apron upon inspection had to be replaced also.

Section II—Discharge Conveyor and Elevator

Removed, cleaned and serviced as required. All rollers, sprockets and chains installed and lubed.
Checked and serviced elevator doors on 1st and 2nd floor.
Replaced all track and guide rollers on elevator.
Also removed cleaned and serviced pallet rollers—drive sprockets and chains in elevator car.

Section III—Infeed Conveyor System

Removed rollers, bearings and shafts. Cleaned inspected and replaced where required.
Replaced belt laggings and belts where required.
Infeed Live Roller Assembly.
Replaced with reconditioned exchange rollers with new bearings and shafts including drive chain and guides with sprockets and take up.

Follow-Up and Work Assigned for Backlog

1. **Flight Bar Chains**—Need replacing

2. **Lid Closers**

   Replace spring on control cylinder rod, replace chain.

3. **Elevator**

   Needs to be shimmed. Too much play in guide rollers.

4. **Discharge Conveyor**

   Needs levelling and secured to floor.

Materials Used

   List Attached!

Man Power Used

Machinist	375 hours
Beltmen	120 hours
Millwrights	240 hours
Electricians	140 hours (est.)

Training

During the last fifteen years, there has been an increase in the use of an overall maintenance group as part of a single local union operation encompassing the entire plant. In such cases, maintenance people lose their identity as part of a particular craft and do a variety of jobs. Naturally, this leads to a smaller work force. It also eases supervision requirements and reduces jurisdictional problems, but does not provide the expertise which one finds in persons who have undergone training in a particular skill. Regardless of what type of shop, supervision must be alert to insure that jobs are being properly done and equipment is properly maintained.

One of the ways in which the job of supervising can be eased is through periodic training programs and the periodic reevaluation of employee performance. Training programs are essential as the sophistication in equipment increases. They are essential when a new piece of equipment is introduced in a particular plant. It is absolutely necessary that the people from the manufacturer conduct programs of training not only for the maintenance people but for the operators, for the lubricators, and *for the supervisors* as well. It is essential that manuals of operation, parts and maintenance be purchased with equipment.

It is almost impossible to over train both supervisory and hourly personnel. One of the basic considerations in training is its cost versus its effectiveness. It is a difficult measurement, but certainly maintenance performance cannot continue to improve without training. Without training, it is almost impossible for maintenance personnel to be aware of industry changes, or to remain alert to them and to what they do to the operation.

SUMMARY

Maintenance is an increasing cost of operation in a brewing organization. As previously mentioned, the make-up of the maintenance cost may vary from company to company, but the relation within a particular company can certainly point out whether a particular plant operation is efficient or not. One may have to consider if the labor contracts in one plant within a company are different from the labor contracts in another plant within the same company to make realistic comparisons. Regardless, no maintenance program can be cost effective unless there is an effort toward planned maintenance, planned accounting for maintenance costs and planned review of those costs. It is imperative that maintenance management be alert to all changes in operation which may affect the cost of maintaining equipment.

The recent introduction of programmable controllers for the modulated flow control of a packaging line means that the line equipment must run steadily and must be maintained for continuous operation without presuming breakdowns. This may mean the maintenance work force must be realigned to permit working on equipment on an off shift as opposed to waiting for something to happen, and then working all weekend to get the equipment ready for the next operating week. It may mean that a line and/or plant might operate only two shifts a day and maintain on the third. These are matters for operating policy which must be based on the degree of sophistication of new equipment.

Regardless of future developments, maintenance costs are today, and will be in the future, an important element of an operation. They must be carefully controlled. Maintenance must be an efficient service organization which gets along with production management and understands the need to be cost effective while fulfilling its primary goal of keeping high speed packaging lines in operation with a minimum of breakdowns or malfunctions of equipment.

CHAPTER XXVI

CLEANING AND SANITATION
BY W.R. GARVIE and A.L. LEITH

INTRODUCTION

There are numerous distinct elements which must be co-ordinated in order to achieve a well organized, efficient packaging operation. One of these, which on occasion may receive less attention than it warrants, is the programme of cleaning and sanitation.

Any good cleaning and sanitation programme in the packaging department must ensure that the following requirements are met:
— Maintenance of product and package quality.
— Maintenance of good housekeeping and safety.
— Protection of equipment.
— Efficiency of operation.
— Adherence to governmental regulations.
The following will attempt to discuss the requirements a good cleaning and sanitation programme must fulfill and suggest a possible format for its implementation and operation. In addition, consideration will be given to water quality, process equipment cleaning and cleaning and sanitizing materials required for the effective functioning of the programme.

PRINCIPLES OF AN EFFECTIVE CLEANING PROGRAMME

The initial step in the development of any effective cleaning programme is the preparation of a detailed, up-to-date cleaning and sanitation manual which must be made readily accessible for the benefit of the cleaning crew and production staff, and which can also be used to aid in the training of the crew and its supervisor.

The manual should establish the frequency and method of cleaning for each major item of equipment. This information can be prepared on the basis of data accumulated from a variety of sources: previous company experience and procedures, reference manuals covering the machinery used, and consultation with representatives from both the equipment manufacturers and suppliers of cleaning materials. Due to the many recent developments in both machinery and cleaning supplies, consultation of this nature is strongly advised during the manual's preparation.

A step-by-step procedure which can be easily followed by the cleaning crew should be set up. The manual should contain information regarding the Daily, Weekly, Monthly and Annual cleaning procedures for each piece of equipment. (An example of the type of outline required can be found in the section on filler cleaning procedures).

Data covering the chemical analysis of all materials and additives being used should be included; this information is required for reference if any materials are being considered as substitutes for existing supplies. In addition, this data permits usage adjustment and permits a check on regulatory approval.

For each cleaning procedure discussed in the manual, information should be given regarding the weight or volume of material used, relative to the amount of water employed, and the concentration of each material involved.

The manual should also include the schedule of routine microbiological assessments or surveys which must be undertaken in order to evaluate the sanitary conditions, and, hence, the effectiveness of the cleaning procedures.

Safety precautions must be adhered to during many of the operations, and these must be outlined, along with any instructions regarding the use of protective clothing and equipment, in the manual.

Finally, it is essential that the manual be kept up-to-date; consequently, it should be the responsibility of an individual within the company to make sure that any necessary changes regarding information in the manual are made.

THE CREW AND SUPERVISION

In many plants, production is carried out on either a single or double shift basis, leaving time available each day for cleaning. Often a separate cleaning crew is employed on the off shift; in smaller operations, however, the regular crew carry out the cleanup at the end of the production run. Establish a reasonable cleaning time for each cleaning job for cost control purposes and possible contractual problems.

Due to the need for greater production and greater utilization of equipment, an increasing number of facilities are being operated on a continuous basis. In this instance, cleaning and maintenance is done either when the line is shut down for one shift during the week or on weekends, and the cleaning is done by the operating crew rather than a specific cleaning crew. Yet, no matter what the operating cycle is, it is essential that the crew carrying out the cleaning operation be well trained; and, if possible, it is advantageous to maintain a regular cleaning crew.

Equally important as the crew is the supervisory staff. The supervisor should also be well trained and should be assigned overall responsibility for the cleaning operation instead of being expected to handle cleanup as a part of his production supervision responsibilities.

A check list should be set up which would allow staff to ascertain whether the cleaning operations have been carried out in the prescribed manner. Many poor production line start-ups can be avoided by assuring that the cleaning procedures have been properly performed prior to start-up. In addition, inspection of cleaned equipment by the cleaning staff can detect developing problems in time to permit correction before production is adversely affected.

WATER QUALITY RELATED TO CLEANING AND SANITATION

Between four and seven gallons of water are required for every gallon of beer packaged; consequently, it is mandatory that a large supply of biologically pure water of suitable hardness is available. It is essential that the water be biologically pure since it is used both to rinse the container prior to filling and to flush any equipment which comes in direct contact with the beer.

Quality of Water Available

The various impurities found in water can all impart undesirable characteristics to it. The three main types of impurities found in water are:

1. Dissolved minerals.
2. Dissolved gases.
3. Suspended solids.

Thorough analyses of the incoming water supply are required during various seasons of the year to assist in the establishment of a suitable treatment programme. These analyses should determine the water's mineral content, microbiological condition, pH, odour, taste and turbidity; in addition, the water should be tested for the presence of organic and particulate matter in the water or for any suspected contaminant.

Corrective Action

All water used within the department should be of high quality, but special emphasis must be placed on the quality of water used in the rinsing of the container prior to filling and the flushing of equipment which comes in contact with the product. The water used in these operations must not be allowed to contain any contaminants; accordingly, steps must be taken to ensure that this water is biologically pure, clear, tasteless, colourless and free of suspended matter.

1. BIOLOGICAL PURITY

The available water supply will often contain many biological impurities; various treatments are available to correct this condition. The most common of these treatments purify the water through the use of one or more of the following:

(a) Chlorination—for sterilization.
(b) Ozonation—for sterilization.
(c) Ultraviolet light—for sterilization.
(d) Sand gravel filters—for removal of suspended matter.
(e) Activated carbon filters—for removal of off-flavors, aromas and trace contaminants.

2. MINERAL CONTENT

The calcium and magnesium salt content of water determines its level of hardness, which is expressed as calcium carbonate equivalents, in p.p.m. Most raw waters contain both temporary and permanent hardness. The bottler is primarily concerned with temporary or carbonate hardness which is present as bicarbonate salts in water.

Levels of hardness may be graded as follows:

Soft Water—15 p.p.m. to 50 p.p.m. $CaCO_3$ hardness

Medium-hard Water—50 to 100 p.p.m. $CaCO_3$ hardness

Hard Water—100 to 200 p.p.m. $CaCO_3$ hardness

High levels of hardness result in carbonate scale precipitation and the formation of a hard deposit when water is heated, or alkalinity increases. The scale forms readily on heating surfaces such as the interior of bottle washer compartments and pasteurizers and creates problems in rinsers which are subject to caustic carryover and alkaline water conditions. The formation of carbonate scale results directly in numerous problems, among them the blockage of manifolds, headers, spray jets, nozzles, pumps, piping and strainers. The indirect consequences of scale formation must also be recognized; these include increased breakdowns, reduced production output and efficiency, increased power consumption, and bottle abrasion. Porous scale is also a microbiological hazard.

In order to achieve adequate, efficient bottle washing and pasteurization, it is clear that regular cleaning and descaling procedures are required.

Water hardness should be controlled at a reasonable level. The economics of treating all or part of the water used must be based on the nature of the incoming supply. For example, water which has in excess of 100 p.p.m. $CaCO_3$ hardness, will cause scale in equipment, and also deposit a white film or "bloom" on the bottles at the washer and pasteurizer discharge.

There are a number of methods of softening water supplies including:

(a) Sodium Zeolite softening.

(b) Lime softening.

(c) Use of sequestrants or chelatants.

CLEANING AND SANITIZING MATERIALS

A full knowledge of the chemical formulation of detergents, cleaners and sanitizers is necessary to permit their proper application in the removal of a variety of soil types and to achieve the degree of disinfection required.

Most cleaning and sanitation is accomplished through the use of compounded cleaner-sanitizers which contain a number of ingredients, each of which contributes to the overall capability of the compound to serve its purpose.

The nature of the formulation must be known in order both to determine the desirable concentration and temperature for use and to permit knowledgeable changes when needed. This information is also required to ensure that all products in use have regulatory agency approval.

To understand the principles of sanitation using proprietary compounds, or basic cleaners and sanitizers separately, it is necessary to appreciate the functions required from the cleaning ingredients involved, as well as the nature of these specific materials or agents. The condition of use will also reflect directly on their performance.

Functions of a Detergent

1. *Emulsification* is a physical breakdown of oils and grease, keeping them dispersed in water until rinsed away.

2. *Saponification* is the action of an alkaline material on a vegetable or animal oil or fat to form a crude soap.

3. *Wetting* is the action of water contacting all surfaces of soil or equipment. The action of wetting agents or surfactants reduces the surface tension and allows improved penetration of the cleaning solution.

4. *Deflocculation or Dispersion* is the action of breaking up aggregates or flocs into individual particles.

5. *Suspension* is the action which prevents the insoluble particles from settling out so they may be readily flushed away.

6. *Peptizing* is the physical formation of a colloidal solution from soils such as protein which may be only partially soluble.

7. *Free Rinsing* is the condition of a cleaning solution which permits it to be easily and completely flushed from a surface. Low surface tension is needed.
8. *Sequestration or Chelation* is the removal or inactivation of water hardness minerals by formation of a soluble complex.
9. *Water Softening* is the removal or inactivation of the hardness of water.
10. *Dissolving* is a chemical reaction which produces a water soluble soil. Lime deposits may be dissolved with an acid. Protein deposits may be dissolved with an alkali. Brewery bottleshops are subject to three major types of cleaning and sanitizing problems. Each is shown below with its respective method of cleaning:

Organic Soil .... Alkaline Detergent
Mineral Soil .... Acid Detergent
Microorganisms .... Sanitizer or Detergent Sanitizer

Organic Soils—Alkaline Detergents

Organic soils are composed of fats, oils, proteins and carbohydrates. Returnable bottles, beer spillage areas, equipment contacting beer and various surface and internal equipment areas subject to biological fouling provide many locations in bottleshops requiring attention.

Alkaline detergents are combinations of individual compounds, each of which contributes desirable properties to the detergent. The removal of soils is vastly improved by the use of the proper blend of materials, which, when mixed with water, provide a cleaning solution greatly superior to that prepared from any single material.

An alkaline detergent of this nature will require:
1. Alkaline salts.
2. Surface active agents.
3. Sequestering or Chelating agents.

See Table I and Table II.

Alkaline Salts

The properties and uses of common alkaline salts used in industrial cleaning are summarized in the above two tables.

Surface Active Agents

Surface active agents are commonly known as surfactants or wetting agents and are usually synthetic organic compounds. When added to water they reduce surface tension and permit the cleaning solution to spread over surfaces, thereby penetrating and removing soils more easily.

Surfactants will remove oil and act as emulsifiers at increased concentrations.

Many cleaners contain one or more surfactants at a concentration of 1-5%. The alkaline salts of the cleaner do most of the work, while the surfactant wets the surface and assists penetration. Surfactants are costly and many are excessive foam producers. Economy dictates low-level use; yet even when used this way, surfactants are still effective. Also, low foaming types can be utilized when necessary.

Surfactants are classified by ionic type or charge:
1. *Anionics*—considered negatively charged. Examples are soap, sulfates, sulfonates and phosphates.
3. *Nonionics*—considered neutral, such as ethoxylates and alkanolamides.
3. *Amphoterics*—have both negative and positive charges, such as amino acids and substituted imidazolines.

TABLE 26-1
DETERGENT COMPONENTS

SEQUESTERANTS		Approx. Calcium Binding Capacity (mg Ca^{++}/g)	Operational pH	Comments
Sodium Tripolyphosphate	STPP	140	10 - 12	threshold effect, reverts to orthophosphate
Sodium Hexametaphosphate	glassy phosphate	200	10 - 12	threshold effect, reverts to orthophosphate
Tetrasodium Pyrophosphate	TSPP	50	10 - 12	good for Mg, reverts
Tetrapotassium Pyrophosphate	TKPP	70	10 - 11	reverts, good for Mg
Ethylene Diamine Tetrasodium Acetate	EDTA.4Na	290	9 - 12	complexes many different metals
Trisodium Nitrilotriacetate	NTA.3Na	365	9 - 12	complexes many different metals
Sodium Gluconate		90*	11 - 14	good in high pH, Fe control
Sodium Glucoheptonate		100	11 - 14	good in high pH, Fe control
Amino Tri(methylene phosphonic acid)	ATMP	520	11 - 14	threshold effect
1-Hydroxyethylidine-1,1 Diphosphonic Acid	HEDP	390	11 - 14	threshold effect
Sodium Citrate		230	10 - 14	good for Fe in high pH
Zeolites	Alumino Silicates	vary	9 - 12	non-polluting, presently expensive

* increases with pH increase

TABLE 26-1 (CON'T)
DETERGENT COMPONENTS

ALKALINITY DONORS, BUFFERS	Alkalinity as % Na₂O	Other Functions
Sodium Carbonate	58.3	absorbs liquids well, filler
Sodium Metasilicate	50.3	corrosion inhibition, prevents redeposition, disperses soil
Sodium Bicarbonate	36.9	buffer at pH 9 - 10
Borates	17.1 (borax decahydrate)	buffer at pH 9
Sodium Hydroxide	77.5	high alkalinity, high conductivity
Potassium Hydroxide	84 (as K₂O)	high alkalinity, high conductivity, neutralization salts soluble
Trisodium Phosphate	18.3	peptizing effect, buffers
INERT FILLERS		
Sodium Sulphate		
Sodium Chloride		
Water		

SURFACE ACTIVE AGENTS

Soap — negatively affected by pH and hard water

Anionic Surfactants — high foaming, good detergency

Nonionic Surfactants — moderate foaming, good emulsifiers, come out of solution with high temp. and electrolyte content, can be defoamers

Cationic Surfactants — moderate to low foaming, substantive, sanitizing effect

Amphoteric Surfactants — behave as anionics or cationics depending on pH, good detergency

Source: DIVERSEY WYANDOTTE INC.

TABLE 26-2
COMMON DETERGENT INGREDIENTS

KEY TO CHART
A .... HIGH VALUE
B .... MEDIUM VALUE
C .... LOW VALUE
D .... NEGATIVE VALUE
* .... VIA PRECIPITATION
• .... VIA SEQUESTRATION
♦ .... ALSO STABLE TO HEAT

	INGREDIENTS	EMULSIFICATION	SAPONIFICATION	WETTING	DISPERSION	SUSPENSION	PEPTIZING	WATER SOFTENING	MINERAL DEPOSIT CONTROL	RINSABILITY	SUDS FORMATION	NON-CORROSIVE	NON-IRRITATING
BASIC ALKALIS	CAUSTIC SODA	C	A	C	C	C	C	C	D	D	C	D	D
	SODIUM METASILICATE	B	B	C	B	C	C	C	C	B	C	B	D
	SODA ASH	C	B	C	C	C	C	C	D	C	C	C	D
	TRI-SODIUM PHOSPHATE	B	B	C	B	B	B	A*	D	B	C	C+	C−
COMPLEX PHOSPHATES	SODIUM TETRA-PHOSPHATE	A	C	C	A	A	A	B•	B	A	C	AA	A
	SODIUM TRI-POLYPHOSPHATE	A	C	C	A	A	A	A*	B	A	C	AA	B
	SODIUM HEXAMETAPHOSPHATE	A	C	C	A	A	A	B•	B	A	C	AA	A
	TETRASODIUM PYROPHOSPHATE	B	B	C	B	B	B	A*	B	A	C	AA	B
ORGANIC COMPOUNDS	CHELATING AGENTS	C	C	C	C	C	A	AA:	A	A	C	AA	A
	WETTING AGENTS	AA	C	AA	A	B	B	C	C	AA	AAA	A	A
	ORGANIC ACIDS	C	C	C	C	C	B	A•	AA	B	C	A	A
	MINERAL ACIDS	C	C	C	C	C	C	A•	AA	C	C	D	D

COMPARATIVE ABILITY

PROVIDED AS A SERVICE BY THE KLENZADE DIVISION, ECONOMICS LABORATORY, INC.

4. *Cationics*—are positively charged, such as quaternary ammonium salts.

The first three types are used in alkaline cleaning, although the nonionics and amphoterics appear more popular for brewery use.

Sequestering and Chelating Agents

Sequestering and chelating agents are inorganic or organic chemicals which remove calcium and magnesium hardness ions (as well as some other ions), from water or from soils by forming a soluble complex. The term sequestrant only will be used.

When formulated with alkaline cleaners they prevent the hardness ions from precipitating and prevent dispersed soils from flocculating and redepositing on surfaces. They assist greatly in the prevention of scale formation and its removal.

Water softening by means of sequestering agents is in contrast to the precipitation of hardness ions by such materials as trisodium phosphate or sodium carbonate.

This subject is based on complex chemistry well beyond the scope of this chapter. However, reference will be made to a few of the better known sequestrants, some of the more recent developments, their functional characteristics and possible applications.

Individual sequestrants should be evaluated on a cost/performance basis. Since performance varies widely, according to their nature and conditions of use, it is most important to choose the one most suitable for the specific job and to use it at the proper concentration.

They vary in sequestering power for certain metallic ions, such as calcium, magnesium, aluminum, or iron, and individual capabilities vary under different temperature and pH conditions. Other factors may influence their suitability for specific applications.

The complex polyphosphates are economical and have detergent action but lose their sequestering power quickly in strongly alkaline solutions where they revert to orthophosphate and precipitate out. However, they are useful scale control agents in bottle rinsers, pasteurizers and as ingredients in compounded cleaners. Both the complex polyphosphates and the more recent organic phosphonates not only sequester scale forming ions, but also operate at very low concentrations by the "Threshold Effect", that is, a few p.p.m. will prevent or retard precipitation of scale on a very economic basis.

Another class contains gluconic acid or sodium gluconate which was a major development for bottle washing. It is commonly used in strong caustic solutions to control water scale formation and sodium aluminate precipitation, which increases in solution when washing bottles with aluminum foil labels. It is heat stable and does not break down, but unfortunately functions best at high pH only, losing most of its sequestering power at lower alkalinity levels. As a result, it does not provide adequate scale control in most post soak tanks or at medium to low pH.

A third class contains E.D.T.A., or ethylenediamine tetraacetic acid and related compounds. It is stable over a wide temperature and pH range and has excellent sequestering power. Cost/performance is a factor in its usage, but it is a popular ingredient in compounded cleaners, and for other uses.

A relatively new class of compounds, the organic phosphonates have excellent sequestering power, have a "Threshold Effect" as noted above, have temperature and pH stability and appear promising. They are used in strong caustic solutions and retain sequestering power at lower pH. They are also a component of a number of anti-corrosion compounds. Cost/performance will prove to be a decisive factor as they receive more attention and experience dictates their place in bottleshop operation.

Many other materials are in use and literature is available from suppliers.

It is evident that the choice of specific ingredients and the proportion used will permit the formulation of a wide range of cleaners varying in strength and suitable for different cleaning requirements. In addition, corrosion inhibitors and sanitizers can be incorporated as desired.

Mineral Soils—Acid Detergents and Sanitizers

The types of mineral soils or scales which form are directly related to the nature of the bottling operations. The most common scale found is calcium and magnesium carbonate which results from the precipitation of temporary or bicarbonate hardness in water. Alkaline pH and elevated temperatures are its major cause. This scale is commonly found, not only in processing equipment but on floors and other areas subject to considerable water contact. Soft water or the use of sequestrants will eliminate or reduce such deposits.

The aluminum on foil labels is dissolved by caustic cleaning solutions during bottle washing. If the caustic does not contain the proper additives to sequester the aluminate or if the sodium aluminate passes solubility limits, then aluminate scale will form. If silica or phosphate is present in the scale it will be hard and tenacious.

Heating surfaces normally are the most prone to scale formation, but overall surfaces in the soaker and particularly the rinser, may become scaled as caustic carryover creates alkaline conditions precipitating water scale.

Fillers may develop beerstone deposits, or oxalate type scale. This is normally well controlled by the careful cleaning and sanitation of this unit.

The removal of common bottleshop scale deposits is best handled by inhibited acid cleaners. Acceptable acids include the mineral acids such as hydrochloric, sulphuric, phosphoric and sodium bisulfate. Typical organic acids include citric, glycollic and sulfamic acid. In practice inhibited hydrochloric acid (muriatic) or inhibited sulfamic acid are the most commonly used in a diluted form for direct acid descaling.

The acids listed above are usually compounded with synthetic detergents of either the nonionic or certain anionic types to provide powder or liquid forms of various acid detergents. All surfaces cleaned with these should be properly flushed to remove all residuals.

Phosphoric acid is often used in the formulation of iodophors and acid-anionic sanitizers, both of which contain surface active agents and provide both good cleaning and sanitizing action, particularly at low pH levels.

Microorganisms as Soils—Sanitizers and Detergent Sanitizers

Some of the materials used in sanitation act as either cleaners or biocides alone, while others provide both detergent and germicidal effect.

It must always be remembered that one cannot sanitize or disinfect any surface unless it has first been thoroughly cleaned to permit intimate contact with the biocidal solution for the time required. It follows that detergent sanitizers will only be effective when the cleaning action is such as to permit the sanitizer the necessary contact. One cannot consider the disinfection of soil surfaces as satisfactory sanitation.

TABLE 26-3
SANITIZERS

SANITIZING AGENT	COMMON ACTIVITY	USE CONC. PPM	RESI-DUAL	SPECTRUM OF KILL	AFFECTED BY PRESENCE OF ORGANICS	ORAL TOXI-CITY	DERMAL TOXI-CITY	CORRO-SIVITY	pH	ODOUR	STORAGE STABILITY	ADVANTAGES	DISADVANTAGES
Sodium Hypochlorite	10.5%	200	no	broad	yes	med.	harsh	some	alk.	some	poor	low cost	must be stored in non-metallic containers
Chlorinated Tri-sodium Phosphate	3.5%	200	no	broad	yes	med.	harsh	some	alk.	some	good-poor	combines detergency & sanitizing	low level of available chlorine
Chlorinated Isocyanurates	55-85%	200	no	broad	yes	med.	harsh	some	alk.	strong	good-poor	high activity	stability fair; very strong oxidizer
Calcium Hypochlorite	33-70%	200	no	broad	yes	med.	harsh	some	alk.	some	good-poor	high activity	forms insoluble calcium salts
Mixed Halogen	variable	50-100	no	broad	yes	med.	harsh	some	alk.	some	good-poor	lower use activity due to synergistic effect	
Iodophor	variable	50	no	broadest	yes	med.	some drying	some	acid	some	poor	lower odour than chlorinated	can cause staining at high conc.
Peroxygen Compounds	variable	vary	no	function of formulation	yes	med.	mod.	nil-low	neut.-alk.	nil	good-poor		stability fair
(Hydrogen Peroxide, Perborates, Percarbonates, Persulphates)													
Quaternaries	variable	200	yes	function of formulation	no	low	mild	nil	neut.-alk.	nil	excellent		easily inactivated; can cause resoiling
Phenol	variable	200	yes	function of formulation	no	high	very harsh	some	acid	strong	excellent		toxicity; effluent control
Cresylic Acid	variable	vary	yes	function of formulation	no	high	very harsh	some	acid	strong	excellent	more effect than phenols	effluent control

TABLE 26-3
SANITIZERS (CON'T)

Alkyl Phenols	variable	vary	yes	function of formulation	no	high	harsh	?	acid or alk.	strong	excellent		solubility normally poor; residual
Chlorinated Phenols	variable	vary	yes	function of formulation	no	high	harsh	?	acid or alk.	strong	excellent	may be combined to give broad spectrum of kill	residual
Bis- Phenols (hexachlorophene)	variable	vary	yes	function of formulation	yes	low	low	nil	neut.	some	excellent	used mainly in hand soaps	regulated for many applications
Trichloro hydroxy diphenyl ether (Irgasan)	variable	vary	yes	function of formulation	yes	low	low	nil	neut.	light	excellent	mainly in hand soaps	
Acid-Anionics	variable	vary	yes	limited	no	low	harsh	low	acid	nil	excellent		Favours GM+
Formaldehyde	up to 40%	gas	yes	depends on temp, activity, RH	some	high	mod.	low	neut.	strong	good	effective on many spore forming types	polymerizes to paraformaldehyde which is difficult to remove; uncertain penetrability
Peracetic Acid	40%	gas or sol'n	no	Cold Sterilent; broad broad	yes	med.	mod.	some	acid	strong	poor	very active bactericide, sporicide; no residue	corrosivity; storage should be in vented containers
Chlorhexidine	variable	vary	yes	limited	no	low	low	low	neut.	nil	excellent	low toxicity; rapid activity vs. vegetative bacteria	limited antifungal activity; some incompatabilities such as anionics, hard water Favours GM+

Source: DIVERSEY WYANDOTTE INC.

Sanitizers or Biocides

See Tables 26-1, 26-2, and 26-3.

Sanitizers or Biocides are basically chemical compounds which have the disinfecting or germicidal power to kill microorganisms. The successful use of such compounds depends on proper concentration and contact time. Monitoring of the treatment addition, residual and effectiveness is essential for both continuous or intermittent treatment.

Other agents such as heat will also destroy such microorganisms.

Caustic soda has excellent germicidal action, dependent upon temperature, contact time and causticity. It is often used in the compounding of alkaline cleaner-sanitizers.

The most important chemical sanitizers used in breweries may be listed in the following groups:

1. Halogen formulations.
   (Iodophors) (Chlorinated Phenols) (Chlorine Compounds)
2. Quaternary ammonium compounds
3. Aliphatic diamines
4. Organo-Tin biocides
5. Acid-anionic surfactant germicides
6. Copper salts
7. Miscellaneous germicidal chemicals

These sanitizers may be further categorized as oxidizing or non-oxidizing biocides. An oxidizing biocide is one which, in addition to its disinfecting power, oxidizes other compounds. Chlorine is a common example.

Halogen Germicides

Chlorine biocides are among the oldest disinfectants for general and specific use and they still retain popularity since they are effective against a wide range of organisms.

Chlorine forms hypochlorous acid in solution, which acts as the main lethal agent. The hypochlorous acid dissociates to the hydrogen ion and hypochlorite ion at alkaline pH. At approximately pH 9 the hypochlorite ion accounts for almost all the chlorine. The efficiency of disinfection becomes minimal. As the pH is lowered to 6.5 the hypochlorous acid fraction increases to near 100% and the killing power moves to the maximum. Determine "Free Available Chlorine". (Figures 26-1 a and b)

An acid or low alkalinity solution becomes more effective, but less stable and may be corrosive. Free chlorine gas may also be released.

Some of the commercial hypochlorite sanitizers are formulated to obtain effective germicidal action at higher pH while retaining stability and minimum corrosiveness.

The more popular chlorine compounds are listed below:

A. *INORGANIC HYPOCHLORITES*

1. Chlorine gas—Liquid cylinders.
   Cylinders contain chlorine under high pressure in the form of part gas and part liquid for use through chlorinators. This form is economical, corrosive, a safety hazard if mishandled, but provides a simple method of chlorinating large quantities of water. Chlorinators may be highly automated.
2. Liquid sodium hypochlorite—economical, corrosive, deteriorates with

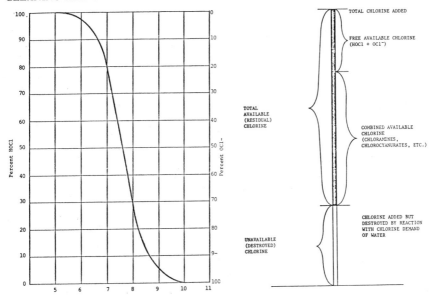

26-1 a, *Distribution of hypochlorous acid and hyperchlorite ion in water at several pH values at 20° C. b, Graphic representation of the relative amounts of* free available chorine, combined available chlorine *and* unavailable chlorine *in a typical sample of chlorinated water. (Source: A. T. I. Information Bulletin)*

storage, normally 12-13% available chlorine.
3. Calcium hypochlorite—basically pure chlorinated lime often compounded; economical, deteriorates with storage, partially insoluble, corrosive, powder (HTH), normally 70-75% available chlorine.
4. Chlorinated trisodium phosphate—dissolves rapidly with slight precipitate, non-corrosive, good detergent, sanitizes, normally has 3.5% available chlorine.

B. ORGANIC CHLORINE COMPOUNDS
1. Chloramine T—stable, low corrosiveness, comparatively slow germicidal action.
2. Chlorinated isocyanurates—stable powders, less corrosive, slowly but totally soluble, effective disinfection similar to the inorganic hypochlorites, available chlorine 60-89%.
3. Chlorinated hydantoins—similar to (2) above.

Formulated detergent sanitizers utilize calcium hypochlorite or the chlorinated isocyanurates, with buffers and other ingredients to produce cleaning products with high levels of available chlorine, (in the order of 2-20%).

Iodine Germicides
Iodophors are the most commonly used type. These are blends of iodine and a solubilizing agent, usually a non-ionic surface active or wetting agent which permits slow liberation of the reactive iodine in a water solution. The surfactant adds good cleaning action to the sanitizing action of iodine.

The free and reactive iodine concentration normally decreases as the alkaline pH range is approached. Since iodophors give their greatest germicidal action at low pH, they are often formulated with phosphoric acid to provide acid detergent sanitizers. In addition to sanitizing they are effective acid cleaners for removal of mineral type deposits.

Iodophors are relatively non-corrosive, stable, non-staining or irritating, effective at low concentrations, and usually do not require rinsing at use concentrations. They exhibit good penetrating power.

In Canada and the U.S. many iodophors are approved for "no rinse" sanitizing applications at 25 p.p.m. I_2. Solution temperatures should be under 122°F (50°C) or volatility occurs.

Bromine Germicides

Bromine-chlorine germicides are composed of a stable hypochlorite and water soluble metal bromides. Brewery use appears limited.

Fluorine Germicides

Fluorides and hydrofluoric acid were once used as effective germicides. Their toxicity and corrosiveness has resulted in general replacement by other agents.

Chlorinated Phenols

Sodium pentachlorophenate alone or in conjunction with sodium trichlorophenate was used at approximately 60 to 100 p.p.m. Toxicity decreases above pH 8.0. While once popular for pasteurizer treatment, the toxicity, odours and resistance to degradation of chlorinated phenols has caused pollution problems. Their use appears to have given way to more recently developed biocides.

Quaternary Ammonium Compounds

A variety of germicidal compounds are formed from the quaternary ammonium salts which are water soluble nitrogen containing surface active compounds, most of which have a chloride anion.

They are non-volatile, highly surface active and have excellent cleaning and germicidal action in solution or on contact surfaces. They form a bacteriostatic film if not washed off. A potable water rinse is not required if the concentration is at or below 200 p.p.m. active ingredients. Compared to the hypochlorites they are more stable and exert a residual effect, but their action as sanitizers is not as rapid.

The quats vary widely in germicidal effectiveness and function with a degree of selectivity to some organisms. To obtain a wide spectrum kill, they are often used in combinations. Shock treatments with other biocides may be used to eliminate a developing tolerance in the microbiological flora.

In the concentrations used they are odourless, colourless, non-toxic, non-corrosive, stable when heated, and most are reasonably stable in hard water and to organic matter.

When formulated with non-ionic surfactants and other cleaners they contribute greatly to detergent sanitizers, but it should be noted that they cannot be used with anionic surfactants which destroy their germicidal power. As a result soap bearing surfaces should be precleaned prior to sanitation with quaternary ammonium compounds.

As a result of their properties, quats have gained major popularity in treating pasteurizer water in many localities and have replaced chlorine and other biocides in many applications. However, since quats are foam depressants they should not be used on surfaces that contact beer.

Aliphatic Diamines
When solubilized and blended with selected surfactants this material provided a new type biocide.

Organo-Tin Biocides
Certain of these biocides have been found biodegradable and now provide another recent development in the biocide field. An example is bis (tributyltin)-oxide.

Acid-Anionic Sanitizers
Acid-anionic surfactant germicides are combinations of organic or inorganic acids with surface active agents. The surfactant is usually of the alkylarylsulfonate type, while the acid is normally phosphoric.

Germicidal activity is provided by the low pH as well as the activity of the surfactant, which also contributes detergency.

These germicides are most effective at a pH of near 2 and as a result the acidity is quite effective in removal of mineral soils, an action similar to that possessed by the iodophors.

They are heat stable, and active against a large number of microorganisms. They form a residual anti-bacterial film, lack odours, remove water scale, are effective in hard water or in the presence of organic matter, are non-corrosive to stainless steel, have a relatively low toxicity and are easily handled. Bacterial action increases at higher temperatures.

Copper Salts
Copper sulfate was commonly used at one time. Use is now limited, as the toxicity of the copper ion is reduced by other ions and organic matter. The copper ion will precipitate as insoluble copper hydroxide at high pH values thus nullifying toxicity.

Proprietary - Biocides
Many proprietary mixes are used to increase the broad spectrum of germicidal activity. There are a number of other specific germicidal chemicals which may be used in formulations.

While chlorine or chlorine-releasing agents are probably used more than any other biocide, it would appear that others are gaining in popularity, particularly for pasteurizer treatment or where residual bacteriostatic films are desired.

The use of new corrosion inhibitor formulations, which are replacing the preferred but environmentally faulted chromates, function at medium alkaline pH levels. Increased alkalinity in the pasteurizer has reduced the effectiveness of chlorine agents, in terms of speed of action.

Treatments that are in common or limited use, individually, or more frequently in combinations, include some of the more recently developed biocides such as:

Quaternary ammonium compounds
Aliphatic Diamines
Organo-Tin Biocides

The diversity of choice in cleaners, sanitizers, sequestrants, wetting agents, or in formulated detergent sanitizers, now offers most bottlers a large selection to solve varied problems.

This entire field has become highly complex. Many plant cleaning or sanitizing problems require specific evaluation if the most suitable agents are to be applied. To achieve satisfactory control in the most economical way will normally require consultation with qualified technical personnel from the formulation companies.

Field experience through a properly established evaluation program should provide the information necessary to establish the most desirable and effective program possible.

The wide diversity in the nature of cleaners, sanitizers or detergent-sanitizers makes it evident that their suitability will also vary widely dependent upon the nature of the soil, type of surface, or use of the equipment involved. The ability to clean and sanitize without corrosion and with either good rinsability, or by leaving a residual film as desired, is important. Obviously, cleaning materials which act as foam depressants would be questioned for cleaning or sanitizing beer contact surfaces.

The scope of this subject is too large to cover in this Chapter, but the interested reader should consult Reference #3, "1980 Selection Guide Cleaning and Sanitizing Compounds."

CLEANING AND SANITIZING PROCESS EQUIPMENT

The avoidance of product contamination is the prime function of any cleaning and sanitizing programme; yet overall cleanliness reflects on the entire packaging operation. An adequate programme contributes to quality packaging, improved operations, reduced breakdowns, and lessens the deterioration of equipment. A high standard of cleanliness helps maintain high employee morale and at the same time ensures that standards set by regulatory agencies are met.

The following section will discuss recommended cleaning principles for the major items of equipment.

Soaker-Rinser Cleaning

The make and model of each machine will determine the nature of its operation, since mechanical and cleaning principles vary widely with different units, (e.g., brush type, dormant soak or hydro units) it follows that cleaning and sanitizing procedures must be adapted as necessary. Manual directions should be followed.

Many other variables will affect the nature and frequency of cleaning. Typical examples would include the presence of label separators, number of hours operated, rate of accumulation of labels, amounts of broken glass and debris, sodium aluminate buildup from foil labels, scale formation, blockage of solution flow and increasing alkalinity in fresh water compartments.

Much of the cleaning and sanitizing can be accomplished with high pressure hosing using water or detergent sanitizers rather than by manual effort.

There are many common areas which require attention at a frequency related to operating conditions. Typical of those which are normally cleaned at the end of each run include the load table, rotary infeed, pre-rinse assembly, tower and sump, rinser drip trough and discharge assembly and conveyors.

Some larger breweries operating bottle washers with many compartments practice cleaning and removal of label pulp from the first series of compartments during normal operation, thus avoiding frequency of shutdown.

The last post-soak and the rinser reservoir tanks are usually drained daily as alkalinity and soils build up. Normally fresh water is introduced continuously into the last post-soak tank for alkalinity and temperature control and this extends operating time. Screens and strainers are removed and cleaned. After draining and cleaning, the last post soak and entire rinser are thoroughly hosed down, and are often treated with a sanitizer before refilling or prior to startup. Routine chlorination or the use of chlorinated materials or residual sanitizers such as the quaternaries or iodophors is a common practice.

The centering rack in a rinser must be kept free of broken glass, labels and other debris, if the bottle is to be rinsed adequately. This may require pressure hosing once or twice per shift. It is also essential to keep the rinser jets open and functional.

Other areas which require considerable attention include the caustic hydro jet assembly, if present, and the rinser assembly. The manifolds or headers with their spray nozzles or jets must be routinely flushed and checked to avoid blockage. In this instance, cleaning frequency varies from daily to weekly.

The soap container under the feed table is usually drained, flushed and cleaned weekly, then recharged with fresh chain lubricant.

Soaker Compartments

The frequency of draining and cleaning varies widely, based on factors previously mentioned.

The first presoak was normally drained to sewer after 1 to 3 weeks' operation, although return to the reclaim system is now common. The first presoak is greatly influenced by the pre-rinse operation. The remaining compartments are cleaned based mainly on label accumulation or sodium aluminate buildup. With good label separation, which is difficult to achieve, the remaining caustic tanks can be expected to function for weeks without cleaning. Sodium aluminate levels above 2% in caustic solution, dependent on temperature and total causticity, tend to precipitate out as a tenacious scale complex which includes silica and calcium and magnesium carbonate. Sequestrants are used to help control such precipitation.

Different breweries approach this problem in various ways which include sewering at specific concentrations, dropping to reclaim and partial reclaim with fresh caustic makeup to dilute the aluminate concentration. Others ignore the concentration, except for maintaining causticity, claiming that it remains at equilibrium at a certain %, without causing scale problems. However, when the solubility limit is passed precipitation must occur.

Basic points to consider when cleaning soaker compartments are:
1. Clean before the residue can dry and harden.
2. After draining, work from the top, this ensures complete drainage. Use a high pressure hose to flush debris from agitators, between carriers and deflectors, and from steam coils or other accessible areas.
3. Move to the access doors and complete hosing down coils, walls, carriers, deflector loops, etc.
4. Debris on the floor can then be flushed out through the lower manholes.
5. Clean sight glasses, windows where present, doors, gaskets and examine hoses and other interior areas for damage and scale.

Floor areas around such units should be adequately curbed and drained. Appropriate protective clothing, equipment and detailed safety procedures are a prerequisite.

Since label accumulation was once the single most important factor controlling cleaning frequency, the development of label separators, such as causti-cleans or caustic renovators such as B.W. or Niagara units, has been a most valuable contribution. If operated and maintained properly, they greatly decrease the need for caustic change and have provided finely screened caustic to hydro-jet units, reducing header and jet blockage.

Cleaning and maintenance of such units is usually an engineering function. Several key points worthy of mention to ensure proper operation of a causti-clean unit are:

1. Operational personnel should regularly monitor their performance based on the quantity of paper discharged to waste.
2. The separator screen should be kept wet to avoid drying and blockage.
3. The unit should be allowed to cycle several times to clear compartment bottoms and separator screens before shutting down.
4. When caustic compartments are drained, label debris may be drawn into the return nozzles of the separator, where it can dry and harden, creating a blockage that affects return circulation of caustic. To avoid this it is desirable to pump water through the system and visually check the return flow at each nozzle in the compartment.
5. Remember that the clearance of screen to screw is critical and that the screen must be kept open at all times for good operation.

The Niagara renovator receives caustic solution with labels from the selected soaker tank into the renovator tank. A perforated stainless steel belt angles through the liquid, retaining the labels on its surface, from which they drop to waste containers after the belt has left the caustic solution and completed its downward turn at the end of the vessel.

The stainless steel screen must be kept clean and free from hardened material to permit caustic drainage through the perforations for reuse.

Other principles, such as ensuring that the return caustic nozzles are not blocked thus preventing adequate flushing across the compartment bottom, should be checked as previously discussed.

Some plants are now using a direct pressure caustic flush across the compartment bottom, thus removing bottom debris to reclaim while continuing normal operation.

Proper operation of these units can change the need for compartmental drainage and cleaning from a weekly basis to an extended period (often months). This appears to be a poorly controlled operation generally, but one with the potential for vast improvement.

If scale formation is troublesome it can be removed by manual effort. Today, removal by acid descaling with inhibited hydrochloric or muriatic acid, or inhibited sulfamic acid, is common practice and has been well documented. Some emphasis has been placed on the proper use of sequestering or chelating agents to prevent or remove scale formations and on the use of acidic cleaners such as the acid-anionics or the iodophors which contribute to scale control.

Those in charge of cleaning operations in any plant which suffers major problems from scale formation must realize that they have not availed themselves of current technology.

It is appreciated that many items, specific to makes or models of soakers have not been covered in this chapter. Units with a label flushing manifold, rocker tees, vibrating screen assemblies for label removal, special caustic sprays or brush type units, will require special procedures. Equipment manuals provide the necessary data.

Filler

When it is considered that the only piece of equipment that comes in direct contact with the beer is the filler, the importance of a good cleaning and sanitizing procedure here cannot be over emphasized.

For effective cleaning of either can or bottle fillers the following is required:

1. Internal cleaning throughout the filler to ensure that all surfaces coming in contact with the beer are thoroughly cleaned and sanitized. This is best achieved by circulation.
2. External cleaning for the removal of glass, debris and soils, plus sanitation, by one or more of the following:
   a) High pressure exterior cleaning and sanitation
   b) Foam type cleaning and sanitation
   c) Use of iodophor type sprays for improved sanitation

Fillers should be cleaned and sanitized after every operating period. If a subsequent start-up is scheduled within a few hours then a cold water flushing through the filler and its passages is all that is necessary. In addition, the beer tank cover should be opened and the water allowed to overflow. Any internal removable parts such as floats, foam rings, etc., should be removed and cleaned as well as the inside of the filler bowl. This varies with different fillers.

The method of filler circulation varies based on filler and brewery involved; e.g. larger Cemco units control liquid level by a Taylor Level Control (ball float) or differential level detector (bubble tube), rather than the mushroom float. Circulation can be through the C.P. line and stuffing box without the need for float removal.

External surfaces should also be cleaned either manually by brushing, or, as is more frequently done, by the use of pressure or foam spray guns. All external parts such as the outside of the filler bowl, valves and tubes, crowner chute, platforms, etc., should be cleaned with a detergent sanitizer solution. The unit should then be thoroughly flushed with hot water at around 130-150°F (55-65°C). Spraying of external surfaces with an iodophor solution of 25 p.p.m. or less is also a common procedure.

SOLUTIONING CYCLE

The cleaning and sanitizing procedure sometimes referred to as the "solutioning cycle" is normally carried out once per week.

There are a number of methods used such as dormant soaking and a variety of circulating systems. The latter method is considered preferable and is the most widely used, with methods varying from the use of separator plates or trough systems to the more popular bottle or can circulation.

Cleaning compounds used depend on the water conditions. There are a great many available and the most suitable for each location should be determined locally. Type of compounds and temperatures of solutions used also vary considerably and are dependent on the type and age of the filler being cleaned. The newer fillers are constructed from materials which can withstand most of the cleaning solutions on the market at temperatures in the 180°F

+ range (82°C). Some older units, however, were constructed from materials which can be seriously attacked by certain types of cleaning solutions and, in addition, should not be subjected to temperatures in excess of 130°F (55°C).

There are now a variety of different fillers in use throughout the industry and each manufacturer has specific recommendat   s for the cleaning of their particular machine. This can vary from cold sol   ons to steam cleaning in certain instances. The general principles outlinec   ove, however, still apply in most cases.

If the cleaning compound chosen for use is received in powder or flake form, care must be taken to ensure that it is completely dissolved before being circulated through the filler, since undissolved particles could cause damage to valve disc, valve arm and faces, etc.

The re-circulation pump pressure should also be kept as low as possible to avoid damage to filler components. A pressure relief valve should be placed at the discharge of the circulating pump and set at a maximum 15 p.s.i. A strainer should also be incorporated in the return line to the circulating tank.

The cleaning equipment used can be either a portable pump and tank unit which can be moved in adjacent to each unit being cleaned, or it can be a central cleaning station remotely located with headers to each filler area.

After cleaning and sanitizing, the filler should be left ready for the next start-up. This procedure can vary depending on the length of time that the unit is going to be out of operation.

A suggested procedure could be as follows:
a) Out of service for less than 8 hours. Bowl should be left filled with water.
b) Out of service between 8 hours and four days. Bowl should be filled with 50 to 100 p.p.m. chlorinated water.
c) Out of service more than 4 days, filler should be left dry.

Earlier in the chapter reference was made to the necessity of having a cleaning manual showing detailed step by step procedures.

A suggested procedure for the weekly circulation cycle for a three tube Cemco filler follows, illustrating the type of detail which should be incorporated in the manual.

Weekly Filler Circulation—Three Tube 72-15 Cemco Bottle or Can Filler.
For Circulation

Prepare cleaning and sanitizing solution as follows:
a) 50 imperial gallons (227 litres) at 120°F (50°C).
b) Add 7½ lbs. (3.4 kgms.) chlorinated trisodium phosphate. Approximately 1.5% T.S.P. and 500 p.p.m. Cl_2.
c) Add 1 imperial fluid ounce (28.4 ml.) of Igepal CO 710. Approximately 0.01% of a nonylphenozypoly ethanol type wetting agent.
d) Add 5 imperial fluid ounces (142 ml.) of Questal Special. Approximately 0.05% tetrasodium ethylenediamine-tetraacetate, or E.D.T.A., as a chelating agent.

Circulate to ensure all additions are completely dissolved. Maintain temperature of 100°F (38°C.) in circulation tank during cleaning. After completion of the routine flushing and external cleaning of the filler, the following circulation procedure should be used.
Refer to Figure 26-2.
(1) Close off beer line shutoff valve "A" and the counterpressure to filler bowl (at control panel).
(2) Remove counterpressure hose "B" and pump pressure switch hose "C" at filler top, and insert plugs. Remove float for manual cleaning and close filler bowl top.
(3) Open all filling valves to "Fill" position draining filler bowl and valve parts.
(4) Open drain valve "D" under filler bowl to drain remainder of bowl.

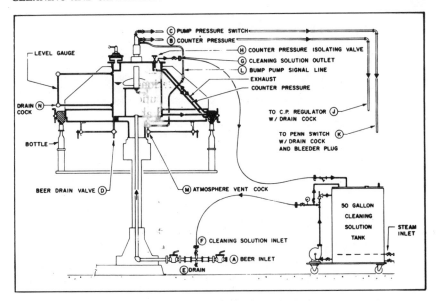

26-2. Arrangement for cleaning and sanitizing Cemco 3 Tube #72-15 Filler.

(5) Open drain valve "E" to drain beer line and vertical beer pipe into filler. Close drain valves "D" and "E".

(6) Insert quick disconnect plugs into both the counterpressure inlet "B" and pump detector inlet "C".

(7) Connect the discharge hose of the detergent circulating pump to solution valve "F". Connect the return line of the detergent supply tank to connection "G" on the vent ring of the filler bowl.

(8) Close four valves "H" on top of the filler bowl vent ring.
NOTE: Care should be taken to ensure that these valves are only snugged down so as not to distort the ring. Slight leakage at these points is unimportant.

(9) Place bottles or cans on lift platforms around the back of the filler, which are not in contact with the pull down cam.

(10) After ensuring that all containers are in alignment with guides, allow the lifters to rise slowly to the sealing position.

(11) Close all valves which do not have sealed containers on their platforms. Remove micromat pressure relief valve and plug opening. Clean manually and replace after filler cleaned and flushed.

(12) Start circulating pump and circulate detergent solution for fifteen to twenty minutes. This will clean beer lines from bowl, all valve ports for beer and the vent or exhaust line for all valves in the "Fill" position. Do not rotate filler or cycle valves during this operation.

(13) Manually change valve position to "Blow Out" and repeat the fifteen-minute cleaning cycle. This step will clean the vent (or exhaust) and counterpressure lines and their passages through the valve and adapter.

(14) Manually close the valves with containers to the "Shut-off" position, lower lift platforms and remove the containers.

(15) Rotate filler 180°F. Repeat steps (9) to (14) inclusive. This will complete the cleaning of all lines and valves.

(16) When cleaning has been completed, shut off circulating pump and remove the plugs from counterpressure inlet "B" and pump detector inlet "C".

(17) Reconnect counterpressure and pump detector hoses to their respective inlets "B" and "C" and pump detergent solution through each for ten minutes. Counterpressure hose

and line "B" will be cleaned back to the counterpressure regulator with solution going to the floor through the drain cocks. Solution will flow back through the "Sleeve Assembly" via the "Bump Pump Signal Line" to the "Pump Pressure Switch Hose" and lines draining to the floor below the "Penn Switch", through the drain cock and bleeder plug. The bleeder cock "N" at the bottom of the "Level Gauge" should also be cracked open to ensure detergent passage through this sight glass and its connections to the bowl. Note that if the float is left in it will block the holes in sleeve assembly preventing solution flow back to Penn Switch.

(18) Disconnect circulating pump hoses and drain all possible detergent.

(19) Remove all containers and store in the specified location.

(20) Open four counterpressure isolating valves "H".

(21) Connect fresh water supply (maximum 15 p.s.i.) to beer inlet "A" and flush out all detergent while rotating the filler and cycling the valves.

NOTE: Cycling of valves is not recommended during cleaning, as beerstone could be forced between teflon valve discs and cause scoring.

(22) During flushing out of the filler with water ensure that all dead end passages and drains are open and adequately flushed. These would include such passages as:

a) Drain valve "E" and cleaning solution inlet and outlet "F" and "G".

b) Counterpressure hose and lines back to counterpressure regulator drain cocks "J" and the bleeder on the machine side of the counterpressure regulator.

c) Sleeve assembly, bump pump signal line "L" and atmosphere vent cock "M", pump pressure switch hose "C" and lines back to Penn switch drain cock and bleeder plug "K".

d) Level gauge or sight glass and fittings at drain cock "N".

e) Filler bowl drain valve "D".

(23) Remove fresh water connection at "A" and let drain. Replace micromat relief valve and float. Flush with hose.

(24) Close all appropriate openings used to flush filler and connections. Run filler at slow speed and flush away detergent from outer surfaces.

(25) Prepare filler for next start-up, or as specified for an out of service period.

(26) Drain and flush out cleaning solution tank and system ensuring that strainer screen is clear.

CAUTION: Water supply for flushing bowl should never exceed 15 p.s.i. This will prevent possible damage to the relief valve diaphragm, bellows in Penn pressure switch, sight glass, etc.

(27) Maintenance should lubricate as necessary and ensure that water and detergent are expelled from bushings, etc.

As previously noted, this detailed cleaning write-up of the 3 tube Cemco bottle filler has been provided specifically to illustrate the type of detailed procedures that should be provided for the "Cleaning Manual".

There are many other excellent fillers, such as the Meyer, Holstein and Kappert, Seitz, Simonazzi and others. Principles of filling, mechanics of operation and materials used all influence individual requirements for adequate cleaning and sanitation.

Since the mechanics of each system varies greatly as to tubes, filling valves, lines, snifting systems, venting, etc., it results in a wide variety of cleaning systems. Combinations of manual cleaning, back washing nozzles, solutioning adapters or sanitation cups for each valve, valve removal, dormant soaks and a variety of circulation systems and other special requirements are needed depending on the filler involved.

It remains essential that all parts of the filler are routinely cleaned and sanitized. Water and acceptable alkaline cleaning solutions at permissible temperatures, plus halogen sanitizers, such as chlorine or iodophor solutions, appear to remain basic to cleaning, whether manual, dormant or circulatory.

Individual cleaning procedures for each type of filler should be based on recommendations from the manufacturer's operating manual and, with experience, from innovations within the brewery which have resulted in satisfactory results based on adequate laboratory testing.

Ultrasonic cleaning baths using cleaning and sanitizing solutions are well known for their effectiveness in cleaning tubes, valves or other such parts, which must be occasionally removed from operating units.

PASTEURIZER CLEANING AND SANITATION

A comprehensive water treatment program based on routine water analyses is needed. Additions should be monitored, desired residuals obtained and maintained as desired. Routine evaluations should be made to determine the effectiveness of the program.

The main control problems are:

1. Scale Formation

Normally scale is calcium carbonate and is controlled by sequestrants such as the polyphosphates at threshold levels of about 5 p.p.m. A very light scale provides corrosion protection.

2. Corrosion

—Chemical

—Electrochemical

Control programs to avoid metal deterioration should include:

(a) Maintenance of an alkaline water pH of approximately 8.0 to 9.0 pH to reduce the overall corrosion potential.

(b) Avoidance of soft or corrosive water as a light scale is protective.

(c) Control of slime and bacteria by biocides and cleaning.

(d) Coatings of various types.

(e) Corrosion inhibitors such as the chromates, phosphates, molybdates, silicates or one of more recent compounded formulations using phosphonates.

3. Microbiological Control

Effective biocidal treatment is required to prevent odour and slime problems. Slime formation clogs screens, pumps, headers and sprays, or the water circulation system in general, reducing the effectiveness of pasteurizer operation and necessitating excessive cleaning.

The simplest and most obvious sources of problems are often neglected. Many plants fail to adequately flush beer foam and label carryover from bottles, or to remove all open bottles, thus supplying the pasteurizer with a constant source of nutrients encouraging microbial growth. Spray nozzles may also be blocked.

Cleaning the Pasteurizer

Frequency and extent of cleaning are mainly governed by the degree of microbial control achieved.

Daily cleaning programs usually cover cleaning screens on a shift basis. In addition to a general daily cleanup, normally the load and discharge ends are cleaned. This may cover dumping and flushing of the end tanks as well as a high pressure cleaning of the interior tops, sides, decks and tanks in the load and discharge areas.

Major cleaning of pasteurizers is common on a weekly basis, although many plants drain and clean their units every two weeks to a month. Those with superior control operate up to six months or longer.

While some plants simply drain each compartment before cleaning, many use an alkaline boil out first, or a high temperature steaming with circulation, prior to drainage and cleaning. Boil outs or steam cleaning are commonly run at 160°F (71°C) to 200°F (94°C) for a period of 1-2 hours.

The actual cleaning is usually started from the top of the pasteurizer. Cleaning ports, manhole doors and the ends of each unit provide further access.

Modern cleaning techniques use high pressure hosing, centralized cleaning stations, high pressure steam or water detergent sanitizer guns, or foam guns which apply a temporary adhesive layer of cleaner sanitizer. Manual cleaning is limited except for outer surfaces.

All accessible interior areas are cleaned from the bottom of cover lids to the bottoms of tank compartments. Any area which is in contact with pasteurizer water is a potential source of slime and infection and should be covered.

Special attention should be given screens, suction boxes, pumps, splash curtains and regeneration lines. If pump delivery pressure to spray headers is abnormal, then pumps should be dismantled and cleaned to eliminate possible slime or glass blockage. One should ensure that the spray headers are flushed out and that spray nozzles are functional, or that spray pan holes are open.

Some pasteurizers have been fitted with fast opening valves at the dead end of each header, permitting desirable frequent flushouts. The normal procedure for flushing glass and debris from headers is to remove the caps from the dead ends and to start-up the pumps involved, flushing foreign matter out to assist in the prevention of nozzle blockage.

Double deck units present difficulties in checking lower deck sprays, but should not be neglected.

Pasteurizer windows, sight glasses, and air filters should be cleaned regularly. The outer parts of the pasteurizer should be kept in good condition by mechanized or manual cleaning.

Descaling is seldom necessary with suitable water treatment, but if required can be accomplished with inhibited hydrochloric or sulfamic acid. Sequestrant additions should control this problem.

After cleaning and rinsing is completed, the different zones should be refilled with fresh water and treated as required. The unit should be operated for at least 10 minutes and the screens recleaned if necessary. Curbed areas and drains should be cleaned.

Some plants spray areas above the water line with biocidal solutions on a weekly basis to prevent slime and odour formation.

To lower water consumption, reduce total wastewater discharge and reduce heat losses, some breweries have made a variety of changes which abandon the principle of separate pasteurizer operation.

Such changes include:

1. The use of cooling towers to recirculate cooling water from pasteurizers was found economically advantageous, as evaporation cooling permitted reuse of the water.
2. The use of a central water system in which a number of pasteurizers are connected to a single regenerative water source for supplying some, or all, of the individual pasteurizer compartments. Usually the overflow water from all compartments is collected in a receiving tank, pumped

to the cooling tower and then into another storage tank. This tank supplies the individual pasteurizers with all their make up water, providing impressive water economies.

The central water supply concept had been adopted by approximately 19 operating breweries in 1979, with systems varying from 2 to 12 pasteurizers.

3. The use of evaporative condensers for water cooling.
4. The use of external side located heat exchangers.
5. The use of external cooling systems for the final cooling water.

The reduction in overflow water which was replaced by fresh water thus creates a much higher potential for heavy biological slime formation and distribution. Algal growth is also a problem with cooling towers or systems subject to sunlight.

It is evident that a more effective sanitation program is required, based on the scheduled application of biocides, which will adequately control the microbiological problems involved.

OTHER EQUIPMENT

The foregoing details cleaning procedures for the major items of equipment in the plant. Additionally there are other items such as conveyors, empty and full bottle (or can) inspectors, labelers, packers, case forming and sealing equipment, etc., which require regular cleaning. Of the above the labeling and case forming and sealing equipment require most attention.

In the case of the labelers the most important factor is to thoroughly clean the glue application equipment at the end of each production period. Care must be taken to ensure that the label holders, picker arms, etc., are not damaged during the cleaning. All excess glue should also be removed from all parts of the machine. More details are given in Chapter X.

As most carton forming and sealing equipment now use hot melt glue systems, it is essential that they be cleaned properly with special emphasis being placed on the cleaning of the glue nozzles.

In the case of inspection machines for both empty and full containers it is recommended that these be wiped off with a dry or damp cloth and that excess water should *not* be used to clean them, as they represent splash proof *not* water tight electronic units.

There are a number of different empty bottle inspectors (E.B.I.'s) made by such companies as Industrial Dynamics, Barry Wehmiller and Meyer, with varied detection systems or capabilities available. Since all empty and full bottle inspection units are optical instruments, it is self evident that the lens must be kept clean if the efficiency of rejection is to be maintained.

Ensure that the soap or lubricant on the conveyor is not excessive, thus permitting the water spray upstream of the starwheel to flush any residual off the bottle permitting proper inspection. The volume of water spray is also important to avoid false rejects, especially if the unit senses liquid carryover in the bottle.

The basic areas requiring cleaning are:
1. The cover over the light source and below the opal or diffuser glass should be cleaned with a damp cloth weekly or as needed.

2. The opal or diffuser glass over which the bottle travels must be clean to permit inspection. One unit has a rotating diffuser plate which is continuously cleaned by a wiper pad. A controlled water drip is applied across the glass and an air jet blows any beads of water off after the scrubber pad. This diffuser glass should be cleaned weekly or as necessary and the wiper pads should be cleaned each shift with soap and water, or as required.

Other type units have a stationary diffuser glass on which water, soap or fine debris may accumulate. This glass should be wiped off several times per shift or as found necessary.

3. The inspection head system cleaning will depend on the detection systems involved.

(a) All E.B.I.'s have an optical trigger system which activates inspection when the bottle is properly located. The trigger beam lens system should be cleaned once per shift with a soft dry cloth.

(b) The inspection head lens system for detection of foreign matter should be cleaned in a similar manner.

(c) The damaged finish detector lens system is treated as above.

There is limited variety of full bottle inspectors available. The Industrial Dynamic Model FT12 is common to many plants. Cleaning should be daily using a soft dry cloth and covering the following parts of the inspection head, if present:

a) The trigger lens or lamp and photocell lens which activate the unit for liquid level detection by gamma ray.

b) The double lamps and photocells for detection of missing labels.

c) The light source and photocell for low or high foam detection.

d) Most missing crown detectors utilize a proximity switch so monthly cleaning suffices. If an optical system is used the lens should be cleaned daily.

The Filtec Model FT 3B is also in use. It uses optics to detect fill level; hence the lens for the lamp and photocell should be cleaned daily.

For other items such as uncasers, packers, conveyors, etc., all debris should be removed, then the machine cleaned thoroughly.

One of the problems encountered during cleaning is the occasional over exuberant use of water hoses and high pressure spray guns; this causes lubricants to be removed from bearings, etc. It is good practice therefore, to have the machine checked after cleaning and lubricated as necessary.

MECHANIZATION OF CLEANING EQUIPMENT

Cleaning equipment is now available which will speed up, simplify, increase accessibility and improve many operations. Cleaning and sanitation can be accomplished with hot or cold water or cleaner-sanitizer solutions delivered at high or low pressure.

Commonly used systems or units include:

1. High pressure hosing.

2. High pressure portable or stationary cleaning stations, with pump supply to cleaning guns. The steam-detergent gun is an alternative.

3. Low pressure portable foam gun units which operate with compressed

air to apply an adhesive foam layer of detergent-sanitizer to various surfaces to increase desired contact time. Individual foam guns are also available which will function directly from normal air, water and detergent supplies.

4. Central pressurized cleaning systems consisting of four main components:
   a) Solution tank with temperature, water level and detergent controls. The location can be remote.
   b) Pressure pump.
   c) Suitable pipe lines to carry the cleaning solution to desired cleaning stations in the bottleshop.
   d) Hose and spray gun connections at the stations to permit the use of cleaning solutions or water rinses.

Systems can be designed for pressures required. Many supply hot cleaning solution at pressures of 500 p.s.i. and higher. The most tenacious soils, in difficult to reach locations, can normally be removed by such spray guns, which have a variety of spray nozzles. Such units have provided cleaning crews with vastly improved capabilities resulting in more effective and economical cleaning.

Any cleaning program, regardless of the equipment involved, will incorporate two fundamental facts:
   a) A detailed write-up of safety procedures and the use of safety equipment for each cleaning and sanitizing job.
   b) The principle of routine visual inspection of all operating equipment, particularly after cleaning, but also to assess cleaning requirements and to ensure that each unit is functioning properly when running.

UTILIZATION OF SERVICE MANUALS AND TECHNICAL ASSISTANCE

Previous reference was made to consultation with both machinery manufacturers and the chemical suppliers' representatives in the section suggesting "Principles" of an effective cleaning programme.

When new equipment is purchased the manufacturer normally provides installational, maintenance and operational manuals for the equipment involved. The operational manual normally covers not only routine maintenance, but also cleaning and sanitizing procedures. Each bottling superintendent or manager should make sure that he has a personal copy and is completely familiar with any manual covering equipment or operation of equipment for which he is responsible.

Both machinery manufacturers and chemical suppliers are highly competitive and have highly qualified members on their staffs who are conversant and experienced in their respective fields. A great deal of assistance can be obtained from either source in setting up an effective cleaning and sanitizing program. Co-operation is high and such technical representatives are available to survey any operation and make recommendations relative to the field involved. Such recommendations will often result in improved equipment operation, or may cover the use of new or better materials or methods of application, which in turn will result in economies to the individual plant.

It is suggested that it would be desirable to have staff from both the above mentioned groups carry out a detailed survey of existing procedures, whether implementing a new cleaning programme or continuing an existing one.

Acknowledgements

We wish to acknowledge help and assistance from: Crown Cork and Seal Co. Ltd., Barry-Wehmiller Co., Geo. J. Meyer Manufacturing Co., Diversey Wyandotte Inc., Oakite Products of Canada, Ltd., Klenzade Division, Economics Laboratory, Inc., Aseptic-Thermo Indicator Co., Industrial Dynamics International Inc., J.W. Anderson Co. Ltd., Water Softening, Monsanto Chemical Company, Pfizer Company Ltd., Wright Chemical Corporation.

REFERENCES FOR ADDITIONAL READING

Articles in Periodicals

1. Greenfield, J.R., *Brewers Digest*, Sequestering and Chelating Agents in the Brewery, October, 66 (1968)
2. Burkhard, P.N., *M.B.A.A. Tech. Quart.*, Brewing Pasteurizer Treatment, Vol. 10, 147 (1973)
3. Forwalter, John, *Food Processing*, 1980 Selection Guide Cleaning and Sanitizing Compounds, February 1980, 40
4. Schultz, Ronald, *Brewers Digest*, Brewery Central Pasteurizer Water Systems, March 44, (1979)
5. Tenney, Robert, *M.B.A.A. Tech. Quart.*, Ozone, the Add-nothing Sterilant, Vol. 10, 35 (1973)
6. Pena, Adolfo: *M.B.A.A. Tech. Quart.*, Chlorination-Concept and Methods, Vol. 8, 229 (1971)
7. Wittl, Gerhard; Marx, Georg; Uhlig, Klaus; Quinters, Eduardo; *M.B.A.A. Tech. Quart.*, Tests and Trials On Bottle-Washing Procedures, Vol. 6, 208 (1969)
8. White, Robert S., *M.B.A.A. Tech. Quart.*, The Role of Iodophors in Brewery Sanitation, Vol. 1,2 (1964)
9. Greenfield, J.R., *M.B.A.A. Tech. Quart.*, A Survey of Sanitizing and Germicidal Agents Used In Brewery Sanitation, Vol. 1, 220 (1964)

Books

1. Ruff, D.G., Becker K., BOTTLING AND CANNING OF BEER, Chicago, Siebel Publishing Co. 1955
2. BETZ HANDBOOK OF INDUSTRIAL WATER CONDITIONING, 7th Edition, Trevose, Betz Laboratories, Inc., 1976

CHAPTER XXVII

PEST CONTROL

BY F.B. JACOBSON

GENERAL PRINCIPLES

Pest Control is inevitably more than chemical or physical control. It is the sum of controlling the environment which insects, rodents and other pests inhabit and frequent. Perhaps it is best described as "Pest Management", and currently it is referred to as "Integrated Pest Management" (IPM).

Integrated Pest Management is based on principles of applied ecology and the ecosystem. This requires an understanding of the interacting relationships between environment, life cycle, insect habits, chemical control, and physical methods of control. The goal of this philosophy is to maximize the forces of natural pest control and to minimize the use of toxicants and pesticides. Unlike agriculture, in a food plant minimization of insect or rodent population can not be accepted; rather, the effort must be such that the pest is eradicated. A modified IPM system can accomplish this purpose. For food processing, packaging, storage and transportation this would include sanitation, proper storage and warehousing practices, good manufacturing practices, chemical and physical treatment as well as regular monitoring of the condition of all of these facilities.

Pest Control requires as a first principle sanitation. The application of any pest control procedure depends upon a clean environment, which includes absence of dust and debris. Any organic matter will act to absorb and neutralize pesticides. They will interfere with baiting and inspection. Improper or inadequate storage practices handicap an applicator in dispensing pesticides properly.

IDENTIFICATION OF PRIMARY PESTS

The insects commonly encountered are the cockroaches, followed closely by sour flies and house flies. Spiders, ground beetles and even occasionally saw tooth grain beetles (in raw wood pallets) are encountered. Book lice (psocids) are also not too unusual in pallets.

Amongst the cockroaches the most common, in returned cases and returned goods are the German cockroaches. The Brown-banded also presents similar problems in some sections of the country. The American and Oriental cockroaches are found in the very wet areas, particularly around soakers, rinsers and pasteurizers.

Flies, particularly house flies, and mosquitoes may enter into the pallet buildings and bottle shops. However, they rarely if ever reproduce where sanitation is reasonable. The problem is that they may enter the containers being filled. Thus, complete control is necessary. On the other hand, sour flies

(Drosophila) are insects which can reproduce in returned containers with residual product. They are frequently found in warehouse areas, even when sanitation is excellent.

Insects in stored product areas are not a major problem in bottling and packaging. Dermestidae (carpet beetles) are very resistant and omnivorous insects and on occasion have been encountered in various storage areas. They may feed on food in cases, other dead insects and various bits of organic matter. They are not considered a primary pest. Silverfish which feed on vegetable and animal matter and frequent warm, moist areas are also found. These too are usually not major pests.

Rodents, which include the roof rat, the Norway rat, house mice and field mice, invade bottle shops and storage buildings with rather great frequency. The return of empty cases and the movement of materials from outside are major factors in the bringing of mice into the building. Probably this can not be totally eliminated, and thus trapping and baiting inside of buildings is essential.

Birds are a problem, but they are restricted in the main to three types: pigeons, sparrows and starlings. The latter two are the more difficult to control, but they can be kept out in somewhat the same way as pigeons—by baiting and trapping and reduction or elimination of feeding areas. Time and patience are required. There is no rapid method of control and it must be continuous.

PHYSICAL ASPECTS

Perhaps the most significant method of controlling pests is the exclusion of pests, whether they be inside rodents or birds.

The examination and inspection of incoming materials is a particularly difficult problem in the high speed, high volume conditions in brewery and beverage packaging. Nevertheless, any effort in this direction can be fruitful.

The inspection of returns, both cases and containers, can be useful in separating out obviously wet and stained units. These frequently are responsible for the entrance of cockroaches, sour flies, mosquitoes and other vermin.

Pallets, too, are problems which should be subject to close examination. From time to time, infestation of psocids (book lice), grain beetles and cockroaches have been detected in green lumber which is to be used for repairs and in old pallets which have been subject to moist and moldy conditions.

Fly screens are of course useful to keep out flying insects. Most packaging warehouses are built to take advantage of natural ventilation and screens are too often not used in these warehouses. Flying insects enter into these areas and then find their way into filling and packaging sections in the same building.

Flashing lights; sonic, supersonic and subsonic sounds have been used to prevent rodents and birds from entering or inhabiting buildings. To date there has been no evidence of long term success in these experiments.and methods.

On the other hand, insect electrocuting grids when properly placed have been very effective in reducing flying insect populations. They are most effective against houseflies, but do have some effect also against night moths, mosquitoes and other flying insects which wander or are drawn into their electrical field. Indoor units should have BL and BLB lamps: night flying insects are attracted to the BL lamp; houseflies and fruitflies to the BLB lamp. They by no means will eliminate all infestation, but do help to reduce it.

Fans are effective to some degree when placed at entrances to buildings. However, in order to operate properly they must cover the entrance and blow out, not in. When this is done, the air can become a severe annoyance to personnel as well, and often the fans are shut off if not properly monitored. In addition, these exclusion fans can be easily damaged so that the fan's direction is slightly changed and thus rendered ineffective or counter-productive. They operate best when the opening is relatively small.

Rodent exclusion means elimination of all rodent entry points. The premises should be checked regularly to locate potential entry points, or to watch for new openings which may occur. A rat can gain entry through any opening larger than ½ inch square; a mouse can enter wherever a man's smallest finger can enter. In addition to the expected areas under and around doors or windows, one should not overlook pipes or conduits going through walls, fan openings, floor drains, and transoms. Any sealing should be done with material which will preclude rodent entry—preferably metal, cement, brick or glass. Rags and papers stuffed into holes are not effective. Holes in floors, around doorways, in walls at ceiling level can also become entrances for rodents.

Inside of a building the trapping of rodents is another method of control not resorting to poisons. This is the oldest control measure, but still of great value. Several types of traps are available, but the efficiency of any type depends upon proper placement and attention. This requires a knowledge of the habits and traits of rodents. The most common and practical traps are the "ketch-all", and other mechanical traps as well as the common snap traps. The former is only useful for mice. It requires no baiting and can contain several mice in one setting. It must be checked regularly to eliminate potential odor problems and unwinding of trap. The snap trap comes in small "mouse" size or larger "rat" types. Expanding the trigger area with thin metal, wire screen and even cardboard will catch any rodent which steps on it whether baited or not. These are very effective in runways.

While traps should be placed in all logical areas of possible infestation as a preventive measure, the greatest success, when rodents are actually present, revolves around a careful inspection and analysis of findings. Which type of rodent is present and the extent of infestation should be considered. If Roof Rats are involved, traps should be placed on beams and overheads. For Norway Rats, traps must be at ground level.

As long as food and water are available, all rodents move in a very limited area. One should not skimp on the number of traps set or the animal will move between traps. It is more efficient to overtrap an area than to undertrap.

For baiting the trap there is no universal food; jam, peanut butter, ground meat, and many other foods have been used successfully. The consistency of the bait should be such that it will not fall off the trigger. It is usually wise to experiment with different baits rather than use one for all situations.

Traps should be checked frequently (daily is best) to remove dead rodents, to reset traps which have been sprung and to maintain fresh bait. Some type of wall marking above traps will help to quickly locate each one, particularly behind stored materials or equipment. As these rodents live in close proximity to man, human scents are not unfamiliar and not objectionable to them.

Another type of trap in use for rodent control is the so called "glue board". These are now made with a plastic type adhesive in self contained trays. They come in small and large sizes for mice and for rats. When placed in rodent runs, or around areas where rodents are known to live, they can be very effective. They also will trap insects, in the same manner as fly paper. They are rendered ineffective by dust and debris and should be inspected on a regular basis.

Trapping is also effective to some degree for insects. The use of "fly paper", or a patented device known as the "Lurestic", using the same principle, has been widely and successfully used. Some insect traps use lures, particularly for fly capture. These have been only moderately successful.

There is currently a great deal of activity in research of pheromones. Pheromones are scents given off by animals and insects which serve as stimuli to others of the same species. These are particularly effective when dealing with sexual responses. Commercial development of these pheromones for cockroaches and houseflies is a distinct possibility in the not-too-distant future.

Trapping is particularly useful for control of various bird species, with pigeons being the most amenable to control by this method. Traps devised by pigeon fanciers have been adapted and commercially manufactured. They permit entrance of the bird, but prevent exit. They capture the bird alive. Pre-baiting with attractive food, is of course, essential. Similar traps are available for sparrows and starlings, but they are not as effective.

In enclosed buildings, positive air pressure has been used to effectively deter insects from entering. This pressure also keeps out dust and foreign matter. Unfortunately, most bottle shops and warehouses are rather wide open. If however, positive pressure can be used, insect invasion can be reduced.

Another method that can be used to reduce infestation is humidity control. Most insects associated with bottling and packaging prefer high humidity. Reduction of moisture and humidity is also useful in reducing or eliminating mold growth and possible infestation. Here also, difficulties are encountered, particularly in bottle shops where soakers, rinsers, pasteurizers and fillers are operating since the process uses large amounts of water. If, however, free humidity can be decreased, control of infestation can be enhanced.

CHEMICAL CONTROL

Legal Aspects

Pesticides and their usage are subject in the United States to Federal Law, namely, the Federal Insecticide, Fungicide and Rodenticide Act (FIFRA). This law provides for the separation of pesticides into "Restricted" or "General" use and for the training and certification of commercial and private pesticide applicators. It further provides for the various states to set up standards and certification supervision.

The restrictions as to which pesticides may be used in food processing, packaging, and storage relate directly to this act, to regulations adopted by the various states and finally to the regulations of the Food & Drug Administration (FDA). FDA has an agreement (a memorandum of understanding) whereby EPA will perform its function in regulating pesticides and FDA will enforce the regulations governing those pesticides relating to Foods, Drugs & Cosmetics. They also can and do place additional strictures on the use of these pesticides.

The label, which is registered under FIFRA, should be the basic and only procedure in how to correctly use the pesticide. The label information includes name and address of the chemical company, list of active ingredients, type of pesticide, kind of formulation, EPA registration number, storage and disposal precautions, hazard statements, directions for use and net contents. Recommended dosages are mandatory, as well as target pests. In some cases compatability, phytotoxicity and common trade name are also included.

It is evident that a complete reading and understanding of the label can do much to reduce or eliminate any accidents and misuse of the pesticide.

In addition to information on the label, other information on usage is available to the user in the Federal Regulations. Title 21 Code of Federal Regulations (CFR) Part 193 provides for Tolerances in Pesticides in Food. This is FDA administered. EPA regulations include Title 40 CFR 180 which provides for tolerances for pesticides on Raw Agricultural Commodities.

Application

Methods of application of pesticides are also delineated by Federal Regulations.

Insecticides may be applied in many ways. One of the most common methods of dispersion is that of space spraying. *Space sprays* are designed to be lethal to flying insects. They are relatively ineffective against crawling insects. The smaller the diameter of the aerosol particles produced by the space spray, the longer it will remain in the air and the more it will penetrate crevices. However there is a lower limit below which the effectiveness decreases due to the lower probability of the particle impinging on the target insect. Aerosol application is sometimes used for flushing of some crawling insects such as cockroaches, and if used with proper residual surface sprays, can be effective.

Space sprays are dispensed in many ways. They include low pressure aerosol dispensers and high pressure aerosol dispensers. The propellants are usually Freon, some Freon combination with other materials, and currently CO_2. Hand operated and compressed air sprayers using compression type atomizers are in use, but they provide a wetter spray than other methods of application.

Mist applicators are based on mechanical dispersion either by means of passing the insecticide through a specially designed device (ULV-Ultra low volume), or by means of a particle impact method wherein the insecticide is ejected into a series of orifices in a rapidly spinning disc. Both shear the liquid carrier and break the insecticide into small particles. The ULV device uses a very high pressure pump to produce aerosol particles in the range of 15 microns. The other method using a spinning disc rarely gets down to this size and usually produces a particle size droplet of approximately 30 microns or larger. While this performance can be improved in some cold aerosol generators, the usual result is a wetter mist.

Thermal aerosol generators can produce aerosol fogs from 0.2 to 9 microns. They operate either electrically or with gasoline motors. The insecticide in oil is drawn into a heated chamber where most of the oil base is vaporized and the resultant smoke is then forced through an opening to be dispersed into the atmosphere. This device is very effective, but suffers from the fact that in some instances the heated chamber may ignite the oil, and also the heated chamber may overheat causing partial destruction of the active insecticidal ingredient. Nonetheless, overall it is a very effective method of dispensing insecticides for flying insects.

While all space sprays are non-residual, as their effectiveness is related to their time in the air, "residual" insecticides are dispensed as wet sprays. In food plants, and food processing, storage and packaging areas all permissible "residual" insecticides are now mandated to be sprayed by "crack & crevice" method, or by "spot treatment".

Crack & crevice has been defined as application in a pin stream (preferably through a nozzle or device designed for this purpose), directly into cracks and crevices such as expansion joints between different elements of construction, between equipment bases and the floor, in wall voids, or hollow equipment legs. Care must be taken to avoid deposition of the product onto exposed surfaces or introduction into the air. Contamination of food and food contact surfaces must be avoided.

Spot treatment is the treatment to selective areas, surfaces and cracks and crevices where insects have either been seen or suspected of harborage. They should be limited to no more than 2 square feet per treatment and not to exceed 20% of the total area being treated in one situation. Of course the same strictures apply that food and food contact surfaces may not be contaminated.

In some instances fogging or surface spraying may not be adequately effective. In that case, fumigation may be resorted to. Fumigation is the application of gas to an enclosed area. Temperature, time and dosage are inherent requirements of any fumigation procedure. This treatment, while effective, must be done only by well trained certified, and in many parts of the country, properly licensed personnel. Unless there is in the employ of the company a well trained and usually full time expert in this treatment, it is recommended that contract experts who perform this type of work on a regular basis be employed. Fumigation is most often used in the dry grain areas, rather than in packaging or warehousing.

Dusts which are finely divided solid particles of a toxic or inert material, or a combination of both, have specialized use in insect control. In packaging and warehouse areas they have particular usefulness in switch boxes, electrical equipment, small voids and crevices, etc. They should be applied with special applicators and care must be taken that they are not likely to be dispersed by air movement, physical activity such as sweeping, and further that the dust cannot become a contaminate of food, food ingredients or food product surfaces.

Rodenticides are used as a supplement in rodent control. The first line of defense, of course is keeping rodents out structurally. The second is trapping and the third is poison baiting. All are equally important, but must be kept in perspective. Rodenticides are most useful in perimeter rodent control, but are useful also in buildings where competitive bait is at a minimum such as warehouse and storage areas, and pallet buildings. They are easily wetted and degraded, so find little use in most areas in packaging buildings. Where bait competition is high and where contamination of food product is possible, they are least useful, and possibly counterproductive. In those cases, of course, trapping and other physical methods of control are more desirable.

Rodenticides should always be used in enclosed fixed bait stations and never used loosely or in open bait cups. They must be made secure against human and animal tampering, as well as accidental spills and contamination of food and food contact surfaces.

Repellents have been used successfully for partial control of pests. At one time a considerable effort was expended in the spraying of returnable beverage cases with a modicum of success. However, with the increase in cost of repellants and repellant application equipment, this procedure has been eliminated as a significant method of control. There are now on the market a number of chemicals being used as bird repellants, for use in baits, or in structural applications. Research is still going on in the investigation of repellants for insects, rodents and birds.

Sometimes it is preferable to use outside pest control operators (PCO) (exterminators). Many of these companies have well trained personnel and are well equipped. However, the burden of their use continues to lie on management of the company employing them. It is recommended that the following requirements be made of any PCO being retained.

1. A certificate of insurance, and a copy of certification for application of restricted pesticides.
2. A list of materials to be used and the method in which they are used. The list should include proper and common name, dosage, and EPA NUMBER. In this respect a copy of the label on file, would in all probability satisfy this requirement.
3. A record of each treatment, including problems encountered and materials used.
4. Location map of all bait stations, traps and devices, as well as results of each visit.
5. A letter or certificate from the PCO advising of the extent of the program.

It is important that at each treatment or visit by the PCO, a responsible, knowledgeable member of management review with the PCO technician what has occurred and what further action is required.

METHODS & MATERIALS

Insecticides—Liquid

Technology and science are continually developing new materials and new approaches to chemical control. Regulations covering their use are in a constant state of change as well. However, at this moment there are a number of basic insecticides which have been approved and which are in constant use.

Table 1 lists the insecticides most commonly in use and currently approved under FDA (Food & Drug Administration) and EPA (Environmental Protection Agency) regulations. They also indicate restrictions in usage.

1. Organophosphates are mixed esters of phosphoric acid. Many contain sulfur. Most are rapidly biodegradable. They are cholinesterase inhibitors and thus they may potentially present toxic hazards to applicators if not used properly.

Organophosphates used in the food industry are considered moderately toxic, and when properly formulated and used correctly are among the safest insecticides. The insecticides acceptable for use in this category are Diazinon, Dichlorvos, Chlorpyrifos and Malathion.

2. Carbamates which include Propoxur and Ficam are organic derivatives of carbamic acid. Their mode of action is similar to that of organic phosphates in that they are cholinesterase inhibitors. They are somewhat safer than organic phosphates to humans.

3. Pyrethrins are plant derived substances, derived from chrysanthemum flowers. They are highly toxic to insects and present a low hazard to man and animals. They can however engender allergic reactions.

4. Synthetic pyrethroids and the synergists used with pyrethrins are, as the names imply, derived by chemical manipulation. They have low toxicity to man, more or less in the order of toxicity of pyrethrins.

5. Synergized pyrethrin and synthetic pyrethroid sprays can be used as space sprays or as residual and contact sprays. They are used in an oil base for fogging in bottle shops, and warehouse storage areas. Due to the irritating effect on insects, causing them to move, they are very useful when fogged

TABLE I
INSECTICIDES APPROVED FOR USE IN FOOD PLANTS (FDA & EPA)

Common Name	Trade Name	Use Concentration	Food Areas Spot	Food Areas Crack & Crevice	Food Areas Space Spray	Non Food Areas	Comments
Propoxur	Baygon	1.1%	No	Yes only	No	Spot & Contact	May crystallize out if too cool.
Diazinon	Diazinon Spectracide	0.5 - 1.0%	No	Yes only	No	Spot & Contact	Available in micro-encapsulated form—has longer effective life in that form.
Dichlorvos	Vapona DDVP Cyanophos	1 - 3% (1-2gms actual DDVP/1000 cu. ft.)	No	No	Yes	Yes	Has a fumigant effect under some conditions. Practically no long term residual effect.
		0.5 - 1.0%	Yes	Yes	No	Spot & Contact	—
Chlorpyrifos	Dursban Lorsban	0.25 - 0.5%	Yes	Yes	No	Spot & Contact	Do not use in food areas in combination with DDVP or pyrethrins. "Paint on"—limited to not over 2% active ingredient Crack & crevice—use not over 2% active ingredient. Adhesive strips—controlled release—not over 10% active.
Ficam-W	same (a methyl carbamate)	0.125 - 0.5%	Yes	Yes	No	Spot & Contact	This is a wettable powder and should be continually agitated to make certain powder does not settle out of suspension.
Malathion	Malathion	1.0 - 3.0%	Yes	Yes	No	Spot & Contact	Some formulations have a distinct objectionable odor.
Pyrethrins	pyrethrins pyrethrum	0.1 - 0.5%	Yes	Yes	Yes	All Methods	Most effective with synergists such as piperonyl butoxide, N-Octyl dicarboximide and N-propyl isome. Ratio is one pyrethrins to 2 to 4 parts synergists. Higher synergist ratios are found in water emulsifiable formulations. Combinations of various synergists are often used with the pyrethrins. Insecticides have low mammailian toxicity, but may be allergic to applicators. Excellent for general use, but residual life very short, except where used in microencapsulated form.
		3.0%	No	No	Yes ULV	Yes ULV	
Synthetic pyrethroid	Resmethrin Synthrin Allethrin	0.2 - 0.5%	No	No	Yes	Same	Less expensive than pyrethrins but also not as effective.

into cracks and crevices where cockroaches harbor. Proper fogging is efficacious in case and pallet storage areas.

Synergized pyrethrins in either water emulsion or in an oil base are effective as a surface or contact spray. They are recommended for use in food preparation areas as well as warehouse areas, with the usual precautions. Thus they are appropriate for use around pasteurizing filling units, soakers, rinsers, labellers, etc.

The microencapsulated forms of pyrethrins do last much longer than the non-encapsulated form and thus they appear to be more useful for residual surface spraying.

Dichlorvos is also a very effective space spray and when properly applied in the storage of empty and return cases performs quite well. It is more toxic to the operator than pyrethrins, but if proper precautions are taken hazards can be minimized. When used in thermal aerosols Dichlorvos becomes "gummy" and clogs up the equipment. However, frequent clean outs and use of other types of equipment does reduce this problem.

Dichlorvos can be obtained impregnated on resin strips for use in specialized warehouse situations where personnel are not present for significant periods of time and where air circulation and ventilation is reduced. It is very effective against flying insects and somewhat effective against crawling insects.

Chlorpyrifos, Propoxur, Diazinon, Ficam and Malathion are all very useful in residual spraying. They can be used in warehouse storage areas for perimeter spraying and to some extent in packaging and labeling areas. However, in the latter case, great care must be taken that they do not contaminate packages, product or product packaging equipment. General conditions of use are noted in Table I, and specific conditions are presented in label directions.

All pesticides should be used only in accordance with label directions. While certain pesticides are approved for use in food processing areas, which includes bottling areas, in all cases foods, and food ingredients, should be removed or covered during treatment. Food contact surfaces should be covered during treatment, or thoroughly cleaned before using.

Treatment should be confined to time periods when facilities are not in operation for areas being treated. This applies particularly to space sprays, which present the greatest risk of product contamination. Food processing need not be stopped while applying a wet spray, spot treatment or crack and crevice sprays, providing proper care is taken and treatment is in accordance with label directions.

Of particular importance to packaging operations is the fact that insecticides invariably include in their formulation solvents, oils, emulsifiers and/or wetting agents. Any one of these can be devastating to the quality of beer or carbonated beverages, even in the smallest amounts.

Water will dilute and degrade insecticides very rapidly. Therefore they should not be applied to wet surfaces and should be permitted to remain without wetting for as long as practical.

Insecticides—Dusts & Baits

Dusts and baits have a special place in pest management systems. This is true, particularly in food and food related operations. While there is a risk of accidental contamination, careful and proper use can minimize or eliminate this risk.

Dusts are dry, finely ground material containing either an insecticide of very low concentration, or a physical agent which can damage or kill the target insect. They usually also contain an inert carrier which serves to increase the bulk and to dilute the active ingredient. Dusts usually adhere best to horizontal surfaces and are moved by strong air currents; thus they are best used in enclosed structures where liquid materials are not desirable.

While sodium fluoride was, in the past, the primary dust used for this purpose, this has been almost entirely replaced due to its high toxicity. Instead, amorphous silica gels sometimes are used with high levels of synergized pyrethrins. Even after the pyrethrins cease to be effective, the silica gel remains effective.

Ficam (a methylcarbamate), in the form of "Ficam D", is a more highly toxic substance, but is also currently being used with success. No doubt other dusts will be developed in the future, but all must be treated with caution as a supplemental part of a pesticide program.

Baits are also used, particularly for German cockroach control. The same precautions which are recommended for dusts are important for baits. In addition, baits should be replaced every 4 to 6 weeks.

Use of covered bait containers is recommended to permit easy disposal and to deter damage. They should be used where insecticides cannot readily be applied or in areas to supplement residual spray treatment. The bait must be specially designed and should be watched carefully to make certain rodents are not attacking the bait. If that is so, then additional rodent control will be required.

Currently two insect baits are in use in the U.S. for cockroach control. One is based on propoxur with the active ingredient at 2% and the other on chlorpyrifos in which the active ingredient is 5%. Others have been used in the past and undoubtedly the future will bring more developments in this field.

For the most part, the use of baits is similar to that of dusts, but one should also include areas under wash basins, in closets, locker rooms, etc. as these are effective as control points.

Rodenticides

Rodenticides have continually undergone major developments and improvements over past few decades. At one time mostly highly toxic poisons were used for the control of rodents. This has been considerably changed and the more modern rodenticides approved for use are not only very effective, but also considerably safer to use. The careful following of label directions is, of course, absolutely necessary in any pesticide usage.

The major rodenticides in use are anticoagulants. Most of these require multiple consecutive feeding. However a few new rodenticides which are anticoagulants can be effective with single feeding. This does reduce the safety factor, but in no way does it eliminate it. These rodenticides remain low hazard poisons when used properly.

A major part of the effectiveness of rodenticides is the bait which is formulated for use with the poison. The ideal bait is one which is attractive to the rodents, will not mold, become infested, will not deteriorate and will not become rancid. The better the bait, the more effective the poison. Knowledge of the rodent to be attracted is the key to the formulations.

"Warfarin" is a coumarin derived material, which is available in forms compatible with grains and other foods. Most formulations include whole or cracked grain, some sweet material such as sugar, a small amount of oil and perhaps an antioxidant. Dried cheese, flaked peanuts, bread crumbs, meat fat and many other items of food are often incorporated into these baits. The method of mixing and incorporation of the poison is important, as a thorough coating and mixing is essential for good results.

"Rozol" is an inandione, another anticoagulant which is very effective. It has been reported to be less susceptable to infestation and reportedly penetrates grain kernels very well.

"Diphacinone", is another effective anticoagulant. It can be obtained in a water soluble form making it useful in rat control.

Both Rozol and Diphacinone have been used very successfully in "bait blocks", which are paraffin wax blocks impregnated with anticoagulant treated grain. It is very mold resistant and can be placed in sewers and wet areas. It is well suited to outdoor perimeter control and particularly helpful in the special conditions found in bottle shops.

"Fumarin", "Pival" and other anticoagulants are competitive products and can be used wherever Warfarin, Rozol, Diphacinone and the others are used.

Two compounds, "Talon" and "Maki" are related. The former is "brodifacoum" and the latter "bromadiolone". These, too, are anticoagulants, but they may act as single dose poisons.

Other rodenticides which have been used and are still being used for special situations in and around food plants are Antu for Norway Rats, Red Squill for rats, Zinc Phosphide for rats and mice and even Strychnine for mice. However, all of these are *highly toxic and present special problems*. They should never be used except where very special circumstances dictate their use.

One of the major problems in the use of rodenticides is that of accidental secondary poisons. Thus, when a poisoned rodent carcass is consumed by another animal or bird, secondary poisoning could occur. Anticoagulants are useful in this regard as low dosages are used, multiple feedings are usually necessary and the combination of the two reduce the secondary poison hazard.

Rodent baits and poisons are available in a number of forms—as paraffin blocks, in pelletized form, in loose grain form, in "bait packs" (often called "toss bags" or "throw bags"), as tracking powder and even individually coated food pellets. The choice is one that should be determined first from the view point of safety and second for effectiveness.

In bottle shop and warehouse operations usage of tracking powder is almost never recommended. The most suitable method appears to be pelletized form enclosed in bait packs, and the entire bait unit further enclosed in a tamper-proof, or tamper-resistant bait station. The only exception to this would be the use of paraffin, or all-weather bait blocks hanging in a closed sewer.

Bait stations should be numbered, locations recorded and service recorded. All stations and traps should be checked no less than monthly, and preferably weekly or bi-weekly. More frequent inspections may be required if active infestation is detected, but no less examinations are desirable.

Complete written records should be kept of activity, inspections, treatment and results. This can aid in more effective treatment over-all.

Fumigants

Fumigants such as Calcium Cyanide may be used outdoors for rodent holes in the earth. While it is very effective, only certified applicators may use this material. Generally, recommendations are to use other methods of control first and if control is not obtained, then to consider Calcium Cyanide. Again, only use after careful and deliberate consideration.

Other fumigants, such as methyl bromide and phosphine, are useful for rodent control, but they are used at much lower levels than for insect control. However, a methyl bromide fumigation requires 24 hours and a phostoxin fumigation at least 72 hours. It appears that such fumigations for either insect or rodent control are impractical in a continuing operation.

In very special situations, such as to control certain insect species in restricted enclosed areas, such fumigations could be considered. However, where other insect or rodent control is possible these should be the method of choice. One hazard to be considered is that dead insects, or dead rodents, may be as much of a problem to a processor as live insects or rodents. They can get into containers or equipment and die there. This is one of the advantages of trapping and of quick acting poisons.

Repellents

Repellency has been used with moderate success in bottle shop and warehouse operations. Case spraying with chemical repellant to insects has been used for many years. Some moderate success has been obtained. However, the materials used are expensive, and there is a serious difficulty in spraying the appropriate areas of the case. These repellent materials were sometimes combined with pyrethrins which irritate the insects and moved them out of the case in instances where outright kill was not attained.

There has been work on impregrating beverage cases with these chemicals, but at the time of this writing, the results have not been successful. Undoubtedly this approach would be very useful if it could be developed successfully. It would prevent roaches from harboring in cases.

Repellency has been attempted also in control of birds. Flashing lights, scrarecrows, model predatory birds, and ultra sound devices have been used. As yet there is no conclusive evidence that these are successful. When first installed they appear to work for a few days or even a week, but the birds evidently become accustomed to them and treat them all in the same manner, with indifference.

On the other hand, some chemical materials do appear to be effective. These include making roosting areas sticky, sharp pronged metal material which makes roosting difficult or impossible, and using certain chemicals to impregnate their food. This evidently disturbs the birds and actively repels them for some time. No method is permanent, but a rather long period of effectiveness is attributed to this latter method.

CONCLUSION

All pest management should concern itself with the safest and most simple methods. Many programs become overly complicated and sophisticated. Simplicity in choice of method and in approach can reduce hazards as well as improve results. Good house keeping and sanitation are the essential first steps in any program.

Contamination of equipment and product remain extremely serious problems to the bottler, and any such probabilities should be eliminated. In so far as contamination and safety are concerned, a pest control program must provide "certainties"!

Implicit following of label directions, education and knowledge, proper supervision and planning are required for an effective and safe pest management program. Training is one segment of this program which is all important. It should include education, textbook information and on-the-job training and experience. Review of on-the-job training should be made by experts in the field. The application of pesticides is as important as any job in the bottle shop!

Inspection of the operation before and after treatment is important. Regularly scheduled inspections, unannounced inspections and partial inspections are the best method of preventing pest problems and remedying problems if they do occur. Records of the inspections together with a check-up and reinspections where deviations or problems occur are essential for pest management and pest control. Supervision should participate in these inspections as much as possible.

REFERENCES

1. EBELING, W. URBAN ENTOMOLOGY—Univ. of California—Berkeley. Cal. (1975)
2. GORHAM, J.R. (Ed.) FDA TECHNICAL BULLETIN #1 PRINCIPLES OF FOOD ANALYSIS FOR FILTH, DECOMPOSITION and FOREIGN MATTER 2nd Ed. Wash. D.C.—Govt. Printing Office (1981)
3. JACOBSON, F.B. Wallerstein Communications vol. XXX, 101 - p33-42 (1967)
4. MALLIS, A HANDBOOK OF PEST CONTROL 6th Ed.—N.Y.—McNair Dorland (1981)

CHAPTER XXVIII

WASTE AND EFFLUENT
BY BRIAN LECLAIR

The treatment and disposal of brewing effluents are governed by the same general considerations that apply to most food processing industrial effluents, that is, to provide an acceptable effluent at lowest cost, which normally means: extensive in-plant by-product recovery, waste stream segregation, point source treatment and final collection and treatment. Accordingly, this chapter will review environmental considerations and industrial waste by-laws. Brewing wastes will be discussed against this background to illustrate the most economical means of disposal.

Generally the degree of treatment required is directly related to the environmental sensitivity of the receiving waters. Treatment and costs increase as the available dilution decreases and the receiving water changes from municipal sanitary sewer, to storm drain to lakes and rivers. Thus most brewery wastewaters are discharged to sanitary sewers connected to municipal treatment systems. Here again the cost to the brewery will depend on the extent to which the waste must be treated by the municipality and the size and age of the municipal wastewater treatment plant.

As the relative ratio of brewery waste to municipal waste increases, the degree of pretreatment required at the brewery increases and added costs are incurred. When the brewing waste fraction becomes a significant fraction of the municipal waste load, the least cost alternative may be a joint-owned and operated municipality-brewery waste treatment facility.

The treatment of a combined waste has several advantages. Brewery wastes are nutrient deficient, whereas municipal wastes generally contain an excess of nutrients. Nutrient removal facilities or nutrient addition requirements are reduced or eliminated. The addition of municipal waste also tends to temper the highly variable brewery load and increases treatment plant size resulting in lower unit treatment costs and more consistent and reliable operations.

WASTE DISCHARGE TO MUNICIPAL SYSTEMS

Most brewery effluents are treated in municipal waste treatment plants.[1, 2, 3]. As municipal waste is normally biodegradable material and inert solids, municipal systems usually employ a biological treatment system to process the waste. These systems use a solids removal process followed by a biological treatment unit. The biological treatment unit utilizes bacteria to convert and reduce the dissolved and particulate organic material in the waste to bacterial solids. These biosolids are then separated from the liquid waste, mixed with the solids removed in the first stage, stabilized by aerobic or anaerobic digestion and disposed of on the land. The liquid leaving the biological stage is chlorinated then discharged to the receiving environment. The design basis for these municipal systems is usually 0.45 m³ of waste per person with a waste strength of 200–400 mg/l biochemical oxygen demand (BOD) and 200–300 mg/l suspended solids (SS).

Municipalities protect their systems by establishing waste bylaws for industrial waste discharges. These bylaws set permissible limits for the important waste parameters, such as hydraulic flow, BOD, SS, pH and daily flow variation (peaking factor). A typical set of regulations is presented in Table I. When a

TABLE I
TYPICAL BYLAWS LEVELS FOR DISCHARGE TO SANITARY EFFLUENTS

	TOWN	CITY
BOD	300 mg/l	500 mg/l
SS	350 mg/l	600 mg/l
pH	5.5–9.5	5.5–10.5
oil/grease	100 mg/l	100 mg/l
oil/greast (mineral)	15 mg/l	15 mg/l
temperature	65°C	65°C
chlorides, sulphates	1500 mg/l	1500 mg/l
metals	n/a	n/a
ammonia	—	—
phosphates	—	—

brewery produces a waste of a strength that exceeds the parameters specified in the bylaw, the municipality may draw up a special agreement with the brewery. These special agreements set new maximum parameter levels for the waste. In some cases, parameter levels have been increased tenfold. Municipalities also set regulations for discharges to storm sewers, Table II. Permissible limits for these discharges generally are an order of magnitude lower than discharges to sanitary sewers, as the storm sewer contents are normally discharged to the receiving environment without treatment. Most municipalities limit storm sewer discharges to surface run off from buildings and grounds. Generally no process wastes are allowed, non-contact cooling waters being the exception in some cases.

TABLE II
TYPICAL BYLAW LEVELS FOR DISCHARGE TO STORM SEWERS

BOD	15 mg/l
SS	15 mg/l
pH	5.5-9.5
oil/grease	15 mg/l

Municipalities charge a fee for the use of the sanitary sewer and waste treatment system. The charge rate is a function of the impact of the waste on the treatment system, the additional cost for treating the waste, and the cost of determining the charges. These factors generally produce two rate formulas—a flat ate and a quality-quantity rate. The flat rate formula is based on city water use and is only applied to small water users. Brewery wastewaters usually have a quality-quantity formula applied. The fee is based on the product of the total totalized daily water use in the brewery corrected for product and evaporation and a semi-annual or annual monitoring of the waste strength by the municipality. When brewery wastewaters exceed bylaw limits and special agreements between the brewery and municipality exist, more detailed rate structures are applied. Continuous flow and waste strength monitoring are required. The fee is a function of the measured flow and the measured quantity of BOD and suspended solids discharged. In some cases, additional charges are added based on the peaking factor, the ratio of the 1 hour average maximum flow and the daily average flow. Average values for the charge rates are: flow—15¢/m^3, BOD—5¢/kg, SS—3¢/kg, total Kjeldahl nitrogen (TKN)—15¢/kg and phosphorus—15¢/kg.

At this point it is of interest to consider comparisons between sanitary waste, total brewery effluent, and packaging wastes. Sanitary waste has a BOD of 200 – 400 mg/l, a suspended solids of 200 – 300 mg/l and an excess of nutrients. Total brewery effluent is characterized by a high BOD (700–2500 mg/l), moderately high levels of suspended solids (400–1000 mg/l) and a pH ranging from 6 to 11. Brewery wastes are generally deficient in nutrients. Of the total brewery effluent, the packaging area contributes about 30–50 percent of the hydraulic load, 15–30 percent of the suspended solids load and a high alkaline pH of 9-13. The large range in the waste load fraction results because returnable and non-returnable containers are used. Returnable containers significantly increase waste loads.

Some degree of pretreatment is necessary if brewery effluents are to meet municipal bylaws. Given the batch nature of the brewery process, the quantity and quality of the effluent discharged during the operating day is time dependent. Flow equalization may also be necessary. Waste flows and loads may be reduced and meet specification through water reuse and by-product recovery. Operator education with regards to the impact of waste generation and good housekeeping practices also significantly reduce waste loads. The origin, quantity and treatment techniques of wastes in the packaging area will be examined with respect to the above factors.

WASTE PRODUCTION AND REDUCTION

The packaging section consists of five waste generation areas. These areas comprise bottle return—container separation and soaker loading, bottle washing, filling, pasteurization, and packing and warehousing. The container separation and soaker loading area produces most of the solid waste, while bottle washing generates a large fraction of the waste volume, suspended solids and alkalinity (waste caustic).

Most of the BOD load, approximately 60 percent, results from beer losses during bottle and can filling and sewering of rejects and returns. A large volume of waste is also generated during production and maintenance cleaning. Relative flows and waste concentrations are presented in Table III.

TABLE III
WASTE FLOW BREAKDOWN

	% OF FLOW	BOD mg/l	SS mg/l
BOTTLE WASHER	35	200-500	200-500
PASTEURIZER	20	20-70	10-50
FILLER	10	300-2500	50-100
CLEAN-UP	30	100-300	100-300
RETURNS, REJECTS	1	70,000	—
OTHER USES	4	—	—

Glass breakage occurs throughout the packaging area. To control glass movement into the sewer, and to reduce maintenance, all floor drains should be covered with strainers. The cullet should be collected every few hours and segregated into clean and dirty glass. The clean glass, that produced between the soaker discharge and labellers, should be crushed and returned to glass recyclers. Dirty glass is normally sent to a sanitary landfill site in bulk lift containers. Glass traps (intercepters) are also necessary in all sewers. The intercepters should be inspected and cleaned 2 to 3 times a year, and the collected solid waste sent to a sanitary landfill site.

SOAKER INFEED AREA

The soaker infeed area produces solid waste consisting of cardboard cartons, broken glass, returned cans and shipping container materials. In most breweries the cardboard cartons are baled and sold to paper recycling firms. Returned cans are crushed, baled and recycled in large breweries, while small breweries generally crush or shred the cans and dispose of them in a sanitary landfill site. These breweries should consider crushing and baling the cans for return to a recycler to reduce waste loads. Broken glass amounting to 50 to 60 percent of the breakage occurs in this area. It is collected and sent to sanitary landfill sites in bulk lift containers. In most cases, returned beer is sewered.

The returned beer along with short fills and rejects, amounting to 25 to 35 percent of the beer losses in the packaging area, may be recovered as by-product alcohol, reducing the BOD load of the waste. A number of breweries utilize this procedure. The waste beer may also be used for energy production through fermentation and distillation using either anaerobic processes or combination evaporation/combustion systems. Evaporation/combustion deserves greater attention because there is no liquid effluent. The dry ash, which contains large amounts of potassium may be used as a fertilizer or soil amendment.[4]

BOTTLE WASHING

The hot caustic return bottle washing process and caustic clean system is a major source of wastewater, solids and alkalinity. Strict supervision of the process and frequent maintenance is necessary to minimize waste loads. Caustic losses generally result from tank overflows and leaking soaker valves. Label pulp removal devices yield less waste when operated continuously. Bottle Washer prerinse screens should be cleaned one or two times a shift and the collected solids disposed of as a solid waste and not dumped to the sewer.

Caustic clean systems utilizing fine screens and settling tanks with sludge dewatering by plate and frame pressure filtration or centrifugation reduce the liquid waste to a minimum.[5] Centrifugation will produce a 10-15 weight percent sludge cake while pressure filtration yields a 40 percent cake. Collected label pulp should be mixed with the settled sludge before filtration to get rapid dewatering rates. Separated solids may be sent to sanitary landfill. Broken glass is normally removed from the soaker during tank cleaning. Utilization of a glass intercepter immediately adjacent to the soaker enhances efficient glass collection for disposal to sanitary landfills.

There are three main sources of wastewater alkalinity in a brewery: continuous dragout from the bottle washer, periodic discharges from the caustic clean system, and the CIP systems.[6] CIP caustic does not pose a problem, as these wastes may be collected and batch neutralized with sulphuric acid at low cost. Caustic losses from the caustic clean system are eliminated when solids dewatering of the settling tank solids is utilized. These practices leave the soaker as the principal alkalinity generator. Whether this stream should be neutralized at source depends on two factors: the wastewater system utilized by the brewery and the pH of the total combined effluent steam leaving the brewery. Breweries with a pH problem that discharge their waste to a municipal system without treatment should practice partial neutralization of the soaker effluent. Breweries with a pH problem with waste treatment facilities should have the neutralization facilities associated with the waste treatment system. One of two neutralization chemicals may be utilized—carbon dioxide[7] or sulphuric acid.[8] It is important that the system be designed to handle spills (the contents of one or two soaker compartments) and controlled dumps following mechanical failures. Two stage sulphuric acid neutralization appears to be the favoured alternative.

FILLERS

Filler operations contribute about 30 – 50 percent of the BOD load generated by the packaging operation. Significant BOD reductions result if wastes from this process are segregated and alcohol recovery is practiced. The procedure is utilized at a number of breweries.

PASTEURIZATION

Waste generation by pasteurization operations is a function of the degree of water recycle practiced.[9] Those breweries utilizing once-through water in the final cooling compartment generate a large volume of weak wastewater. Suspended solids and BOD values are generally less than 50. This waste may be discharged to municipal systems without treatment, bypassing any in-plant waste treatment facilities. When central water systems with cooling towers are utilized wastewater flows are reduced. However, waste strength increases markedly as bactericides and fungicides must be used to control slime formation. Waste treatment of the blowdown is normally required.

PRETREATMENT OF EFFLUENTS BEFORE DISCHARGE

The activated sludge process is the most popular biological waste treatment system utilized by breweries. Many variations have been employed. These include low rate processes, such as extended aeration and the Carrousel process; medium rate processes, such as the modified Hatfield process, and high rate processes, such as the Deep Shaft.[10, 11] Although not ideally suited for brewery wastes, the contact stabilization process has also been utilized. BOD removals of 80 percent and SS removals of 30 to 70% have been obtained. However, sludge bulking has been a persistent problem.[11] Trickling filters employing plastic media have enjoyed success in Europe and North America. With rising energy costs, energy producing anaerobic processes and lower energy cost land application systems have appeared on the scene. Generally low rate systems, such as extended aeration, require a large land area, but do not require neutralization or equalization and have low sludge yields. As oxidation rates increase, plant size decreases, and neutralization and equalization requirements along with sludge yields increase. Operator requirements and nutrient addition rates similarly increase as oxidation rates increase.

ACTIVATED SLUDGE PROCESSES

The Coors brewery at one time employed a high-rate (1.1 kg BOD/d/m^3) activated sludge system using a modified version of the Hatfield process to treat its effluent before discharge to the receiving environment. Neutralization to pH 7 and solids removal comprised primary treatment. Wastes are subject to equalization (4 hrs.) prior to secondary treatment. Mixed liquor contact time in the basins was about 18 hours. Nitrogen was added at a rate of 1.6 kg per 100 kg of BOD. Surface aeration amounting to 365 KW was used to maintain a dissolved oxygen level of 2 mg/l. The treatment system routinely removed 96% of the incoming BOD and 90% of the suspended solids. Sludge from the secondary clarifier was pumped to the aeration basin at a rate of 30% of total flow. Some digested anaerobic sludge was also added to the aeration basin to suppress filamentous growth. Excess sludge was produced at a rate of 1.1 kg per kg of BOD removed. Waste activated sludge was concentrated by air flotation and then combined with the primary sludge. Lime and ferric chloride were used as coagulants to dewater the sludge mixture on vacuum filters to 16% solids.[12]

The Miller brewery in Fulton utilizes a similar rate activated sludge process (0.7 kg BOD/m^3/d) to treat its effluent before discharge to the receiving environment. Numerous additional control measures are incorporated to prevent filamentous growth. The sludge yield is 1 kg solids per kg BOD removed. Waste activated sludge is concentrated by centrifugation and combined with primary sludge. Lime and ferric chloride are used as coagulants to dewater the sludge mixture in a plate and frame pressure filter to 45% solids (13).

The use of commercial oxygen in aerobic biological treatment has received considerable attention. Some of the reported adventages are: smaller aeration tanks, reduced sludge yield, lower power requirements and increased settleability of the sludge. Experiments conducted at Jacksonville, using the UNOX process, demonstrated that combined brewery and domestic effluents can be treated by pure oxygen aeration. When operated at F/M ratios ranging from

0.6 to 1.6, the treatment system achieved better than 95% BOD and SS removals.[14] The pure oxygen activated sludge modification was shown to eliminate most of the problems associated with conventional air activated sludge and fixed film treatment systems.[15] However, the operating costs of the system appear to be greater than conventional systems.[16]

The Coors brewery currently employs a high purity oxygen activated sludge process. The strong brewery wastes are separated from sanitary wastes at the brewery, in order to market the sludge generated from the brewing process wastes as an animal food supplement. The primary treatment portion of this plant includes: screening, grit/grain removal, flow equilization, primary clarification and pH and nutrient adjustment. Secondary treatment is accomplished with a high purity oxygen activated sludge plant. This plant accomplishes 98% BOD removal and 94% suspended solids removal of the 4 MGD flow which is returned to the nearby stream.

The sanitary wastes from the brewery and the municipal wastes from the town of Golden are treated by Coors in a second waste treatment plant which features an extended aeration activated sludge process and aerobic sludge digestion. This effluent is also suitable to be returned to the stream.

The biodisc has also been found appropriate for treating combined brewery and sanitary waste. BOD removals of 80 percent were attained in the treatment of combined wastewaters. However, removals appeared to be a function of influent load.[17] Pure oxygen was added to a rotating disc plant to improve sedimentation and reduce excess sludge production.[18] Greater than 98 percent BOD removals were reported. The use of step feed to the biodisc also improved the performance.[19]

The Molson brewery plant in Barrie utilizes a low rate extended aeration process (0.2 kg BOD/m^3/d) to pretreat its effluent before discharge to a municipal system. Neutralization and equalization are not necessary. Mixed liquor contact time in the aeration basins is 8 days and the sludge residence time is 30 days. Surface and diffused aeration amounting to 323 KW is used. Nitrogen and phosphorus are added at rates of 100:2.3 and 100:0.2 respectively. Excess sludge is produced at a rate of 0.6 kg per kg of BOD removed. The treatment system routinely removes 95% of the incoming BOD and 90% of the suspended solids. The excess sludge is aerobically digested and dewatered in a belt press to 15 wt% solids. Polymer and ferric chloride are used as coagulants (20). The brewery also uses a high rate Deep Shaft process (11 kg BOD/m^3/d) to treat its waste. The process consists of two 152 m deep, 1.37 m diameter shafts with a total aerated volume of 450 m^3. For solids separation, two flotation tanks, with an effective area of 65 m^2, are used. Polymer is added to aid flocculation. Flow equalization of 11 hrs. is provided; however, neutralization is not necessary as anaerobic activity reduced the pH to required levels. Nitrogen and phosphorus are added at a BOD:N:P ratio of 100:5:1.2. Approximately 168 KW is required to provide aeration, with 50% of the oxygen entering the shaft being transferred. The liquid residence time in the aeration section is 6 hours while the sludge age is 2 days. Filamentous growth is not observed. Excess sludge production rates averaged 0.8–0.9 kg solids per kg of BOD removed. The overall treatment plant performance was considered good with an average removal of 95% of the applied BOD load. The effluent COD averaged 175 mg/l (the effluent BOD/COD ratio is 0.2), while the effluent suspended solids averaged 70 mg/l. The excess sludge is aerobically digested and dewatered on a belt press.[21,22]

TRICKLING FILTER PROCESSES

A number of breweries utilize trickling filters with plastic media for pre-treatment or complete treatment of brewery wastewater.[23] When discharge is to the receiving environment the trickling filter is followed by an activated sludge process. The Pabst plant at Perry, Georgia, is an excellent example.[24, 25] Neutralization and solids removal comprise primary treatment. Flow equalization may also be employed.[26] The nutrients, nitrogen and phosphorus are added, then the waste is fed to a two-stage trickling filter loaded at 0.35 l/m (5.6 kg BOD/m^3/d) with a treatment efficiency of 44%. The trickling filters are followed by a contact stabilization process loaded at 0.8 kg BOD/m^3/d utilizing high capacity rotor brush type mechanical aerators. The treatment plant BOD removal averaged 98%. The final effluent had a mean BOD value of 45 mg/l and a mean suspended solids of 62 mg/l. Excess sludge production from the process, which amounted to 0.65 kg solids per kg BOD removed, was applied to the land using the spray irrigation technique.

LAND APPLICATION

Land application of brewery wastewater is a method of treatment which may be utilized in areas where the land has a net water deficit. Anheuser-Busch employs the process at their Jacksonville brewery.[27] Economical and successful operation demands a nutrient-rich waste and the harvesting of a cash crop having a large nitrogen requirement. Waste application rates are generally limited to the nitrogen utilization rate of the crop. The nitrogen application rate at Jacksonville is 650 kg/hec/yr or 20000 kg BOD/d.

ANAEROBIC PROCESSES

Anaerobic treatment of brewery wastewater is currently receiving increasing attention because of its anticipated low cost.[28, 29] The economics are favourable, since: anaerobic treatment requires 25% of the nutrients of aerobic processes; anaerobic processes produces 20% of the excess sludge of an aerobic process and anaerobic processes produce methane gas, an energy source, making the process a net producer of energy where aerobic processes are net users of energy; anaerobic treatment processes operate at much higher loadings (10-20 kg BOD/m^3/d) than aerobic processes (0.5-4 kg BOD/m^3/d) significantly reducing plant size.[30, 31]

Anaerobic treatment followed by aerobic treatment has been recommended as an effective and economical treatment alternative for plants discharging to the receiving environment.[32] A commercial process utilizing this technique is the Anamet process. An anaerobic tank converts solubles to methane, a second tank strips ammonia and raises the pH, and a final aerobic tank completes treatment. Removals of 99 percent have been reported. The Heileman brewery at LaCrosse has installed a high rate anaerobic treatment system, which utilizes the upflow anaerobic sludge blanket or Biothane process. The design loading is 5–11 kg $BOD/m^3/d$ with a liquid retention in the reactor of 5 hours. Excess sludge production is expected to be about 0.1 kg solids per kg BOD removed with BOD reductions of 80 percent.[33, 34]

REFERENCES

1. Le Seelleur, L.A. *MBAA Tech. Quart.*, *8*, 1, 52 (1971).
2. Ramsey, T.G. *MBAA Tech. Quart.*, *8*, 3, 152 (1971).
3. Joyce, M.E. et al. USEPA, EPA-600/2-77-048 (1977).
4. Nilsson, M. *Int. Sugar J.*, *83*, 259 (1981).
5. Arbour, R.G. *MBAA Tech. Quart.*, *16*, 2, 73 (1979).
6. Lom, T. *MBAA Tech. Quart.*, *14*, 1, 50 (1977).
7. Naecker, J. and Goettsche, R. *Int. Brew. & Distil.*, 3, 23 (1973).
8. Hoyle, D.L. *Plant Eng.*, 3, 75 (1975).
9. Schultz, R. *Brew. Digest*, 3, 44 (1979).
10. Beszedits, S. *Wat. & Poll. Control* 10, 10 (1977).
11. Schwartz, H.G. and Jones, R.H. Proc. 3rd Nat. Sym. Food Processing Wastes, Washington, D.C., 371 (1972).
12. Anon. EPA Tech. Transfer Capsule Rept. no. 6, EPA, Washington, D.C.
13. Schwartz, H.G. Popowchak, T., and Becker, K. *JWPCF*, *52*, 2977 (1980)
14. Dedeke, W.C. and Stankewich, M.J. Proc. 24th Oklahoma Ind. Waste Conf., Oklahoma State Univ., Oklahoma (1973).
15. Fuggle, R.W. *Chem. Ind.* (G.B.), *13*, 453 (1981).
16. Hill, F. Effl. Treat. Biochem. Ind., Conf. Pap., Process Biochem. Int. Conf., 3rd, no. 5 (1980).
17. Beak Consultants, EPS 3-WP-74-2, Environment Canada, Ottawa (1973).
18. Ishigiero, M., and Fukumoto, T. *Kamkyo Gijutsu* (Jap.), *8*, 1194 (1979).
19. Richard, D., et al. *JWPCF*, *50*, 869 (1978).
20. Love, L.S., Guilaume, F., and Weiks, H. *MBAA Tech. Quart.*, *10*, 3, 134 (1973).
21. Gallo, T., and Sandford, D.S. Amer. Inst. Chem. Eng. Sym. Series—Water, *76*, 197, 288 (1980).
22. Knudsen, F.B. *Brew. Digest.*, *53*, 46 (1978).
23. Biesinger, M.G., et al., Proc. 35th Ind. Waste Conf., Purdue Univ., Ann Arbor Science, 596, (1981).
24. McWhorter, T.R., and Zielinski, R.J. Proc. 26th Ind. Waste Conf., Purdue Univ., 604 (1971).
25. Zielinski, R.J., and McWhorter, T.R. Proc. 31st Ind. Waste Conf., Purdue Univ., 240 (1977).
26. Seddon, A.W., and Woodland, R. *MBAA Tech. Quart.*, *18*, 1, 49 (1981).
27. Keith, L.W. *MBAA Tech. Quart.*, *18*, 4, 201 (1981).
28. Lovan, C.R., and Foree, E.G. Proc. 26th Ind. Waste Conf., Purdue Univ., 1074 (1971).
29. Keenan, J.D., and Kormi, I. *JWPCF*, *53*, 1, 66 (1981).
30. Donnolly, T. *Brew. Distilling Int.*, *10*, 78 (1980).
31. Rippon, G.M., Effl. Treat. Biochem. Ind., Conf. Pap., Process Biochem. Int. Conf. 3rd., Wheatland, no. 19 (1980).
32. Skogman, H. *Process Biochem.*, *14*, 5 (1979).
33. Richards, E.A. *Brewers Digest*, *56*, 10, 8 (1981).
34. Anon. *Biothane Digest*, *2*, 1 (1982).

INDEX